Calculus
For The Life Sciences

**Calculus with Applications
Math 11A**

University of California, Santa Cruz

Schreiber • Smith • Getz

Wiley Custom Learning Solutions

ISBN 978-1-118-80711-8

10 9 8 7 6 5 4 3 2

CONTENTS

Figure 1 Mathematics has been used to model many biological systems on Earth, ranging from global climatic processes to viral dynamics.

NOAA/NASA GOES Project

Preview of Modeling and Calculus

Is calculus relevant?

The interface between mathematics and biology presents challenges and opportunities for both mathematicians and biologists. Unique opportunities for research have surfaced within the past ten to twenty years because of the explosion of biological data with the advent of new technologies and because of the availability of advanced and powerful computers that can organize the data. For biology, the possibilities range from the level of the cell and molecule to the biosphere. For mathematics, the potential is great in traditional applied areas such as statistics and differential equations, as well as in such nontraditional areas as knot theory.

These challenges: aggregation of components to elucidate the behavior of ensembles, integration across scales, and inverse problems, are basic to all sciences, and a variety of techniques exist to deal with them and to begin to solve the biological problems that generate them. However, the uniqueness of biological systems, shaped by evolutionary forces, will pose new difficulties, mandate new perspectives, and led to the development of new mathematics. The excitement of this area of science is already evident, and is sure to grow in the years to come.

(Executive Summary, National Science Foundation (NSF)-sponsored workshop led by Simon Levin, 1990).

The above quotation, which is as true today as when it was written, hints at the exciting opportunities that exist at the interface of mathematics and biology. The goal of this course is to provide you with a strong grounding in calculus, while at the same time introducing you to various research areas of mathematical biology and inspiring you to take more courses at this interdisciplinary interface. In Chapter 1, we will set the tone for the entire book and review some of the skills needed to work at this interface. But first, in this preview, the idea of mathematical modeling is introduced to give you are underlying understanding of this important concept. Throughout the book you will find real-life problems that can be solved using mathematics. For example, in Olympic weightlifting, medals are awarded to individuals in different weight classes, as heavier individuals tend to lift more weight. In Chapter 1, we use mathematics and a basic physiological principle to predict how much an individual can lift scales with their body weight. Using the resulting mathematical model, we identify one of the greatest weightlifters of all time, Pocket Hercules (see Figure 1).

Models come in many guises: Architects make buildings models that are either small-scale replicas or, more recently, visual images created using computer-aided design packages. Political scientists, through debate and discussion, create verbal and written models that simulate the potential outcomes of a proposed policy. Artists make sketches and small-scale sculptures before starting a large-scale project. Flight simulators allow people to gain skills in piloting without the dangers associated with flying. Scientists in many disciplines (e.g., physics, biology, economics, chemistry, sociology, and even psychology) use mathematical models to investigate important phenomena.

Real-world problems inspired the creation of quantitative tools to grapple with their complexity. The counting and division of flocks of birds influenced the early development of number theory. The measurement and division of land led to the development of geometry. Understanding the motion of the planets and the forces of electricity, magnetism, and gravity resulted in the development of calculus. More recently, the study the dynamics of population growth and population genetics led to many of the basic topics in stochastic processes. The immense success of mathematical models in understanding physical processes was recognized by E. P. Wigner in "The Unreasonable Effectiveness of Mathematics in the Natural Sciences" (*Communications in Pure and Applied Mathematics* 13 (1960): 1–14)—his now famous essay—in which he states:

The miracle of the appropriateness of the language of mathematics for the formulation of the laws of physics is a wonderful gift which we neither understand nor deserve. We should be grateful for it, and hope that it will remain valid in future research and that it will extend, for better or for worse, to our pleasure even though perhaps also to our bafflement, to wide branches of learning.

As highlighted in the quotation from the NSF-sponsored workshop, one of the areas to which mathematics has extended most dramatically over the past half century is the biological sciences. The importance of this mathematics-biology interface is threefold. First, field and laboratory experiments are generating an explosion of data at both the cellular and environmental levels of study. To make these data meaningful requires extracting patterns within the data (e.g., correlations among variables, clustering of points in time and space). Mathematics, which from one viewpoint is the study of patterns (e.g., numerical, geometrical), provides a powerful methodology to identify and extract these patterns. This power of mathematics is reflected in the following statement of one of the founders of calculus, Sir Isaac Newton (1642–1727), in his book.

The latest authors, like the most ancient, strove to subordinate the phenomena of nature to the laws of mathematics.

Second, mathematics is a language that permits the precise formulations of assumptions and hypotheses. Consider the words of another founding father of calculus, Gottfried Wilhelm Leibniz (1646–1716), in his book.

In symbols one observes an advantage in discovery which is greatest when they express the exact nature of a thing briefly and, as it were, picture it; then indeed the labor of thought is wonderfully diminished.

Third, mathematics provides a logical, coherent framework to deduce the implications of one's assumptions.

One of the goals of this book is to help you understand how, when, and why calculus can be used to model biological phenomena. To achieve this understanding, you will be expected to develop simple models, to understand more complicated models sufficiently well to slightly modify them, to determine the appropriate techniques to analyze the models (e.g., numerical vs. analytical, stability vs. bifurcation analysis), and to interpret the results of your analysis. Examples of biological phenomena that we will encounter include epidemic outbreaks, blood flow, population extinctions, tumor regrowth after chemotherapy, population genetics, regulatory genetic networks, mechanisms for memory formation, enzyme kinetics, and evolutionary games. Another goal of this book is to provide you with a thorough grounding in calculus: concepts and applications, analytical techniques, and numerical methods. In the remainder of this introduction, we briefly address two basic questions: What is mathematical modeling? and What is calculus?

What is mathematical modeling?

A real-life situation is usually far too complicated to be precisely or mathematically defined. When confronted with a problem in the real world, therefore, it is usually necessary to develop a mathematical framework based on certain assumptions about the real world. This framework can then be used to find a solution that will tell us something about the real world. The process of developing this mathematical framework is referred to as mathematical modeling.

What, precisely, is a mathematical model? It is an abstract description of a real-life problem that does not have an obvious solution. The first step involves abstraction in which certain assumptions about the real world are made, variables are defined, and appropriate mathematical expressions are developed.

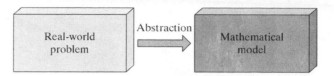

In this text, we discuss modeling biological systems. Consequently, as we progress through the book, we spend some time identifying the features associated with molecular, physiological, behavioral, life history, and population-level processes of many species and biological processes. After abstraction, the next step in modeling is to simplify the mathematics or derive related mathematical facts from the mathematical model.

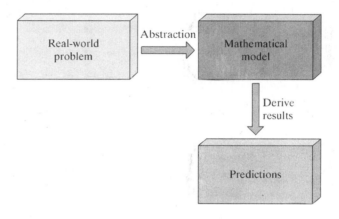

The results derived from the mathematical model should lead us to some predictions about the real world. The next step is to gather data from the situation being modeled and to compare those data with the predictions. If the two do not agree, then the gathered data are used to modify the assumptions underlying the model, and the process repeats.

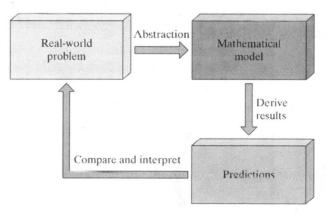

One use of the modeling process is predicting world population size, that is, the total number of humans living on Earth. Predicting world population size is of critical importance in determining future impacts of humans on their environment and future needs for energy, food, shelter, and other resources. Table 1 reports world population sizes over the past millennium.

Table 1 Human world population sizes over the past 1000 years

Year AD	Population size (in billions)	Year AD	Population size (in billions)
1000	0.31	1930	2.07
1250	0.40	1940	2.30
1500	0.50	1950	2.52
1750	0.79	1960	3.02
1800	0.98	1970	3.70
1850	1.26	1980	4.44
1900	1.65	1990	5.27
1910	1.75	1999	5.98
1920	1.86	2010	6.86

It is clear that the world population is growing. But how fast is it growing? As a first guess, we might try modeling with a linear function $N(t) = a + bt$, where t is the year and $N(t)$ is the population size. Using the first two data points from Table 1 yields this relationship (try this for yourself!):

$$N(t) = 0.31 + 0.00036\,t \text{ billion individuals in year } t$$

Plotting this linear model against the data yields the left panel of Figure 2. Although this linear model does a reasonable job of predicting population sizes from 1000 to 1500 AD, it clearly underpredicts for the remainder of the millennium. This limitation stems from the assumption that the population size is increasing at a rate independent of its size. Clearly, this assumption is not reasonable as our population appears to be growing more and more rapidly over the centuries. A better model, as we will discuss in Sections 1.4 and 1.6, is exponential growth in which the population growth rate is proportional to the population size. The exercises of Section 1.4 will ask you to fit an exponential model to the data. This exponential model fitted to the first few data points slightly improves the predictive power of the model, as seen in the middle panel of Figure 2. However, the new model also substantially underpredicts world population sizes after 1750 AD. One possible explanation for this underprediction is that the model does not account for successive cultural revolutions, such as the Industrial Revolution, that led to surges in population size during the nineteenth and twentieth centuries. In Chapter 6, we examine a model that accounts for population growth that is faster than exponential: so-called super-exponential model. Developing and analyzing this model requires simultaneously the tools from differential and integral calculus, which we discuss next. In Section 6.2, you will fit this super-exponential growth model to the world population data and find that its predictive power (as seen in the right panel of Figure 2) is significantly better than the simpler models. Hence, after several iterations of model formulation and comparison to data, we arrive at a much better model for predicting future population sizes.

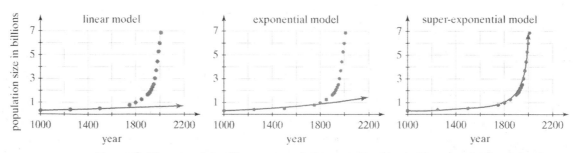

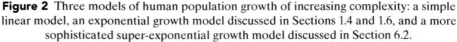

Figure 2 Three models of human population growth of increasing complexity: a simple linear model, an exponential growth model discussed in Sections 1.4 and 1.6, and a more sophisticated super-exponential growth model discussed in Section 6.2.

What is calculus?

Very likely, you have enrolled in a course that requires that you use this book. If you read the preface, you know that the intended audience is students who wish to learn about calculus but are majoring in an area related to biology. You might think of calculus as the culmination of all of your mathematical studies. To a certain extent, that is true, but it is also the beginning of your study of mathematics as it applies to how the real world changes in time and across space. All your prior work in mathematics is elementary. With calculus, you cross the dividing line between using elementary and advanced mathematical tools for studying a variety of applied topics. Calculus is the mathematics of motion and change over time and space.

What distinguishes calculus from your previous mathematics courses of algebra, geometry, and trigonometry is the transition from discrete static applications to those that are dynamic and often continuous. For example, in elementary mathematics you considered the slope of a line, but in calculus we define the (nonconstant) slope of a nonlinear curve. In elementary mathematics you found average changes in quantities such as the position and velocity of a moving object, but in calculus we can find instantaneous changes in the same quantities. In elementary mathematics you found the average of a finite collection of numbers, but in calculus we can find the average value of a function with infinitely many values over an interval.

The development of **calculus** in the seventeenth century by Newton and Leibniz was the result of their attempt to answer some fundamental questions about the world and the way things work. These investigations led to two fundamental concepts of calculus, namely, the idea of a *derivative*, which deals with rates of change, and that of an *integral*, which deals with accumulated change. The breakthrough in the development of these concepts was the formulation of a mathematical tool called a *limit*.

1. **Limit.** The limit is a mathematical tool for studying the *tendency* of a function as its variable *approaches* some value.
2. **Derivative.** The derivative is defined in the context of a limit. One of its used is to compute rates of change and slopes of tangent lines to curves. The study of derivatives is called *differential calculus*. Derivatives can be used in sketching graphs and in finding the extreme (largest and smallest) values of functions. Biologists use derivatives to calculate, for example, the rates of change to the biochemical states of cells within individuals, rates of growth of populations, and rates of the spread of disease within populations.
3. **Integral.** The integral is found by taking a special limit of a sum of terms, and it is used initially to compute the accumulation of change. The study of this process is called *integral calculus*. Area, volume, work, and degree-days (the latter used to monitor the development of plants and "cold blooded" animals) are a few of the many quantities that can be expressed as integrals. Biologists can use integrals to calculate, for example, the amount of fat bears store before going into hibernation, the time it takes an insect to develop from an egg into an adult as a function of temperature, the probability that an individual will die before a certain age, or the number of infected people as a disease spreads through a population.

Let us begin our study by taking an intuitive look at each of these three essential ideas of calculus.

The Limit

Zeno (ca. 500 BC) was a Greek philosopher who is known primarily for his famous paradoxes. One of these concerns a race between Achilles, a legendary Greek hero, and a tortoise. When the race begins, the (slower) tortoise is given a head start, as shown in Figure 3.

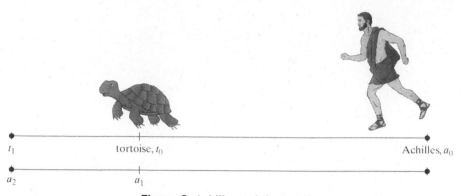

Figure 3 Achilles and the tortoise.

Is it possible for Achilles to overtake the tortoise? Zeno pointed out that by the time Achilles reaches the tortoise's starting point, $a_1 = t_0$, the tortoise will have moved ahead to a new point, t_1. When Achilles gets to this next point, a_2, the tortoise will be at a new point, t_2. The tortoise, even though much slower than Achilles, keeps moving forward. Although the distance between Achilles and the tortoise is getting smaller and smaller, the tortoise will apparently always be ahead.

Of course, common sense tells us that Achilles will overtake the slow tortoise, but where is the error in this reasoning? The error is in the assumption that an infinite amount of time is required to cover a distance divided into an infinite number of segments. This discussion is getting at an essential idea in calculus, the notion of a limit.

Consider the successive positions for both Achilles and the tortoise:

Achilles: $a_0, a_1, a_2, a_3, a_4, \cdots$

Tortoise: $t_0, t_1, t_2, t_3, t_4, \cdots$

After the start, the positions for Achilles, as well as those for the tortoise, form sets of positions that are ordered by the counting numbers. Such ordered listings are called *sequences*, which we introduce in Section 1.7. As we discuss in our first example below, and explore further in Chapter 2, the limit of a sequence of values $t_0, \cdots, t_n$ can be bounded above by some value T, say, so that for all values of n, no matter how large, we have $t_n < T$. In the context of the Achilles paradox, this means that Achilles will pass the tortoise at time T, if T is the smallest of all values that satisfies this inequality.

Example 1 Sequences: an intuitive preview

The sequence

$$\frac{1}{2}, \frac{2}{3}, \frac{3}{4}, \frac{4}{5}, \cdots$$

can be described by writing a *general term*: $\dfrac{n}{n+1}$ where $n = 1, 2, 3, 4, \cdots$. Can you guess the value L that $\dfrac{n}{n+1}$ approaches as n gets large? This value is called the *limit of the sequence.*

Solution   We say that L is the number that $\dfrac{n}{n+1}$ tends toward as n becomes large without bound. We define a notation to summarize this idea:

$$L = \lim_{n \to \infty} \frac{n}{n+1}$$

As we consider larger and larger values for n, we find a sequence of fractions:

$$\frac{1}{2}, \frac{2}{3}, \frac{3}{4}, \cdots, \frac{1,000}{1,001}, \frac{1,001}{1,002}, \cdots, \frac{9,999,999}{10,000,000}, \cdots$$

It is reasonable to guess that the sequence of fractions is approaching the number 1.

The Derivative: Rates of Change

The derivative provides information about the rate of change over small intervals (in fact, infinitesimally small!) of time or space. For instance, in trying to understand the role of humans in global climate change, we may be interested in the rate at which carbon dioxide levels are changing. In Section 1.2, we show that it is possible to come up with a function that describes how carbon dioxide levels (in parts per million) vary as a function of time. The relationship between this function and the data is illustrated in Figure 4.

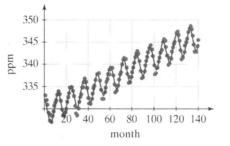

Figure 4 Carbon dioxide levels (in parts per million) as a function of months after April 1974.

In a scientific discussion about carbon dioxide levels, we might be interested in the rate of change of carbon dioxide levels at a particular time, say the second month (June 1974) of this data set. To find the rate of change from the second to tenth month, we could find the change in carbon dioxide levels, $331.8 - 331.0 = 0.8$ parts per million, and divide it by the change in time, $10 - 2 = 8$ months, to get the rate of change

$$\frac{331.8 - 331.0}{10 - 2} = 0.1 \text{ ppm per month}$$

over this eight-month period. Note that this rate of change corresponds to the slope of the **secant line** passing through the points $P = (2, 331.0)$ and $Q = (10, 331.8)$ as illustrated in Figure 5a. Although this rate of change describes what happens over the eight-month period, it clearly does not describe what is happening around the second month. Indeed, during the second month, the carbon dioxide levels are decreasing not increasing. Consequently, we expect the rate of change to be negative.

To get the **instantaneous rate of change** at the beginning of the second month, we can consider moving the point Q along the curve to the point P. As we do so, the points P and Q define secant lines that appear to approach a limiting line. This limiting line, as illustrated in Figure 5b, is called the **tangent line**.

The slope of this line corresponds to the instantaneous rate of change for carbon dioxide levels at the beginning of the second month of the data set. Later you will be able to find the exact value of this instantaneous rate of change, which is approximately -1.24 ppm per month. The slope of this limiting line is also known as the derivative at P. The study of the derivative is called **differential calculus**.

Integration: Accumulated Change

The integral deals with accumulated change over intervals of time or space. For instance, consider the 1999 outbreak of measles in the Netherlands. During this outbreak, scientists collected information about the **incidence rate**: the number of reported new cases of measles per day. How this incidence rate varied over the course of the measles outbreak is shown in Figure 6. To find the total number of cases of measles during the outbreak, we want to find the area under this incidence "curve." Indeed, each rectangle in the left-hand side of this figure has a base of width "one day" and a height with units of measles per day. Hence, the area of each of these

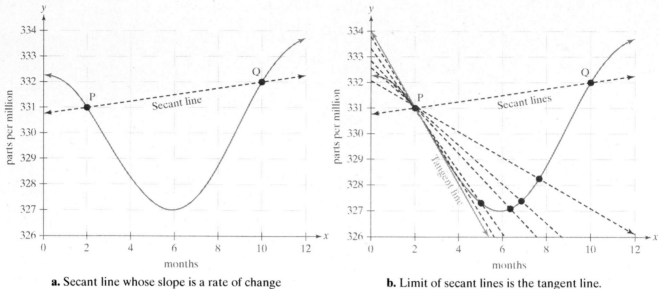

a. Secant line whose slope is a rate of change

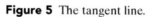

b. Limit of secant lines is the tangent line.

Figure 5 The tangent line.

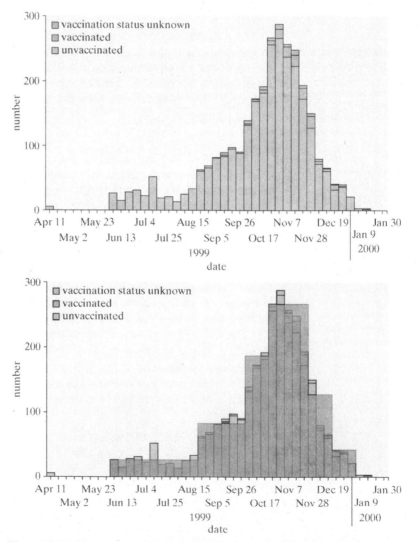

Figure 6 Incidence rate of the 1999 outbreak of measles in the Netherlands.
Source: Centers for Disease Control and Prevention.

rectangles corresponds to the number of measles cases in one day. Summing up the area of these rectangles gives us the total number of measles cases during the outbreak. To get a rough estimate of this accumulated change, we can approximate the area under the incidence curve using the six larger rectangles imposed on the data, as illustrated in the right-hand side of Figure 6.

Computing these areas yields an estimate of

$$11 \cdot 25 + 6 \cdot 80 + 3 \cdot 200 + 5 \cdot 250 + 3 \cdot 125 + 3 \cdot 50 = 3130 \text{ cases of measles}$$

The actual number of reported cases was 3292. Hence, our back of the envelope estimate was pretty good.

Integrals are a refined version of the calculation that we just made. Given any curve (e.g., incidence function) as illustrated in Figure 7, we can approximate the area by using rectangles.

If A_n is the area of the nth rectangle, then the total area can be approximated by finding the sum

$$A_1 + A_2 + A_3 + \cdots + A_{n-1} + A_n$$

This process is shown in Figure 8. To get better estimates of the area, we use more rectangles with smaller bases. The limit of this process leads to the *definite integral*, the key concept for **integral calculus**.

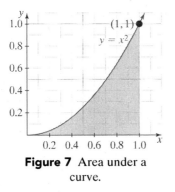

Figure 7 Area under a curve.

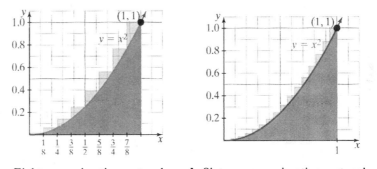

a. Eight approximating rectangles   **b.** Sixteen approximating rectangles

Figure 8 Approximating the area using circumscribed rectangles

In Chapter 1, we introduce some modeling concepts while reviewing basic mathematical concepts such as real numbers and functions—including linear, periodic, power, exponential, and logarithmic functions. Using these functions, we model the cyclic rise of carbon dioxide concentrations in the atmosphere, dangers facing large versus small organisms, population growth, and the binding of receptor molecules. We also introduce the basic notions of sequences and difference equations. Using these constructs, we encounter the dynamics of oscillatory populations, drug delivery, and gene frequencies. In the ensuing chapters, we develop the ideas of differential and integral calculus, and along the way, build necessary skills in biological modeling. Using these ideas and skills, you will model a diversity of biological topics such as disease outbreaks, blood flow, population extinctions, tumor regrowth after chemotherapy, genetics of populations, genetic networks, mechanisms for memory formation, enzyme kinetics, and evolutionary games.

Figure 1.1 Mathematical models are used in Section 1.3 to identify the great Pocket Hercules as one of the all-time greatest weightlifters.

CHAPTER 1

Modeling with Functions

MIKE HASKEY KRT/Newscom

Preview

"Mathematicians do not study objects, but relations between objects."

Henri Poincare, 1854–1912.

Although all readers taking a first course in calculus have a background in algebra, geometry, and trigonometry, the depth of exposure and choice of material covered can be quite variable. The material in this chapter is designed to provide a common framework upon which to build an introductory course in calculus for students who have a strong interest in the life sciences. In reviewing real numbers and functions, our intention is also to develop the notation we will use throughout the book. As students, you must become familiar with this notation if you want to be fluent in reading the mathematical text in this book. We also introduce data—and concepts around working with data—early on, because this component of the mathematical modeling process is critical to testing model predictions in the context of real-world problems (as discussed in the introduction to this book). We pay particular attention to power, exponential, and logarithmic functions since these all play a critical role in the development of differential and integral calculus. Trigonometric functions are important but less fundamental, and they have been dealt with extensively in precalculus mathematics courses. Thus, we provide only a brief review; we expect students who are rusty on this topic to go back and review trigonometry functions themselves. The topics dealt with in the function building section and inverse function subsection provide the kinds of skills that are needed in model building. Finally, we introduce the notion of sequences. Sequences are important both for introducing the concept of limits and in the context of dynamics, where consecutive terms in sequences can be used to represent the changes in the state of some object over a sequence of points in time—an idea that is central to the application of calculus to all branches of science.

Real Numbers and Functions

You may have had a medical test in which an electrocardiograph, as shown in Figure 1.2, was used to check whether your heart was beating normally. In order to analyze graphs such as this, we need to seek unifying ideas relating graphs, data, tables, and equations. The mathematical concept that unifies these elements is the notion of a *real-valued* function, which is at the core of the development of both differential and integral calculus.

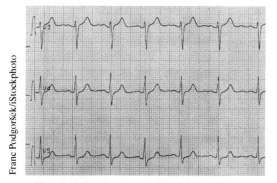

Figure 1.2 Portion of an electrocardiograph.

In this section, we discuss real numbers, functions, and basic properties of functions. To do this, we use the set notation $\{x : \text{statement}\}$, which means the set of all values of x or points x on the number line that satisfies or is defined by the statement following the colon.

Real numbers

Historically, the concept of numbers arose to address a need to count and keep exact records of land and property and to facilitate commerce. This process began with the counting numbers, now referred as the **natural numbers**, as depicted in Table 1.1.

Table 1.1 Sets of numbers

Name	Symbol	Set	Examples
Natural numbers	$\mathbb{N}$	$\{1, 2, 3, 4, 5, \cdots\}$	$6793, \sqrt{4}$
Integers	$\mathbb{Z}$	$\{\cdots -2, -1, 0, 1, 2, \cdots\}$	$-\sqrt{25}, \dfrac{18}{6}$
Rational numbers	$\mathbb{Q}$	$\left\{\dfrac{p}{q} : p, q \text{ are integers}, q \neq 0\right\}$	$\dfrac{5}{3} = 1.\bar{6}, \ -7.46\overline{31}$, where the overbar indicates a repeating decimal
Irrational numbers	$\mathbb{Q}'$	Numbers whose decimal representation does not terminate or repeat	$\sqrt{2}, \ -\sqrt{3}, \ \pi, e$
Real numbers	$\mathbb{R}$	All rational and irrational numbers	

It took a surprisingly long time for human civilization to add zero to this group to obtain the whole numbers. Negative numbers, which by some historical accounts first appeared in India and China around the seventh century, were then added to obtain the **integers**. The integers, however, are not closed under the operation of division: for example, $-4/2 = -2$ is an integer, but $4/3$ is not. Ancient Egyptian surveyors were well aware of fractional numbers, but only after negative numbers were widely accepted could the set of all positive and negative fractions, called the **rational numbers**, be defined.

Rational numbers are extremely useful for the measurements of "continuous" traits such as weight, height, humidity, and temperature, which are often measured by counting. For instance, we measure lengths by counting the number of marked intervals (e.g., inches, centimeters) on a tape measure. By subdividing these intervals into smaller and smaller fractions, we obtain more and more accurate measurements. We might expect that if we allow for all possible fractional divisions, then we can measure the precise length of anything. It came as a shock to the Greeks that this expectation is wrong! For instance, the Greeks proved that the length of the diagonal of a unit square (i.e., sides of length one) cannot be expressed as a rational number (see the 𝔥𝔦𝔰𝔱𝔬𝔯𝔦𝔠𝔞𝔩 𝔔𝔲𝔢𝔰𝔱 in Problem Set 1.1). Because this length corresponds to a number that cannot be found in the set of rational numbers, it is called *irrational* (not rational). It is denoted by the symbol $\sqrt{2}$ and its value can be approximated as precisely as we want by bounding it above and below by sequences of rational numbers that approach it in the limit! Intuitively, if we have a ruler with all fractional divisions, we can measure arbitrarily close approximations of this length.

To deal with irrational numbers, mathematicians extended the rational numbers to a larger set of numbers that we call the **real numbers**, $\mathbb{R}$. One can think of the real numbers as living on the edge of an infinitely long ruler with demarcations at all powers of ten. A real number is a point on this line and can be represented in a decimal form with its integer part before the decimal and tenths, hundredths, thousandths, ten thousandths, and so on, after the decimal. Rational numbers on this line have decimal representations that terminate or repeat, while the irrational numbers have decimal representations that do not terminate (see Table 1.1). For example, $\pi = 3.141592\ldots$ has a decimal representation that does not terminate or repeat and, consequently, is an irrational number—as is the Euler number e that we will encounter later in this chapter. Since $\sqrt{2} = 1.4142135\ldots$ is irrational, its decimal representation also does not terminate or repeat itself.

Intervals of real numbers arise so frequently in calculus that it is worthwhile giving them special names and notations. An **open interval** from a to b is denoted

$$(a, b) = \{x : a < x < b\}$$

Notice that this interval includes all the real numbers between a and b but does not include a and b themselves. A **closed interval** from a to b is denoted

$$[a, b] = \{x : a \leq x \leq b\}$$

Unlike an open interval, a closed interval includes the end points. In addition to these finite intervals, we are often interested in **infinite intervals**. These are intervals where either the right side of the interval extends infinitely far in the positive direction or the left side extends infinitely far in the negative direction, or both. In the first case, to denote this situation, we use the symbol ∞ on the right side of the interval, and in the second case we use the symbol $-\infty$ on the left side of the interval, as follows:

$$(a, \infty) = \{x : x > a\}, [a, \infty) = \{x : x \geq a\}, (-\infty, b) = \{x : x < b\}, \quad \text{and} \quad (-\infty, b] = \{x : x \leq b\}$$

The typical graphical depictions of these intervals on the real line is shown in Figure 1.3. For infinite intervals, it is important to realize there is no number "∞"

or "$-\infty$." These symbols are only used to indicate numbers in the interval whose magnitudes are arbitrarily large and positive or large and negative, respectively.

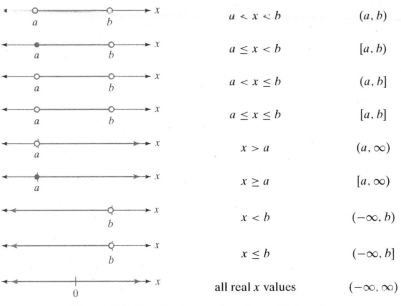

Figure 1.3 Graphical representations of intervals.

Often domains of functions are not a single interval but consist of the union of two or more intervals. We denote the **union of two (or more) intervals** with the notation $\cup$. For instance,

$$(a, b) \cup (c, d) = \{x : a < x < b \quad \text{or} \quad c < x < d\} \quad \text{and}$$

$$[a, b) \cup (c, d] = \{x : a \le x < b \quad \text{or} \quad c < x \le d\}$$

Functions

Biologists, mathematicians, and other researchers often study relationships between two quantities. The mathematical study of such relationships involves the concept of a function.

Function

A **function** $f : X \to Y$ is a rule that assigns to each element x of a set X (called the **domain** D) a unique element y of a set Y. The element y is called the **image** of x under f and is denoted by $f(x)$, read as "f of x." The set of all images $f(x)$ for x in X is called the **range** R of f.

A function can also be regarded as follows:

- A rule that assigns a unique "output" in the set Y to each "input" from the set X (Figure 1.4a)

- A graph that corresponds to the set of ordered pairs $\{(x, f(x)) : x \in D\}$ in the xy plane (Figure 1.4b)

- A machine that into which values of x are inserted and, after some internal operations are performed, a unique value $f(x)$ is produced (Figure 1.4c)

- An algebraic equation (Figure 1.4d)

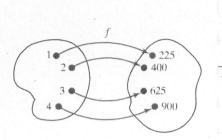

a. Function as a mapping

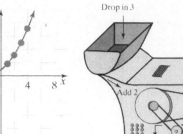

b. Function as a graph

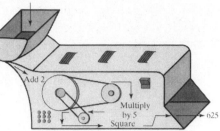

Some number drop out; in this case, we drop in a 3 and 625 drops out; this number is called f of 3 and is written $f(3) = 625$. The output for the other members of the domain is shown:

$$f(x) = [(x + 2)5]^2$$

d. Function as an equation

c. Function as a machine

Figure 1.4 Different representations of a function.

Example 1   Identifying functions

Determine whether the following rules are functions. If one is a function, identify its domain and (if possible) its range.

a. To the real number r assign the area of a circle with radius r.

b. To each person in Atlanta assign his or her telephone number.

c. To the irrational reals, assign the value 1; to the rational reals, assign the value 0.

d. To each month from May 1974 to December 1985 assign the average carbon dioxide (CO_2) concentration measured at the Mauna Loa Observatory of Hawaii. The data are graphed in Figure 1.5.

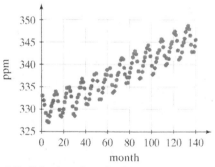

Figure 1.5 CO_2 (ppm) at the Mauna Loa Observatory.

Data Source: Komhyr, W. D., Harris, T. B., Waterman, L. S., Chin, J. F. S. and Thoning, K. W. (1989), Atmospheric carbon dioxide at Mauna Loa Observatory 1. NOAA Global monitoring for climatic change measurements with a nondispersive infrared analyzer, 1974–1985; J. Geop. Res., v. 94, no. D6, pp. 8533–8547. http://www.seattlecentral.org/qelp/sets/016/016.html

e. To each (adjusted) income of a married individual filing jointly assign the federal tax rate for 2009.

Solution

a. This function can be expressed algebraically as

$$\text{area} = \pi r^2$$

Since a radius of a circle can only be nonnegative, the domain of this function is the nonnegative reals, $[0, \infty)$. The range of this function is also $[0, \infty)$.

b. Assigning telephone numbers to individuals in Atlanta is not a function for two reasons. First, not everyone has a phone number. For these individuals no assignment can be made. Second, many people may have more than one phone number, in which case the rule does not specify which of these phone numbers to associate with such an individual. By appropriately shrinking the domain, this rule becomes a function. For instance, if the domain is restricted to individuals in Atlanta with a single home phone number, assigning the home phone numbers to these individuals is a function.

c. Assigning 1 to irrationals and 0 to rationals defines a function whose domain is the reals and whose range is the set $\{0, 1\}$. This function is known as the *Dirchlet function* and is effectively impossible to graph for reasons that will become clearer in Chapter 2.

d. Assigning average monthly CO_2 concentrations from May 1974 to December 1985 is a function whose domain is the set

$$\{\text{May 1974, June 1974, July 1974}, \ldots, \text{March 1986, April 1985}\}$$

Alternatively, if we identify any natural number n with n months after April 1974 until December 1985, then the domain of this function is

$$\{1, 2, 3, \ldots, 140\}$$

as there are eleven years and eight months of monthly data recordings. To determine the range, we would have to find the values of the collected data. These data are illustrated in Figure 1.5 and suggest the range is contained in the interval $[327, 350]$. While these data, in themselves, cannot be precisely described by a simple algebraic formula, we shall see in Section 1.3 that this function is well approximated by a simple algebraic formula.

e. Assign each adjusted income for a married individual filing jointly in 2009 the federal tax rate. Since each adjusted income for a married individual filing jointly has one and only one tax rate, this rule, which is described in the tax tables, is a function. For instance, an adjusted income of greater than \$372,950 is assigned a tax rate of 35%. We will reconsider this in Example 6.

As the preceding example and figure illustrate, functions can be represented in a variety of ways: verbally, algebraically, numerically, or graphically. Being able to move freely between these representations of a function is a skill that this book tries to cultivate.

Example 2   **From words to algebraic representations**

For regular strength Tylenol, each tablet contains 325 mg of acetaminophen. According to the *Handbook of Basic Pharmacokinetics*,* approximately 67% of the drug is removed from the body every four hours. Suppose Professor Schreiber had x mg of acetaminophen in his body four hours ago and just swallowed two more tablets of regular strength Tylenol. Write a formula in terms of x for the amount A of acetaminophen in Schreiber's body.

---

*W. A. Ritschel, *Handbook of Basic Pharmacokinetics*, 2nd ed. (Hamilton, IL: Drug Intelligence Publications, 1980): 413–426.

Solution   Since $100\% - 67\% = 33\%$ of the acetaminophen from four hours ago remains in Schreiber's body now, $0.33x$ is the amount of acetaminophen that is still in his body from four hours ago. Since Schreiber just swallowed two tablets of 325 mg per tablet, the total amount of acetaminophen in his body is

$$A = 0.33x + 325 \cdot 2 = 0.33x + 650 \text{ mg}$$

We will use this function in Section 1.7 to examine how the amount of acetaminophen in Schreiber's body varies in time whenever he takes two tablets every four hours.

In this book, unless otherwise specified, the domain of a function is the set of real numbers for which the function is a well-defined real number determined by the context of the problem. We call this the **implied domain** convention. For example, if $f(x) = \dfrac{1}{x-2}$ and $g(y) = \sqrt{y}$, we need $x \neq 2$ and $y \geq 0$, respectively. Alternatively, if n is the number of people in an elevator, the context requires that n is a whole number.

Example 3   From algebraic expressions to graphs

Find the domain D of the following functions.

a. $y = \sqrt{1-x}$

b. $y = \dfrac{1}{(1-x)(x-2)}$

Solution

a. Because the argument of square roots must be nonnegative whenever we are dealing with real numbers, the domain in this case is $D = \{x : 1 - x \geq 0\}$. Equivalently $D = (-\infty, 1]$.

b. Because we cannot divide by zero, the domain consists of x such that $x \neq 1, 2$. Equivalently, the domain is $D = (-\infty, 1) \cup (1, 2) \cup (2, \infty)$.

Plants use light energy, in the form of photons, to synthesize glucose from carbon dioxide and water while excreting oxygen as a byproduct of this process called *photosynthesis*. Plants then use the sugars to fuel other processes associated with their maintenance and growth while the oxygen is used by animals and other creatures for respiration. Thus, photosynthesis is a key process not only for plants but also for animal life on Earth!

Example 4   From verbal descriptions to graphs

Let $P(t)$ denote the photosynthetic activity of a leaf as function of t, where t is the number of hours after midnight. Sketch a rough graph of this function. Assume the sunrise is at 6 A.M. and the sunset is at 8 P.M.

Solution   Noting that there is no photosynthetic activity prior to the sunrise, we have $P(t) = 0$ for $0 \leq t \leq 6$. At sunrise, the photosynthetic activity slowly increases with the availability of light and reaches some maximum during midday. As the sun begins to set, the photosynthetic activity of the plant declines to zero and remains zero for the rest of the day. The graph of this function is shown in Figure 1.6.

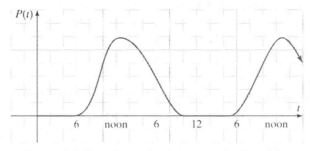

Figure 1.6 Sample graph of photosynthetic activity.

In Example 1, you were asked to identify functions. We extend this question to deciding if a given graph is the graph of a function. By looking at the definition of a function, we see that its graph has one point for a given element of the domain. Graphically, this idea can be stated in terms of the following **vertical line test**.

Vertical Line Test	A set of points in the xy-plane is the graph of a real valued function if and only if every vertical line intersects the graph at, at most, one point.

Example 5   Vertical line test in action

Determine which of the given graphs is the graph of a function.

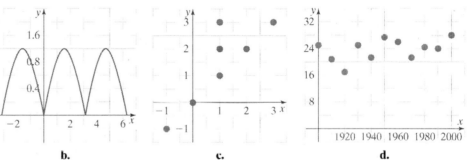

a.   **b.**   **c.**   **d.**

Solution   In panel **a** (below), a vertical line intersects the curve at two points for $x = -0.5$. Hence, this curve fails the vertical line test and is not the graph of a function. In fact, this curve is an ellipse given by the set of points that satisfy

$$x^2 + \frac{y^2}{4} = 1$$

The upper and lower halves of this ellipse can be described by the *pair* of functions

$$y = 2\sqrt{1 - x^2} \quad \text{and} \quad y = -2\sqrt{1 - x^2}$$

In panel **b** (below), this curve does satisfy the vertical line test for all points x, as shown below for $x = 1$. In fact, recalling your trigonometric functions (see the next section), it is the graph of the function $y = |\sin x|$.

In panel **c** (below), this set of points is not the graph of a function as the vertical line at $x = 1$ intersects three points.

In panel **d** (below), this set of points is the graph of a function as it passes the vertical line test for all x, as shown below for $x = 1970$. In fact, these points are the graph of the average annual temperature in New York as a function of time (in years).

a.   **b.**   **c.**   **d.**

Piecewise-defined functions

In the real world sometimes functions must be defined with more than one formula; therefore, these are called **piecewise-defined functions** or just piecewise functions for short.

Example 6   Income tax rates

The federal income tax rates for married filing jointly in 2009 can be described as 10% for (adjusted) incomes up to $16,700, 15% for the component of income between $16,701(rounding up) and $67,900, 25% for the component of income between $67,901 and $137,050, 28% for the component of income between $137,051 and $208,850, 33% for the component of income between $208,851 and $372,950, and 35% for the component of income greater than $372,950. Express the income tax rate $f(x)$ for an individual in 2009 with adjusted income x as a piecewise function. Graph the income tax rates over the interval $(0, 500000]$ (note the point 0 is not included).

Solution   An algebraic representation of this piecewise function is given by

$$f(x) = \begin{cases} 0.1 & \text{if } 0 < x \le 16,700 \\ 0.15 & \text{if } 16,700 < x \le 67,900 \\ 0.25 & \text{if } 67,900 < x \le 137,050 \\ 0.28 & \text{if } 137,050 < x \le 208,850 \\ 0.3 & \text{if } 208,850 < x \le 372,950 \\ 0.35 & \text{if } x > 372,950 \end{cases}$$

The graph of this piecewise function over the interval $(0,500,000]$ is shown in Figure 1.7. This graph consists of linear pieces with jumps between income brackets.

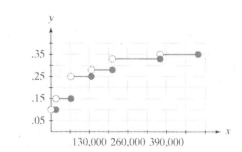

Figure 1.7 Graph of 2009 income tax rates for married filing jointly.

A particularly important piecewise-defined function is the **absolute value function**.

Absolute Value Function	The **absolute value function** $y = |x|$ is defined by
	$$|x| = \begin{cases} x & \text{if } x \geq 0 \\ -x & \text{if } x < 0 \end{cases}$$

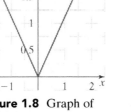

Figure 1.8 Graph of $y = |x|$.

When x is nonnegative, the absolute value of x is itself. When x is negative, the absolute value of x is the negative of itself. Hence, the graph of the absolute value function is shown in Figure 1.8.

Increasing and decreasing functions

There are several different **properties of functions** that are useful in a variety of ways.

Increasing and Decreasing Functions	Let I be an interval in the domain of a function. Then
	f is **increasing** on I if $f(x) < f(y)$ for all $x < y$ in I; that is, its graph rises from left to right on I
	f is **decreasing** on I if $f(x) > f(y)$ for all $x < y$ in I; that is, its graph falls from left to right on I
	f is **constant** on I if $f(x) = f(y)$ for every x and y in I; that is, the graph is flat on I

These classifications are shown graphically in Figure 1.9.

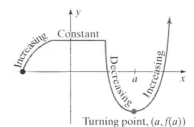

Figure 1.9 Classifications of functions.

Example 7   Classifying a function

Consider the function f defined by the following graph on the interval $I = [-2, 3]$.

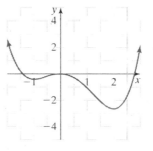

Find the intervals on which f is increasing and the intervals on which f is decreasing.

Solution   The function f is decreasing on $[-2, -1)$, increasing on $(-1, 0)$, decreasing on $(0, 2)$, and increasing on $(2, 3]$. Note that the interval is open at points where the function switches from increasing to decreasing or vice versa.

PROBLEM SET 1.1

Level 1 DRILL PROBLEMS

Determine whether the descriptions in Problems 1 to 6 represent functions. If a description is a function, find the domain and (if possible) the range.

1. **a.** $\{(4, 7), (3, 4), (5, 4), (6, 9)\}$
   b. $\{6, 9, 12, 15\}$
2. **a.** $\{(5, 2), (7, 3), (1, 6), (7, 4)\}$
   b. $\{(x, y) : y = 4x + 3\}$
3. **a.** $\{(x, y) : y \leq 4x + 3\}$
   b. $\{(x, y) : y = 1$ if x is positive and $y = -1$ if x is negative$\}$
4. **a.** $\{(x, y) : y$ is the closing price of IBM stock on July 1 of year $x\}$
   b. $\{(x, y) : x$ is the closing price of Apple stock on July 1 of year $y\}$
5. **a.** $\{(x, y) : (x, y)$ is a point on a circle of radius 4 passing through $(2, 3)\}$
   b. $\{(x, y) : (x, y)$ is a point on an upward-opening parabola with vertex $(-3, -4)\}$
6. **a.** $\{(x, y) : (x, y)$ is a point on a line passing through $(2, 3)$ and $(4, 5)\}$
   b. $\{(x, y) : (x, y)$ is a point on a line passing through $(4, 5)$ and $(-3, 5)\}$

Use the vertical line test in Problems 7 to 9 to determine whether the curve is a function. Also state the probable domain and range.

7. **a.**   **b.**

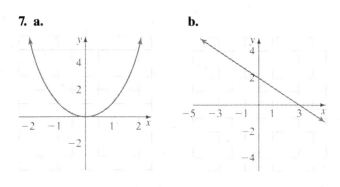

8. **a.**   **b.**

9. **a.**   **b.**

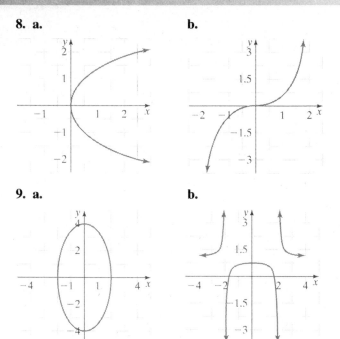

Problems 10 to 12 show the output you might find for a calculator graph. The Xmin and Xmax values show the input x values and the Ymin and Ymax values show the input y values. The scale for each tick mark on the x and y axis is also shown. These values determine the extent of the box that is shown. Using these calculator images use the vertical line test to determine whether the curve is a function. Also state the probable domain and range if you assume that a curve reaching a boundary of the frame continues in the same fashion as it continues beyond the shown screen.

10. **a.**   **b.**

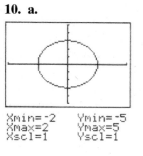

```
Xmin=-2    Ymin=-5
Xmax=2     Ymax=5
Xscl=1     Yscl=1
```

```
Xmin=-7.580645...
Xmax=7.5806451...
Xscl=1
Ymin=-5
Ymax=5
Yscl=1
```

11. a.

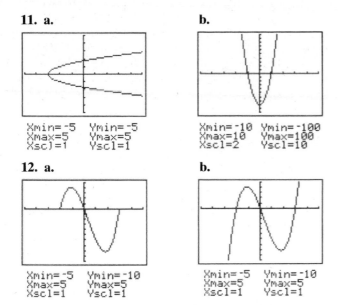

Xmin=-5   Ymin=-5
Xmax=5   Ymax=5
Xscl=1   Yscl=1

b.

Xmin=-10 Ymin=-100
Xmax=10   Ymax=100
Xscl=2   Yscl=10

12. a.

Xmin=-5   Ymin=-10
Xmax=5   Ymax=5
Xscl=1   Yscl=1

b.

Xmin=-5   Ymin=-10
Xmax=5   Ymax=5
Xscl=1   Yscl=1

In Problems 13 to 18 find the domain of f and compute the indicated values or state that the corresponding x-value is not in the domain.

13. $f(x) = -x^2 + 2x + 3$; $f(0)$, $f(1)$, $f(-2)$

14. $f(x) = 3x^2 + 5x - 2$; $f(1)$, $f(0)$, $f(-2)$

15. $f(x) = \dfrac{(x+3)(x-2)}{x+3}$; $f(2)$, $f(0)$, $f(-3)$

16. $f(x) = (2x - 1)^{-3/2}$; $f(1)$, $f\left(\dfrac{1}{2}\right)$, $f(0)$

17. $f(x) = \begin{cases} -2x + 4 & \text{if } x \le 0 \\ x + 1 & \text{if } x > 0 \end{cases}$; $f(3)$, $f(1)$, $f(0)$

18. $f(x) = \begin{cases} 3 & \text{if } x < -1 \\ x + 1 & \text{if } -1 \le x \le 5 \\ \sqrt{x} & \text{if } x > 5 \end{cases}$; $f(-6)$, $f(5)$, $f(16)$

19. Consider a function machine

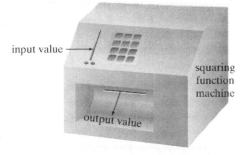

input value

squaring function machine

output value

that yields the table of values

Input values	Output values
1	1
2	4
3	9
−5	25

Algebraically, define the simplest function F you can think of for input values x from the domain $D = \mathbb{R}$.

20. Consider a function machine

secret function machine

that yields the table of values

Input values	Output values
0	3
1	5
2	7
3	9
4	11

Algebraically, define the simplest function S you can think of for input values t from the domain $D = [0, \infty)$.

21. Suppose you are given a machine that multiplies the input value by 3 and then subtracts 7. Complete the table of values given below

Input values	Output values
3	2
5	
0	
−3	

and algebraically, define a function M for input values x from the domain $D = \mathbb{R}$.

22. Suppose there is super-secret machine the produces the table

Input values	Output values
0	5
1	6
2	9
3	14
4	21

Algebraically define the simplest function, T, for input values t from the domain $D = \mathbb{R}$.

Find the domain and range for the graphs indicated in Problems 23 to 28. Also tell where the function is increasing, decreasing, and constant.

23.

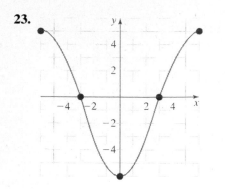

24.

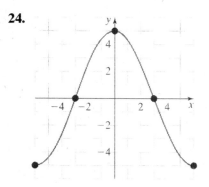

25.

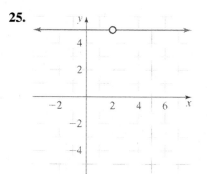

26.

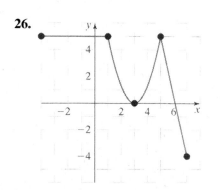

27.

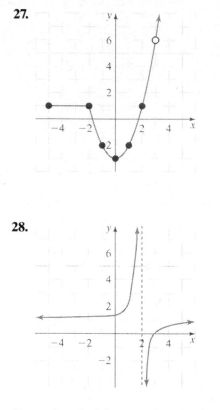

28.

For each verbal description in Problems 29 to 32, write a rule in the form of an equation, state the domain, and then graph the function.

29. For each number x in the domain, the corresponding range value, y, is found by multiplying by 3 and then subtracting 5.

30. For each number x in the domain, the corresponding range value, y, is found by squaring and then subtracting 5 times the domain value.

31. For each number x in the domain, the corresponding range value, y, is found by subtracting the domain value from 5 and then taking the square root.

32. For each number x in the domain, the corresponding range value, y, is found by taking 5 added to 5 times the domain value and then dividing this by the result of adding 1 to the domain value.

33. From a square whose side has length x (in inches), create a new square whose side is 5 inches longer. Find an expression for the difference between the area of the two squares (in square inches) as a function of x. Graph this expression for $0 \le x \le 10$.

34. From a square whose side has length x (in meters), create a new square whose side is 10 meters longer. Find an expression for the sum of the areas of the two squares (in square meters) as a function of x. Graph this expression for $0 \le x \le 10$.

35. Find the area of a square as a function of its perimeter P.

36. Find the area of a circle as a function of its circumference C.

Level 2 APPLIED AND THEORY PROBLEMS

37. Recall from Example 2, a tablet of regular strength Tylenol contains 325 mg of acetaminophen and approximately 67% of the drug is removed from the body every four hours. Suppose Professor Schreiber had x mg of acetaminophen in his body four hours ago and just swallowed two more tablets of regular strength Tylenol. Write a formula in terms of x for the amount A of acetaminophen in Schreiber's body four hours from now.

38. Diazepam is a medication used for the management of anxiety disorders. Approximately 68% of the drug is removed from the body every 24 hours. Suppose a patient had x mg of diazepam in his body 24 hours ago and just took an oral dose of 30 mg. Write a formula in terms of x for the amount A of diazepam in the patient's body 24 hours from now.

39. Professor Getz mows his backyard lawn every Saturday. Draw a graph of the height of the grass in the lawn over a two-week period, beginning just after Getz mowed his lawn one Saturday.

40. Continuous morphine infusion (CMI) is a means of providing a continuous dosage of medication (morphine) for acute pain. Morphine is administered continuously by a computerized pump connected to the patient by an intravenous tube (IV). Graph the concentration of morphine in a patient's blood (in milligrams/liter) over a three-day period. Assume the patient initially had no morphine in the blood stream and the concentration of morphine was relatively constant at 1 mg/liter on the last day.

41. Biologists have found that the speed of blood in an artery is a function of the distance of the blood from the artery's central axis (Figure 1.10). According to *Poiseuille's law*, the speed (centimeters/second) of blood that is r centimeters from the central axis of an artery is given by the function

$$S(r) = C(R^2 - r^2)$$

where R is the radius of the artery and C is a constant that depends on the viscosity of the blood and the pressure between the two ends of the blood vessel. (The law and the unit *poise*, a unit of viscosity, are named for the French physician Jean Louis Poiseuille, 1799–1869.) Suppose that for a certain artery

$$C = 1.76 \times 10^5 \text{ cm/s}$$

and

$$R = 1.2 \times 10^{-2} \text{ cm}$$

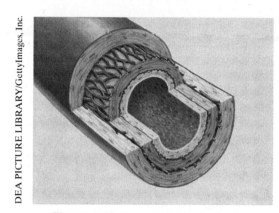

DEA PICTURE LIBRARY/GettyImages, Inc.

Figure 1.10 Cutaway view of an artery.

a. Compute the speed of the blood at the central axis of this artery.

b. Compute the speed of the blood midway between the artery's wall and central axis.

c. What is the domain for the function defined by the ordered pairs (r, S)?

d. Graph this function for $S \geq 0$.

42. The reaction rate of an autocatalytic reaction is given by the formula

$$R(x) = kx(a - x)$$

for $0 \leq x \leq a$, where a is the initial concentration of substance A and x is the concentration of X.

a. What is the domain?

b. Graph this function for $k = 3$ and $a = 8$.

43. Consider the function defined to study the rate at which animals learn when a psychology student performed an experiment in which a rat was sent repeatedly through a laboratory maze. Suppose that the time (in minutes) required for the rat to traverse the maze on the nth trial is modeled by the function

$$f(n) = 3 + \frac{12}{n}$$

a. What is the domain of the function f if n is a continuous variable?

b. What is the domain of the function f in the context of the psychology experiment?

c. Graph the function f defined in part **b** for n on interval $[1, 20]$.

d. What will happen to the time required for the rat to traverse the maze as the number of trials increases? Will the rat ever be able to traverse the maze in less than three minutes?

44. Consider the function defined by

$$f(x) = \frac{150x}{200 - x}$$

  a. What is the domain of the function f?

  b. Suppose that during a nationwide program to immunize the population against a certain form of influenza, public health officials found the cost (in millions of dollars) of inoculating $x\%$ of the population is modeled by f. For what values of x does $f(x)$ have a practical interpretation in this context?

  c. Graph the function for its interpretable range for the problem at hand.

  d. Compare the cost of inoculating the first 50% of the population with the cost for the second 50%.

45. *Friend's rule* is a method for calculating pediatric drug dosages in terms of a child's age (up to $12\frac{1}{2}$ years). If A is the adult dose (in milligrams) and n is the age of the child (in years), then the child's dose is given by

$$D(n) = \frac{2}{25}nA$$

  a. What is the domain for the function defined by (n, D)?

  b. Graph this function for continuous $0 \le n \le 12.5$ and $A = 100$.

  c. If a 3-year-old child receives 100 mg of a certain drug, what is the corresponding dose for a 5-year-old child?

46. *Young's rule* is another method for calculating pediatric drug dosages in terms of a child's age. If A is the adult dose (in milligrams) and n is the age of the child (in years), then the child's dose is given by

$$D(n) = \frac{n}{n + 12}A$$

  a. What is the domain for the function defined by (n, D) if the formula is applied to individuals up to age 16?

  b. Graph this function for continuous $0 \le n \le 16$ and $A = 100$.

  c. If a 6-year-old child receives 120 mg of a certain drug, what is the corresponding dose for an 8-year-old child?

47. *Clark's rule* is a method for calculating pediatric drug dosages based on a child's weight (w) in pounds (lb). If A denotes the adult dose (in milligrams) then the corresponding child's dose is given by

$$D(w) = \left(\frac{w}{150}\right)A$$

  a. What is the domain for the function defined by (w, D)?

  b. Graph this function for $A = 200$ mg.

  c. If a 70-lb child receives 90 mg of a certain drug, what is the corresponding dose for an adult?

48. Table 1.2 tabulates the estimated number of HIV/AIDS cases diagnosed each year in the United States from 1999 to 2002.

Table 1.2 Number of diagnosed cases of HIV/AIDS by year

Age at diagnosis (years)	1999	2000	2001	2002
< 13	187	163	206	162
13–14	28	31	33	30
15–24	2,646	2,803	2,926	2,926
25–34	7,817	7,386	7,221	7,338
35–44	9,115	9,289	9,119	9,450
45–54	3,887	4,212	4,408	4,675
55–64	1,112	1,250	1,303	1,450
> 64	382	386	427	432

Source: **Survey Report Volume 14 from the Center of Disease control, Division of HIV/AIDS Prevention.**

  a. Use these data to draw a graph of the number of cases being diagnosed each day during the period starting at the beginning of 1999 and ending at the end of 2002 for the age group 25–34. This should be done by assuming that the average daily rate each year holds at the beginning of the year and then joining these points by a "continuous" curve (i.e., a curve with no jumps or breaks). The concept of continuity will be made more precise in the Chapter 2.

  b. Use these data to draw a graph of the number of new cases diagnosed each day for all age groups.

49. 𝔥istorical 𝔔uest

Courtesy of Karl Smith

Pythagoras (ca. 569–475 BC)

Throughout the text, you will find problems called Historical Quest. These problems are not just historical notes to help you see mathematics and biology as living disciplines; rather, these problems are designed to involve you in the quest of pursuing great ideas in the history of science. Yes, they relate some interesting history, but they will also lead you on a quest that you may find interesting.

Even though we know little about the man himself, we do know that Pythagoras was a Greek philosopher who is sometimes described as the first true mathematician in the history of mathematics. He founded a philosophical and religious school in Croton and attracted many followers, known today as the Pythagoreans. The Pythagoreans were a secret society who had their own philosophy, religion, and way of life. This group investigated music, astronomy, geometry, and number properties. Because of their strict secrecy, much of what we know about them is legend, and it is difficult to tell what work can be attributed to Pythagoras himself. We also know that it was considered impious for a member of the Pythagoreans to claim any discovery for himself. Instead, each new idea was attributed to their founder Pythagoras. No doubt you know the Pythagorean theorem, but do you know that the Pythagoreans believed that all things are numbers and that by a *number* they meant the ratio of two whole numbers? For this $\mathfrak{Historical\ Quest}$ you are to use these two ideas to prove that $\sqrt{2}$ is an irrational number.

There is a legend (not historical fact) that one day a group of Pythagoreans were out in a boat seeking truth. One person on board came up with the following argument: Construct a right triangle with legs of length 1 unit. By the Pythagorean theorem, the length of the hypotenuse is (using modern notation) exactly $\sqrt{2}$ units long. Is the length of this side a rational number or an irrational number? Let $\sqrt{2} = \frac{p}{q}$. (Remember, they believed that all numbers could be expressed as the ratio of two whole numbers; thus, assume that $\sqrt{2}$ is a rational number.) Assume that $\frac{p}{q}$ is a reduced fraction (if it is not reduced, simply reduce it and work with the reduced form). See if you can reproduce the work done in the boat; that is, show the details outlined here. Square both sides of the equation and prove that p is an even number. If p is even, then it can be written as $p = 2k$. Use this fact to show that q is even. Thus, the fraction $\frac{p}{q}$ is not reduced. Now, if you understand logic as did the Pythagoreans, you can see the contradiction. What is it? How can you use this information to prove that $\sqrt{2}$ is irrational. Legend has it that this contradiction bothered those on the boat so much that they tossed the person who came up with this argument overboard—and pledged themselves to secrecy!

1.2   Data Fitting with Linear and Periodic Functions

In the previous section we presented data about carbon dioxide (CO_2) collected at the top of the Mauna Loa volcano since 1958 by the U.S. government's Climate Monitoring Diagnostics Laboratory. These data are plotted in Figure 1.5. Scientists routinely collect data involving two variables x and y and refer to such data as *bivariate*. In many cases, a list of bivariate points, such as the Mauna Loa CO_2 data, can be modeled by a relatively simple functional relationship of the form $y = f(x)$ that passes, if not through all points, then close by all points. The advantages of the model are that it describes the data more concisely than a list, it can make predictions for uncollected data values, and it can generate hypotheses. For instance, if we had a function that did a good job of describing how carbon dioxide concentrations fluctuate in time, then we could make predictions about future levels of carbon dioxide concentrations. The importance of these predictions stems from the fact that carbon dioxide is a greenhouse gas. It prevents the escape of heat radiating from the Earth. Consequently, carbon dioxide in the atmosphere influences the Earth's temperature, and many people would like to know what the temperature might be twenty or fifty years from now so that they can plan accordingly.

The most commonly fitted function is a *linear function*: a function that depicts a constant rate of change with respect to unit changes in the argument of the function. In this section, we review basic facts about linear functions and briefly discuss how to fit linear functions to data sets, a process referred to in statistics as *linear regression*. For instance, the data in Figure 1.5 suggest that carbon dioxide concentrations in the atmosphere are tending to increase across years. Using linear regression, we can determine at what rate this increase across years is occurring. In addition to exhibiting a linear trend, the carbon dioxide data clearly exhibit seasonal fluctuations. These seasonal fluctuations can be modeled by periodic functions. Consequently, the section continues by reviewing basic properties of periodic and trigonometric functions and fitting trigonometric functions to data sets. Using a combination of linear and trigonometric functions, we arrive at surprisingly good model of CO_2 fluctuations.

Linear functions

Linear functions play a fundamental role in differential calculus as they can be used to approximate functions locally (i.e., over a relatively small interval of the domain of the variable x). A **linear function** is a function of the form

$$y = f(x) = mx + b$$

where m is the **slope** and b is the **vertical** or **y-intercept** of the linear function. The vertical intercept b is the value of y when x equals zero. Equivalently, it is the y-value at which the graph of $y = f(x)$ intercepts the y-axis; that is, $b = f(0)$. In contrast, the slope m of the line tells us that if we increase the x-value by an increment, say 0.2, then the corresponding y-value increases by m times that increment, $0.2m$. Equivalently, the change in y divided by the corresponding change in x is always the constant m. This leads us to a **slope formula**.

Slope of a Line	A nonvertical line that contains the points $P_1 = (x_1, y_1)$ and $P_2 = (x_2, y_2)$ has slope $$m = \frac{y_2 - y_1}{x_2 - x_1}$$

When the function $y = mx + b$ is regarded as a relationship between the paired variables (x, y), x is called the **independent variable** and y the **dependent variable**, because the relationship is designed to answer this question: What value of y corresponds to a given value for x?

Example 1   From graphs to equations

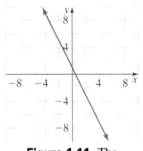

Figure 1.11 The equation $y = -2x + 1$.

Let $y = f(x)$ be the linear function whose graph is shown in Figure 1.11. Find the equation for $f(x)$.

Solution   Looking at the graph, we see that the y intercept is given by $b = 1$. Since $y = 1$ when $x = 0$ and $y = 0$ when $x = 0.5$, we see that y decreases by 1 when x increases by 0.5. Thus,

$$m = \frac{1 - 0}{0 - 0.5} = -2$$

and the equation of this line is

$$y = -2x + 1$$

Example 2   From equations to graphs

Let $y = f(x)$ be a linear function such that $f(2) = 3$ and $f(-2) = -1$. Write a formula for $f(x)$ and sketch the graph.

Solution   Since $f(x)$ is linear, we write $f(x) = mx + b$ where we need to determine the constants m and b. The slope is given by

$$m = \frac{f(2) - f(-2)}{2 - (-2)} = \frac{3 - (-1)}{4} = 1$$

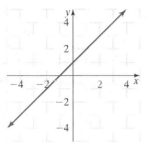

Figure 1.12 Graph of $y = x + 1$.

Therefore, $f(x) = x + b$. To find b, we solve

$$f(2) = 3$$
$$b + 2 = 3$$
$$b = 1$$

Hence, $y = f(x) = x + 1$. To graph this function, it suffices to draw a line that passes through the points $(-2, -1)$ and $(2, 3)$ as shown in Figure 1.12. ■

Fitting linear functions to data

Many data sets exhibit trends that can be reasonably described by linear functions. We can fit linear functions to data using either formal or informal approaches. Informal approaches include eyeballing how well a selected line passes through a given set of data or fitting a line to two suitably chosen points in the data set. Formal statistical methods provide ways for finding the **best-fitting line** in some well-defined mathematical sense, which we describe after the next example.

Example 3   **Carbon dioxide output from electric power plants**

In Figure 1.13 the carbon dioxide emissions of most of the electricity generation plants in California are plotted as a function of the heat input for the year 1997. The heat input units are a million British thermal units (i.e., 10^6 BTU or 1 MMBTU) and CO_2 emissions are measured in metric tons.

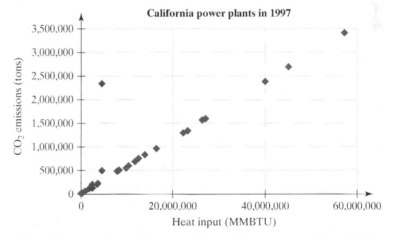

Figure 1.13 Data from the Emissions and Generation Resource Integrated Database.

In Table 1.3, six points that appear in Figure 1.13 are listed.

a. Since the data in Figure 1.13 look linear, use the first two data points in Table 1.3 to find a line that passes through the data. Graph this line.

Table 1.3 California power plants in 1997

Heat input (MMBTU)	CO_2 output (tons)
45.179×10^6	2.685×10^6
1.00×10^6	0.058×10^6
1.902×10^6	0.113×10^6
3.334×10^6	0.197×10^6
0.086×10^6	0.005×10^6
13.897×10^6	0.826×10^6
$\vdots$	$\vdots$

b. One data point in Figure 1.13 looks like it does not fit the rest of the data. This data point corresponds to a heat input of 4.488×10^6 MMBTU with a corresponding output of around 2.3×10^6 metric tons. Use the linear function in part **a** to estimate the CO_2 output for this plant. Then use the graph to estimate the actual output.

Solution

a. To find the line $y = mx + b$ that passes through $(45.179 \times 10^6, 2.685 \times 10^6)$ and $(1 \times 10^6, 0.058 \times 10^6)$, we first solve for the slope:

$$m = \frac{2.685 - 0.058}{45.179 - 1} \approx 0.059$$

Using the point-slope formula (see Problem 17 in Problem Set 1.2) for a line yields

$$y - 2.685 \approx 0.059(x - 45.179)$$
$$y \approx 0.059x - 0.019 \times 10^6 \text{ tons of } CO_2$$

Sketching this line over the data graph shown in Figure 1.13 yields the following graph.

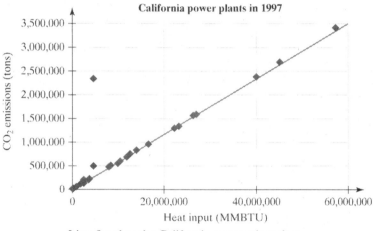

Line fitted to the California power plant data.

This is a very good fit considering we just used the first two data points. Such a good fit does not always happen.

b. Substituting $x = 4.488$ into our linear equation yields

$$y = 0.059(4.488) - 0.019 \approx 0.25 \times 10^6 \text{ tons of } CO_2$$

This is significantly smaller than the value of 2.3×10^6 tons of CO_2 given in the data. Thus, the power plant represented by this point on the graph pollutes almost ten times as much as it should compared with other power plants of similar energy output.

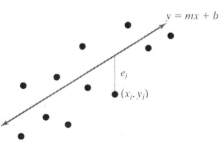

Figure 1.14 Vertical distance of data from a line.

Sometimes we can get a good fit to data by appropriately choosing two data points and finding the line that passes through these points. However, this method is quite ad hoc, because it depends on the two points selected and thus yields many different possible lines. Statisticians have solved this problem by inventing a method called **linear regression**. It is used to find a line that best fits that data in the following sense: The slope parameter m and y-intercept parameter b are chosen to minimize the sum of the squared vertical distances e_i of the data from the line (see Figure 1.14). The values e_i are called the *residuals* because they represent "what is left over once the linear fit has been taken into account."

Why squared distances? To find the answer to this question and to learn the statistical underpinnings of linear regression, you need to take an introductory statistics course! However, we note without further details (see any elementary statistics text for details) that a *sum-of-squares* measure of the fit leads to relatively simple formulas for the slope and y-intercept of the best-fitting line (which can be easily computed with calculators, computer software, and on line web applications). Part of this simple formula is derived in Chapter 4 as an application of differentiation.

Example 4 CO_2 concentrations in Hawaii

Table 1.4 describes how CO_2 concentrations (in ppm) have varied from May 1974 to December 1985 at the Mauna Loa Observatory in Hawaii. A plot of these data (where time is measured in months) was given by Example 1 of Section 1.1.

Table 1.4 CO_2 concentrations at the Mauna Loa Observatory of Hawaii

Month	CO_2	Month	CO_2	Month	CO_2	Month	CO_2	Month	CO_2	Month	CO_2
1	333.2	25	334.8	49	338.0	73	341.5	97	344.3	121	347.5
2	332.1	26	334.1	50	338.0	74	341.3	98	343.4	122	346.8
3	331.0	27	332.9	51	336.4	75	339.4	99	342.0	123	345.4
4	329.2	28	330.6	52	334.3	76	337.8	100	339.8	124	343.2
5	327.4	29	329.0	53	332.4	77	336.0	101	337.9	125	341.3
6	327.3	30	328.6	54	332.3	78	336.1	102	338.1	126	341.5
7	328.5	31	330.1	55	333.8	79	337.2	103	339.3	127	342.8
8	329.5	32	331.6	56	334.8	80	338.3	104	340.7	128	344.4
9	330.7	33	332.7	57	336.2	81	339.4	105	341.5	129	345.0
10	331.4	34	333.2	58	336.7	82	340.5	106	342.7	130	345.9
11	331.8	35	334.9	59	337.8	83	341.7	107	343.2	131	347.5
12	333.3	36	336.0	60	339.0	84	342.5	108	345.2	132	348.0
13	333.9	37	336.8	61	339.0	85	343.0	109	345.8	133	348.7
14	333.4	38	336.1	62	339.2	86	342.5	110	345.4	134	348.1
15	331.8	39	334.8	63	337.6	87	340.8	111	344.0	135	346.6
16	329.9	40	332.5	64	335.5	88	338.6	112	342.0	136	344.6
17	328.6	41	331.3	65	333.8	89	337.0	113	340.0	137	343.0
18	328.5	42	331.2	66	334.1	90	337.1	114	340.2	138	342.9
19	329.3	43	332.4	67	335.3	91	338.5	115	341.4	139	344.2
20	*	44	333.5	68	336.7	92	339.9	116	343.0	140	345.6
21	331.7	45	334.7	69	337.8	93	340.9	117	343.9		
22	332.7	46	335.2	70	338.3	94	341.7	118	344.6		
23	333.5	47	336.5	71	340.1	95	342.8	119	345.2		
24	334.8	48	337.8	72	340.9	96	343.7	120	347.1		

Data source: Komhyr, W. D., Harris, T. B., Waterman, L. S., Chin, J. F. S. and Thoning, K. W. (1989), Atmospheric carbon dioxide at Mauna Loa Observatory 1. NOAA Global monitoring for climatic change measurements with a nondispersive infrared analyzer, 1974–1985; *J. Geop. Res.*, v. 94, no. D6, pp. 8533–8547.

a. Find the best-fitting line to the CO_2 data. Plot this line against the data.

b. Determine at what rate (in ppm/year) the concentration of CO_2 has been increasing.

c. Estimate the CO_2 concentration for December 2004 using your best-fitting line. How does this compare with the average level of 338 ppm over the period May 1974 to December 1985?

d. For the CO_2 concentration in each data point, subtract the CO_2 concentration predicted by the best-fitting line. Plot the resulting residuals. What do you notice?

Solution

a. Downloading the data from the website and entering it into a graphing calculator or to a computer spreadsheet, and then running a linear regression routine, yields the best-fitting curve

$$y = 0.1225x + 329.3$$

STOP: Do not just read this—do it! Plotting this line against the data results in Figure 1.15.

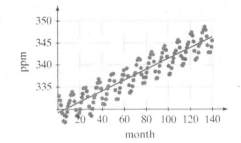

Figure 1.15 Best-fitting line for CO_2 at the Mauna Loa Observatory in Hawaii.

b. Since the slope of the line is 0.1225, the rate that CO_2 concentration has been increasing on average is 0.1225 ppm/month. Multiplying by 12 yields an annual rate of 1.47 ppm/year.

c. The number of months between December 2004 and May 1974 is $12 \cdot 30 + 8 = 368$. Substituting $x = 368$ into the best-fitting line yields a prediction of

$$y = 0.1225 \cdot 368 + 329.3 \approx 374.4$$

The estimated CO_2 concentration for December 2004 is 374.4 ppm. This is $374.4 - 338 = 36.4$ ppm higher than the average level from May 1974 to December 1985.

d. Subtracting the best-fitting line from the data and plotting the first five years yields Figure 1.16. This figure illustrates that with the removal of the linearly increasing trend, the residual CO_2 concentrations exhibit reasonably well-defined oscillations that seem to roughly repeat themselves over a twelve-month cycle.

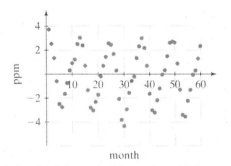

Figure 1.16 Residuals for the CO_2 at the Mauna Loa Observatory in Hawaii once the values predicted by the best-fitting line have been subtracted from the data.

Periodic and trigonometric functions

Many biological and physical time series exhibit oscillatory behavior, as just shown by Example 4. These types of data sets can be described by **periodic functions** that repeat their values at evenly spaced intervals. More formally, we make the following definition.

Periodic Function

A real-valued function f is **periodic** if there is a real number $T > 0$ such that

$$f(x) = f(x + T)$$

for all x. The smallest possible value of T is called the **period** of f. The **amplitude** (if it exists) of a periodic function is half of the difference between its largest and smallest values.

Example 5   Estimating periods and amplitudes

Estimate the period and amplitude for the CO_2 data in Figure 1.16.

Solution   A quick examination of the CO_2 data reveals that the time between peaks is approximately twelve months, so the period is a year. From the plot of the residuals in Figure 1.16, we see that the largest values of the data seem to be around 3 ppm, while the smallest values are typically around -3 ppm. Hence, the amplitude is approximately $(3 - (-3))/2 = 3$ ppm.

Two important periodic functions that you have encountered previously in pre-calculus mathematics studies are the **cosine** and **sine** functions. The cosine function, $y = \cos x$, is defined for all reals and has a range of $[-1, 1]$. Hence, the amplitude of cosine is 1. As with all trigonometric functions used here, we assume x is measured in radians. You may recall the an angle of $90°$ is a right angle, which is equal to $\pi/2$ radians. Consequently, the full period of the sine and cosine function is 2π. In other words, $\sin(x) = \sin(x + 2\pi)$ and $\cos(x) = \cos(x + 2\pi)$ for any value of x measured in radians. The graphs of both functions are shown in Figure 1.17. Since the graph of sine is the graph of cosine shifted to the right by $\pi/2$, it follows that

$$\sin x = \cos\left(x - \frac{\pi}{2}\right)$$

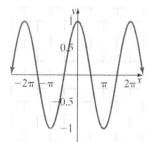   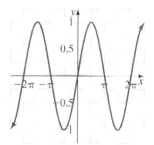

a. cosine curve period: 2π; amplitude: 1   **b. sine curve** period: 2π; amplitude: 1
Figure 1.17 Graphs of cosine and sine.

Curves with the shape of sine or cosine functions are called **sinusoidal**. An important two-parameter family of sinusoidal functions are functions of the form

$$y = f(x) = a\,\cos(bx)$$

where a is a real number and b is a nonzero real number. Since the range of $f(x)$ is $[-|a|, |a|]$, the amplitude of $f(x)$ is $|a|$. To find the period $T > 0$ of $f(x)$, we need to find the smallest $T > 0$ such that

$$a\,\cos(bx) = a\,\cos(b(x + T)) = a\,\cos(bx + bT)$$

This occurs when $bT = 2\pi$. Therefore, the period of f is $2\pi/b$. In the following example, we put this information to use.

Example 6   Fitting the CO₂ data

Consider

$$y = f(x) = a\cos(bx)$$

where a and b are positive constants.

a. Write an equation $f(x)$ that provides a good fit to the CO_2 residual data shown in Figure 1.16 from the Mauna Loa Observatory and plot this equation against the given data.

b. Let $g(x) = 0.1225x + 329.3$ be the best-fitting line shown in Figure 1.15 and $f(x)$ the equation you have just obtained. Plot $h(x) = f(x) + g(x)$ against the data shown in Table 1.4. Use h to predict the carbon dioxide level in March 2006, and compare to what you find online.

Solution

a. We found in Example 5 that the amplitude for the data in Figure 1.16 is approximately 3 ppm and the period is 12 months. Therefore, we need to choose $a = 3$ and find b. To get a period of 12 months, we need $2\pi/b = 12$. Therefore, $b = \pi/6$ and we get the equation

$$f(x) = 3\cos\left(\frac{\pi}{6}x\right)$$

The graph of this equation against the data is shown here.

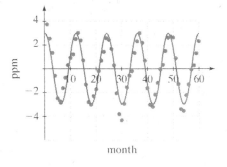

b. Plotting $h(x) = f(x) + g(x)$ against the data yields the following graph.

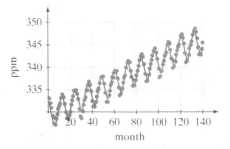

A truly remarkable fit! Next, calculate $h(12 \cdot 31 + 11) = h(383) = f(383) + g(383) = 2.60 + 376.2 = 378.8$. According to one website, the March measurement was 381 ppm. Hence, CO_2 may well be increasing slightly faster than predicted by the model, possibly due to an accelerating rate of CO_2 emissions. ▪

Other important trigonometric functions that you will encounter in this book are given by taking either reciprocals or ratios of the sine and cosine functions. For example, the tangent function is

$$y = \tan x = \frac{\sin x}{\cos x}$$

Because $\cos x = 0$ for odd integer multiples of $\pi/2$, the domain of tangent is all real numbers except these odd integer multiples of $\pi/2$. Furthermore, as we discuss further in Chapter 2, $\tan x$ approaches $+\infty$ as x approaches $\pi/2$ from the left and approaches $-\infty$ as x approaches $\pi/2$ from the right. Consequently, the domain of tangent excludes all points $x = n\pi/2$ for any odd integer n, and its range is the entire reals. Also it does not have a well-defined amplitude but is periodic, with period π, as shown in Figure 1.18. Like tangent, the other trigonometric functions—namely, cotangent $\cot x = \dfrac{\cos x}{\sin x}$, secant $\sec x = \dfrac{1}{\cos x}$, and cosecant $\csc x = \dfrac{1}{\sin x}$—are not defined for all reals, have no well-defined amplitude, but also have a well-defined period as shown in Figure 1.18. Since these functions are all expressed in terms of the sine and cosine functions, and cosine is the sin function with a $\pi/2$ shift in its argument, the properties of all the trigonometric functions can be directly deduced from the properties of the sine function.

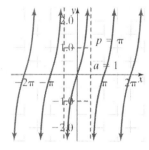

Figure 1.18 Graphs of the trigonometric functions $y = \tan(x)$, $y = \cot(x)$, $y = \sec(x)$, and $y = \csc(x)$.

PROBLEM SET 1.2

Level 1 DRILL PROBLEMS

Solve for y as a function of x and graph the resulting function for Problems 1 to 10.

1. $5x - 4y - 8 = 0$

2. $x - 3y + 2 = 0$

3. $100x - 250y + 500 = 0$

4. $2x - 5y - 200 = 0$

5. $3x + y - 2 = 0$, $-7 \le x \le 1$

6. $2x - 2y + 6 = 0$, $1 \le x \le 5$

7. $y = 4 \cos x$

8. $y = \cos(4x)$

9. $y = (\sin x)/2$, $-8 \le x \le 8$

10. $y = \sin(x/2)$, $-8 \le x \le 8$

Using the information in Problems 11 to 16, find the formula for the line $y = mx + b$.

11. Slope 3, passing through $(1, 3)$

12. Slope $\dfrac{2}{5}$; passing through $(5, -2)$

13. Passing through $(-1, 2)$ and $(0, 1)$

14. Passing through $(5, 6)$ and $(7, 6)$

15. y-intercept 4 passing through $(3, 4)$

16. horizontal line through $(-2, 5)$

17. Show that
$$y - k = m(x - h)$$
is the equation of the line passing through the point (h, k) with slope m.

18. Derive the equation of vertical line passing through (h, k). Does this set of points represent a function?

Classify each graph in Problems 19 to 24 as a linear function or a periodic function. If it is linear, estimate the slope and write an equation of the form $y = mx + b$. If it is periodic, estimate the period and the amplitude and write an equation of the form $y = a \cos(bx)$, $a > 0$.

A

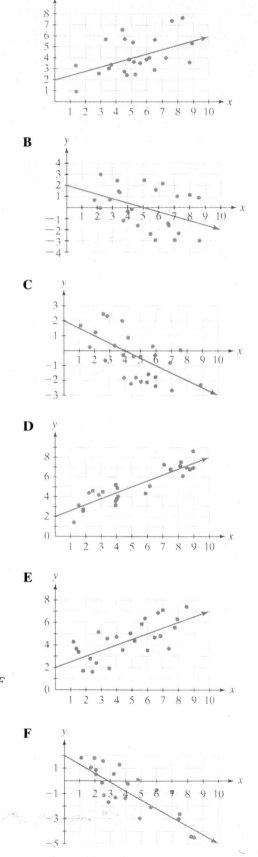

19.

20.

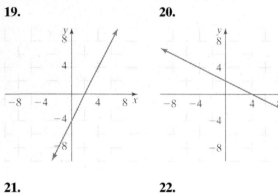

21.

22.

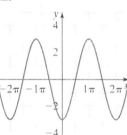

23.

24.

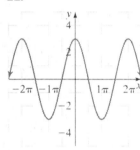

Match the equations in Problems 25 to 30 along with the scatter diagrams and best-fitting lines in figure panels A–F below.

25. $y = 0.6x + 2$

26. $y = 0.5x + 2$

27. $y = 0.4x + 2$

28. $y = -0.4x + 2$

29. $y = -0.5x + 2$

30. $y = -0.7x + 2$

Consider some standard trigonometric curves shown in Figure 1.19. Specify the period and amplitude for each graph (if exists) in Problems 31 to 36, and graph each curve.

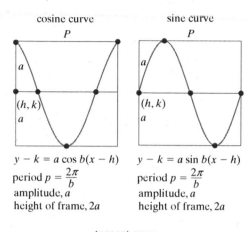

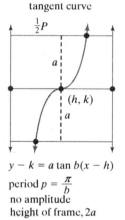

Figure 1.19 Standard cosine, sine, and tangent curves.

31. $y = \dfrac{1}{2} \cos(x + \pi/6)$

32. $y = 2 \sin(x - \pi/4)$

33. $y = 2 \sin 2\pi x$

34. $y = 3 \cos 3\pi x$

35. $y = \tan(2x - \pi/2)$

36. $y = \tan(x/2 + \pi/3)$

Level 2 APPLIED AND THEORY PROBLEMS

37. A life insurance table indicates that a woman who is now A years old can expect to live E years longer. Suppose that A and E are linearly related and that $E = 50$ when $A = 24$ and $E = 20$ when $A = 60$.

　a. At what age may a woman expect to live 30 years longer?

　b. What is the life expectancy of a newborn female child?

　c. At what age is the life expectancy zero?

38. In certain parts of the world, the number of deaths N per week has been observed to be linearly related to the average concentration x of sulfur dioxide in the air. Suppose there are 97 deaths when $x = 100$ mg/m^3 and 110 deaths when $x = 500$ mg/m^3.

　a. What is the functional relationship between N and x?

　b. Use the function in part **a** to find the number of deaths per week when $x = 300$ mg/m^3. What concentration of sulfur dioxide corresponds to 100 deaths per week?

　c. Research data on how air pollution affects the death rate in a population. You may find the following articles helpful: D. W. Dockery, J. Schwartz, and J. D. Spengler, "Air Pollution and Daily Mortality: Associations with Particulates and Acid Aerosols," *Environmental Research* 59 (1992): 362–373; Y. S. Kim, "Air Pollution, Climate, Socioeconomics Status and Total Mortality in the United States," *Science of the Total Environment* (1985): 245–256. Summarize your results in a one-paragraph essay.

39. The chart in Figure 1.20 shows the fat intake compared with death rates in several countries.

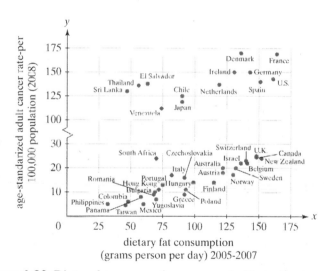

Figure 1.20 Dietary fat consumption compared with death rate.
Source: World Health Statistics, World Health Organization.

It can be shown that the best-fitting line is one of the following:

A. $y = -0.281x + 111$

B. $y = 0.274x + 109$

C. $y = 0.086x + 110$

Which do you think is the correct one? Use your choice to estimate the number of deaths per 100, 000 population to be expected from an average fat intake of 150 g/day (roughly the fat intake in the United States).

40. The chart in Figure 1.21 shows a comparison of Foude number with stride length for humans, kangaroos, and others.

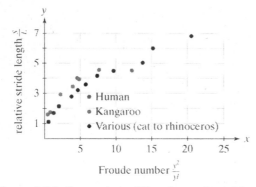

Figure 1.21 Comparison of Froude number with stride length.

Data Source: Graph by Patricia J. Wynne, from "How Dinosaurs Ran," by R. McNeill Alexander, *Scientific American*, April 1991, p. 132 ©1991 by Scientific American, Inc. All rights reserved.

It can be shown that the best-fitting line is one of the following:

A. $y = 0.31x$

B. $y = 0.221x + 2$

C. $y = 0.29x + 1$

Which do you think is the correct one? Use your choice to estimate the relative stride length that corresponds to a Froude number $x = 4$.

41. In a classic study by Julian Huxley, the weight X, in milligrams, of the small fiddler crab (*Uca pugnax*) is compared with the weight of the large claw (Y, in milligrams). The data are shown in Table 1.5.

Table 1.5 Comparison of the weight of the fiddler crab with the weight of its large claw

X	Y	X	Y
57.6	5.3	355.2	104.5
80.3	9.0	420.1	135.0
109.2	13.7	470.1	164.9
156.1	25.1	535.7	195.6
199.7	38.3	617.9	243.0
238.3	52.5	680.6	271.6
270.0	59.0	743.3	319.2
300.2	78.1		

Data source: Julian S. Huxley, 1932. Problems of Relative Growth. Reprinted by The Johns Hopkins University Press, 1993.

a. Plot the points in the table. Does this look like a linear model to you?

b. Plot the line $y = 0.47x - 49$ on the axis for the points you plotted in part **a**. Does this look like a best-fitting line? Do you think you can find a better fitting line?

42. The data in Table 1.6 compare the mandibles of the male stag-beetle (*Cyclommatus tarandus*) where X is the total length (body and mandibles) in millimeters and Y is the length of the mandibles in millimeters.

Table 1.6 Comparison of body weight with the length of the mandibles of the male stag-beetle

X	Y	X	Y
20.38	3.88	36.13	12.08
24.01	5.31	37.32	12.73
26.38	6.33	38.44	14.11
27.76	7.32	39.26	14.70
29.65	8.17	41.34	15.84
32.20	9.73	43.22	17.39
33.11	10.71	45.51	18.83
35.01	11.49	46.32	19.19

a. Plot these points. Does this look like a linear model to you?

b. Plot the line $y = 0.62x - 9.7$ on the axis for the points you plotted in part **a**. Does this look like a best-fitting line? Do you think you can find a better-fitting line?

43. Table 1.7 shows the census figures (in millions) for the U.S. population since the first census.

Table 1.7 U.S. population

Year	Population	Year	Population
1780	2.8	1900	76.0
1790	3.9	1910	92.0
1800	5.3	1920	105.7
1810	7.2	1930	122.8
1820	9.6	1940	131.7
1830	12.9	1950	150.7
1840	17.1	1960	179.3
1850	23.2	1970	203.3
1860	31.4	1980	226.5
1870	39.8	1990	248.7
1880	50.2	2000	281.4
1890	62.9	2010	310.5

a. Plot these points where 1780 represents $x = 0$. Does this look like a linear model can provide a good fit?

b. Plot the line $y = 1.3x - 50$ on the axis for the points you plotted in part **a.** Does this look like a best-fitting line? Do you think you can find a better-fitting line?

44. Ethyl alcohol is metabolized by the human body at a constant rate (independent of concentration). Suppose the rate is 10 milliliters per hour.

  a. Express the time t (in hours) required to metabolize the effects of drinking ethyl alcohol in terms of the amount A of ethyl alcohol consumed (in milliliters).

  b. How much time is required to eliminate the effects of a liter of beer containing 3% ethyl alcohol?

  c. Discuss how the function in part **a.** can be used to determine a reasonable "cutoff" value for the amount of ethyl alcohol A that each individual may be served at a party.

45. In a 1971 study by Savini and Bodhaine, data for velocity of water versus depth were collected for the Columbia River below Grand Coulee Dam. The data are reported in Table 1.8 and were measured 13 feet from the shoreline.

Table 1.8 Depth and flow of Grand Coulee Dam

Depth (feet)	Velocity (feet/second)
0.7	1.55
2.0	1.11
2.6	1.42
3.3	1.39
4.6	1.39
5.9	1.14
7.3	0.91
8.6	0.59
9.9	0.59
10.6	0.41
11.2	0.22

Data source: Savini, J. and Bodhaine, G. L. (1971), Analysis of current meter data at Columbia River gaging stations, Washington and Oregon; USGS Water Supply Paper 1869-F.

  a. Plot these points.

  b. Find the lines defined by the first two data points and the first and last data points. Plot these lines against the data and decide which fits the data better.

  c. Use technology to find the best-fitting data line.

  d. Estimate the velocity of the river at a depth of 12 feet and 20 feet. Discuss the answers you obtain.

46. Eighty-eight samples of shells of the native butter clam (*Saxidomus giganteus*) were collected **Quantitative Environmental Learning Project (QELP)** Web Site at http://seattlecentral.edu/qelp/index.html. These clams grow to lengths of 12–13 cm and live for more than 20 years. A scatter plot of their data is given in Figure 1.22.

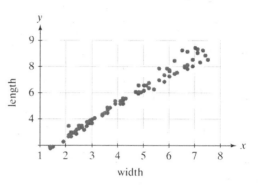

Figure 1.22 Plot of length and width of clam samples.

  a. A pair of points on this data set are given by $(1.3, 1.7)$ and $(7.3, 8.9)$. These two points are drawn in black in the Figure 1.22. Sketch the line passing through these points and find the formula for this line.

  b. Use your line to estimate the width of a butter clam whose length is 12 cm.

47. Temperature fluctuations in many parts of the world exhibit sinusoidal patterns. Consider, for example, the average monthly temperature in Chappaqua, New York, reported in Table 1.9.

Table 1.9

Month	Temp.	Month	Temp.
August	77	February	35.5
September	70	March	42.5
October	59	April	53
November	48.5	May	63
December	39	June	72.5
January	35	July	77.5

  a. Plot these data.

  b. Approximate the amplitude of the data and the period.

  c. Find a and b such that $56.25 + a\cos(bx)$ has the same amplitude and period as your data, and plot this function against your data. Let x represent months after July.

48. Problem 47 illustrates temperature oscillations on a yearly time scale corresponding to the seasons. Temperatures also vary daily: cooler at night and warmer at noon. Consider, for example, the average

July hourly temperature in Abeerdeen, New York, shown in the following table.

Hour	Temp.	Hour	Temp.
1	79.9	13	62.3
2	78.6	14	62.7
3	76.4	15	65.1
4	73	16	67.7
5	69.9	17	70.3
6	67.8	18	72.8
7	65.9	19	76
8	66.6	20	76.8
9	64.6	21	77.7
10	63.8	22	78.9
11	63	23	79.7
12	62.1	24	79.8

a. Plot these data.

b. Approximate the amplitude of the data and the period.

c. Find a and b such that $70.8 + a\cos(bx)$ has the same amplitude and period as your data, and plot this function against your data. Let x represent months after July.

1.3   Power Functions and Scaling Laws

Why can an ant lift a hundred times its weight whereas a typical man can only lift about six-tenths of his weight? Why is getting wet life-threatening for a fly but not for a human? Why can a mouse fall from a skyscraper and still scurry home, while a human who falls is likely to be killed? Why are elephants' legs so much thicker relative to their length than are gazelles' legs? A class of functions called *power functions* provides a means to answer these questions.

Power functions and their properties

Power Functions

A function $f(x)$ is a **power function** if it is of the form

$$y = f(x) = ax^b$$

where a and b are real numbers. The variable x is called the **base**, the parameter b is called the **exponent**, and the parameter a is called the **constant of proportionality**.

Note that $\frac{5}{7}x^{-1}$ and x^3 are power functions, while 3^x is not because, in this latter case, the exponent rather than the base is the variable.

Example 1   Graphing power functions

Graph each of the following sets of functions and discuss how they differ from one another and what properties they have in common.

a. $y = x^2$, $y = x^4$, and $y = x^6$

b. $y = x^3$, $y = x^5$, and $y = x^7$

c. $y = x^{1/2}$, $y = x$, and $y = x^{3/2}$

d. $y = \dfrac{1}{x}$ and $y = \dfrac{1}{x^2}$

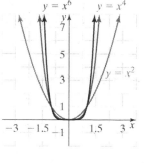

Solution

a. Graphing $y = x^2$, $y = x^4$, and $y = x^6$ gives the figure on the left.

All of these graphs tend to "bend" upward and are "U-shaped." All three of these graphs intersect at the points $(0, 0)$, $(-1, 1)$, and $(1, 1)$. On the interval $[-1, 1]$ the function with the smallest exponent grows most rapidly as you move away from $x = 0$, and on the intervals $(-\infty, 1)$ and $(1, \infty)$ the function with the largest exponent increases most rapidly.

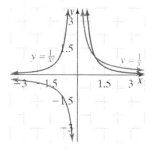

b. Graphing $y = x^3$, $y = x^5$, and $y = x^7$ gives the figure on the left.

All of these graphs are "seat shaped," bending downward for negative x and bending upward for positive x. All three of these graphs intersect at the points $(0, 0)$, $(-1, -1)$ and $(1, 1)$. On the interval $[-1, 1]$ the function with the smallest exponent grows most rapidly, and on the intervals $(-\infty, 1)$ and $(1, \infty)$ the function with the largest exponent grows most rapidly.

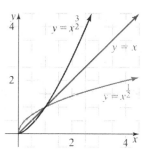

c. Graphing $y = x^{1/2}$, $y = x$, and $y = x^{3/2}$ gives the figure on the left.

We graphed over the domain $[0, \infty)$ of $y = x^{1/2}$ and $y = x^{3/2}$. All of these graphs increase as x increases and pass through the points $(0, 0)$ and $(1, 1)$. The graph of $x^{1/2}$ becomes steeper and steeper at 0, while the graph of $x^{3/2}$ becomes flatter and flatter. Moreover, the graph of $x^{1/2}$ bends downward, while the graph of $x^{3/2}$ bends upward.

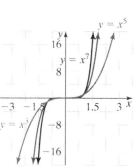

d. Graphing $y = \dfrac{1}{x}$ and $y = \dfrac{1}{x^2}$ gives the figure on the left.

Both of these functions pass through the point $(1, 1)$ and approach positive or negative infinity (i.e., have a vertical asymptotes) as x approaches 0, although the function $\dfrac{1}{x}$ does so by approaching $-\infty$ in the third quadrant while the "other branch" of $\dfrac{1}{x^2}$ approaches $+\infty$ in the second quadrant. Branches of the graphs lying above the x axis, bend upward, while parts lying below bend downward.

To algebraically manipulate power functions, we review some properties of exponents.

Laws of Exponents	Let x, y, a, and b be any real numbers. Then provided that both sides of the equality are well defined, the following five rules govern the use of exponents:

1. Addition law: $x^a x^b = x^{a+b}$

2. Subtraction law: $\dfrac{x^a}{x^b} = x^{a-b}$

3. Multiplication law: $(x^a)^b = x^{ab}$

4. Distributive law over multiplication: $(xy)^a = x^a y^a$

5. Distributive law over division: $\left(\dfrac{x}{y}\right)^a = \dfrac{x^a}{y^a}$

Example 2 Using Laws of Exponents

Simplify the following expressions using the laws of exponents.

a. $\dfrac{x^2}{x}$ **b.** $(x^3)^{1/3}x$ **c.** $\left(\dfrac{1}{\sqrt{x}}\right)^4$

Solution

a. Since $\frac{1}{x} = x^{-1}$, we obtain

$$\frac{x^2}{x} = x^2 x^{-1}$$
$$= x^{2-1} = x \qquad \textit{by the addition law for } x \neq 0$$

b. We have

$$(x^3)^{1/3}x = x^{3/3}x \qquad \textit{by the multiplication law}$$
$$= x^1 x^1 = x^2 \qquad \textit{by the addition law}$$

c. Since $\sqrt{x} = x^{1/2}$, we have

$$\left(\frac{1}{\sqrt{x}}\right)^4 = (x^{-1/2})^4 \qquad \textit{by the subtraction law for } x > 0$$
$$= x^{-2} \qquad \textit{by the multiplication law for } x > 0$$

Proportionality and geometric similarity

In his essay, "On Being the Right Size,"* John B. S. Haldane (1892–1964), noted biologist and one of the founders of the field of population genetics, wrote:

"A man coming out of a bath carries with him a film of water of about one-fiftieth of an inch in thickness. This weighs roughly a pound. A wet mouse has to carry about its own weight in water. A wet fly has to lift many times its own weight and, as everybody knows, a fly once wetted by water or any other liquid is in a very serious position indeed."

You might wonder how Haldane came up with these conclusions. To see why, consider power laws in the context of proportionality, which is defined as follows.

Proportionality	We say that y is **proportional** to x if there exists some constant $a > 0$ such that $y = a x$ for all $x > 0$. When y is proportional to x, we write $$y \propto x$$

Example 3 Geometric similarity

Figure 1.23 A cubical critter (a C^3).

Imagine a world in which all individuals are cubical critters of different types: one such critter is drawn in Figure 1.23. The size of each critter can be characterized using one measurement, L meters, which denotes the length of the critter in any of its three dimensions.

a. Argue that the surface area, S, and volume, V, of the cubical critter are proportional to L^b for appropriate choices of b.

b. If we assume that these cubical critters are essentially "ugly bags of mostly water" (*Star Trek* fans may remember this line as an alien's description of humans who are mostly water encased in a bag of skin; the "ugly" part is a matter of extraterrestrial taste), argue that body

*John B. S. Haldane, "On Being the Right Size," *The Harper's Monthly*, March 1926, pp. 424–427.

mass, M, is also proportional to L^b for an appropriate choice of b. In your argument, you may use the fact that 1 cubic meter of water has a mass of 1000 kilograms.

Solution

a. Since the surface area of a cube is $6L^2$ and the volume of a cube is L^3,

$$S \propto L^2 \qquad V \propto L^3$$

In other words, surface area is proportional to length squared and volume is proportional to length cubed.

b. Since we are assuming the cubical critters are made of water and the density of water is 1000 kg/m^3, the mass is $M = 1000 \cdot V = 1000 \cdot L^3$. Hence,

$$M \propto L^3$$

Notice that this proportionality would not change even if we used a different density constant. ■

Geometrical similarity is not confined to cubical critters. So long as all dimensions of an organism scale in the same way, the organisms are geometrically similar. Moreover, for any measurement of length L (e.g., height, arm length, chest circumference), surface area S (e.g., palm surface area, cross-sectional area of a muscle), and mass M (e.g., mass of a hair or the entire body), the relationships $S \propto L^2$ and $M \propto L^3$ continue to hold.

To work with proportionality relationships, we need to remember a few basic rules. Essentially these rules have this effect: we can treat a proportionality symbol for manipulative purposes like an equality sign.

Rules of Proportionality.

- **Transitive property:** If $x \propto y$ and $y \propto z$, then $x \propto z$.
- **Power-to-root property:** If $y \propto x^b$ with $b \neq 0$, then $x \propto y^{1/b}$.
- **General transitive property:** If $x \propto y^b$ and $y \propto z^c$, then $x \propto z^{bc}$.

Example 4   Rules of proportionality

Demonstrate that proportionality satisfies the properties listed in the box above.

Solution

Transitive property: Since $x \propto y$, then there exists a constant $a > 0$ such that $x = ay$. Since $y \propto z$, then there exists a constant $b > 0$ such that $y = bz$. Therefore,

$$x = ay = a(bz) = (ab)z$$

This equality implies that $x \propto z$ with proportionality constant ab.

Power-to-root property: If $y \propto x^b$, then there exists a constant $a > 0$ such that $y = ax^b$. Solving for x in terms of y yields

$$x = \left(\frac{y}{a}\right)^{1/b} = a^{-1/b} y^{1/b}$$

Hence, $x \propto y^{1/b}$ with proportionality constant $a^{-1/b} > 0$.

General transitive property: This property is really just a simple extension of the transitive property, but it is easily demonstrated directly. If $x \propto y^b$ and $y \propto z^c$, then there exist $a_1 > 0$ and $a_2 > 0$ such that $x = a_1 y^b$ and $y = a_2 z^c$. Therefore, $x = a_1 (a_2 z^c)^b = a_1 a_2^b z^{bc}$. Hence, $x \propto z^{bc}$ with proportionality constant $a_1 a_2^b$. ■

Example 5   **Dangers of getting wet**

To understand the dangers of getting wet, it is reasonable to assume that the mass, W, of the water on your body of mass M after getting wet is proportional to the surface area, S, of your body.

a. For cubical critters find the value of b such that $W \propto M^b$.

b. Suppose you had two cubical critters: a man-sized cubical critter with mass 60 kg, and a mouse-sized cubical critter with mass 0.01 kg. Moreover, assume when the man gets wet, the mass of water clinging to his skin is 0.6 kg. Using proportionality, find the mass of water on the mouse. Compare the ratios $\dfrac{W}{M}$ for the two critters.

c. Graph the ratio $\dfrac{W}{M}$ as a function of M and discuss its implications for the danger of getting wet.

Solution

a. To solve this problem, we use the rules of proportionality found in Example 4. Since we have assumed that $W \propto S$ and $S \propto L^2$, the transitive property implies $W \propto L^2$. Since $M \propto L^3$, the power-to-root property implies $M^{1/3} \propto L$. The general transitive property implies that

$$S \propto L^2 \propto (M^{1/3})^2 = M^{2/3}$$

In other words, $W \propto M^b$ for $b = 2/3$.

b. Since W is proportional to $M^{2/3}$, there exists some number $a > 0$ such that

$$W = a M^{2/3}$$

The man-sized cubical critter has mass $M = 60$ with $W = 0.6$. Substituting these values into $W = a M^{2/3}$ allows us to solve for a:

$$0.6 = a 60^{2/3}$$
$$a \approx 0.04$$

The ratio of water mass to body mass for the man is

$$\frac{W}{M} = \frac{0.6}{60} = 1\%$$

The mouse-sized critter has mass $M = 0.01$ kg with $W = 0.04(0.01)^{2/3} \approx 0.00186$ kg. The ratio of water mass to body mass for the mouse is

$$\frac{W}{M} \approx \frac{0.00186}{0.01} \approx 18.6\%$$

We see that the wet cubical man has to lift only 1% of his body mass while the wet cubical mouse has to lift approximately 19% of its body mass.

Note that this calculation does not take into account that a mouse is hairier than a man and therefore likely to retain more water per surface area of body than a man. This calculation assumes that the retention properties for each unit of surface area are the same.

c. We have

$$\frac{W}{M} = \frac{a M^{2/3}}{M} = a M^{-1/3} \approx 0.04 M^{-1/3}$$

The graph of the ratio of water mass to body mass, $y = M^{-1/3}$, is shown in Figure 1.24.

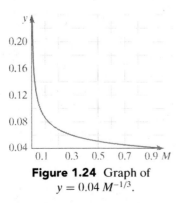

Figure 1.24 Graph of $y = 0.04 M^{-1/3}$.

This graph illustrates that the bigger creature (i.e., M becomes larger), the amount of water one has to carry relative to one's body mass decreases. Hence, getting wet is much worse for a fly than a human. ∎

The previous example shows how we can use *geometric similarity* to understand the implications of getting wet for critters of vastly different sizes—from humans to flies. In Problem 39 of Problem Set 1.3, we pose a counterpoint analysis of how smaller animals are favored when it comes to the dangers of falling from high places. Although it is true that organisms are often geometrically quite dissimilar, it turns out that in many cases analyses using the approximation of geometric similarity are quite good.

Example 6   Olympic weightlifting

The heaviest weight classes are excluded, as individuals in this class have no weight restriction and therefore are often not geometrically similar to their lighter counterparts.

Table 1.10 reports the body mass and the winning lifts (in kilograms) for the male gold medalists in the 1988, 1992, and 1996 Olympic Games. In this example, we develop a simple model relating body mass to mass lifted.

Table 1.10 Body mass versus winning lift (Olympic gold medalists)

Class	1988 Mass	Lift	Class	1992 Mass	Lift	Class	1996 Mass	Lift
≤ 52	51.85	270.0	≤ 52	51.8	265	≤ 54	53.91	287.5
≤ 56	55.75	292.5	≤ 56	55.9	287.5	≤ 59	58.61	307.5
≤ 60	59.7	342.5	≤ 60	59.9	320	≤ 64	63.9	335
≤ 67.5	67.2	340.0	≤ 67.5	67.25	337.5	≤ 70	69.98	375.5
≤ 75	74.8	375.0	≤ 75	74.5	357.5	≤ 76	75.91	367.5
≤ 82.5	82.15	377.5	≤ 82.5	81.8	370	≤ 83	82.06	392.5
≤ 90	89.45	412.5	≤ 90	89.25	412.5	≤ 91	90.89	402.5
≤ 100	99.7	425.0	≤ 100	97.25	410	≤ 99	96.78	420
≤ 110	109.55	455.0	≤ 110	109.4	432.5	≤ 108	107.32	430

a. A basic physiological principle is that the strength of a muscle is proportional to the cross-sectional area of that muscle. Assuming that Olympic male weightlifters are geometrically similar, as illustrated in Figure 1.25, argue that for a lifter of mass M the amount ℓ he can lift is proportional to M^b, and find the value of b for which this should be true.

Lars Baron/Getty Images, Inc.

Heavy weight   Middle weight   Light weight

Figure 1.25 Geometrically similar weightlifters.

b. The relationship $\ell \propto M^b$ from part **a** implies $\ell = a\,M^b$ for some $a > 0$. Find a using the data point $(\ell, M) = (287.5, 53.91)$ (table entry for the category ≤ 54 in year 1996 that leads to a good fit). Plot $\ell = a\,M^b$ for the values of a and b that you obtain.

c. Since the power law you find in part **a.** does a relatively good job of predicting lift as a function of body weight, you can use it to determine an overall winner among the weight classes. Namely, associate a score

$$y = \text{lift}/(\text{body mass})^b$$

with each weightlifter and declare the individual with the largest score to be the overall winner. Use this approach to find the overall winner in the 1988 Olympics.

Solution

a. Let L be a measurement of length (e.g., height), M the mass, and S the cross-sectional area of the weightlifter. Since we assume that weightlifters are geometrically similar, we have $M \propto L^3$ and $S \propto L^2$. Thus,

$$S \propto L^2 \propto (M^{1/3})^2 = M^{2/3}$$

Since we have assumed that $\ell \propto S$, we can conclude that

$$\ell \propto M^{2/3}$$

b. We substitute the data point $(\ell, M) = (287.5, 53.91)$ into the equation $\ell = a\,M^{2/3}$ to find

$$287.5 = a(53.91)^{2/3}$$

$$a \approx 20.15$$

The plot $\ell = 20.15\,M^{2/3}$ against the data as shown in Figure 1.26 illustrates a remarkable fit of the model to the data.

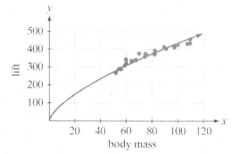

Figure 1.26 Graph showing data points and graph of $\ell = 20.15\,M^{2/3}$.

c. Calculating the individuals scores y for each of the 1988 Olympic lifters in Table 1.10, we get the values $19.42\ (= 270.0/51.85^{2/3})$, 20.04, 22.42, 20.57, 21.12, 19.98, 20.62, 19.77, 19.87. The overall winner here is the Gold Medal winner in the third lightest weight class with a score of 22.42. A quick search shows that this medal winner is Naim Süleymanoğlu, pictured in Figure 1.1, who has been nicknamed Pocket Hercules because of his feats of strength for his small size. ◾

Allometric scaling

Although geometric similarity works wonders, it is not universal. When the shape of an animal (or organ or bone) deviates from geometrical similarity with size, then we say that it scales **allometrically** (*allo* = different, *metric* = measure) if we can find a power law that relates one particular measure (e.g., length of the mammalian femur) denoted by, say, x to another (e.g., cross-sectional area of the mammalian femur) denoted by, say, y as the size of an individual increases. In this case, the fundamental **allometric formula** posits the relationship

$$y = ax^b \qquad \text{or} \qquad y \propto x^b$$

for some constants $a > 0$ and b.

Haldane made the key observation in "On Being the Right Size" that a structure breaks when a load that is proportional to the volume of an organism (cubic dimension) acts on the cross-sectional area (square dimension) of the structure supporting this organism. The essence of this issue is presented in the next example.

Example 7   Breaking bones

a. From physics we know that the force per unit area at the base of a cube, which we denote here using the symbol K, is given by:

$$K = \text{gravitational acceleration} \times \frac{\text{density} \times \text{volume}}{\text{area}}$$

Calculate the dimensions of a sugar cube that would crush under its own weight at the surface of the Earth where the gravitational acceleration is 9.81 m/s^2, given that the sugar cube's density is 1040 kg/m^3 and its crushing strength (the maximum value of K that it can resist) is 5.17×10^6 newtons/m^2.

b. Thomas McMahon collected data on lengths L and diameters D of bones for various cloven-hoofed animals. If these animals were geometrically similar, we would expect $L \propto D$. However, the data suggest that $L \propto D^{2/3}$, as illustrated in Figure 1.27, where lengths are measures in millimeters (mm).

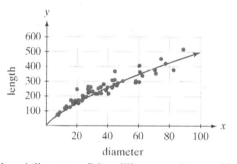

Figure 1.27 Lengths L and diameters D in millimeters of bones for various cloven-hoofed animals and fitted curve.

Data Source: T. A. McMahon (1975). "Allometry and Biomechanics: Limb Bones in Adult Ungulates." *The American Naturalist*, Vol. 109, No. 969, pp. 547–563.

In this data set, the humerus bone of an African impala has a length of 173 mm and a diameter of 22.5 mm. Use this information to estimate the length of a wildebeest humerus whose diameter is 42.6 mm.

Solution

a. From the formula, the force per unit area at the base of the sugar cube is $K = 9.81 \times 1040 L^3/L^2 = 10202.4L$ Newtons per meter squared where L is the length of one side of the base of the cube. Since the crushing strength of sugar is 5,170,000 Newtons per meter, the cube gets crushed under its own weight if

$$10202L \geq 5,170,000$$

$$L \geq 506.74 \text{ meters!}$$

b. Assume that $L = aD^{2/3}$ where L is length and D is diameter measured in millimeters. For an African impala, we are given that $L = 173$ and $D = 22.5$. Solving for the proportionality constant a yields

$$173 = a(22.5)^{2/3}$$

$$a = 173/(22.5)^{2/3} \approx 21.7$$

Using the relationship $L = 21.7D^{2/3}$ with $D = 42.6$ yields $L \approx 264.7$ mm for the length of the wildebeest humerus. The actual value from the data set is 256. Hence, our estimate from the scaling law is not too bad.

PROBLEM SET 1.3

Level 1 DRILL PROBLEMS

Simplify the functions in Problems 1 to 9, and determine whether the functions are power functions. If a function is a power function, write it in the form $y = ax^b$.

1. a. $y = \dfrac{x}{3}$ **b.** $y = \dfrac{1}{3x}$ **c.** $y = 3^x$

2. a. $y = 10$ **b.** $y = x^{10}$ **c.** $y = 10^x$

3. $y = \dfrac{1}{3} + \dfrac{1}{x}$

4. $y = \dfrac{2x + 15}{5x}$

5. $y = \dfrac{1}{\sqrt{16x^3}}$

6. $y = \dfrac{5\sqrt{x}}{7x^2}$

7. $y = 2^x 3^{2x} 5^x$

8. $y = \dfrac{\sqrt{36x}}{6x^5}$

9. $y = \dfrac{\sqrt{144x^3}}{2x^2}$

10. $y = (2x^3)^2$

11. If $y \propto x^2$ and y increases from 10^3 to 10^{15}, what happens to x?

12. If $y \propto 6x$ and $x \propto t$, how does t change when y increases from 2×10^2 to 6×10^4?

13. If $y \propto 10x^3$ how is y proportionally related to x?

14. If $x \propto 100y$ and $y \propto 45z$, then how does z change as x decreases from 95 to 12?

15. If $x \propto y^2$ and $y \propto z^3$, then how is x proportionally related to z?

16. If $x \propto \sqrt{y}$ and $y \propto z^2$, then how is x proportionally related to z?

Graph the functions in Problems 17 to 22. By inspection, state the intervals where the function is increasing and the intervals where it is decreasing.

17. $y = 2x^2$

18. $y = \dfrac{1}{8}x^4$

19. $y = -x^3$

20. $y = 0.1x^5$

21. $y = 12x^{1/2}$

22. $y = \dfrac{2}{x}$

23. The linear function

$$y = 3x + b$$

represents a **family of functions** whose graphs all look the same except for the relative placement with respect to the y-axis. On the same coordinate axis, graph the members of this family for the values $b = 0, 4, -3,$ and $\sqrt{2}$ and state which of these are power functions.

24. The quadratic function $y = ax^2$ represents a **family of functions** whose graphs all look the same except for the relative placement with respect to the y-axis. On the same coordinate axis, graph the members of this family for the given parameter, $a = 0, 4 - 3, \sqrt{2},$ and state which of these are power functions.

25. A spherical cell of radius r has volume $V = \frac{4}{3}\pi r^3$ and surface area $S = 4\pi r^2$. Express V as a function of S. If S is quadrupled, what happens to r?

26. Consider a cylinder of radius r and height $5r$. Express the volume and surface area of this cylinder as a function r. If r is doubled, what happens to the volume? If S is quadrupled, what happens to r?

27. Consider a cone of height h and radius $h/2$ at the top. Express the volume and surface area of this cone as a function of h. If h is doubled, what happens to S?

Drug doses for dogs and cats are known to scale with their surface area S. When body mass W is measured in kilograms, then surface area S in square meters is given by

$$S = \dfrac{K \times W^{2/3}}{100},$$

where for dogs $K = 10.1$ and for cats $K = 10.4$. Further, when converting human drug doses of an average adult to pet drug doses, this formula is used:

$$pet's\ drug\ dose = \dfrac{pet's\ S}{1.73} \times human\ adult\ drug\ dose$$

In Problems 28 to 33, the human adult dose of a drug is given. Calculate the drug dose (rounded to the nearest milligram) that you would give your dog or cat of the indicated weight.

28. 100 mg of aspirin and your dog weighs 7 kg

29. 200 mg of aspirin and your cat weighs 4.6 kg

30. 250 mg of an antibiotic and your dog weighs 16 kg

31. 500 mg of a renal drug and your cat weighs 5.3 kg

32. 50 mg of an anticoagulant and your dog weighs 31 kg

33. 50 mg of an anticoagulant and your cat weighs 4.8 kg

Level 2 APPLIED AND THEORY PROBLEMS

30. An ant weighs approximately 1/500 ounce and can lift 1/5 ounce, which is approximately 100 times its weight. Assume that strength is proportional to the cross-section of a muscle and that all organisms on Earth (ants and humans) are geometrically similar. Using these assumptions, determine how much a 150-pound person on Earth can lift.

31. A comic book explained Superman's strength by stating that on Krypton an organism's strength is directly proportional to its body mass. Based on this assumption and assuming that Krypton ants are like Earth ants (see Problem 30), how much can a 150-pound person on Krypton lift?

32. In a sample of twenty-six trees of a particular species, wood density, $D\,(\text{kg/m}^3)$, is related to breaking strength, $S\,(\text{MPa})$, according to the relationship $D \propto S^{0.91}$. If one of the points that this relationship passed through was $(D, S) = (300, 10)$, find the equation and sketch its graph.

33. A sample based on nineteen mountain ash trees of different sizes yielded a relationship between the leaf area, $A\,(\text{m}^2)$, of the tree and the stem diameter at breast height (DBH), d (cm). The relationship obtained was $A \propto d^{2.99}$. If one of the points that this relationship passed through was $(d, A) = (30, 78)$, find the equation and sketch its graph.

34. In Julian Huxley's classic book *Problems of Relative Growth*, there are data showing an allometric relationship between the mass (C milligrams) of the large claw (chela) and that of the rest of the body (B milligrams) in the male fiddler crab (*Uca pugnax*). The exponent of this relationship is approximately 1.6, that is $C = a B^{1.6}$, and it passes through the point $(B, C) = (1000, 500)$. Calculate the parameter a and then graph the relationship for the growth of a large claw mass as a function of an individual's body mass (excluding claw) over the range $50 \le x \le 2200$ mg.

35. In 1936, Sinnott showed that there is an allometric relationship between the length (L) and width (W) of gourds, when observed from ovary to maturity. (See Roger V. Jean, *Differential Growth, Huxley's Allometric Formula and Sigmoid Growth* (COMAP, Incorporated, Lexington MA, 1984) UMAP Module 635, p. 421.) He obtained the exponents of $m = 0.95$ for pumpkins (*Cucurbita pepo*) to $m = 2.2$ for the snake gourd (*Trichosanthes*). Plot these relationships on the same graph for both types of gourds over the interval $[1, 50]$ centimeters, if they both pass through the point $(L, W) = (10, 10)$.

36. Professor Smith's house (10 m wide, 20 m long, 4 m high—just a hovel, really) has a 30,000 watt furnace that just barely keeps him warm on cold winter nights. He's thinking of building a larger house to accommodate his growing insect collection and needs advice on the output of the new furnace. The new house will be three times as high, three times as wide, and three times as long.

   a. If he assumes that the furnace size should be proportional to the volume of the house, then what size furnace should he install?

   b. If heat loss depends on the surface area of exterior walls, roof, and floor exposed to the winter cold rather than on the volume of the house, then what size furnace would you recommend?

37. Consider the following quote from Jonathan Swift's *Gulliver's Travels*:

"The reader may be pleased to observe, that, in the last article of the recovery of my liberty, the emperor stipulates to allow me a quantity of meat and drink sufficient for the support of 1724 Lilliputians. Some time after, asking a friend at court how they came to fix on that determinate number, he told me that his majesty's mathematicians, having taken the height of my body by the help of a quadrant, and finding it to exceed theirs in the proportion of twelve to one, they concluded from the similarity of their bodies, that mine must contain at least 1724 of theirs, and consequently would require as much food as was necessary to support that number of Lilliputians. By which the reader may conceive an idea of the ingenuity of that people, as well as the prudent and exact economy of so great a prince."

Let F denote the amount of food an individual eats and L the height of an individual. This quotation implicitly assumes that $F \propto L^b$ for an appropriate choice of b. Find this b value and provide a biological explanation for this choice of b.

38. Suppose the main loss of energy is heat loss through the surface. For the quotation in Problem 37, determine the appropriate choice of b so that $F \propto L^b$. Under the assumption, how much should the Lilliputians feed Gulliver?

39. The following quote from Haldane (*On Being the Right Size*, p. 424) illustrates the dangers of being large:

To the mouse and any smaller animal, [gravity] presents practically no dangers. You can drop a mouse in a thousand-yard mine shaft; and, on arriving at the bottom, it gets a slight shock and walks away. A rat would be probably killed, though it can fall safely from the eleventh story of a building; a man is killed, a horse splashes. For the resistance presented to movement by air is proportional to the surface of a moving object. Divide an animal's length, breadth, and height each by ten; its weight is reduced to a thousandth, but its surface only to a hundredth. So the resistance to falling in the case of the small animal is relatively ten times greater than the driving force.

Consider a cubical critter being dropped down a mine shaft. Let A denote the force due to air resistance that the cubical critter experiences and let M denote the critter's weight. Assume that A is proportional to surface area and M is proportional to volume.

a. Determine the value of b for which $\dfrac{M}{A} \propto M^b$.

b. Graph $y = M^b$ and discuss the implications for a falling cubical critter.

1.4 Exponential Growth

Without doubt, the linear function $y = ax + b$ is the most important elementary function in mathematics. In the context of calculus, its importance is equaled only by the function we introduce in this section, the exponential function. Just why this function is so critical in calculus will become apparent once we introduce the concept of a derivative. In this section, we show that the exponential function is suitable for describing how populations, income, beer froth, and the radioactivity of unstable isotopes change over time.

Exponential growth and exponential functions

The following table provides data on the growth of the United States from 1815 until 1895.

Year	Population (in millions)
1815	8.3
1825	11.0
1835	14.7
1845	19.7
1855	26.7
1865	35.2
1875	44.4
1885	55.9
1895	68.9

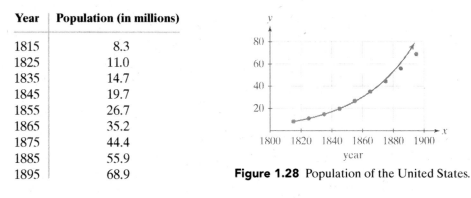

Figure 1.28 Population of the United States.

These data, which are plotted in Figure 1.28, indicate around a tenfold (also referred to as an *order of magnitude*) increase in the U.S. population size during the nineteenth century. To get a finer understanding of the actual rate of growth, we can divide the size of the population in any given year by its size one decade earlier. For example,

$$\frac{\text{population in 1825}}{\text{population in 1815}} = \frac{11}{8.3} \approx 1.3253$$

and

$$\frac{\text{population in 1835}}{\text{population in 1825}} = \frac{14.7}{11.0} \approx 1.3363$$

These calculations tell us that population increased by a factor of approximately 33% over both decades. Let us assume that the population increases by 33% every decade. If t corresponds to the number of decades that have elapsed since 1815 and t is a positive integer, then we might estimate the population size by

$$(8.3) \underbrace{1.33 \times 1.33 \times \cdots \times 1.33}_{t \text{ terms}} = 8.3(1.33)^t$$

More generally, for any real t, we can model the population size $N(t)$ at t decades after 1815 by the exponential function

$$N(t) = 8.3(1.33)^t \text{ million people}$$

The graph of $N(t)$ is plotted in Figure 1.28 against the data, and reasonably approximates the data until 1880, after which it begins to overestimate the population size.

In the previous section, we introduced power functions $y = x^a$ for which the independent variable x is raised to some fixed power. In contrast, the function $N(t)$ has its exponent as the independent variable t and its base is a fixed constant. Such functions are termed *exponential functions*.

> **Exponential Function**
>
> An **exponential function** is a function of the form
>
> $$y = f(x) = a^x$$
>
> where the parameter $a \neq 1$ (the base) is a positive real number and the variable x (the exponent) is a real number.

The graphs of exponential functions have three different shapes, depending on the value of the base, as shown in the following example.

Example 1   Sketching exponential functions

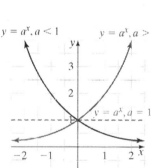

Figure 1.29 Graph for $y = a^x$.

Sketch the exponential function

$$y = a^x$$

where $a > 1$, $a = 1$, and $0 < a < 1$ on the same coordinate axes, and comment on each of the graphs.

Solution   The graphs are shown in Figure 1.29.

The graph of $y = a^x$ passes through $(0, 1)$ for all values of a. We also notice:

- If $a < 1$, the graph is increasing for all x.
- If $a = 1$, the graph is a horizontal line (a constant function).
- If $a < 1$, the graph is decreasing for all x.

Example 1 illustrates that if the base of the exponential function is greater than one, then the exponential function is an increasing function. In the context of population change, this increase corresponds to population growth. A fundamental quantity associated with population growth is the *doubling time*; how long before the population size doubles? The following example illustrates this concept.

Example 2   Malthus's estimate for doubling time

In *An Essay on the Principal of Population* (http://www.gutenberg.org/files/4239/4239-h/4239-h.htm), Thomas Malthus wrote:

In the United States of America, where the means of subsistence have been more ample, the manners of the people more pure, and consequently the checks to early marriages fewer, than in any of the modern states of Europe, the population has been found to double itself in twenty-five years.

Let $N(t) = 8.3(1.33)^t$ be our model of population growth in the United States from 1815 onward.

a. Determine whether the population size doubles from 1815 until 1840. Recall that the units of t are decades.

b. Determine whether the population size doubles over every twenty-five year period for our model $N(t)$.

Solution

a. Since t is decades after 1815, 25 years after 1815 corresponds to $t = 2.5$. To determine whether the population doubles between 1815 and 1840, we compute the ratio of the population sizes in those years

$$\frac{N(2.5)}{N(0)} = \frac{8.3(1.33)^{2.5}}{8.3} = 1.33^{2.5} \approx 2.04$$

Hence the population increases by just over a factor of 2.

b. Consider any time t. To determine whether the population doubles between t and $t + 2.5$, we compute the ratio of the population sizes in those years

$$\frac{N(t + 2.5)}{N(t)} = \frac{8.3(1.33)^{t+2.5}}{8.3(1.33)^t} = 1.33^{2.5} \approx 2.04 \qquad \textit{using laws of exponents}$$

We see that Malthus's prediction conforms reasonably well with our model. Notice that we could not test the prediction directly with data, as data are reported only in ten-year intervals.

In Example 2, we used a law of exponents (discussed earlier in Section 1.3). These laws are extremely useful for manipulating exponential functions, so you may review them. For example, using these laws, we uncover a key property of exponential functions. Namely, if $f(x) = a^x$ and h is a real number, then by the law of exponents

$$\frac{f(x + h)}{f(x)} = \frac{a^{x+h}}{a^x} = a^{x+h-x} = a^h$$

In other words, over any interval of length h, the exponential function changes by a fixed factor a^h. In the case of Example 2, this observation implies that the population approximately doubles over any twenty-five-year period.

Exponential growth is much faster than polynomial growth, as we explore in the next example.

Example 3   **Exponential growth versus polynomial growth**

- -

Use technology to graph the functions $y = 2^x$ and $y = x^4$. Which function takes on larger values when x is large?

Solution   Figure 1.30 shows both functions plotted on a the intervals $[0, 2]$, $[0, 8]$, and $[0, 20]$. Over the $[0, 2]$ interval $y = 2^x$ initially takes on larger values than $y = x^4$, but at the end of this interval $y = x^4$ takes on the larger values. The graphs on the intervals $[0, 8]$ suggest that $y = x^4$ continues to be larger. On the interval $[0, 20]$, we see the curves again cross at $x = 16$, and for $x > 16$, we see that $y = 2^x$ is larger.

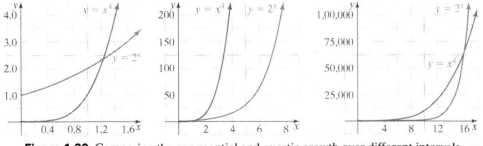

Figure 1.30 Comparing the exponential and quartic growth over different intervals.

The fact that exponential functions with base greater than one grow faster than any polynomial led the economist Thomas Malthus to make a dire prediction about the future of humankind.

Example 4 Malthus's law of misery

In *An Essay on the Principle of Population,** Thomas Malthus wrote:

Let us then take this for our rule, though certainly far beyond the truth, and allow that, by great exertion, the whole produce of the Island might be increased every twenty-five years, by a quantity of subsistence equal to what it at present produces. The most enthusiastic speculator cannot suppose a greater increase than this. In a few centuries it would make every acre of land in the Island like a garden.

To illustrate the meaning of this quote, consider the United States to be the "island" and farms to be the "garden." Let $N(t) = 8.3(1.33)^t$ (in millions) be the population size t decades after 1815. Assume that in 1815, the amount of food produced in this year is equivalent to 10 million yearly rations. Further, assume, as suggested by Malthus, that the production of food in the United States will increase every twenty-five years by 10 million yearly rations.

a. Write a formula for the number $R(t)$ of yearly rations (in millions) produced over time.

b. Graph and compare the functions $R(t)$ and $N(t)$.

c. Determine the first year in which there is just enough food to provide everyone with one ration per year.

Solution

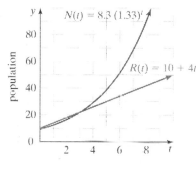

a. As the amount of yearly rations increases by 10 million every twenty-five years, $R(t)$ is a linear function with slope $\frac{10}{2.5} = 4$. Since $R(0) = 10$, the intercept of this linear function is 10 and we have

$$R(t) = 10 + 4t$$

b. Using technology to plot $R(t)$ and $N(t)$ gives the graph shown on the left. In the long term, the predicted population size is much greater than the availability of food.

c. By inspection, it looks like the graphs of $N(t)$ and $R(t)$ intersect at $t = 4$. Hence in forty years, every individual in the population will get one yearly ration every year.

Table 1.11 Froth height decay

Time t (seconds)	Froth height H (centimeters)
0	17.0
15	16.1
30	14.9
45	14.0
60	13.2
75	12.5
90	11.9
105	11.2
120	10.7

Exponential decay

When the base of an exponential function is less than one, the exponential function is decreasing and exhibits so-called *exponential decay*. An amusing example of exponential decay resulted in Arnd Leike, a professor of physics at Universität München, winning the 2002 Ig Nobel Prize. The Ig Nobel Prize is annually awarded to scientists who firstly make people laugh, and secondly make them think. Leike received his award for his paper, "Demonstration of the Exponential Decay Law Using Beer Froth" (*European Journal Physics* 23 (2002): 21–26.) This paper reports an experiment that Leike performed with a mug of the German beer Erdinger Weissbier. After pouring the beer, Leike measured the height of the beer froth at regular time intervals. The measured values are shown in Table 1.11.

*http://www.gutenberg.org/files/4239/4239-h/4239-h.htm.

If we consider the ratios of heights at subsequent time intervals, we find

$$\frac{\text{height at 45 seconds}}{\text{height at 30 seconds}} = \frac{14}{14.9} \approx 0.94$$

and

$$\frac{\text{height at 60 seconds}}{\text{height at 45 seconds}} = \frac{13.2}{14} \approx 0.94$$

Note that 0.94 represents 6% decay. If we assume, as the data suggest, every 15 seconds the height of the froth decays by a factor of 6%, then we can write an expression (formula) for the froth height and see how well it fits the data.

Example 5   Modeling the decay of beer froth

Find values for the parameters a and b of the function

$$H(t) = ab^t$$

that ensure the function passes through the first data point in Table 1.11 and that the height of the froth declines 6% every 15 seconds. Use technology to graph $H(t)$ alongside the data. How well does the function fit the data? Assume that t is measured in seconds.

Solution   Since the initial height of the froth is 17 cm and $H(0) = ab^0 = a$, we set $a = 17$. On the other hand, assuming that the froth decays by a factor of 6% every 15 seconds means that

$$0.94 = \frac{H(15)}{H(0)} = \frac{ab^{15}}{a} = b^{15}$$

Hence, $b = 0.94^{1/15} \approx 0.99588$. Therefore, we have (in centimeters)

$$H(t) = 17(0.99588)^t$$

The graph is shown in Figure 1.31 and appears to fit the data very well.

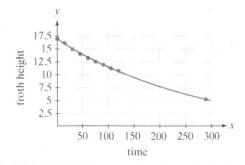

Figure 1.31 Froth height equation plotted with data points.

One way of understanding this exponential decay is to think of the froth as a large collection of bubbles. According to our calculations, approximately every 15 seconds, 6% of the bubbles will pop, leaving only 94% of the original head of froth. As the bubbles continue to pop, there are fewer and fewer that can pop. Consequently, as shown in Figure 1.31, the number of bubbles left to pop declines to zero over time in a way that seems to be modeled rather well by a function that has a variable appearing as the exponent of some base value. For this reason, the decline is called *exponential decay*. In the problem set and in the next section, you will see that exponential decay arises in many biological contexts: exponential decay of a tumor following radiation therapy, exponential decay of a drug in the body, and exponential decay of endangered populations.

The number e

There is one choice of a base a for exponential functions a^x that plays a particularly important role in calculus. It is Euler's number e named after the Swiss mathematician Leonhard Euler (1707–1783). Its importance will become apparent only when we get into the machinery of calculus. The following example, however, introduces you to this constant, and in providing an economic interpretation of its value.

Example 6   Continuously compounded interest

Jacob Bernoulli (1655–1705), another Swiss mathematician, discovered the irrational number e while exploring the compound interest on loans. Consider a bank account starting with one dollar. If the bank (never to be seen in the real world!) gives you 100% interest on this dollar after a year, you will have $2.00 after one year. What happens to your initial dollar if the bank compounds the interest more frequently?

a. How much money will you have in the account one year from now if the bank gives you 50% interest six months from now and another 50% interest on the total amount in your account a year from now? This corresponds to compounding a 100% interest rate twice a year.

b. How much will you have in the account if the bank compounds the interest quarterly? In other words, it gives you 25% interest on the total amount in your account four times a year.

c. Create a table corresponding to compounding your dollar monthly, daily, hourly, and every minute. Does the amount in your bank account after one year appear to approach a limiting value?

Solution

a. After the first six months, you will have $1.00(1.5) = $1.50. After a year, the total amount of money $1.00(1.5) in your account gets 50% interest and you will have $1.00(1.5)^2 = $2.25.

b. After the first three months, you will have $1.00(1.25) = $1.25. After the first six months, you have $1.00(1.25)^2 = $1.5625. After the first nine months, $1.00(1.25)^3 = $1.953125. After one year, $1.00(1.25)^4 \approx $2.44.

c. Following the approach from parts **a** and **b**, we get the following table of values.

Number of times compounded	Dollar amount at end of year
1 (annually)	$2.00
2 (half-yearly)	$1.00(1 + 1/2)^2 = $2.25
4 (quarterly)	$1.00(1 + 1/4)^4 \approx $2.4414
12 (monthly)	$1.00(1 + 1/12)^{12} \approx $2.61304
365 (daily)	$1.00(1 + 1/365)^{365} \approx $2.71457
8760 (hourly)	$1.00(1 + 1/8760)^{8760} \approx $2.71813
525600 (minutely)	$1.00(1 + 1/525600)^{525600} \approx $2.71828

The table suggests that the amount in the account is approaching some value near $2.71828 as you compound more and more frequently.

This example suggests that the quantity $(1 + 1/n)^n$ approaches a limiting value near 2.71828 as n gets very large. The actual limiting value is Euler's number e. We state this definition formally using the concept of a limit discussed in the introduction to this book. Limits are discussed extensively in Chapter 2.

Euler's Number e

$$e = \lim_{n \to \infty} \left(1 + \frac{1}{n}\right)^n \approx 2.7182818\ldots$$

Based on Example 6, we can interpret e as the value of one dollar a year from now in a continuously compounded bank account at a rate of 100%. The exponential function $y = e^x$ has many properties that are particularly convenient for calculus. We will see some of these properties in Chapter 2 when we discuss derivatives.

With continuous compounding, we compound interest not quarterly, or monthly, or daily, or even every second, but *instantaneously*, so that the future amount of money A in the account grows continuously. In other words, we compute A as the limiting value of

$$P\left(1 + \frac{r}{n}\right)^{nt}$$

as the number of compounding periods n grows without bound. We denote by $A(t)$ the future value after t years. As with the definition of e, we denote this by the limit notation $n \to \infty$:

$$A(t) = \lim_{n \to \infty} P\left(1 + \frac{r}{n}\right)^{nt} \quad \text{\textit{Let }} k = \frac{n}{r}, \text{ \textit{so that} } krt = nt \text{ \textit{and} } \frac{r}{n} = \frac{1}{k};$$
$$\text{\textit{also} } k \to \infty \text{ \textit{as} } n \to \infty.$$

$$= \lim_{k \to \infty} P\left(1 + \frac{1}{k}\right)^{krt}$$

$$= \lim_{k \to \infty} P\left[\left(1 + \frac{1}{k}\right)^k\right]^{rt}$$

$$= P\left[\lim_{k \to \infty} \left(1 + \frac{1}{k}\right)^k\right]^{rt} \quad \text{\textit{Scalar rule for limits.}}$$

$$= Pe^{rt} \quad \text{\textit{Definition of }} e$$

These observations are now summarized.

Future Value

If P dollars are compounded n times per year at an annual rate r, then the **future value** after t years is given by

$$A(t) = P\left(1 + \frac{r}{n}\right)^{nt}$$

and if the compounding is continuous, the future value is

$$A(t) = Pe^{rt}$$

Since $e > 1$, the exponential function $y = e^x$ increases rapidly. To get a sense of how quickly this exponential function increases, you will use technology in the next example to determine how long it would take the continuously compounded bank account with one dollar to yield $10,000. An analytical approach to solving this problem is given in Section 1.6, after we introduce logarithm functions.

Example 7 Naïve approach to solving an exponential equation

Graph $y = e^x$ and $y = 10,000$ to solve the equation $e^x = 10,000$.

Solution Graphing $y = e^x$ and $y = 10,000$ yields the following graph (with units on the y-axis in units of 10,000).

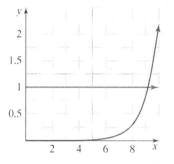

We estimate the x value at which the intersection occurs to be $x \approx 9$. ■

PROBLEM SET 1.4

Level 1 DRILL PROBLEMS

Graph the exponential functions in Problems 1.4 to 6.

1. $y = 2^x$

2. $y = \left(\dfrac{1}{2}\right)^x$

3. $y = 3^{-x}$

4. $y = e^{2x}$

5. $y = 0.1^{-x}$

6. $y = \pi^{ex}$

Graph the exponential function $y = f(x)$ and the polynomial function $y = g(x)$ using the same domain (x-values) and range (y-values) in Problems 7 to 10. Estimate for what value of x that $f(x) \geq g(x)$.

7. $f(x) = 2^x$ and $g(x) = 2x$.

8. $f(x) = e^x$ and $g(x) = 2x$.

9. $f(x) = \pi^x$ and $g(x) = x^4 - 4$.

10. $f(x) = 1.1^x$ and $g(x) = 5x^5 + x + 1$.

Use a graphical approach to estimate the solution to the equations specified in Problems 11 to 18. Note that the solution may be negative.

11. $e^{2x} = 10$

12. $e^{x/2} = 1/2$

13. $e^{-x} = x$

14. $e^{-x} = -3x$

15. $e^{x/3} = x$

16. $e^{-x} = -x^2$

17. $e^x = -x^2 + 2$

18. $e^x = x^2 + 2x$

Assume that $1,000$ is invested for t years at r percent interest compounded in the frequencies given in Problems 19 to 24. Calculate the future value.

19. $t = 25, r = 0.07$; annual compounding

20. $t = 10, r = 0.12$; semiannual compounding

21. $t = 1, r = 0.01$; continuous compounding

22. $t = 5, r = 0.02$; continuous compounding

23. $t = \frac{1}{3}$ (4 months), $r = 0.16$; monthly compounding

24. $t = \frac{1}{2}$ (6 months), $r = 0.08$; monthly compounding

Find the equation for the exponential function $f(x) = b\,a^x$ that passes through the two indicated points in Problems 25 to 28.

25. $(0, 2)$ and $(1, 5)$

26. $(-2, 32)$ and $(2, 8)$

27. $(1/2, 3)$ and $(1, 1)$

28. $(-2, 1/2)$ and $(2, 2)$

Level 2 APPLIED AND THEORY PROBLEMS

29. In Example 5, we modeled the height of the beer froth (in centimeters) as $H(t) = 17(0.99588)^t$ where t is measured in seconds. Plot this function over a four-minute time interval and estimate at what time the froth is one half of its original height.

30. In Example 2, we modeled the population size (in millions) of the United States as $N(t) = 8.3(1.33)^t$ where t is measured in decades after 1815. Plot this function over a fifty-year period and estimate the time at which the population would triple in size. How does this compare to the actual time that the population tripled in size?

31. Consider $100 in a bank account that has annual interest rate of 20%.

   a. Compute the amount in the bank account one year later if the money is compounded once a year, twice a year, and four times a year.

   b. Find an expression for the amount of money in the bank account if the money is compounded n times a year.

   c. Evaluate this expression for larger and larger n and estimate the value it appears to be approaching.

32. Consider $1,000 in a bank account that has annual interest rate of 5%.

   a. Compute the amount in the bank account one year later if the money is compounded once a year, twice a year, and four times a year.

   b. Find an expression for the amount of money in the bank account if the money is compounded n times a year.

   c. Evaluate this expression for larger and larger n and estimate the value it appears to be approaching.

33. Consider a bacterial species that produces ten offspring per day. Assume that you start with one bacterial cell, no cells die, and all cells reproduce at the same rate.

   a. Compute the bacterial population size in one year if the cells reproduce only once per day, twice per day, and four times per day.

   b. Find an expression for the population size if the population reproduces n times per day.

   c. Evaluate this expression for larger and larger n and estimate the value it appears to be approaching.

34. Consider a bacterial species that produces five offspring per day. Assume that you start with twenty bacterial cells, no cells die, and all cells reproduce at the same rate.

   a. Compute the bacterial population size in one year if the cells reproduce only once per day, twice per day, and four times per day.

   b. Find an expression for the population size if the population reproduces n times per day.

   c. Evaluate this expression for larger and larger n and estimate the value it appears to be approaching.

35. The following functions give the population size $P(t)$ in millions for four fictional countries where t is the number of decades since 1900.

   Country 1: $P_1(t) = 3(1.5)^t$

   Country 2: $P_2(t) = 10(1.1)^t$

   Country 3: $P_3(t) = 20(0.95)^t$

   Country 4: $P_4(t) = 2(1.4)^t$

   a. Which country had the largest population size in 1900?

   b. Which country has the fastest population growth rate? By what percentage does this population grow every decade?

   c. Is any of these populations decreasing in size? If so, which one and by what fraction does the population size decrease every decade?

36. The following functions give the froth height (in centimeters) of three fictional beers where t represents time (in seconds).

   Beer 1: $H_1(t) = 20(0.99)^t$

   Beer 2: $H_2(t) = 40(0.9)^t$

   Beer 3: $H_3(t) = 15(0.98)^t$

   a. Which beer has the highest froth initially? What is the height?

   b. Which beer has the slowest decay of froth? For this beer, what percentage of the height is lost in ten seconds? Twenty seconds?

   c. Which beer has the highest froth height after ten seconds?

37. Hyperthyroidism is a condition in which the thyroid gland makes too much thyroid hormone. The condition can lead to difficulty concentrating, fatigue, and weight loss. One treatment for hypothyroidism is the administration of replacement thyroid hormone such as thyroxine (T4). The concentration of this hormone in a patient's body exhibits exponential decay with a half-life of about seven days. Consider an individual that has taken 100 mcg of T4.

   a. How much of the T4 is in the body after fourteen days?

   b. Write an expression for the amount of T4 in the body after t days.

   c. Use a graph to estimate the time required for the amount of T4 to be reduced to 10 mcg.

38. In Problem 37, we discussed hyperthyroidism. For individuals with this conditions, the body converts thyroxine (T4) into triiodothyronine (T3), which is the hormone that the body uses at the cellular level. The bodies of some individuals are unable to do this conversion; consequently these people are given injections of T3. The half-life of T3 is about ten hours. Consider an individual who has taken 100 mcg of T3.

   a. How much of the T3 is in the body after thirty hours?

   b. Write an expression for the amount of T3 in the body after t hours.

   c. Use a graph to estimate the time required for the amount of T3 to be reduced to 10 mcg.

39. Carbon-14 has a half-life of 5,730 years. How much is left of 500 g of C-14 after t years?

40. If a bacterial population initially has twenty individuals and doubles every 9.3 hours, then how many individuals will it have after three days?

41. Scientists estimate that whale numbers were 350 in 1981 and growing at 12% per year. "Whale Numbers up 12% a Year" was a headline in a 1993 Australian newspaper. A thirteen-year study had found that the humpback whale (*Megaptera novaeangliae*) off the coast of Australia was increasing significantly. When the study began in 1981, the humpback whale population consisted of 350 individuals.

   a. Write an expression for $P(t)$, the population size at t years after 1981.

   b. Estimate the size of the population in 2010.

42. The population size (in millions) of Mexico in the early 1980s is reported in Table 1.12.

Table 1.12 Population in Mexico

Year	Population (in millions)
1980	67.38
1981	69.13
1982	70.93
1983	72.77
1984	74.66
1985	76.60

   a. Assume the population growth in Mexico is exponential. Use the first two data points to find a formula for $P(t)$, the population size (in millions) t years after 1980.

   b. Plot $P(t)$ against the data. Discuss the quality of the fit.

   c. Estimate the size of the population in 2004.

   d. Look up Mexico's actual population size in 2004. Does your model overpredict or underpredict the population size? Discuss your answer.

43. Consider an instant lottery game in which you buy a scratch-off card and there is a certain chance p of winning a prize. If you buy N scratch-off cards, the chance of *not* winning a prize is $(1 - p)^N$, that is, the chance you didn't win the prize on the first card times the chance you didn't win the prize on the second card, and so on. Therefore, the chance of winning a prize with N cards is $1 - (1 - p)^N$.

   a. If there is a 1/10 chance of winning a prize and you buy ten cards, what is the chance you win a prize?

   b. If there is a chance 1/100 of winning a prize and you buy 100 cards, what is the chance you win a prize?

   c. If there is chance $1/N$ of winning a prize and you buy N cards, what is the chance you win a prize? What value does this approach for large N?

44. In an experimental study performed at Dartmouth College, two groups of mice with tumors were treated with the chemotherapeutic drug cisplatin. Prior to the therapy, the tumor consisted of proliferating cells (also known as clonogenic cells) that grew exponentially with a doubling time of approximately 2.9 days. Assume the initial tumor size was $0.1 \, \text{cm}^3$.

   a. Write an expression for the tumor size after t days.

   b. Use graphing to estimate at what time the tumor is $0.5 \, \text{cm}^3$ in size.

45. In the experimental study described in Problem 44, each of the mice was given a dosage of 10 mg/kg of cisplatin. At the time of the therapy, the average tumor size was approximately $0.5 \, \text{cm}^3$. Assume all the cells became quiescent (i.e., no longer dividing) and decay with a half-life of approximately 5.7 days.

   a. Write an expression for the tumor size after t days of treatment.

   b. Use graphing to estimate at what time the tumor is $0.05 \, \text{cm}^3$ in size.

46. By comparing the graphs of $\sqrt{x}^{\pi}$ and $\pi^{\sqrt{x}}$ determine which is larger:

   a. $(\sqrt{3})^{\pi}$ or $\pi^{\sqrt{3}}$

   b. $(\sqrt{5})^{\pi}$ or $\pi^{\sqrt{5}}$

   c. $(\sqrt{6})^{\pi}$ or $\pi^{\sqrt{6}}$

   d. From parts **a–c**, notice that $(\sqrt{x})^{\pi}$ is larger for some values of x, while $\pi^{\sqrt{x}}$ is larger for others. For $x = \pi^2$

$$(\sqrt{x})^{\pi} = \pi^{\sqrt{x}}$$

is obviously true (since $\pi^{\pi} = \pi^{\pi}$). Using a graphical method, find another value (approximately) for which the given statement is true.

In calculus the number e is sometimes introduced using slopes. In Problems 47 to 49 explore this idea.

47. a. Draw the graph of $y = 2^x$ and plot the points $(0, 1)$ and $(2, 4)$, which are on the graph.

b. Consider the secant line passing through these points. Now, consider the slope of the secant line as the point $(2, 4)$ slides along the curve toward the point $(0, 1)$. Draw the line that you think will result when the point $(2, 4)$ reaches the point $(0, 1)$. This is the *tangent line* to the curve $y = 2^x$ at $(0, 1)$.

c. Using the tangent line, and the fact that the slope of a line is RISE/RUN, estimate (to the nearest tenth) the slope of the tangent line.

48. a. Draw the graph of $y = 3^x$ and plot the points $(0, 1)$ and $(2, 9)$, which are on the graph.

b. Consider the secant line passing through these points. Now, consider the slope of the secant line as the point $(2, 9)$ slides along the curve to-ward the point $(0, 1)$. Draw the line that you think will result when the point $(2, 9)$ reaches the point $(0, 1)$. This is the *tangent line* to the curve $y = 2^x$ at $(0, 1)$.

c. Using the tangent line, and the fact that the slope of a line is RISE/RUN, estimate (to the nearest tenth) the slope of the tangent line.

49. a. Draw a line passing through $(0, 1)$ with slope 1.

b. Compare the graphs of $y = 2^x$ (Problem 47) and $y = 3^x$ (Problem 48). Now, it seems reasonable that there exists a number between 2 and 3 with the property that the slope of the tangent through $(0, 1)$ is 1. Draw such a curve.

c. On the same coordinate axes, draw the graph of $y = e^x$. How does this curve compare with the curve you drew in part **b**? In calculus, the number between 2 and 3 with the property that the slope of the tangent through $(0, 1)$ is 1 is used as the number e.

1.5   Function Building

We have reviewed basic properties of linear, periodic, exponential, and power functions. By combining these functions, we can greatly enlarge our "toolbox" of functions. With this larger toolbox, we can describe more data sets and model more biological processes. For instance, in this section we develop models of the waxing and waning of tides and the rates at which microbes consume nutrients.

Shifting, reflecting, and stretching

The simplest way to create the graph of a new function from the graph of another function is to shift the graph vertically or horizontally.

Horizontal and Vertical Shifts

Let $y = f(x)$ be a given function with $a > 0$.

Horizontal shifts:

$y = f(x - a)$ shifts the graph of $y = f(x)$ to the right a units

$y = f(x + a)$ shifts the graph of $y = f(x)$ to the left a units

Vertical shifts:

$y = f(x) + a$ shifts the graph of $y = f(x)$ upward a units

$y = f(x) - a$ shifts the graph of $y = f(x)$ downward a units

To understand why these shifts occur, consider $y = f(x - a)$. Substituting $x + a$ for x yields $y = f(x + a - a) = f(x)$. Hence, the function $y = f(x - a)$ has the same value as the function $y = f(x)$ when you "shift x" to the right by a.

Example 1   **Shifting graphs**

Consider the function $y = f(x)$ whose graph is given by Figure 1.32.

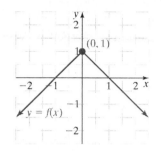

Figure 1.32 Graph of $y = f(x)$.

Sketch the graphs of $y = f(x - 0.5)$, $y = f(x) - 0.5$, and $y = f(x + 1) + 1$.

Solution $y = f(x - 0.5)$ shifts the graph right 0.5 units. $y = f(x) - 0.5$ shifts the graph down 0.5 units. $y = f(x + 1) + 1$ shifts the graph left 1 unit and up 1 unit. These graphs are shown in Figure 1.33

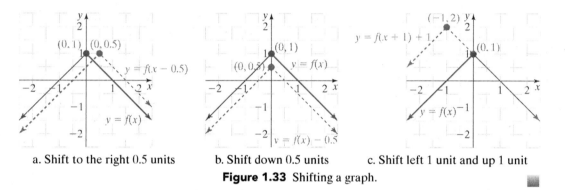

a. Shift to the right 0.5 units   b. Shift down 0.5 units   c. Shift left 1 unit and up 1 unit

Figure 1.33 Shifting a graph.

In addition to shifting graphs, we can reflect graphs across axes.

Reflections

Let $y = f(x)$ be a given function.

The graph of $y = -f(x)$ is the **reflection across the x axis**. It is found by replacing each point (x, y) on the graph with $(x, -y)$.

The graph of $y = f(-x)$ is the **reflection across the y axis**. It is found by replacing each point (x, y) on the graph with $(-x, y)$.

Example 2   **Reflecting a function**

Consider the function $y = f(x)$ whose graph is given by

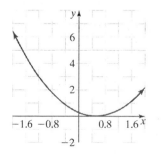

a. Sketch $y = f(-x)$.

b. Sketch $y = -f(x)$.

Solution

a. Reflecting the graph about the y axis yields the desired graph in red in the left panel below.

b. Reflecting the graph about the x axis yields the desired graph in red in the right panel below.

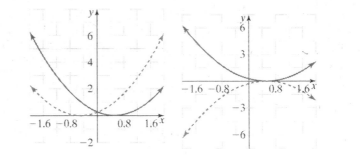

A curve can be stretched or compressed in either the x-direction, the y-direction, or both, as shown in Figure 1.34.

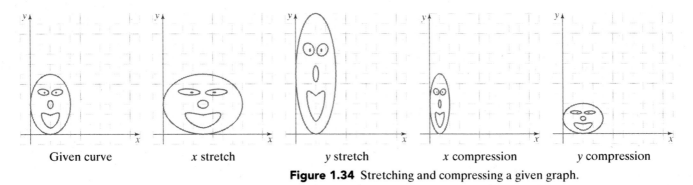

| Given curve | x stretch | y stretch | x compression | y compression |

Figure 1.34 Stretching and compressing a given graph.

Stretching and Compressing

Let $y = f(x)$ be a given function.

To sketch the graph of $y = f(bx)$, replace each point (x, y) with $(\frac{1}{b}x, y)$. If $0 < b < 1$, then we call the transformation an **x-dilation** (or x stretch). If $b > 1$, then we call the transformation an **x-compression**.

To sketch the graph of $y = c\, f(x)$, replace each point (x, y) with (x, cy). If $c > 1$, then we call the transformation a **y-dilation** (or y stretch). If $0 < c < 1$, then we call the transformation a **y-compression**.

Example 3   Stretching and compressing

Consider the function $y = f(x)$ defined by

$$f(x) = \begin{cases} 0 & \text{if } x < 0 \\ x & \text{if } 0 \le x < 1 \\ 1 & \text{if } x \ge 1 \end{cases}$$

Find and sketch the functions $y = f(2x)$ and $y = 3f(2x)$.

Solution   We begin by sketching the function $y = f(x)$ which is 0 for negative x, linear with slope 1 from $x = 0$ to $x = 1$, and equal to 1 for $x \geq 1$ to obtain the left panel below.

Since $2x < 0$ if and only if $x < 0$, we get the function $y = f(2x)$ equals 0 for $x < 0$. Since $0 \leq 2x < 1$ if and only if $0 \leq x < 1/2$, $y = f(2x) = 2x$ for $0 \leq x < 1/2$. Finally, $y = f(2x) = 1$ for $x \geq \dfrac{1}{2}$. Therefore, we have shown

$$f(2x) = \begin{cases} 0 & \text{if } x < 0 \\ 2x & \text{if } 0 \leq x < 1/2 \\ 1 & \text{if } x \geq 1/2 \end{cases}$$

Plotting this function, we get the center panel below. Hence, $y = f(2x)$ compresses the function $y = f(x)$ by a factor of 2 in the horizontal direction.

The function $y = 3f(2x)$ stretches the function $y = f(2x)$ by a factor of 3 in the vertical direction. Hence, we get

$$3f(2x) = \begin{cases} 0 & \text{if } x < 0 \\ 6x & \text{if } 0 \leq x < 1/2 \\ 3 & \text{if } x \geq 1/2 \end{cases}$$

Plotting this function, we get the right panel below.

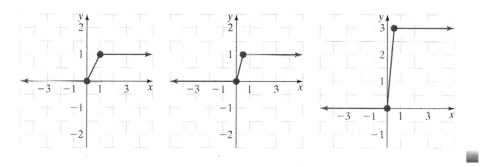

By compressing and stretching sinusoidal functions, we can model periodic phenomena like tidal movements.

Example 4   Modeling tidal movements

The tides for Toms Cove in Assateague Beach, Virginia, on August 19, 2004, are listed in the table on the left.

Assume that this can be modeled by

$$T(t) = A\cos[B(t + C)] + D$$

where T denotes the height (in feet) of the tide t hours after midnight. Find values of A, B, C and D such that the function fits the Assateague tide data.

Time	Height) (ft)	Tide
5:07 A.M.	0.4	Low
10:57 A.M.	4.0	High
5:23 P.M.	0.4	Low

Solution   The data suggest that the period of T is approximately twelve hours, in which case $B = \dfrac{2\pi}{12} = \dfrac{\pi}{6}$. The amplitude of the tide is given by $A = \dfrac{4 - 0.4}{2} = 1.8$. Since the graph of cosine is always centered around the horizontal axis, we need to vertically shift the graph up by the midtide height, $D = (4.0 + 0.4)/2 = 2.2$. Finally, since the high tide occurs approximately at $t = 11$, we can choose $C = -11$ to shift

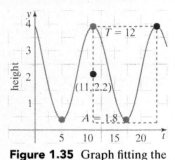

Figure 1.35 Graph fitting the Assateague tide data.

the graph left by 11. Putting this all together yields

$$T(t) = 1.8\cos\left[\frac{\pi}{6}(t-11)\right] + 2.2$$

To graph this function, we note $(h, k) = (11, 2.2)$; amplitude, $A = 1.8$; and period $T = 12$, as shown in Figure 1.35.

Adding, subtracting, multiplying, and dividing

The easiest way to create new functions is to perform arithmetic operations on old functions. The first three of these operations result in a function whose domain is the intersection of the domains of the original functions, where the symbol $\cap$ is used to denote *set intersection*. Since division by zero is not permitted, division can further reduce the domain of the new function.

Functional Arithmetic

Let f and g be functions with domains A and B, respectively. Then,

$f + g$ is defined by $(f + g)(x) = f(x) + g(x)$ with domain $A \cap B$

$f - g$ is defined by $(f - g)(x) = f(x) - g(x)$ with domain $A \cap B$

fg is defined by $(fg)(x) = f(x)g(x)$ with domain $A \cap B$

f/g is defined by $(f/g)(x) = f(x)/g(x)$ with domain consisting of points x in $A \cap B$ such that $g(x) \neq 0$

Example 5 Combining functions

Consider the functions $f(x) = \sqrt{100 - x^2}$ and $g(x) = \sin x$. Find the domains for $f + g$, fg, and f/g.

Solution The domain of $f(x)$ is $[-10, 10]$ and the domain of $g(x)$ is $(-\infty, \infty)$. Thus it follows that the domains of $f + g$ and fg are $[-10, 10]$. Multiplying the graphs pointwise yields a graph that does not alter the domain, but taking the quotient f/g requires that we remove points on $[-10, 10]$ where $g(x) = 0$; that is the values $0, \pm\pi, \pm2\pi, \pm3\pi$.

Two important classes of functions that we get by adding, multiplying, and dividing power functions are polynomials and rational functions.

Polynomials and Rational Functions

Let n be a whole number. A *polynomial function of degree n* is a function of the form

$$y = a_0 + a_1 x + a_2 x^2 + \cdots + a_n x^n$$

where $a_0, a_1, \ldots, a_n$ are constants.

A *rational function* is a function of the form

$$y = \frac{a_0 + a_1 x + a_2 x^2 + \cdots + a_n x^n}{b_0 + b_1 x + \cdots + b_m x^m}$$

where division by zero is excluded, n, m, are natural numbers, $a_0, a_1, a_2, \ldots, a_n$, $b_0, b_1, b_2, \ldots, b_m$ are constants, and the denominator is not a factor of the numberator (i.e. it cannot be cancelled out).

Rational functions arise in biology in many ways, particularly in the context of the rate at which organisms extract resources from their environments. Bacteria, for example, have special molecular receptors embedded in their cell membrane to ingest nutrients, such as glucose, into their cell bodies. These receptors "capture" nutrient molecules outside of the cell and transport them into the cell body. This process is illustrated in Figure 1.36.

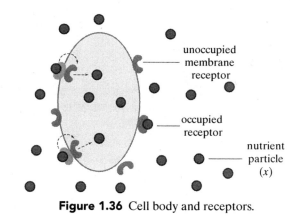

Figure 1.36 Cell body and receptors.

The rate at which nutrients can be brought into the cell body is called the *uptake rate*. The uptake rate is limited by the number of receptors and the time it takes a receptor to bring a nutrient particle into the cell body. The next example derives the Michaelis-Menton uptake function named after biochemists Leonor Michaelis (1875–1947) and Maud Menten (1879–1960). In addition to describing nutrient uptake, this function is used to describe enzyme kinetics and the consumption rates of organisms such as foxes eating rabbits, or ladybugs eating aphids.

Example 6   Michaelis-Menten glucose uptake rate

This problem is divided into two parts: the derivation of the Michaelis-Menten uptake function in part **a** and application of this function in part **b**.

a. To find the amount of glucose brought into the cell per hour, let T be the amount of time a receptor is unbound and can bind to a glucose molecule. The total number of receptors on the cell is R and x is the concentration of nutrients. Assume the number N of glucose molecules brought into the cell per hour by one receptor is proportional to T and x (i.e., more time for binding or higher glucose concentrations lead to more glucose uptake):

$$N = aTx$$

where $a > 0$ is the proportionality constant. If a bound receptor requires b hours (b is much less than 1) to bring a glucose molecule into the cell, then T satisfies

$$T = \text{one hour} - \text{time spent bound to glucose} = 1 - bN = 1 - baTx$$

Solve for T in terms of x and derive an expression for the total uptake rate $f(x)$ in terms of x.

b. In the 1960s, scientists at Woods Hole Oceanographic Institution measured the uptake rate of glucose by bacterial populations from the coast of Peru.* In one

---

*R. F. Vaccaro and H. W. Jannasch (1967). "Variations in uptake kinetics for glucose by natural populations in seawater." *Limnology and Oceanography.* 12:540–542.

field experiment, they collected the following data:

Glucose concentration (micrograms per liter)	Uptake rate for 1 liter of bacteria (micrograms per hour)
0	0
20	12
40	16
60	18
80	19
100	20

By an appropriate change of variables (see Problem set 1.5), one can use linear regression to estimate the parameters for the uptake function. Doing so yields $f(x) = \dfrac{1.2078x}{1 + 0.0506x}$. How does this relate to the expression for $f(x)$ derived in part **a**? Use technology to plot this function against the data. How good is the fit?

Solution

a. Solving for T, we get

$$T = 1 - ba\,Tx$$
$$T + ba\,Tx = 1$$
$$T(1 + bax) = 1$$
$$T = \frac{1}{1 + bax}$$

Substituting this expression into the expression $N = aTx$, we get

$$N(x) = \frac{ax}{1 + bax}$$

Since N is the number of molecules handled by each receptor and the cell has R receptors, the total uptake rate of the cell is

$$f(x) = \frac{NRax}{1 + bax}$$

b. The function $f(x)$ has an identical form to the function derived in part **a**, with $ba = 0.0506$ and $aNR = 1.2078$, where B is the number of bacterial cells in one liter of solution. Using technology to plot the function against the data yields the following graph.

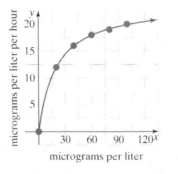

The fact that the function fits the data so well gives us confidence that the arguments used to construct the function are sound! One interesting question to ask is what happens to the uptake rate $f(x)$ as x gets very large (i.e., approaches $+\infty$)? In the next chapter, we will develop ideas to tackle this question.

Composing

Situations often arise in biology where the relationship between two variables x and z is mediated by a third variable y. For example, the rate z at which a population of mice or shrews grows is related to the number y of insects the animals consume per unit time, and this rate y is related to the density x of insects in the area where these animals feed. Let f be the function that relates consumption rate y to resource density x; that is $y = f(x)$. Let g be the function that relates the per capita population growth rate z of the population to the consumption rate y; that is, $z = g(y)$. Then by substitution, we obtain $z = g(f(x))$. We have expressed the growth rate as a function of resource density through the process of taking a function of a function. This process is known as **composition** and is shown in Figure 1.37.

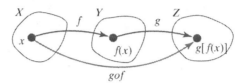

Figure 1.37 Composition of two functions.

Composite Functions

Let f and g be functions with domains A and B, respectively. The **composite function** $g \circ f$ is defined by

$$(g \circ f)(x) = g[f(x)]$$

The domain of $g \circ f$ is the subset of A for which $g \circ f$ is defined.

To visualize how functional composition works, think of $f \circ g$ in terms of an assembly line in which f and g are arranged in series, with output f becoming the input of g.

Example 7   Composing functions

Let $f(x) = 2x + 1$ and $g(x) = \sqrt{x}$. Find the composite functions $g \circ f$ and $f \circ g$ and their domains.

Solution   The function $g \circ f$ is defined by

$$g[f(x)] = g(2x + 1) = \sqrt{2x + 1}$$

Notice that $g \circ f$ means that f is applied first, then g is applied. Since $g \circ f$ is defined only for $2x + 1 \geq 0$ or $x \geq -\dfrac{1}{2}$, the domain of $g \circ f$ is $\left[-\dfrac{1}{2}, \infty\right)$.

The function $f \circ g$ is defined by

$$f(g(x)) = f(\sqrt{x}) = 2\sqrt{x} + 1$$

In this part, first apply g then apply f. Since $f \circ g$ is defined only for $x \geq 0$, we see the domain of $f \circ g$ is $[0, \infty)$.

Example 7 illustrates that functional composition is not, in general, commutative. That is, in general,

$$f \circ g \neq g \circ f$$

Sometimes it can be useful to express a function as the composite of two simpler functions.

Example 8   Decomposing functions

Express each of the following functions as the composite $f \circ g$ of two functions f and g.

a. $\sin^2 x$ 　　　　　　　　　　　　　**b.** $(2 + \cos x)^3$

Solution

a. A good way of thinking about this is to think about how you would use a calculator to evaluate this expression. You would first find sine of x, and then square the result. Hence, let $g(x) = \sin x$ and $f(x) = x^2$ so that

$$f[g(x)] = f(\sin x) = (\sin x)^2 = \sin^2 x$$

b. To evaluate the function $y = (2 + \cos x)^3$, first take cosine of x, add two, and raise the result to the power x. Since the evaluation of this function takes three steps, there is more than one way that we can represent it as a composition of two functions.

Let $g(x) = \cos x + 2$ and $f(x) = x^3$. Then,

$$f[g(x)] = f(\cos x + 2) = (\cos x + 2)^3$$

Alternatively, let $g(x) = \cos x$ and $f(x) = (2 + x)^3$. Then,

$$f[g(x)] = f(\cos x) = (2 + \cos x)^3$$

The next example involves the composition of two well-known functions in ecology: (1) the consumption function $y = f(x)$ that relates the rate at which an organism is able to consume a resource of density x in the environment (also known as the *functional response*) and (2) the per capita growth rate of an organism $g(y)$ that is a function of the consumption rate y.

The example is based on data pertaining to the daily rates at which individual short-tailed shrews (*Blarina brevicauda*), as shown in Figure 1.38, gather cocoons of the European pine sawfly (*Neodiprion sertifer*) buried in forest-floor litter. These data, as a function of cocoon density x per thousandth acre (i.e., acres $\times 10^{-3}$), can be fitted reasonably well by the function

$$y = f(x) = \frac{320x}{110 + x} \qquad \text{cocoons per day.}$$

Figure 1.38 Short-tailed shrew (*Blarina brevicauda*).

This function is directly equivalent to the Michaelis-Menten uptake function derived in Example 6.

Example 9   Short-tailed shrews exploiting cocoons

Consider the shrew population studied by the Canadian ecologist C. S. Holling, "Some Characteristics of Simple Types of Predation and Parasitism," *The Canadian Entomologist* 91(1959): 385–398. Suppose we are given the information that under ideal conditions (i.e., when the number of sawfly cocoons per shrew is essentially unlimited) each pair of shrews produces an average of around twenty female and twenty male progeny per year.

a. Use these data to estimate the maximum per capita growth rate r per day in the growth rate function[*] $g(y) = r\left(1 - \dfrac{b}{y}\right)$, where y is the number of cocoons

---

[*]W. M. Getz, "Metaphysiological and Evolutionary Dynamics of Populations Exploiting Constant and Interactive Resources: *r-K* Selection Revisited," *Evolutionary Ecology* 7(1993): 287–305.

consumed per day per shrew, r is the *maximal per capita growth rate of the population*, and $b = 100$ is the *growth breakeven point*, that is, $g(b) = 0$.

  b. Use functional composition on this growth rate function and Holling's response function $f(x) = \dfrac{320x}{110 + x}$ on the daily rate at which shrews collect cocoons to find the daily per capita growth rate $G = g \circ f$ as a function of cocoon density x.

Solution

  a. Under ideal conditions, the per capita growth rate is given by 20 pairs/year. To convert this yearly rate to a daily rate, we divide by 365 days/year to get an estimate for the maximal per capita growth rate

$$r = \frac{20}{365} \approx 0.055 \text{ pairs/day}$$

Setting $b = 100$, we get the per capita growth rate as a function of cocoons consumed per day y:

$$g(y) = 0.055 \left(1 - \frac{100}{y} \right)$$

  b. Taking functional composition of g and f now yields the per capita growth rate as a function of the cocoon density:

$$G(x) = g[f(x)] = 0.055 \left(1 - \frac{100}{f(x)} \right)$$
$$= 0.055 \left(1 - \frac{100(110 + x)}{320x} \right)$$
$$= 0.055 \left(\frac{320x - 100x - 11{,}000}{320x} \right)$$
$$= \frac{0.055(220x - 11{,}000)}{320x} \text{pairs/day}$$

PROBLEM SET 1.5

Level 1 DRILL PROBLEMS

Let $y = f(x)$ be the function whose graph is given by Figure 1.39. Sketch the graph of the functions in Problems 1 to 6.

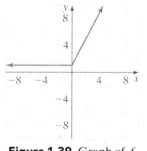

Figure 1.39 Graph of f.

1. $y = f(x) + 2$
2. $y = f(x + 1)$
3. $y = f(x - 2) + 1$
4. $y = 2f(x + 2)$
5. $y = -f(x)$
6. $y = f(-x + 2)$

Sketch the graph of the functions in Problems 7 to 10 by appropriately shifting, stretching, or translate the graph of $y = \cos x$

7. $y = \cos \left(x - \dfrac{\pi}{2} \right)$
8. $y = 3 \cos(2x)$
9. $y = 3 \cos \dfrac{x}{2}$
10. $y - 2 = 2 \cos \left(x + \dfrac{2\pi}{3} \right)$

In Problems 11 to 19 sketch the graph of each function without the aid of technology.

11. $y = (x - 2)^2$
12. $y = (x - 2)^2 + 1$
13. $y = -1.25(x - 2)^2$
14. $y = (x + 1)^3 + 5$
15. $y = (2x + 1)^3 + 5$
16. $y = (2x + 1)^3 / 2$

17. $y = 1 - e^{-x}$ **18.** $y = -|x|/2$

19. $y = 1 - 2|x|$

20. Find the indicated values given the functions
$f = \{(0, 1), (1, 4), (2, 7), (3, 10)\}$ and
$g = \{(0, 3), (1, -1), (2, 1), (3, 3)\}$

  a. $(f + g)(1)$

  b. $(f - g)(2)$

  c. $(fg)(2)$

  d. $(f/g)(0)$

  e. $(f \circ g)(2)$

21. Find the indicated values given the functions

$$f(x) = \frac{2x^2 - 5x + 2}{x - 2}$$

and

$$g(x) = x^2 - x - 2$$

  a. $(f + g)(-1)$

  b. $(f - g)(2)$

  c. $(fg)(9)$

  d. $(f/g)(99)$

  e. $(f \circ g)(0)$

22. Let $f(t)$ be a periodic function with period $p = 2\pi$ and amplitude $a = 1$. Show that the given functions are periodic and find their period and amplitude.

  a. $f(t - 1) + 2$

  b. $5f(t)$

  c. $f\left(\dfrac{t}{\pi}\right)$

  d. $2f\left(t + \dfrac{\pi}{2}\right) - 3$

23. Let $f(t)$ be a periodic function with period $p = T$ and amplitude $a = A$. Show that the following functions are periodic and find their period and amplitude.

  a. $f(t + 1) - 2$

  b. $4f(t)$

  c. $-2f(3t)$

  d. $2f(t - 4) + 1$

Express each of the functions in Problems 24 to 29 as the composition $f \circ g$ of two functions f and g. (Answers are not unique.)

24. $y = (2x^2 - 1)^4$

25. $y = \sqrt{1 - \sin x}$

26. $y = e^{-x^2}$

27. $y = e^{1 - x^2}$

28. $y = |x + 1|^2 + 6$

29. $y = (x^2 - 1)^3 + \sqrt{x^2 - 1} + 5$

For each of the functions in Problems 30 to 33, find $f + g$, fg, and, f/g. Also give the domain of each of these functions.

30. $f(x) = \dfrac{x - 2}{x + 1}$ and $g(x) = x^2 - x - 2$

31. $f(x) = \dfrac{2x^2 - x - 3}{x + 1}$ and $g(x) = x^2 - x - 2$

32. $f(x) = \sqrt{1 - x}$ and $g(x) = \sqrt{4 - x^2}$

33. $f(x) = \sqrt{4 - x^2}$ and $g(x) = \sin(\pi x)$

Level 2 APPLIED AND THEORY PROBLEMS

34. The tides for Hell Gate, Wards Island, New York, on September 6, 2004, are given by the following table:

Time	Height (ft)	Tide
12:08 A.M.	2.1	Low
5:19 A.M.	5.8	High
12:00 noon	2.1	Low

Let

$$T(t) = A\cos[B(t + C)] + D \text{ feet}$$

denote the height of the tide t hours after midnight. Find values of A, B, C, and D such that the function fits the Hell Gate tide data.

35. The tides for Bodega Bay, California, on March 10, 2005, are given by the following table:

Time	Height (ft)	Tide
4:36 A.M.	1.1	Low
10:43 A.M.	5.8	High
5:02 P.M.	−0.4	Low

Let

$$T(t) = A\cos[B(t + C)] + D \text{ feet}$$

denote the height of the tide t hours after midnight. Find values of A, B, C, and D such that the function fits the Bodega Bay tide data.

36. Enzymes are nature's catalysts because they are compounds that enhance the rate (speed) of biochemical reactions. Enzymes are used according to the body's need for them. Some enzymes aid in blood clotting and some aid in digestion. Even enzymes within the cell are needed for specific reactions. In this problem, you will derive a model of a biochemical reaction where there is a substance (e.g., glucose) that is converted to a new substance (e.g., fructose) by an enzyme (e.g., isomerase). Let $f(x)$ be the amount of substance produced per minute as a function of the substrate concentration x. To model this reaction rate, assume that enzymes are either "occupied" (i.e., processing a substrate particle) or are "unoccupied" (i.e., waiting to bind to another substrate particle).

a. Let t be the fraction of time that an enzyme is unoccupied. Assuming that $1 - t$ is proportional to x, find t as a function of x.

b. Assuming that $f(x)$ is proportional to $1 - t$, find an expression for $f(x)$.

c. Below are data for glucose-6-phosphate converted to fructose-6-phospate by the enzyme phosphoglucose isomerase.

Substrate concentration (micromolar)	Reaction rate (micromolar/minute)
0.08	0.15
0.12	0.21
0.54	0.70
1.23	1.1
1.82	1.3
2.72	1.5
4.94	1.7
10.00	1.8

Using linear regression on the transformed data, the uptake rate can be approximated by
$$f(x) = \frac{1.95x}{1 + 0.95x}.$$ Graph this function against the data.

37. In several applications it has been useful to fit a function of the form $y = f(x) = \dfrac{bx}{1 + ax}$ to a data set. Consider the change of variables given by $t = 1/x$ and $z = 1/y$.

a. Write an expression for z in terms of t.

b. Consider the following data set

Substrate concentration y (micromolar)	Reaction rate x (micromolar/minute)
0.08	0.15
0.12	0.21
0.54	0.70
1.23	1.1
1.82	1.3
2.72	1.5
4.94	1.7
10.00	1.8

Take the reciprocals of the (x, y) data values to get the corresponding (t, z) values. Use technology to fit a line to the (t, z) data. If this line is given by $z = c + dt$, use your work in **a** to find the parameters a and b in $y = \dfrac{bx}{1 + ax}$.

38. Environmental studies are often concerned with the relationship between the population of an urban area and the level of pollution. Suppose it is estimated that when p hundred thousand people live in a certain city, the average daily level of carbon monoxide in the air is

$$L(p) = 0.07\sqrt{p^2 + 3}$$

ppm. Further, assume that in t years there will be

$$p(t) = 1 + 0.02t^3$$

hundred thousand people in the city. Based on these assumptions, what level of air pollution should be expected in four years?

39. The volume, V, of a certain cone is given by

$$V(h) = \frac{\pi h^3}{12}.$$

Suppose the height is expressed as a function of time, t, by $h(t) = 2t$.

a. Find the volume when $t = 2$.

b. Express the volume as a function of elapsed time by finding $V \circ h$.

c. If the domain of V is $[0, 6]$, find the domain of h; that is, what are the permissible values for t?

40. The surface area, S, of a spherical balloon with radius r is given by

$$S(r) = 4\pi r^2.$$

Suppose the radius is expressed as a function of time t by $r(t) = 3t$.

a. Find the surface area when $t = 2$.

b. Express the surface area as a function of elapsed time by finding $S \circ r$.

c. If the domain of S is $(0, 8)$, find the domain of r; that is, what are the permissible values for t?

41. The ecologist C. S. Holling mentioned in Example 9 also collected data on the daily rates at which individual masked shrews (*Sorex cinereus*), gathered European pine sawfly cocoons in forest-floor litter. His data for this species are fitted by the functional response

$$f(x) = 110 \frac{x^4}{300^4 + x^4} \qquad \text{cocoons per day}$$

where x is the density of cocoons on the forest floor. If breeding pairs for this species produce approximately four female and four male progeny per year under favorable conditions and the growth breakeven point is $b = 400$ cocoons per day, then find the specific form of the per capita hyperbolic growth rate r per day: $g(y) = r(1 - b/y)$ for this species. Use this to derive the composite per capita growth rate function $G = (g \circ f)(x)$. Plot a graph of this composite function.

42. Suppose the number of hours between sunrise and sunset in Los Angeles, is modeled by

$$H = 12.17 + 1.5 \sin\left(\frac{2\pi n}{365} - 1.5\right)$$

where n is the number of the day in the year ($n = 1$ on January 1 and $n = 365$ on December 31, except in leap years when $n = 366$). On what days of the year in 2011 were there approximately twelve hours of daylight in Los Angeles?

43. According to the model in Problem 42, when will the length of the day in Los Angeles be about thirteen hours?

44. In an experimental study performed at Dartmouth College, two groups of mice with tumors were treated with the chemotherapeutic drug cisplatin. In Problems 44 and 45 in Section 1.4, we modeled the growth of the volume of these tumors before and after chemotherapy. A key feature missing in the model was that tumors often consist of a mixture of quiescent (i.e., nondividing) cells and proliferating cells. To add this important component to the model, assume (as was observed in the experiments), that 99% of cells are quiescent and 1% are proliferating following chemotherapy. Furthermore, assume that the volume of tumors at the time of therapy is 0.5 cm^3, the quiescent cells have a half-life of 5.7 days, and the proliferating cells have a doubling time of 2.9 days.

  a. Write a function of the tumor growth as a function of t in days.

  b. Graph this function over a twenty-day period and describe what you see.

45. The following graph posted at the Global Warming Art website indicates regular oscillations to observed sunspot activity over the past 400 years.

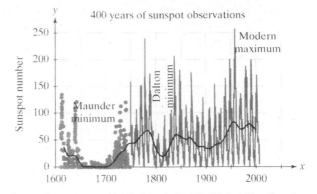

Source: Image created by Robert A. Rohde/Global Warming Art. Reprinted with permission.

Find a trigonometric function of the form $y = a + b\cos(cx + d)$, where x is in years, that provides a good fit to the data from the minimum that occured around 1844 to the minimum that occurred in 1997.

46. The following is a graph of a famous data set on the number of lynx pelts handled by the Hudson Bay Company from 1821 to 1910.

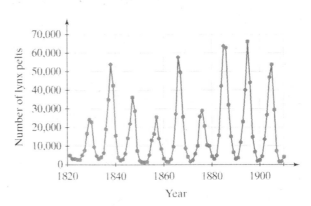

Data Source: Taken from Krebs, C J., R. Boonstra, S. Boutin and A. R. E. Sinclair, "What Drives the 10-year Cycle of Snowshoe Hares?" *BioScience* 51(1)(2001): 25–35. First published by Elton, C., and M. Nicholson, "The Ten-Year Cycle in Numbers of the Lynx in Canada," *Journal of Animal Ecology* 11 (1942): 215–244.

Write a trigonometric function of the form $y = a + b\cos(cx + d)$, where x is in years, that provides a good fit to these data.

1.6 Inverse Functions and Logarithms

Sometimes when we are given the output of a function, we want to know what inputs could generate the observed output. For instance, consider the function that assigns to each gene the protein that it encodes. If in an experimental study we observe certain proteins at high abundance, we might want to know what genes might have been expressed. At another time we might be interested in how long before a population doubles in size or reaches a specific size. Here, we introduce the concepts of one-to-one functions and inverse functions to tackle such questions. A particularly important family of inverse functions consists of logarithm functions. As you will discover, logarithmic functions are extremely convenient for examining questions about scaling laws, population growth, and radioactive decay.

Table 1.13 U.S. population size N as a function of time t

Year t	$N = f(t)$ Population size (in millions)
1815	8.3
1825	11.0
1835	14.7
1845	19.7
1855	26.7
1865	35.2
1875	44.4
1885	55.9
1895	68.9

Table 1.14 Year t as a function of U.S. population size N

N Population size (in millions)	Year $t = f^{-1}(N)$
8.3	1815
11.0	1825
14.7	1835
19.7	1845
26.7	1855
35.2	1865
44.4	1875
55.9	1885
68.9	1895

Inverse functions

Let's reexamine the U.S. population growth data introduced at the beginning of Section 1.4 and shown again in Table 1.13.

We can view this table as defining a function $f(t)$ that associates each year t with the U.S. population size $N = f(t)$ in that year. The domain of this function is $\{1815, 1825, 1835, 1845, 1855, 1865, 1875, 1885, 1895\}$ and its range is $\{8.3, 11, 14.7, 19.7, 26.7, 35.2, 44.4, 55.9, 68.9\}$. An important feature of this function is for each value N in its range, there is only a single year t in the domain such that $f(t) = N$. For example, there are 19.7 million people in the United States only in 1845 and 55.9 million people in the United States only in 1885. Functions that have this feature are called *one-to-one*. This one-to-one feature of $N(t)$—that is, two different inputs lead to two different outputs (some people refer to this as *two-to-two*)—allows us to define a new function $t = f^{-1}(N)$ that sends each population size N (in millions) to the year t corresponding to that population size N. This function is the *inverse function of N* and is shown in Table 1.14.

While the U.S. population data function $N = f(t)$ is one-to-one and that allows us to define an inverse function, not all functions are one-to-one. For example, consider the quadratic function $y = f(x) = x^2$. Since there are two values of $x = 2, -2$ such that $f(x) = 4$, this function is not one-to-one.

One-to-One (Two-to-Two)

A function $f : X \to Y$ is **one-to-one** if $f(a) = f(b)$ for some a and b in X implies that $a = b$ for all such pairs in X (this can also be thought of as two different x in X to two different y in Y).

Example 1 Checking for one-to-one

Determine whether each of the following functions is one-to-one.

a. $y = f(x) = x^3$

b. $y = f(x) = \sin x$

Solution

a. Suppose that $a^3 = b^3$. Taking the cube root of both sides of this equation, the laws of exponents imply $a = (a^3)^{1/3} = (b^3)^{1/3} = b$. Therefore, $y = x^3$ is one-to-one as we have shown that $f(a) = f(b)$ implies $a = b$.

b. We know that sine takes on the value 0 infinitely often. In particular, $\sin 0 = \sin \pi = 0$. Since we found $a = 0$ and $b = \pi$ such that $a \neq b$ but $f(a) = f(b)$, the function $f(x) = \sin x$ is not one-to-one.

In Section 1.1, we used the vertical line test to determine if a given relation is a function. We have a similar test, called the **horizontal line test**, to determine if a given function is one-to-one.

Horizontal Line Test

A function f is one-to-one if and only if every horizontal line over the function's domain intersects the graph of $y = f(x)$ in at most one point.

Example 2   Using the horizontal line test

Determine which of the following functions are one-to-one.

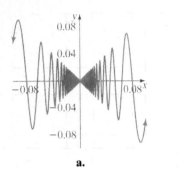

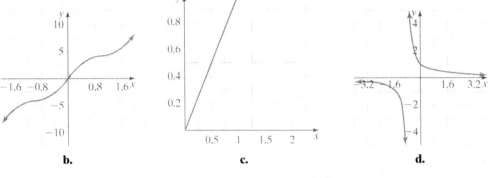

a.   b.   c.   d.

Solution

a. Since any horizontal line would intersect multiple points on the graph of $y = f(x)$, this function is not one-to-one.

b. Since any horizontal line only intersects the graph of $y = f(x)$ in one point, this function is one-to-one.

c. Since the horizontal line $y = 1$ passes through an infinite number of points of the graph, this function is not one-to-one.

d. Since any horizontal line intersects the graph in at most one point, this function is one-to-one.

When a function $y = f(x)$ is one-to-one, we can associate a single value in its domain with a single value in its range. This association defines the **inverse function** of $f(x)$.

Inverse Function

Let f be a one-to-one function with domain D and range R. The **inverse** f^{-1} of f is the function with domain R and range D such that

$$f^{-1}(y) = x \text{ if and only if } y = f(x)$$

Equivalently,

$$f^{-1}(f(x)) = x \text{ for all } x \text{ in } D$$

The second characterization of an inverse function states that if we take the output from the function f as the input to the function f^{-1}, then we get back the input into the function f. Hence, the inverse function f^{-1} can be viewed as a "machine that undoes" the work of the function f.

Example 3   Using the definitions of the inverse function

a. Find $f^{-1}(2)$ and $f^{-1}(-3)$ for a one-to-one function $y = f(x)$ satisfying $f(-3) = 4$, $f(1) = 2$, $f(2) = 0$, and $f(4) = -3$.

b. Show that $g(x) = (x - 3)^{1/3}$ is the inverse function of $f(x) = x^3 + 3$.

Solution

a. To find $f^{-1}(2)$, we need to find x such that $f(x) = 2$. This is $x = 1$. Therefore, $f^{-1}(2) = 1$. To find $f^{-1}(-3)$, we need to find x such that $f(x) = -3$. This is $x = 4$. Therefore, $f^{-1}(-3) = 4$.

b. Since the range of f is all of the real numbers, the domain of g should be all of the reals. For any real number x, we have that

$$(g \circ f)(x) = (f(x) - 3)^{1/3}$$
$$= (x^3 + 3 - 3)^{1/3}$$
$$= (x^3)^{1/3} = x$$

Thus, g is f^{-1}.

In part **b** of the previous example, we expressed the inverse function g as a function of x instead of as a function of y. This choice corresponds to the convention that x is considered the independent variable and y is the dependent variable. For the U.S. population growth example at the beginning of the section, we did not interchange the names of N and t, as N and t had different units, that is, population size (in millions) and years. In general, it is not necessary to interchange the names of x and y if we are comfortable expressing the inverse function as $x = f^{-1}(y)$.

To find the inverse of a function algebraically, there is a simple procedure to follow.

Finding the Inverse

Let $y = f(x)$ be a one-to-one function with domain D and range R. To find the inverse function, follow these steps:

Step 1. Solve the equation $y = f(x)$ for x in terms of y (provided this is possible).

Step 2. (Optional) To express the inverse function as a function of x, interchange the xs and ys in the solution from Step 1. This results in the equation $y = f^{-1}(x)$.

Example 4   Finding inverses

Find the inverses for the following functions.

a. The function defined by the equation

$$y = f(x) = \frac{1}{1 + x}$$

b. The function defined by this verbal description: to every $r \geq 0$ associate the area of a circle of radius r

Solution

a. We begin by solving for x in terms of y for the equation $y = f(x)$:

$$y = \frac{1}{1+x} \qquad \textit{assuming } x \neq -1$$

$$1 + x = \frac{1}{y}$$

$$x = \frac{1}{y} - 1$$

Interchanging the roles of x and y, we get $y = f^{-1}(x) = \frac{1}{x} - 1$ for all $x \neq 0$. Notice that the range of $f(x)$ is all the real numbers but zero, and this range corresponds to the domain of the function $f^{-1}(x)$ that we found.

b. The area A of a circle of radius $r \geq 0$ is given by $A = \pi r^2$. The range of A is $[0, \infty)$. To find the inverse, for every $A \geq 0$, solve for r in terms of A

$$A = \pi r^2$$

$$r = \sqrt{\frac{A}{\pi}}$$

In words, the radius of a circle is the square root of its area divided by π. Since there are no conventions associated with the variable names A and r, we do not bother to interchange the names, especially because A stands for *area* and r stands for *radius* and we do not want to mix these up.

The idea of interchanging the roles of x and y to find the equation of an inverse function also can be used to graph an inverse function. Indeed, if $(x, y) = (a, b)$ is a point on the graph of $y = f(x)$, then $f(a) = b$. Therefore, $a = f^{-1}(b)$ and $(x, y) = (b, a)$ is a point on the graph of $y = f^{-1}(x)$.

Graphing Inverses

If f is one-to-one, then the graph of its inverse $y = f^{-1}(x)$ is given by reflecting the graph of $y = f(x)$ about the line $y = x$.

Example 5   **Graphing inverses**

Consider the function $y = f(x)$ whose graph is shown below,

Sketch the graph of $y = f^{-1}(x)$ by hand.

Solution   If we sketch the line $y = x$ in blue, then reflecting the graph about the line $y = x$ yields the graph of $y = f^{-1}(x)$, shown in red.

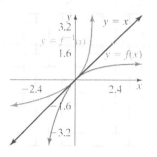

Logarithms

Consider the exponential function $y = a^x$ where $a > 0$. Suppose that $x_1 \neq x_2$ are such that $a^{x_1} = a^{x_2}$. Then by the laws of exponents, $1 = a^{x_1} a^{-x_2} = a^{x_1 - x_2}$. Since $x_1 - x_2 \neq 0$, a must equal 1. Hence, we may conclude that $y = a^x$ is a one-to-one function provided that $a \neq 1$. Therefore, $y = a^x$ has an inverse function provided that $a \neq 1$. This inverse is the *logarithm function with base a*.

Logarithm

Let $a > 0$ and $a \neq 1$. Then

$$y = \log_a x \text{ if and only if } a^y = x$$

$y = \log_a x$ is the **logarithm** of x with base a.

The statement "$y = \log_a x$" should be read as "y is the exponent on a base a that gives the value x." *Do not forget that a logarithm is an exponent.*

Example 6   Using the definition of logarithm

Find x such that

a. $x = \log_2 16$ **b.** $x = \log_4 16$ **c.** $\log_{10} x = 3$ **d.** $\log_e x = 2$

Solution
a. "x is the exponent on a base 2 that gives 16"; Since $2^4 = 16$, $x = 4$.
b. "x is the exponent on a base 4 that gives 16"; Since $4^2 = 16$, $x = 2$.
c. "3 is the exponent on a base 10 that gives x"; $x = 10^3 = 1,000$.
d. "2 is the exponent on a base e that gives x"; $x = e^2$.

In elementary work, the most commonly used base is 10, so we call a logarithm to the base 10 a **common logarithm** and agree to write it without using a subscript 10. Thus, part **c** of the previous example is usually written $\log x = 3$. In biological applications dealing with natural growth or decay, the base e is more common. A logarithm to the base e is called a **natural logarithm** and is denoted by $\ln x$. The expression $\ln x$ is often pronounced "ell en ex" or "lawn ex." In some texts, especially those pertaining to information theory in computer science, the function $\log_2 x$ is of theoretical importance and it is written simply as $\lg x$. Its use, however, is not common in differential or integral calculus.

Logarithmic Notations

- **Common logarithm:** $\log x$ means $\log_{10} x$.
- **Natural logarithm:** $\ln x$ means $\log_e x$.

To **evaluate** a logarithm means to find an exact answer if possible (e.g., $\log_9 81 = 2$), or to calculate a decimal approximation to a required number of decimal places. Find the keys labeled $\boxed{\text{LOG}}$ and $\boxed{\text{LN}}$ on your calculator. Verify the following calculator evaluations using your own calculator:

$$\log 5.03 \approx 0.7015679851 \qquad \ln 3.49 \approx 1.249901736 \qquad \log 0.00728 \approx -2.137868621$$

Since logarithms are exponents, the following properties of logarithms follow immediately from the properties of exponents and the definition of logarithms.

Laws of Logarithms

Additive law: $\log_a x + \log_a y = \log_a xy$

Subtractive law: $\log_a x - \log_a y = \log_a \dfrac{x}{y}$

Multiplicative law: $y \log_a x = \log_a(x^y)$

Change of base: $\log_b x = \dfrac{\log_a x}{\log_a b}$

Cancellation properties: $\begin{aligned} \log_a a^x &= x \\ a^{\log_a x} &= x, \ x > 0 \end{aligned}$

Example 7 **Graphing logarithmic functions**

Use technology to graph the logarithmic functions $y = \log x$, $y = \ln x$, and $y = \log_2 x$ on the same coordinate axes. Discuss the common properties of these graphs.

Solution   The graphs (using technology) are shown in Figure 1.40.

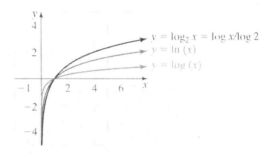

Figure 1.40 Graphs of logarithmic functions.

In all cases, the function has a domain of $(0, \infty)$ and range of $(-\infty, \infty)$—that is, the range is the real number line **R**. The x-intercept is $(1, 0)$. Additionally, the graph appears to be increasing from $-\infty$ as x increases from 0, and the steepness of the graph is decreasing with increasing x.

Example 8 **Solving exponential equations**

Approximate the solutions to two decimal places.

a. $10^x = 0.5$ **b.** $e^x = 10{,}000$ **c.** $1.33^t = 2$ **d.** $\ln(2x) = 1$ **e.** $\log_2 4^x = 3$

Solution   Be sure to duplicate the results below using your calculator.

a. This means x is the exponent on a base 10 which gives 0.5: in symbols, $x = \log 0.5$. Then evaluate with your calculator to find $x = \log 0.5 \approx -0.30$.

b. Using the definition, $x = \ln 10{,}000 \approx 9.21$.

c. We note t is the exponent on a base 1.33 which is 2. That is,

$$t = \log_{1.33} 2 = \frac{\log 2}{\log 1.33} \approx 2.43$$

d. We have

$$\ln(2x) = 1$$
$$e^1 = 2x \qquad \textit{definition of logarithm}$$
$$x = \frac{e}{2} \approx 1.36$$

e. We have

$$\log_2 4^x = 3$$
$$x \log_2 4 = 3 \qquad \textit{by cancellation proprieties}$$
$$x \cdot 2 = 3$$
$$x = \frac{3}{2} = 1.5$$

Logarithmic functions are key to finding half-lives of exponentially decaying quantities and to finding doubling times for exponentially growing quantities:

Exponential half-life. In a process $x(t)$ decaying exponentially, its half-life is the time $t = T$ that it takes to change from its current size $x(0)$ to $x(T) = x(0)/2$.

Exponential doubling time. In a process $x(t)$ growing exponentially, its doubling time is the time $t = T$ that it takes to change from its current size $x(0)$ to $x(T) = 2x(0)$.

In the next example, we solve for these quantities for processes introduced in Section 1.4.

Example 9 Half-life and doubling time

a. In Example 5 of Section 1.4, the function $H(t) = 17(0.99588)^t$ denoted the height of the beer froth at time t seconds. Find the time T at which half of the froth has been lost.

b. In Section 1.4, we modeled population growth in the United States with the function $N(t) = 8.3(1.33)^t$ where N is measured in millions of individuals and t is decades after 1815. In Example 2b of Section 1.4, we estimated the doubling time for the population as twenty-five years. Find a more precise estimate for the doubling time T.

Solution

a. The half-life is the solution T to the equation

$$\frac{H(T)}{H(0)} = 0.5 \qquad \textit{given equation}$$

$$(0.99588)^T = 0.5 \qquad \textit{evaluate functions}$$

$$T = \log_{0.99588} 0.5 \qquad \textit{definition of logs}$$

$$= \frac{\log 0.5}{\log 0.99588} \qquad \textit{change of base}$$

$$= 167.89 \qquad \textit{evaluate}$$

Thus, it takes the froth around 168 seconds, which is almost three minutes, to decay to half its height!

b. The doubling time T is the solution to the equation

$$\frac{N(T)}{N(0)} = 2 \qquad \text{\textit{given equation}}$$

$$1.33^T = 2 \qquad \text{\textit{evaluate functions}}$$

$$\ln 1.33^T = \ln 2 \qquad \text{\textit{take logs}}$$

$$T \ln 1.33 = \ln 2 \qquad \text{\textit{multiplicative law}}$$

$$T = \frac{\ln 2}{\ln 1.33} \approx 2.431 \qquad \text{\textit{evaluate}}$$

Since T is in decades, the doubling of the population occurs approximately in twenty-four years and four months.

Table 1.15 Body sizes of different organisms

Organism	Approximate body size
Mycoplasma	< 0.1 picogram
Average bacterium	0.1 nanogram
Large amoeba	0.1 milligram
Bee	100 milligrams
Hamster	100 grams
Human	100 kilograms
Blue whale	100 metric tons
Sequoia	5,000 metric tons

The logarithmic scale

Organisms vary greatly in their body mass. On the one hand, mycoplasma, which are bacteria without cell walls, weigh less than a tenth of a picogram (i.e., less than 10^{-13} grams). On the other hand, an ancient sequoia weighs as much as 5,000 tons (i.e., 10^{10} grams). Body sizes of other species are shown in Table 1.15. Marking all of these body sizes on an axis would be exceedingly difficult (try it!). However, if we take the log of these body sizes in grams, we can mark these sizes easily on a single axis as shown in Figure 1.41. An equivalent means of representing the data is to mark the body sizes on a *logarithmic scale* where powers of 10 are equally spaced. Doing so yields the lower panel in Figure 1.41, which simply corresponds to replacing the log body sizes in the upper panel of Figure 1.41 with the actual body sizes. Each unit increase on the logarithmic scale thus represents a tenfold increase in the underlying quantity.

-13	-10	-4	-1	2	5	8	10
mycoplasma	bacterium	amoeba	bee	hamster	human	blue whale	sequioa

10^{-13}	10^{-10}	10^{-4}	10^{-1}	10^2	10^5	10^8	10^{10}
mycoplasma	bacterium	amoeba	bee	hamster	human	blue whale	sequioa

Figure 1.41 Log body sizes (upper panel) and body sizes on a logarithmic scale (lower panel) of the organisms listed in Table 1.15.

Example 10   Using the log scale

Mark the numbers 0.00005, 0.1, 20, and 60,000 on a logarithmic scale.

Solution   Applying log to the numbers 0.00005, 0.1, 20, and 60,000, we get -4.3, -1, 1.3, and 4.8. Marking these log values on an x-axis yields

To turn this figure into a logarithmic scale, we replace the exponents x with 10^x.

$$10^{-5} \quad 10^{-4} \quad 10^{-3} \quad 10^{-2} \quad 10^{-1} \quad 10^{0} \quad 10^{1} \quad 10^{2} \quad 10^{3} \quad 10^{4} \quad 10^{5}$$

When plotting functions in the xy plane, it can be useful to plot one or both axes on the logarithmic scale.

Semi-log plots correspond to using the logarithmic scale on one axis and arithmetic scale on the other axis.

Log-log plots correspond to using the logarithmic scale on both axes.

The next example illustrates how plotting on semi-log or log-log plots can transform the graphs of nonlinear functions into the graphs of linear functions.

Example 11   Exponentials and power functions on logarithmic scales

a. Plot the function $y = 8.3(1.33)^x$ with the y axis on a logarithmic scale and the x axis on an arithmetic scale.

b. Plot the function $y = 5/x$ with the y and x axes on logarithmic scales.

Solution

a. To plot the y values on a logarithmic scale, we take the log of y

$$\log y = \log(8.3(1.33)^x)$$
$$= \log(8.3) + \log(1.33)x \qquad \textit{using laws of logarithms}$$

Plotting $\log y$ against x yields the left panel below, while replacing the values on the $\log y$ axis with ten raised to the power of these values produces the semi-log plot in the right panel below.

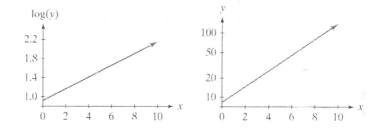

b. Taking the log of y yields

$$\log y = \log(5/x) = \log 5 - \log x$$

Plotting $\log y$ as a function of $\log x$ yields the left panel below, while replacing the values on the $\log y$ axis and $\log x$ axis with ten raised to the power of these values produces the log-log plot in the right panel below.

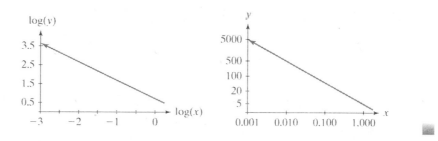

The previous example illustrates how the graphs of exponential functions and power functions are linear when using logarithmic scales appropriately.

Exponentials, Power Functions, and the Logarithmic Scale

If $y = b\,a^x$ is an exponential function with $b > 0$, then $\log y = \log b + x \log a$ is a linear function of x. Therefore, exponential functions appear linear on a semi-log plot.

If $y = a\,x^b$ is a power function with $a > 0$, then $\log y = \log a + b \log x$ is a linear function of $\log x$. Therefore, power functions appear linear on log-log plots.

These observations allow us to apply data fitting techniques discuss in Section 1.2 to exponential and power functions.

Example 12   Linear regression on a logarithmic scale

The metabolic rate of an organism is the rate at which it builds up (anabolism) and breaks down (catabolism) the organic materials that constitute its body. A famous data set exhibiting an allometric scaling law for relating metabolic rate y to body mass x was first published by Max Kleiber and is reproduced here in Table 1.16.

Table 1.16 Metabolic data

Animal	Weight	kCal/day
Mouse	0.021	3.6
Rat	0.282	28.1
Guinea pig	0.410	35.1
Rabbit	2.980	167
Rabbit 2	1.520	83
Rabbit 3	2.460	119
Rabbit 4	3.570	164
Rabbit 5	4.330	191
Rabbit 6	5.330	233
Cat	3.0	152
Monkey	4.200	207
Dog	6.6	288
Dog 2	14.1	534
Dog 3	24.8	875
Dog 4	23.6	872
Goat	36	800
Chimpanzee	38	1,090
Sheep	46.4	1,254
Sheep 2	46.8	1,330
Woman	57.2	1,368
Woman 2	54.8	1,224
Woman 3	57.9	1,320
Cow	300	4,221
Cow 2	435	8,166
Cow 3	600	7,877
Heifer	482	7,754

Source: M. Kleiber, *The Fire of Life* (Krieger Pub. Co., Huntington, NY, Revised edition (June 1975), 205.

Since the data should exhibit allometry, we would expect that there exist real numbers $a > 0$ and b such that

$$y = ax^b$$

a. Apply the natural log to all of the data in Table 1.16 and use technology to find the best-fitting line for the converted data.

b. 1 data point missing from Table 1.16 is for the elephant. Use the best-fitting line to estimate the metabolic rate of an African elephant with mass of 6,800 kilograms.

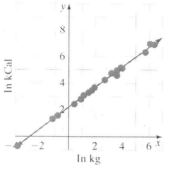
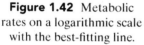

Figure 1.42 Metabolic rates on a logarithmic scale with the best-fitting line.

Solution

a. Taking logarithms of the masses and metabolic rates in Table 1.16 and plotting the new data yields the red dots in Figure 1.42. This figure illustrates that the data on a logarithmic scale appear linear.

As before, we use technology to find the best-fitting line:

$$\ln y = 0.755917 \ln x + 4.20577$$

The $\ln y$-intercept is $(0, 4.20577)$ and the slope is $0.755917 \approx \dfrac{3}{4}$. There have been many theoretical attempts to explain this scaling exponent.

b. To predict the metabolic rate, y, for an elephant of mass $x = 6,800$, we substitute this x value into the equation for the best-fitting line and solve for y.

$$\ln y = 0.755917 \ln x + 4.20577$$
$$\ln y = 0.755917 \ln 6{,}800 + 4.20577$$
$$\ln y = 10.8765$$
$$y = e^{10.8765} \approx 52{,}918$$

The elephant will burn off approximately 53,000 kilocalories per day.

In the problem set that follows you will see that a similar approach can be used for fitting exponential functions to data.

PROBLEM SET 1.6

Level 1 DRILL PROBLEMS

Determine whether the functions defined by the tables in Problems 1 to 4 are one-to-one. For the functions that are one-to-one, write the inverse function.

1.

x	$f(x)$
1	0
2	2
3	4
4	2
5	6

2.

x	$f(x)$
2	0
−3	14
44	22
5	6

3.

x	$f(x)$
11.9	0
17	1
−2	4
4	2
5	6

4.

x	$f(x)$
1	2
3	4
5	6
4	4
−1	0

Use the horizontal line test to determine which of the functions in Problems 5 to 8 is one-to-one. For the functions that are one-to-one, sketch the inverse.

5.

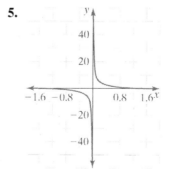

6.

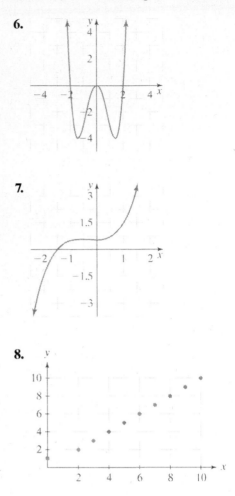

7.

8.

Find the inverse of the functions in Problems 9 to 14. State the domain and range of the inverse.

9. $y = \dfrac{x}{1 + x}$

10. $y = e^{2x+1}$

11. $y = (x + 1)^3 - 2$

12. $y = \exp(x^2)$ on $[0, \infty)$

13. $y = \exp(x^2)$ on $(-\infty, 0]$

14. $y = \sqrt{\ln x}$

Find x in Problems 15 to 19 using the definition of logarithm (do not use a calculator).

15. a. $x = \log 10$　　　　**b.** $x = \log 0.001$

16. a. $x = \ln e^2$　　　　**b.** $x = \ln e^{-4}$

17. a. $x = \log_5 125$　　　**b.** $x = \log_8 64$

18. a. $5 = \log x$　　　　　**b.** $18 = \ln x$

19. a. $\ln x = 3$　　　　　**b.** $\log x = 4.5$

Simplify the expressions given in Problems 20 to 22.

20. a. $2^{8\log_2 x}$　　**b.** $3^{3\log_3 x}$　　**c.** $5^{-2\log_5 x}$

　　d. $2^{3\log_{1/2} x}$　　**e.** $3^{-\log_{1/3} x}$

21. a. $\log_2 8^x$　　**b.** $\log_3 81^x$　　**c.** $\log_4 64^x$

　　d. $\log_{1/2} 32^x$　　**e.** $\log_3 9^{-x}$

22. a. $e^{4\ln x}$　　**b.** $e^{3\ln(x^2+1)}$　　**c.** $e^{-2\ln(x^2-1)}$

　　d. $e^{-3\ln(1/x)}$　　**e.** $e^{-\ln(1/(x^2+1))}$

In Problems 23 to 25 write the expressions in terms of base e and simplify where possible.

23. a. 5^x　　　**b.** $\dfrac{1}{2^x}$　　　**c.** $5^{1/x}$

　　d. 4^{x^2}　　**e.** 3^{x^e}

24. a. 3^{1-x}　　**b.** 3^{x+2}　　**c.** $2^{1/x+e}$

　　d. 4^{x^2}　　**e.** 3^{-3x-2}

25. a. $\log(x + 1)$　　　　**b.** $\log(ex + e)$

　　c. $\log_2(x^2 - 2)$　　　**d.** $\log_7(2x - 3)$

Simplify the expressions in Problems 26 to 30 using the definition of logarithm (do not use a calculator).

26. $\log 100 + \log \sqrt{10}$

27. $\ln e + \ln 1 + \ln e^{542}$

28. $\log_8 4 + \log_8 16 + \log_8 8^{2.3}$

29. $10^{\log 0.5}$

30. $\ln e^{\log 1,000}$

Sketch the indicated points on a logarithmic scale in Problems 31 to 34.

31. $0.002, 0.5, 10, 25000$

32. $0.0003, 0.01, 0.1, 1, 200$

33. $0.00004, 0.2, 10, 200000$

34. $7, 10, 2000, 10000000$

Level 2 APPLIED AND THEORY PROBLEMS

35. In Example 6 of Section 1.5, you modeled the uptake rate of glucose by bacterial populations with the Michaelis-Menten function $U = \dfrac{1.2078\,C}{1 + 0.0506\,C}$ micrograms/hour where C is the concentration of glucose (mg/l) (micrograms/liter).

　　a. If the observed uptake rate of glucose was 1 mcg/hour, find the concentration of glucose per liter.

b. Find the inverse function of the uptake rate function and be sure to identify the appropriate units for this function.

36. In Example 9 of Section 1.5, you modeled the per capita growth rate for a shrew population with the function $F = \dfrac{0.055(220\,C - 11,000)}{320\,C}$ pairs/day where C is the cocoon density (cocoons per thousandth acre).

    a. If the observed shrew per capita growth rate was 0.02 pairs/day, find the density of cocoons.

    b. Find the inverse function of the per capita growth rate function and be sure to identify the appropriate units for this function.

37. In Problem 41 of Section 1.4, you modeled the population size of humpback whales off of the coast Australia with the exponential function $N(t) = 350(1.12)^t$ where t is measured in years since 1981. Estimate the doubling time for this population of whales.

38. In Problem 42 of Section 1.4, you modeled the population size (in millions) of Mexico with the function $P(t) = 67.38(1.026)^t$, where t is years after 1980. Find the doubling time for the population.

39. In an experimental study performed at Dartmouth College, two groups of mice with tumors were treated with the chemotherapeutic drug cisplatin. Prior to the therapy, the tumor consisted of proliferating cells (also known as *clonogenic cells*) that grew exponentially with a doubling time of approximately 2.9 days. In Problem 44 from Section 1.4, you modeled the volume of the tumor with the function $V(t) = 0.1(2)^{t/2.9}$ cm^3, where t is measured in days. Find an exact expression for the time at which the tumor size is 0.5 cm^3.

40. In the experimental study described in Problem 39, each of these mice was given a dose of 10 mg/kg of cisplatin. At the time of the therapy, the average tumor size was approximately 0.5 cm^3. Assume all the cells became quiescent (i.e., no longer dividing) and assume decay with a half-life of approximately 5.7 days. In Problem 45 from Section 1.4, you modeled the volume of this tumor with the function $V(t) = 0.5(1/2)^{t/5.7}$. Find an exact expression for when the tumor size is 0.1 cm^3.

41. Figure 1.43 shows a plot of the weight W (in grams) versus length L (in meters) for a sample of 158 male and 167 female western hognose snakes (*Heterodon nasicus*) from Harvey County, Kansas. The females are represented by open circles, and the males by closed circles. The scale is log-log.

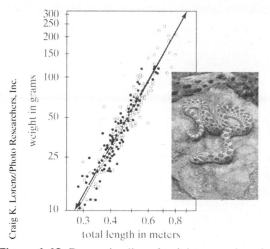

Figure 1.43 Regression line of weight versus length.

Data Source: D. R. Platt, *Natural History of the Hognose Snakes Heterodon platyrhinos and Heterodon nasicus* (Natural History Museum of the University of Kansas. Reprinted with permission.)

It appears that when $L = 0.4$ cm, the corresponding weight on the best-fitting line is $W = 28$ g; likewise, $L = 0.6$ m appears to correspond to $W = 100$ g. Assuming an allometric relationship $W = cL^m$, we have

$$28 = c(0.4)^m \quad \text{and} \quad 100 = c(0.6)^m$$

Find the allometric relationship between weight and length (round c to the nearest integer).

42. It is known that fluorocarbons have the effect of depleting ozone in the upper atmosphere. Suppose the amount Q of ozone in the atmosphere is depleted by 15% per year, so that after t years, the amount of original ozone Q_0 that remains may be modeled by

$$Q = Q_0(0.85)^t$$

    a. How long (to the nearest year) will it take before half the original ozone is depleted?

    b. Suppose through the efforts of careful environmental management, the ozone depletion rate is decreased so that it takes 100 years for half the original ozone to be depleted, what is the new rate (to the nearest hundredth of a percent)?

43. Allison and Cicchetti reported data on body weight (in kilograms) and corresponding brain weight (in grams) for sixty-two different terrestrial mammals (no whales). A partial list of the data is given below.

Body weight (kg)	Brain weight (g)
6654.000	5712.00
1.000	6.60
3.385	44.50
0.920	5.70
2547.000	4603.00
10.550	179.50
0.023	0.30
160.000	169.00
3.300	25.60
52.160	440.00
0.425	6.40
465.000	423.00
0.550	2.40
187.100	419.00
0.075	1.20
3.000	25.00
0.785	3.50
0.200	5.00
1.410	17.50
60.000	81.00

Data source: Allison, T., and D. V. Cicchetti. (1976). "Sleep in Mammals: Ecological and Constitutional Correlates." *Science* 194, pp. 732–734.

a. Plot the log of brain size against the log body weight.

b. Find the best-fitting line using least squares regression on the log-transformed data.

44. Rivers and streams carry small solid particles of rock and mineral downhill, either suspended in the water column ("suspended load") or bounced, rolled, or slid along the river bed ("bed load"). Solid particles are classified according to their mean diameter from smallest to largest as clay, silt, sand, pebble, cobble, and boulder. During low velocity flow, only very small particles (clay and silt) can be transported by the river, whereas during high velocity flow, much larger particles may be transported.

Table Torrential invertebrate fauna

Diameter of objects moved (mm)	Speed of current (m/sec)	Classification of objects
0.2	0.10	Mud
1.3	0.25	Sand
5	0.50	Gravel
11	0.75	Coarse gravel
20	1.00	Pebbles
45	1.50	Small stones
80	2.50	Large stones (fist sized)
180	3.50	Boulders

Data soure: Nielsen A. (1950). "The Torrential Invertebrate Fauna," *Oikos* 2: 176–196.

a. Plot the log of diameter against the log of the speed.

b. Find the best-fitting line using least squares regression on the log-transformed data.

45. Rainbow trout taken from four different localities along the Spokane River (eastern Washington) during July, August, and October 1999 were analyzed for heavy metals for the Washington State Department of Ecology. As part of this study, the length (in millimeters) and weight (in grams) of each trout were measured; age determinations using scales are currently underway.

Length (mm)	Weight (g)
457	855
405	715
455	975
460	895
335	472
365	540
390	660
368	581
385	609
360	557
346	433
438	840
392	623
324	387
360	479
413	754
276	235
387	538
345	438
395	584

Data source: Johnson, A. *Results from Analyzing Metals in 1999 Spokane River Fish and Crayfish Samples* (Washington State Dept. of Ecology report, 2000).

a. Plot the log of weight against length.

b. Find the best-fitting line using least squares regression on the transformed data.

46. Consider the first four entries presented in the table below one estimate of the world's population levels over the first half of the second millennium AD:

Year AD (t)	Population size x (in billions)
1000	0.31
1250	0.40
1500	0.50
1750	0.79

Provide a semi-log plot of the points $(t, \ln x)$ and find and graph the best-fitting line through these points on the same plot. From this line, provide an estimate of the average growth rate exponent r for the population size function $x(t) = ce^{rt}$ over this period of 750 years.

47. Consider the entries presented in the table below one estimate of the world's population levels over the period 1750 to 1920:

Year AD (t)	Population size x (in billions)
1750	0.79
1800	0.98
1850	1.26
1900	1.65
1910	1.75
1920	1.86

Provide a semi-log plot of the points $(t, \ln x)$ and find and graph the best-fitting line through these points on the same plot. From this line, provide an estimate of the average growth rate exponent r for the population size function $x(t) = ce^{rt}$ over this 170-year period.

48. Consider the entries presented in the table below one estimate of the world's population levels over the period 1920 to 2010:

Year AD (t)	Population size x (in billions)
1920	1.86
1930	2.07
1940	2.30
1950	2.52
1960	3.02
1970	3.70
1980	4.44
1990	5.27
1999	5.98
2010	6.86

Provide a semi-log plot of the points $(t, \ln x)$ and find and graph the best-fitting line through these points on the same plot. From this line, provide an estimate of the average growth rate exponent r for the population size function $x(t) = ce^{rt}$ over this 90-year period.

1.7   Sequences and Difference Equations

Often, experimental measurements are collected at discrete intervals of time. For example, the number of elephants in wildlife park in Africa may be counted every year to ensure that poachers are not exterminating the population. Blood may be drawn on a weekly basis from a patient infected with HIV and the number of CD4+ cells produced by the patient's immune system counted to monitor patient response to treatment. Data obtained in this regular fashion can be represented by a sequence of numbers over time. In this section, we describe the basic properties of such *sequences* and demonstrate that some sequences can be generated recursively using a relationship called a *difference equation*. These equations are formulated using a function from the natural numbers to the real numbers.

Sequences

We begin with the idea of a sequence, which is simply a succession of numbers that are listed according to a given prescription or rule. Specifically, if n is a natural number, the sequence whose nth term is the number a_n can be written as

$$a_1, a_2, a_3, \ldots, a_n, \ldots$$

The number a_1 is called the first term, a_2 the second term, $\ldots$, and a_n the nth term.

Sequence   A **sequence** is a real-valued function whose domain is the set of natural numbers.

When working with sequences, we alter the usual functional notation. For a function a from the natural to the real numbers we should write $a(1)$, $a(2)$, $a(3)$, $\ldots$, but for convenience we write a_1, a_2, a_3, $\ldots$. The function $a(n)$ is written a_n and is called the *general term*.

Example 1   **Finding the sequence, given the general term**

Find the first five terms of the sequences whose general term is given.

a. $a_n = n$ **b.** $a_n = \sin \dfrac{\pi n}{2}$ **c.** $a_n = \dfrac{n}{1+n}$

d. a_n is the digit in the nth decimal place of the number π

Solution

a. Since n is the general term, we have $1, 2, 3, 4,$ and 5 for the first five terms.

b. For $n = 1$, $\sin \dfrac{\pi}{2} = 1$; for $n = 2$, $\sin \dfrac{2\pi}{2} = 0$; for $n = 3$, $\sin \dfrac{3\pi}{2} = -1$; for $n = 4$, $\sin \dfrac{4\pi}{2} = 0$; and for $n = 5$, $\sin \dfrac{5\pi}{2} = 1$. Thus the first five terms are $1, 0, 1, 0, 1$.

c. Take the first five natural numbers (in order) to find: $\dfrac{1}{1+1} = \dfrac{1}{2}, \dfrac{2}{1+2} = \dfrac{2}{3}, \dfrac{3}{1+3} = \dfrac{3}{4}, \dfrac{4}{1+4} = \dfrac{4}{5},$ and $\dfrac{5}{1+5} = \dfrac{5}{6}$

d. Since $\pi \approx 3.141592\cdots$, we see the first five terms of this sequence are: $1, 4, 1, 5,$ and 9.

To visualize a sequence, one can graph the sequence of points

$$(1, a_1), (2, a_2), (3, a_3), \ldots$$

in the coordinate plane. The first several terms of the first four sequences from Example 1 are graphed in Figure 1.44. Since the domain consists of the natural numbers, the graph consists of discrete points.

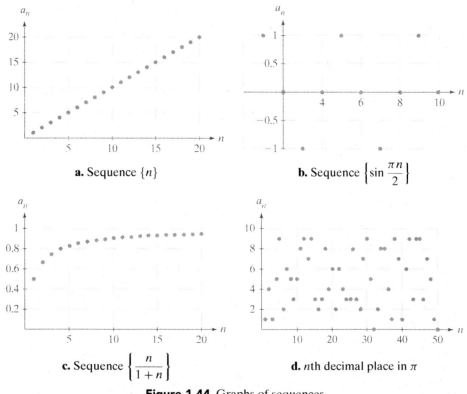

a. Sequence $\{n\}$ **b.** Sequence $\left\{\sin \dfrac{\pi n}{2}\right\}$

c. Sequence $\left\{\dfrac{n}{1+n}\right\}$ **d.** nth decimal place in π

Figure 1.44 Graphs of sequences.

Difference equations

Beyond specifying a sequence by its general term, sequences can also be generated term by term using a rule called a *difference equation*, which specifies how to calculate each term in the sequence from the values of preceding terms. For example, the difference equation

$$a_{n+1} = ra_n \quad \text{and} \quad a_1 = r$$

generates the *geometric sequence*

$$a_1 = r$$
$$a_2 = ra_1 = r^2$$
$$a_3 = ra_2 = r^3$$
$$a_4 = ra_3 = r^4$$
$$\vdots$$
$$a_n = ra_{n-1} = r^n$$
$$\vdots$$

Similarly, the difference equation

$$a_{n+1} = a_n + d \quad \text{and} \quad a_1 = d$$

generates the *arithmetic sequence*

$$a_1 = d$$
$$a_2 = a_1 + d = 2d$$
$$a_3 = a_2 + d = 3d$$
$$a_4 = a_3 + d = 4d$$
$$\vdots$$
$$a_n = nd$$
$$\vdots$$

Example 2   Geometric decay of acetaminophen

Example 2 of Section 1.1 stated that a tablet of regular strength Tylenol contains 325 mg of acetaminophen and that approximately 67% of the drug in the body is removed from the body every four hours. Assume Professor Schreiber just swallowed two tables of Tylenol. Let a_n be the amount in milligrams of acetaminophen in his body $4n$ hours after taking the two tablets.

a. Find a_1 and find r such that $a_{n+1} = ra_n$.

b. Find and plot the amount of acetaminophen in Professor's Schreiber's body over the next twenty-four hours, that is, $n = 1, 2, 3, 4, 5, 6$.

Solution

a. Initially, there is 650 mg in his body. Hence, after four hours, there is only $(1 - 0.67)650 = 214.5$ mg. Since the fraction of acetaminophen remaining in the body after each four hour time interval is 0.33, we have $a_{n+1} = 0.33a_n$ and $r = 0.33$.

b. Using the difference equation from part **a**, we get $a_1 = 214.5$, $a_2 = 0.33a_1 = 70.785$, $a_3 = 0.33a_2 \approx 23.359$. $a_4 = 0.33a_3 \approx 7.708$, $a_5 = 0.33a_4 \approx 2.544$, and $a_6 = 0.33a_5 \approx 0.839$. Plotting these values produces the following figure.

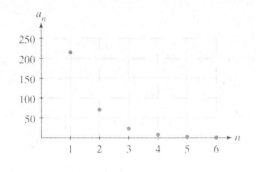

More generally, for any real-valued function f, we can make the following definition.

Difference Equation	Let f be a real-valued function. Then $$a_{n+1} = f(a_n)$$ is a **difference equation**. A sequence $a_1, a_2, a_3, \ldots$ satisfying this equation for all n is a **solution to the difference equation**. By specifying a particular value of a_1 and applying the $a_{n+1} = f(a_n)$ inductively, one can generate solutions to the difference equation, provided f is well-defined at every step.

Difference equations allow us to describe how quantities evolve over discrete intervals of time. For example, the difference equation $a_{n+1} = 0.33a_n$ in Example 2 described the decay of a drug in the body. A similar equation could describe the weekly growth of a bacterial culture in a laboratory, or even a population of California condors that were reintroduced to a wild area where they had previously become extinct because of use of the pesticide DDT.

From a modeling perspective, discrete intervals of time implied by the iteration of the difference equation (e.g., daily, weekly, or annual growth rules) correspond to one of two factors: synchronized events of the system (e.g., daily injections of a drug, annual reproductive cycles in a population) or intervals separating experimental measurements of the system (e.g., daily blood cell counts, annual population counts).

Example 3   The difference equation implicit in taking repeated square roots

Enter any nonzero number into your calculator. Press the square root key $\boxed{\sqrt{}}$ and record your answer. Press again and record repeatedly. Let a_n denote the nth number displayed on the screen.

a. Find a difference equation for a_n.

b. Graph the first twenty terms of the sequence when $a_1 = 4$ and then when $a_1 = 0.1$. Discuss what happens to a_n in each case as n gets very large.

c. What happens when $a_1 = 1$?

Solution

a. For any selected value a_1, after pressing the square root key, the calculator generates the number $a_2 = \sqrt{a_1}$. Similarly, after the second iteration the number $a_3 = \sqrt{a_2} = \sqrt{\sqrt{a_1}}$ is obtained. Proceeding inductively yields

$$a_{n+1} = \sqrt{a_n}.$$

Thus, the difference equation in this case is $a_{n+1} = f(a_n)$ with $f(x) = \sqrt{x}$.

b. Plotting the first twenty terms of the sequence with $a_1 = 4$ and $a_1 = 0.1$ respectively yields Figures 1.45a and 1.45b. Both plots suggest that as n gets larger, a_n approaches the value 1 (but does not become 1).

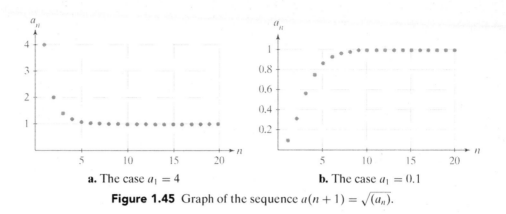

a. The case $a_1 = 4$ **b.** The case $a_1 = 0.1$

Figure 1.45 Graph of the sequence $a(n+1) = \sqrt{(a_n)}$.

c. If $a_1 = 1$, then $a_2 = \sqrt{a_1} = \sqrt{1} = 1$. Proceeding inductively, $a_n = 1$ for all integers $n \geq 1$.

Difference equations can be used to model a variety of biological phenomena. The next two examples illustrate their usage in modeling repeated drug dosages and the purging of a lethal recessive gene from a population.

Example 4   **Drug delivery**

In Example 2, Professor Schreiber took only two tablets of Tylenol. However, the directions recommend taking two tablets every four to six hours and not taking more than ten tablets in twenty-four hours. Suppose Schreiber takes two tablets every four hours. To model how the amount of drug in Schreiber's body changes in time, let a_n be the amount of drug in his body right before taking the nth dose.

a. Write a difference equation for a_n.

b. Find a_1, a_2, a_3.

c. What is the maximum amount of acetaminophen in Schreiber's body during the first twelve hours of taking Tylenol?

d. Suppose contrary to the directions, Schreiber kept on taking doses every four hours for several day (which you should not do unless directed to do so by your physician). What value does a_n seem to approach?

Solution

a. If a_n is the amount of drug in the body just before taking the nth dose, then the amount of drug in the body after taking the nth dose is $a_n + 650$ mg. Since we know from Example 2 that 67% of the drug leaves the body in four hours, the amount of drug left in the body before taking the next dose is $(1 - 0.67)(a_n + 650) = 0.33\, a_n + 214.5$. Therefore,

$$a_{n+1} = 0.33\, a_n + 214.5$$

b. Without being told, there is no way for us to know what the value of a_1 is. It is reasonable to assume that before taking the first dose, Schreiber has no acetaminophen in his body, in which case $a_1 = 0$. In this case, for $n = 2$ and $n = 3$, we obtain $a_2 = 0.33 \cdot 0 + 214.5 = 214.5$ mg and $a_3 = 0.33(214.5) + 214.5 = 285.285$ mg.

c. The maximum amount of acetaminophen in the body occurs right after taking a dose. The amounts of acetaminophen in the body after taking the first, second, and third dose are $650, 214.5 + 650 = 864.5$ mg, and $285.285 + 650 = 935.285$ mg. Hence, the maximum is given by 935.2853 mg.

d. Computing a_n for $n = 1, 2, \ldots, 20$, yields this table of values:

n	a_n	n	a_n
1	0	11	320.14
2	214.50	12	320.15
3	285.29	13	320.15
4	308.64	14	320.15
5	316.35	15	320.15
6	318.9	16	320.15
7	319.74	17	320.15
8	320.01	18	320.15
9	320.10	19	320.15
10	320.14	20	320.15

This table suggests that a_n is approaching a value that rounded to two decimal places is 320.15 mg.

The difference equation $a_{n+1} = 0.33a_n + 214.5$ in Example 4 is an example of a *linear difference equation*: the right-hand side of the difference equation depends linearly on a_n. In Problem Set 1.7, you are asked to write explicit solutions for linear difference equations.

Difference equations arise in biology whenever we consider how certain quantities change over regular, discrete intervals of time:

- From one fifteen-second period to the next, as in the beer froth problem considered in Section 1.4

- From one four-hour period to the next, as in this example

- From one day to the next, as in the tumor growth problems presented in Problem Sets 1.4–1.6

- From one month to the next, as in the carbon dioxide concentration problem considered in Section 1.2

- From one year to the next, or even one decade to the next, as discussed in the U.S. population growth problem in Section 1.4

Now we consider a model of how a particular quantity changes from *one generation to the next*!

The quantity to model is the proportion of a particular *allele* (i.e., a variant of a particular gene) responsible for a genetic disease, such as Tay-Sachs or cystic fibrosis, that has a lethal effect when untreated. The model we present is the simplest example of a class, of models, that traces the proportion of a particular allele a in a *diploid* organism that has two possible alleles a and A associated with the gene in question and thus has *genotypes* $aa, a A = Aa$ and AA. These models are *only valid for large populations*, where the assumption that one can replace the concept of probabilities with proportions holds.

Specifically, if one flips a coin four times and represents the proportion of heads using the variable x, then it is unreasonable to assume that half of the flips were heads and half were tails (i.e., $x = 0.5$), since quite often one might land up with three heads and five tails ($x = 3/8$), five heads and three tails ($x = 5/8$), or values of x even closer to 0 or 1. On the other hand, if one flipped the coin a million times, then one can safely assume, to a very good approximation, that half of the flips were heads and half were tails, that is, $x = 0.50$.

In such models, we apply the following principle of Gregor Mendel (1822–1884), derived from his work on plant hybridization

Random mating and Mendelian inheritance principle: Under the assumptions of individuals choosing mates at random, and alleles segregating randomly and independently, it follows that if x and $(1 - x)$ are the proportion of alleles A and a in a population, then the proportion of *genotypes* among the progeny, before evaluating their ability to survive, is as follows:

- x^2 for type aa

- $2x(1 - x)$ for type Aa (the 2 arises because $aA = Aa$)

- $(1 - x)^2$ for type AA

This accounts for all possible genotypes, which we check by adding these three genotype frequencies to obtain the value 1:

$$x^2 + 2x(1 - x) + (1 - x)^2 = x^2 + 2x - 2x^2 + 1 - 2x + x^2 = 1$$

Example 5   Lethal recessive genes

Suppose a disease in humans is primarily due to the existence of a *lethal recessive allele a*. By **lethal recessive**, we mean that individuals of type aa die from the disease, whereas individuals of type AA and Aa are not affected by the disease.

a. If x_n denotes the proportion of alleles a in generation n in a population of size N (i.e., for a total of $2N$ alleles), where N is very large, write an expression for x_{n+1} in terms of x_n under a random mating and Mendelian inheritance assumption. Also, assume all aa genotypes die while genotypes Aa and AA successfully reproduce one copy of themselves each.

b. Use technology to plot x_n for $n = 1, \ldots, 100$.

Solution

a. If x_n is the proportion of alleles in generation n, then under random mating and Mendelian inheritance principles we expect the proportion of genotypes aa, Aa, and AA in the progeny to be in proportion x_n^2, $2x_n(1 - x_n)$ and $(1 - x_n)^2$. However, since all the aa genotypes die so that a occurs only in the heterozygote genotypes Aa, in generation $n + 1$ the proportion of a alleles in a population of size N is

$$x_{n+1} = \frac{\text{number of } a \text{ alleles}}{\text{total number of alleles}}$$

$$= \frac{x_n(1 - x_n)N}{2x_n(1 - x_n)N + (1 - x_n)^2 N}$$

$$= \frac{x_n}{2x_n + (1 - x_n)}$$

$$= \frac{x_n}{1 + x_n}$$

b. Using technology to compute $x_2, \ldots, x_{100}$, we get the plot illustrated in Figure 1.46. This plot shows two things. First, when the initial proportion of the lethal allele is high, the proportion of this lethal allele initially decreases very rapidly. However, as the proportion of the allele gets low, it decreases much less rapidly (e.g., in Problem Set 1.7, you will be asked to show that it takes approximately 1000 generations for the alleles to reach a proportion of 0.1%).

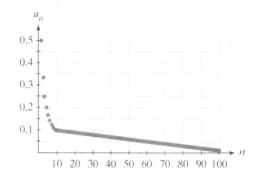

Figure 1.46 Rate of decline of a recessive lethal gene over n generations when initially at a proportion of 0.5 in the population.

In Figure 1.47, experiments on the fruit fly show that the difference equation $x_{n+1} = \dfrac{x_n}{1 + x_n}$ does a reasonable job of describing observed frequencies of the lethal allele, *Glued*, in fruit flies. The observed trajectories illustrate that even if you start with the same initial conditions (i.e., 50% with Glued), random birth and death events can result in different experimental trajectories. Hence, the model can only be expected to describe what happens for the "average" experiment.

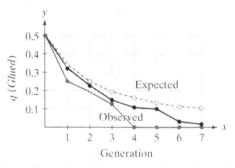

Figure 1.47 Data on the decline of the Glued gene in fruit flies compared with the expected rate predicted by the model in Example 5.

Source: Genetics 83: 793–810 August, 19iG Dynamics of Correlated Genetic Systems. I. Selection in the Region of the Glued Locus of Drosophila Melanogaster, M. T. Clegg, J. F. Kidwell, M. G. Kidwell and N. J. Daniel.

In Examples 3 and 5 we saw that for certain initial values the difference equations generating the sequences in question produced a string of constant values. Specifically, in Example 3 the difference equation $a_{n+1} = \sqrt{a_n}$ produced the sequence $1, 1, 1, \ldots$ for $a_1 = 1$ (i.e., the square root of 1 is 1) and in Example 5 the difference equation $x_{n+1} = \dfrac{x_n}{1 + x_n}$ produced the sequence $0, 0, 0, \ldots$, when $x_1 = 0$ (i.e., if the lethal allele is not present initially, it never appears). Such starting values are called **equilibria** for the equations in question.

| **Equilibrium** | An **equilibrium** of the difference equation |

$$a_{n+1} = f(a_n)$$

is an initial value a_1 such that $f(a_1) = a_1$. From this it easily follows that $a_1 = a_2 = a_3 = \cdots$.

Example 6   Finding equilibria

Find the equilibria for the following three difference equations. Discuss how the answers you find relate to what was observed in Examples 3, 4, and 5.

a. $a_{n+1} = \sqrt{a_n}$ **b.** $a_{n+1} = 0.33a_n + 214.5$ **c.** $x_{n+1} = \dfrac{x_n}{1 + x_n}$

Solution

a. To find the equilibria, we need to solve $a = \sqrt{a}$. Since the only numbers whose square roots are themselves are 0, 1, the equilibria for this difference equation are given by 0 and 1. In Example 3, we saw that for various positive initial conditions, the sequence a_n approaches the equilibrium 1 as n gets large.

b. To find the equilibria, we need to solve

$$a = 0.33a + 214.5$$
$$0.67a = 214.5$$
$$a \approx 320.15$$

In Example 4, we observed that for the initial condition $a_1 = 0$, the sequence a_n would approach this equilibrium value.

c. To find the equilibria, we need to solve, $x = \dfrac{x}{1 + x}$. One solution to this equation is $x = 0$. Any other solution must satisfy $1 = \dfrac{1}{1 + x}$. Cross-multiplying yields $1 + x = 1$. Hence, $x = 0$ is the only equilibrium. In Example 5 it appeared the sequence corresponding to $x_1 = 0.5$ might be approaching this equilibrium. However, since the approach seems quite slow, it is not obvious that x_n becomes arbitrarily close to zero.

In Chapter 2, we explore more carefully the sequence approach that identified equilibria in Example 6. The next example illustrates that an equilibrium is not always approached. It is based on a model for population biology.

In 1981, Thomas Bellows investigated how the survivorship of different species of stored grain beetles depended on the population abundance x. Some of the data from this experiment are illustrated in Figure 1.48. Bellows showed that the function $s(x) = \dfrac{1}{1 + (ax)^b}$ with x corresponding to population density, $a > 0$ and $b > 0$, could describe all of these data sets. The function $s(x)$ describes the fraction of grain beetles surviving as a function of population abundance. If $r > 0$ is the average number of progeny produced by an individual, then the population model arising from this is

$$x_{n+1} = r x_n s(x_n)$$

with the specific form considered by Bellows given in the next example.

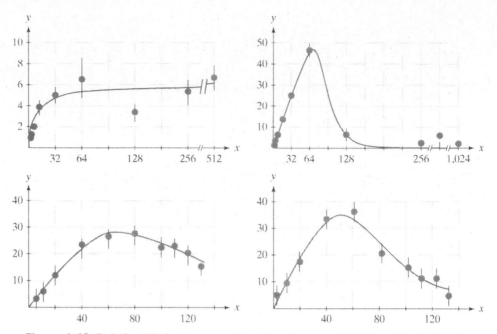

Figure 1.48 Relationship between number of survivors and initial egg density for four species of stored product beetles.

Source: After T. S. Bellows, "The Descriptive Properties of Some Models for Density Dependence," *Journal of Animal Ecology* 50(1)(1981): 139–156. Reprinted with permission.

Example 7   **Generalized Beverton-Holt Dynamics**

If x_n is the population density in generation n, then the population model

$$x_{n+1} = \frac{r\, x_n}{1 + (a x_n)^b}$$

(sometimes referred to as the generalized Beverton-Holt model) produces solutions with behavior that depends on the three parameters r, a, and b.

a. For $r = 2$ and $a = 0.01$, find the equilibria of the model and show that they do not depend on the specific value of b.

b. For $b = 3$ and $b = 6$, with r and a as above, compute and graph for the first fifty terms of the sequence starting with the initial condition $x_1 = 99$. Compare the sequences obtained for $b = 3$ and $b = 6$.

Solution

a. To find the equilibria, we need to solve

$$x = \frac{2x}{1 + (x/100)^b}$$

for x. Clearly, $x = 0$ is a solution. For $x \neq 0$, we obtain

$$1 = \frac{2}{1 + (x/100)^b}$$
$$1 + (x/100)^b = 2$$
$$(x/100)^b = 1$$
$$x/100 = 1$$
$$x = 100$$

Thus, $x = 100$ is an equilibrium value regardless of the value of $b > 0$.

b. Using technology for $b = 3$:

$$x_{n+1} = \frac{2x_n}{1 + (x_n/100)^3}$$

and $x_1 = 99$, yields Figure 1.49a. It appears that the sequence is approaching the equilibrium value of $x = 100$.

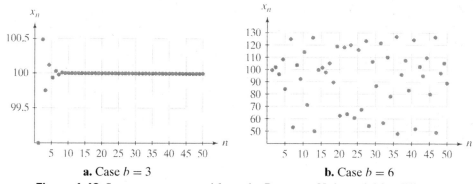

a. Case $b = 3$ **b.** Case $b = 6$

Figure 1.49 Sequences generated from the Beverton-Holt model for different values of the parameter b.

c. Using technology for $b = 6$:

$$x_{n+1} = \frac{2x_n}{1 + (x_n/100)^6}$$

and $x_1 = 99$, yields Figure 1.49b. Despite starting near the equilibrium abundance of $x = 100$, this sequence exhibits oscillatory bursts of population growth and decline without any other characterizable pattern of behavior. In Chapter 4, we will discuss methods to distinguish among these different outcomes. ▪

Cobwebbing

Another way to visualize sequences determined by a difference equation

$$a_{n+1} = f(a_n)$$

is via a graphical technique known as **cobwebbing**.

Before describing this technique, we provide a graphical characterization of equilibria.

Finding Equilibria Graphically

To find equilibria of $a_{n+1} = f(a_n)$, it suffices to look for intersection points of the graphs of $y = x$ and $y = f(x)$

Cobwebbing

To create a **cobweb** for the difference equation $a_{n+1} = f(a_n)$ with initial condition a_1, follow these steps:

Step 1. Graph the functions $y = f(x)$ and $y = x$ in the xy plane.

Step 2. Draw a vertical line segment from (a_1, a_1) to $(a_1, f(a_1))$ and draw a horizontal line segment from $(a_1, f(a_1))$ to $(f(a_1), f(a_1))$. Since $a_2 = f(a_1)$, you will have ended at the point (a_2, a_2).

Step 3. Repeat this procedure as desired. More specifically, if you are the point (a_n, a_n), then draw a vertical line segment from (a_n, a_n) to $(a_n, f(a_n))$ and draw a horizontal line segment from $(a_n, f(a_n))$ to $(f(a_n), f(a_n)) = (a_{n+1}, a_{n+1})$.

Example 8   Cobwebbing square roots

Consider the difference equation $a_{n+1} = f(a_n)$ where $f(x) = \sqrt{x}$. Use cobwebbing to visualize the first ten terms of the sequence determined by

a. $a_1 = 4$ **b.** $a_1 = 0.1$

Solution

a. We begin with the graphs of $y = \sqrt{x}$ and $y = x$ (Figure 1.50**a**). To visualize the first two terms of the sequence, we start at the point $(4, 4)$ and draw a vertical line down to the graph of $y = f(x)$ followed by a horizontal line to the graph of $y = x$ (Figure 1.50**b**). To visualize the next term, draw a vertical down from $(2, 2)$ to the graph of $y = f(x)$ followed by a horizontal line to the graph of $y = x$ (Figure 1.50**c**). Proceeding in this manner for seven more iterates gives the cobweb diagram depicted in Figure 1.50**d**. This figure shows that the sequence of a_n values down the diagonal $y = x$ are getting closer to the value 1, as we found in Example 3.

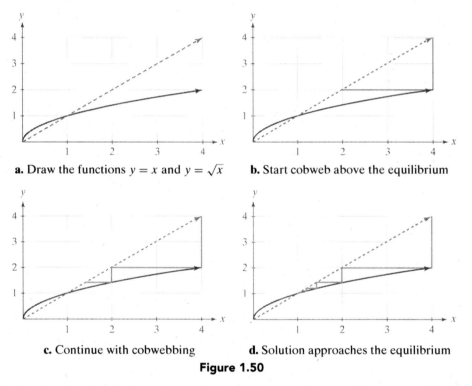

a. Draw the functions $y = x$ and $y = \sqrt{x}$ **b.** Start cobweb above the equilibrium

c. Continue with cobwebbing   **d.** Solution approaches the equilibrium

Figure 1.50

b. To visualize the first ten terms of the sequence with $a_1 = 0.1$, start at $(0.1, 0.1)$, draw a vertical line to the graph of $y = f(x)$ and then a horizontal line to the graph of $y = x$ (Figure 1.51**a**). As you continue, the cobwebbing shows that the sequence of a_n values are getting closer to the value 1 (Figure 1.51**b**).

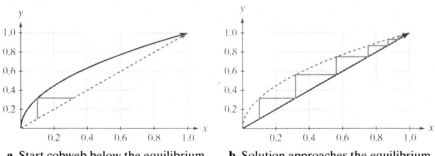

a. Start cobweb below the equilibrium   **b.** Solution approaches the equilibrium

Figure 1.51 Cobwebbing for the difference equation $a_{n+1} = \sqrt{a_n}$.

Cobwebbing an increasing function, such as the square root function, is relatively simple. The cobweb diagram gets more complicated when the function is both increasing and decreasing over its relevant domain (see next example).

Example 9   Cobwebbing a hump-shaped function

Use cobwebbing to visualize the first forty terms of the sequence determined by the equation

$$a_{n+1} = \frac{3a_n}{1 + (a_n/100)^6}$$

from starting value $a_1 = 50$. Discuss the primary difference between this example and Example 8.

Solution   We begin by drawing the graphs of $y = f(x) = \dfrac{3x}{1 + (x/100)^6}$ and $y = x$ (Figure 1.52**a**). To visualize the first two terms of the sequence, start at $(50, 50)$ and draw a vertical line up to the graph of $y = f(x)$ followed by a horizontal line to the graph of $y = x$ (Figure 1.52**b**). To visualize the next term, draw a vertical down from $(150, 150)$ to the graph of $y = f(x)$ followed by a horizontal line to the graph of $y = x$ (Figure 1.52**c**). Unlike our previous cobwebbing, we see that the sequence is already exhibiting some oscillation. In fact, continuing for the remaining thirty-seven terms yields the wild web depicted in Figure 1.52**d**.

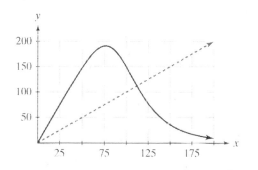

a. Draw functions $y = x$ and $y = f(x) = \dfrac{3x}{1 + (x/100)^6}$

b. Start cobweb at a convenient initial value

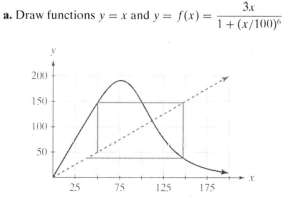

c. Continue with cobwebbing

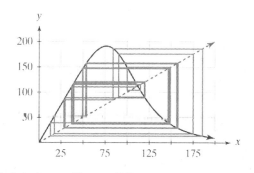

d. Solution oscillates wildly around the equilibrium

Figure 1.52 Cobwebbing for the difference equation $a_{n+1} = \dfrac{3a_n}{1 + (a_n/100)^6}$.

PROBLEM SET 1.7

Level 1 DRILL PROBLEMS

Find and graph the first five terms for the sequences in Problems 1 to 10.

1. $a_n = 1 - \dfrac{1}{n}$

2. $a_n = (-1)^{n+1}$

3. $a_n = \cos\left(\dfrac{\pi n}{2}\right)$

4. $a_n = \dfrac{\cos(2n\pi)}{n}$

5. a_n is the nth digit of the decimal representation of the number $\dfrac{1}{7}$

6. a_n is the nth digit of e

7. $a_1 = 256, a_{n+1} = \sqrt{a_n}$

8. $a_1 = 2, a_{n+1} = a_n^2, n \geq 2$

9. $a_1 = -4, a_2 = 6, a_n = a_{n-1} + a_{n-2}, n \geq 3$

10. $a_1 = 1$ and $a_2 = 2, a_{n+1} = a_n a_{n-1}, n \geq 3$

Find a_5 for each difference equation in Problems 11 to 20.

11. $a_{n+1} = a_n + 8; a_1 = 0$

12. $a_{n+1} = 3a_n; a_1 = 1$

13. $a_n = \dfrac{1}{2}a_{n-1} + 2; a_1 = 100$

14. $a_n = \dfrac{1}{10}a_{n-1} + 2; a_1 = 1,000$

15. $a_{n+1} = 5a_n + 2; a_1 = 0$

16. $a_{n+1} = 1 - 2a_n; a_1 = 0$

17. $a_{n+1} = 2a_n + 1; a_1 = 8$

18. $a_{n+1} = 1 - \dfrac{1}{2}a_n; a_1 = 0$

19. $a_{n+1} = \dfrac{2a_n}{1 + a_n}; a_1 = 1$

20. $a_{n+1} = 2a_n(1 - a_n); a_1 = 1$

Find the equilibria of $a_{n+1} = f(a_n)$ and sketch cobwebbing diagrams for the values of a_1 given in Problems 21 to 26.

21. $f(x) = 2x(1 - x)$ with $a_1 = 0.1$

22. $f(x) = x(2 - x)$ with $a_1 = 0.4$

23. $f(x) = \dfrac{3x}{1 + x}$ with $a_1 = 0.1$

24. $f(x) = \dfrac{3x}{1 + x}$ with $a_1 = 3$

25. $f(x) = 1 + x/2$ with $a_1 = 0$

26. $f(x) = \dfrac{1}{1 + x}$ with $a_1 = 3$

Find the equilibria of $a_{n+1} = f(a_n)$ where the graph of $y = f(x)$ is shown in Problems 27 to 30, and sketch the cobwebbing diagrams starting with the given a_1 value.

27. $a_1 = 1$

28. $a_1 = 1$

29. $a_1 = 0.5$

30. $a_1 = 1$

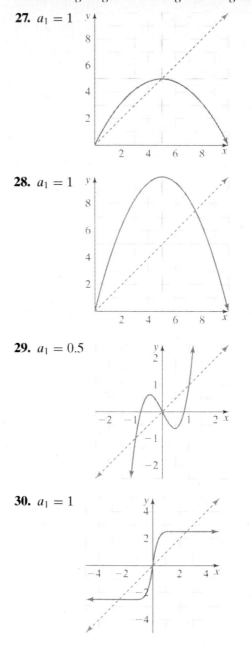

Level 2 APPLIED AND THEORY PROBLEMS

31. A drug is administered into the body. At the end of each hour, the amount of drug present is half what it was at the end of the previous hour. What percentage of the drug is present at the end of four hours? At the end of n hours?

32. A friend has a really bad headache. He decides to take 500 mg of aspirin every four hours. At the end

of each four-hour period, the body clears out 80% of the aspirin in his body. Let a_n denote the amount of aspirin in your friend's body at the time he takes the nth aspirin.

a. Write a difference equation for a_n and identify the value of a_1.

b. Write the first five terms of a_n assuming initially there is no aspirin in your friend's body.

c. Find the equilibrium of this difference equation.

33. Consider the general case of a patient who is taking a drug for a health issue. Let A be the amount the patient takes each time and c be the fraction of the drug cleared by the body between doses. Define a_n to be the amount of drug in the body *immediately prior* to taking the nth dose.

a. Write a difference equation for a_n.

b. Find the equilibrium of the difference equation in **a**.

c. Determine under what conditions the equilibrium amount of drug in the body (prior to taking the next dose) is greater than the dose A being taken by the patient.

34. A doctor has prescribed a drug for a patient. Let A be the amount the patient takes each time and c be the fraction of drug cleared by the body between doses. Define a_n to be the amount of drug in the body *immediately after* taking the nth dose.

a. Write a difference equation for a_n.

b. Find the equilibrium of the difference equation in part **a**.

c. Determine under what conditions the equilibrium amount of drug in the body (right after taking a dose) is greater than twice the dose A being taken by the patient.

35. The wildebeest (or gnu) is a ubiquitous species in the Serengeti of Africa. The following data about wildebeest abundance were collected by the Serengeti Research Institute.

year	1961	1963	1965	1967	1971	1972	1977	1978
population size in thousands	263	357	439	483	693	773	1444	1249

a. Assuming $x_{n+1} = a\,x_n$ can be used to model the data, find the constant value of a that would cause the population to grow from size 263 in 1961 to size 1,249 seventeen years later.

b. Generate the sequence $x_{n+1} = a\,x_n$ for $n = 1$ corresponding to year 1961 to $n = 18$ corresponding to the year 1978. Plot this sequence together with the data on the same diagram. How well does the model fit the data?

c. Suppose poachers kill 150 wildebeest each year. Modify the difference equation found in part **a** to account for this poaching and calculate the sequence of values it predicts from 1978 to 1997 (twenty years), if poaching started in 1978. From your answer, what can you deduce?

36. The Ricker model of a dynamic salmon population is given by

$$a_{n+1} = b\,a_n\,e^{-c\,a_n}$$

where b is the total number of progeny produced per individual per generation and $e^{-c\,a_n}$ represents the fraction of progeny that survives after accounting for the effects of adult cannibalism of very young fish. Find all the equilibria for this model and determine under what conditions they are positive. Sketch cobwebbing diagrams for $b = 0.9, b = 2.0$, $b = 8.0$, and $b = 20.0$. In these diagrams, let $c = 1.0$ and $a_1 = 2$.

37. A simple **continued fraction** is an expression of the form

$$b_0 + \cfrac{1}{b_1 + \cfrac{1}{b_2 + \cfrac{1}{b_3 + \cdots}}}$$

where $b_0, b_1, \ldots$ are real numbers. The simplest continued fraction occurs when $1 = b_0 = b_1 = b_2 = \ldots$. This continued fraction is generated by the sequence

$$a_{n+1} = 1 + \frac{1}{a_n} \qquad a_1 = 1$$

a. Find the first five terms of this sequence in "expanded form" (i.e., no algebraic reductions) and in simplified form.

b. Find the equilibrium of the difference equation.

c. Use cobwebbing to determine the asymptotic behavior of a_n for the case $a_1 = 1$.

38. 𝔥𝔦𝔰𝔱𝔬𝔯𝔦𝔠𝔞𝔩 𝔔𝔲𝔢𝔰𝔱

Fibonacci
1170–1250

Leonardo of Pisa, also known as Fibonacci, was one of the best mathematicians of the Middle Ages. He played an important role in reviving ancient mathematics and introduced the Hindu-Arabic place-value decimal system to Europe. His book, *Liber abaci*, published in 1202, introduced Arabic numerals, as well as the famous *rabbit problem*, for which he is best remembered today. To describe Fibonacci's rabbit problem, we consider a sequence whose *n*th term is defined by a difference equation. Suppose rabbits breed in such a way that each pair of adult rabbits produces a pair of baby rabbits each month.

The first month after birth, the rabbits are adolescents and produce no offspring. However, beginning the second month, the rabbits are adults, and each pair produces a pair of offspring every month. The sequence of numbers describing the number of rabbits is called the *Fibonacci sequence*, and it has applications in many areas, including biology and botany.

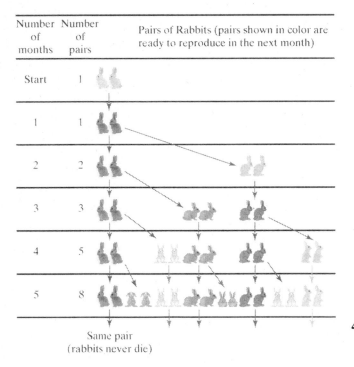

Number of months	Number of pairs	Pairs of Rabbits (pairs shown in color are ready to reproduce in the next month)
Start	1	
1	1	
2	2	
3	3	
4	5	
5	8	

Same pair
(rabbits never die)

In this 𝕳𝖎𝖘𝖙𝖔𝖗𝖎𝖈𝖆𝖑 𝕼𝖚𝖊𝖘𝖙 you are to examine some properties of the Fibonacci sequence. Let a_n denote the number of pairs of rabbits in the "colony" at the end of n months.

a. Explain why $a_1, a_2 = 1, a_3 = 2, a_4 = 3$, and, in general,

$$a_{n+1} = a_{n-1} + a_n$$

for $n = 2, 3, 4, \ldots$

b. The *growth rate* of the colony during the $(n+1)^{th}$ month is

$$r_n = \frac{a_{n+1}}{a_n}$$

Compute r_n for $n = 1, 2, 3, \ldots, 10$.

c. Show that r_n satisfies the difference equation $r_{n+1} = 1 + \dfrac{1}{r_n}$ (Hint: combine the difference equations in parts **a** and **b**) and solve for the equilibrium of this difference equation.

39. Consider the difference equation $x_{n+1} = \dfrac{x_n}{1 + x_n}$ introduced in Example 5. Let x_1 be given.

a. Write explicit expressions for $x_2, x_3, x_4,$ and x_5 in terms of x_1.

b. Use part **a** to find a reasonable guess for an explicit expression of x_n in terms of x_1.

c. Verify your guess by making sure it satisfies the difference equation.

40. A biologist discovers that a gene has a lethal allele a that is not purely recessive: genotypes of the form aa all die before reproducing and half the genotypes of the form Aa also die before reproducing.

a. Show, in contrast to Example 5, that the difference equation describing the proportion x_n of the lethal gene from one generation to the next is now given by the difference equation

$$x_{n+1} = \frac{x_n}{2}$$

b. Calculate the first ten terms of the resulting sequence starting from $x_1 = 0.5$.

c. Find all equilibrium solutions.

d. Compare the sequence you obtain in part **b** with the first ten terms of the sequence obtained in Example 5 (you have to calculate these). What do you notice about how rapidly the allele disappears?

41. A biologist discovers that a gene has a lethal allele a that is not purely recessive: genotypes of the form aa all die before reproducing and two thirds of the genotypes of the form Aa also die before reproducing.

a. Show, in contrast to Example 5, that the difference equation describing the proportion x_n of the lethal gene from one generation to the next is now given by the difference equation

$$x_{n+1} = \frac{x_n}{3 - x_n}$$

b. Calculate the first ten terms of the resulting sequence starting from $x_1 = 0.5$.

c. Find all equilibrium solutions.

d. Compare the sequence you obtain in part **b** with the first ten terms of the sequence obtained in Example 5 (you have to calculate these). What do you notice about how rapidly the allele disappears?

42. A biologist discovers that a gene has a lethal allele a that is not purely recessive: genotypes of the form aa all die before reproducing and one third genotypes of the form Aa also die before reproducing.

a. Show, in contrast to Example 5, that the difference equation describing the proportion x_n of the lethal gene from one generation to the next is now given by the difference equation

$$x_{n+1} = \frac{2x_n}{3 + x_n}$$

b. Calculate the first ten terms of the resulting sequence starting from $x_1 = 0.5$.

c. Find all equilibrium solutions.

d. Compare the sequence you obtain in part **b** with the first ten terms of the sequence obtained in Example 5 (you have to calculate these). What do you notice about how rapidly the allele disappears?

43. Compare the first ten terms of the sequences obtained from the difference equations derived in Example 5 and in Problems 40, 41, and 42. What do you conclude about the effect of a lethal allele in the population when it has a partial effect on the genotypes Aa. What happens when the lethal allele kills all Aa genotypes before they have a chance to reproduce?

CHAPTER 1 REVIEW QUESTIONS

1. Let $y = \sqrt{\log x + 1}$.

a. State the domain and range of this function.

b. Find the inverse of this function. State its domain and range as an inverse function.

2. The maximum temperature on a fall day in Woodland, California, was 92°F at 5 PM. The minimum temperature was 52°F at 5 AM. Let $T(t)$ be the temperature in degrees at the tth hour after midnight. Write a sinusoidal function of the form $T(t) = A + B\cos(C(t - D))$ that could be used to describe the temperatures on this warm fall day.

3. Find the equilibrium of $a_{n+1} = f(a_n)$ where the graph of $y = f(x)$ is shown. Sketch the cobwebbing diagram for $a_1 = 1$.

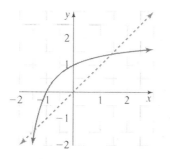

4. Sketch the x values $0.0001, 0.1, 0.3$, and $3,000,000$ on a logarithmic axis.

5. Calculate the residuals of the graphs $y = x$ and $y = \frac{x}{2} + 1$ with respect to the data set $\{(0, 0.7), (1, 1.1), (2, 2.2)\}$. Use the sum-of-squares criterion to decide which of these two curves fits the data best.

6. The time for cooking a roast is approximately proportional to its surface area.

a. How does the cooking time scale with the weight of the roast?

b. How much longer should it take to cook a 20-lb roast compared to a 10-lb roast?

7. John Damuth hypothesized a power function relationship $y = cx^m$ between the body mass x of individuals and the density y of populations belonging to related species.* The data he presented for five species of apes, where the units of x are kilograms and y are numbers/square kilometer: the western lowland gorilla, $(127, 1.8)$; the common chimpanzee, $(45.0, 2.5)$; the bonobo chimpanzee, $(22.7, 4.0)$; the Bornean orangutan, $(53.0, 2.0)$; and the agile gibbon, $(5.9, 5.1)$. By plotting these data on a semi-log scale, what would you estimate to the nearest integer that the power of the allometric relationship is between abundance and body mass?

*John Damuth, "Interspecific Allometry of Population Density in Mammals and Other Animals: The Independence of Body Mass and Population Energy-use," *Biological Journal of the Linnean Society*, 31 (2008): 193–246.

8. Consider a bank account with initially $1,000. The annual interest rate in this account is 10%.

   a. Find the amount in the account one year from now if the interest is compounded once a year, twice a year, three times a year.

   b. What value is the amount in the account approaching as the number n of times the money is compounded in the year approaches ∞?

9. An exponential function $y = ab^x$ is plotted below on a semi-log plot. Find a and b.

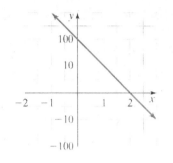

10. Hypothyroidism is a condition in which the thyroid gland makes too little thyroid hormone. One treatment for hypothyroidism is administration of replacement thyroid hormone such as thyroxine (T4). The concentration of this hormone in a patient's body exhibits exponential decay with a half-life of about seven days. Consider an individual who takes 100 mcg of T4 once a week. Let a_n denote the amount of T4 in the individual's body right before the nth dose.

    a. Write a difference equation for a_n.

    b. Find the equilibrium for the difference equation in part **a** and describe in words what this equilibrium means.

    c. In the long term, what is the greatest amount of T4 in the individual's body?

11. Consider a population with two alleles, A and a, at a single locus such that all individuals born with the genotype aa die immediately, 10% of individuals with genotype Aa die immediately, and individuals with the genotype AA always survive to reproduce. Let x_n denote the fraction a alleles in the population in generation n.

    a. Write a difference equation for x_n.

    b. Find x_2, x_2, x_4 given that the initial proportion of a is $x_1 = 0.9$.

12. Data points with a curve fit to those points are shown. Decide whether the data are better modeled by an exponential or a logarithmic function that is possibly shifted with respect to either axis.

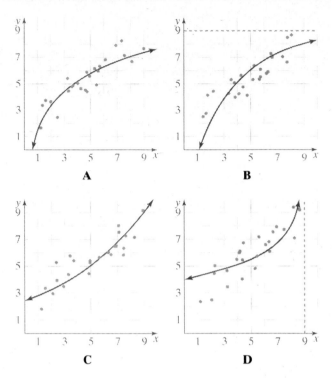

13. Let $y = f(x)$ be the function whose graph is given in Figure 1.53.

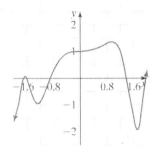

Figure 1.53 Graph of f.

Mix and match the following functions with their corresponding graphs.

   a. $y = f\left(\dfrac{x}{2}\right)$

   b. $y = 2f(x)$

   c. $y = f(-x)$

   d. $y = -f(x)$

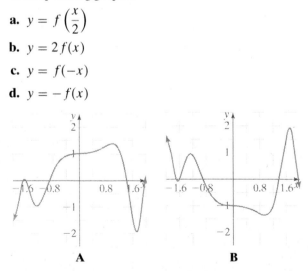

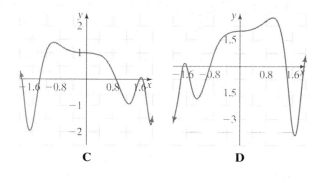

C   D

14. As a result of recovery efforts, the size of the whooping crane population in Wood Buffalo Park grew from 20 individuals in 1941 to 518 individuals in 2007. Assume that you can model the population growth of the whooping cranes as $N(t) = ae^{rt}$ individuals where t is years after 1941.

   a. Find a and r.

   b. Use the model to estimate the doubling time for the whooping crane population.

15. Find the first five terms for the given sequences.

   a. $a_n = 2 - \dfrac{n}{n+1}$

   b. $a_n = \left(\dfrac{1}{2}\right)^{n-1}$

   c. a_n is the nth prime number.

16. The pollution level, P, in Lake Bowegon varies during a typical year according to the formula

$$P(t) = 50 - 30\cos\left(\frac{2\pi t}{365}\right)$$

   where t is the number of days from the beginning of the year. A treatment program initiated by the Department of Wildlife is 50% effective against this pollution. When does the model predict, for the first time, that the pollution will be at a level of 40?

17. The number of apples, n, in a tree is a function of the population density, d, of bees pollinating the apple orchard. This function can be modeled by the formula

$$n(d) = \frac{500d}{6+d}$$

The average weight, w, in grams, of an apple at time of harvest is the following decreasing function of the number apples:

$$w(n) = 70 - \frac{n}{10}$$

Are either of these linear functions?

   a. Graph the weight of the apple as a function of the density of bees. What is the domain of w?

   b. As the number of bees increases, what can you say about the average weight of an apple?

18. The amount of solids discharged from the MWRA (Massachusetts Water Resources Authority) sewage treatment plant on Deer Island (near Boston Harbor) is given by the function

$$f(t) = \begin{cases} 130 & \text{if } 0 \le t \le 1 \\ -30t + 130 & \text{if } 1 < t \le 2 \\ 100 & \text{if } 2 < t \le 4 \\ -5t^2 + 25t + 80 & \text{if } 4 < t \le 6 \\ 1.25t^2 - 26t + 161 & \text{if } 6 < t \le 10 \end{cases}$$

where $f(t)$ is measured in tons per day, and t is measured in years, from 1992.

   a. How many more tons per day were discharged in 2002 than in 1996?

   b. Sketch the graph of f.

19. A female moth (*Tinea pellionella*) lays nearly 150 eggs and then dies. In one year, up to five generations may be born, and each female larva eats about 20 mg of wool. Assume that two thirds of the eggs die, and 50% of the remaining moths are females. Use an exponential population growth model to estimate the largest amount of wool that may be destroyed by the female descendants of one female over a period of one year.

20. The level of a certain pollutant in the Los Angeles area has been decreasing linearly since 1990 when a new pollution control program began. The level of pollution was 0.17 ppm in 2000 and had fallen to 0.11 ppm in 2010.

   a. Let P be the level of pollutant (in parts per million) at time t (years after 2000). Express P as a function of t.

   b. Air with a pollutant level of 0.05 ppm is considered clean. If the present trend continues, when will this clean level be achieved?

GROUP PROJECTS

Seeing a project through on your own, or working in a small group to complete a project, teaches important skills. The following projects provide opportunities to develop such skills.

Project 1A   Heart rates in mammals

Smaller mammals and birds have faster heart rates than larger ones. If we assume that evolution has determined the best rate for each, why isn't there a single best rate? Is there a model that leads to a correct rule relating heart rates? A warm-blooded animal uses large quantities of energy to maintain body temperature because of heat loss through its body surfaces. Cold-blooded animals require very little energy when they are resting. The major energy drain on a resting warm-blooded animal seems to be maintenance of body temperature.

The amount of energy available is roughly proportional to blood flow through the lungs—the source of oxygen. Assuming the least amount of blood needed is circulated, the amount of available energy will equal the amount used. In this project, you are to develop a model of blood flow and heart pulse rates as a function of body size and validate the model using the data in Tables 1.17 and 1.18. Be sure to address the following points:

- Set up a model based on geometric similarity relating body weight to basal (resting) blood flow through the heart. State your assumptions.

- There are many animals for which pulse rate data are available but not blood flow data. Set up a model based on geometric similarity that relates body weight to basal pulse rate.

- Test your ideas using the data in Tables 1.17 and 1.18. In addition to finding the best-fitting lines, determine how the data support your assumptions about geometric similarity.

Table 1.17 Weight and blood flow data on humans and some mammals

Animal	Weight (kg)	Blood flow (deciliters/min)
Human (age 5)	18	23
Human (age 10)	31	33
Human (age 16)	66	52
Human (age 25)	68	51
Human (age 33)	70	43
Human (age 47)	72	40
Human (age 60)	70	46
Rabbit	4.1	5.3
Goat	24	31
Dog 1	16	22
Dog 2	12	12
Dog 3	6.4	11

Data source: W. S. Spector, *Handbook of Biological Data* (1956).

Table 1.18 An across species comparison of the mammalian heart

Animal	Weight (kg)	Pulse (1/min)	Heart weight (g)	Ventricle length(cm)
Shrew	0.004	660		
Mouse	0.025	670	0.13	0.55
Rat	0.2	420	0.64	1.0
Guinea pig	0.3	300		32.00
Rabbit	2	205	5.8	2.2
Dog	5	120		
Dog 2	30	85	102	4.0
Sheep	50	70	210	6.5
Human	70	72		
Horse	450	38	3900	16
Ox	500	40	2030	12
Elephant	3000	48		

Data source: A. J. Clark, *Comparative Physiology of the Heart*, Macmillan (1972).

Project 1B: The mouse to elephant curve

The most universal feature of living organisms is their turnover of energy. Animals, with few exceptions, obtain energy by the oxidation of organic compounds, and the rate of energy turnover (the metabolic rate) is often measured by the rate of oxygen consumption. The fact that there is a regular relationship between the metabolic rate, or rate of oxygen consumption, and the body size of animals is thoroughly familiar to biologists. In the early part of the twentieth century, French scientists realized that the heat dissipation from warm-blooded animals must be roughly proportionate to their free surface. Since smaller animals have a larger relative surface, they must also have a higher relative rate of heat production than larger animals. In this project, you are to develop a model to explore this relation. Use the data in Table 1.19 to assess the accuracy of your model and its assumptions. The project needs to address the following point:

- Develop a model based on geometric similarity to describe surface area of a mammal as a function of body size. Be sure to state all of your assumptions.

- Develop a model based on geometric similarity to describe the metabolic rate of an organism as a function of body size.

- Test your models using the data in Table 1.19.

- The curve described by the data in Table 1.19 is called the *mouse-to-elephant curve*. However, the original data set from which the curve was derived did not include the relevant numbers for the elephant. Find the weight of an elephant and determine what the models predict for its metabolic rate. If possible, compare this prediction with the actual value.

- In 1847, Carl Bergmann, a German biologist, formulated what later became known as *Bergmann's rule*, which states that animals that live in colder climates are of larger body size than their relatives from warmer climates. Based on your analysis, does this rule make sense?

Table 1.19 Data on the relationship between the weight of individuals and their basal metabolic rate

Animal	Body mass (kg)	kCal/day
Mouse	0.021	3.6
Rat	0.282	28.1
Guinea pig	0.410	35.1
Rabbit	2.980	167
Rabbit 2	1.520	83
Rabbit 3	2.460	119
Rabbit 4	3.570	164
Rabbit 5	4.330	191
Rabbit 6	5.330	233
Cat	3.0	152
Monkey	4.200	207
Dog	6.6	288
Dog 2	14.1	534
Dog 3	24.8	875
Dog 4	23.6	872
Goat	36	800
Chimpanzee	38	1,090
Sheep	46.4	1,254
Sheep 2	46.8	1,330
Woman	57.2	1,368
Woman 2	54.8	1,224
Woman 3	57.9	1,320
Cow	300	4,221
Cow 2	435	8,166
Cow 3	600	7,877
Heifer	482	7,754

Project 1C: Golden Ratio

Around 300 BC, the greatest of the ancient Greek geometers, Euclid of Alexandria, defined what he called the "extreme and mean ratio," now better known as the *golden ratio*. (See Mario Livio, *The Golden Ratio: the Story of Phi*, the Worlds Most Astonishing Number, New York: Broadway Books, 2002, p. 3.) Euclid's ratio states:

A straight line is said to have been cut in extreme and mean ratio when, as the whole line is to the greater segment, so is the greater segment to the lesser segment.

Specifically, if we look at the line illustrated in Figure 1.54, this statement can be expressed mathematically as

$$(a + b)/a = a/b$$

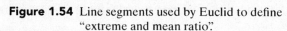

$a + b$ is to a as a is to b

Figure 1.54 Line segments used by Euclid to define "extreme and mean ratio".

The *golden rectangle* is the rectangle whose sides conform to the golden ratio. The beauty, and astonishing perfection, of the golden rectangle arises from this fact: If you add one additional edge parallel to a short side of the rectangle to form a square within the rectangle, the smaller rectangle so formed (now oriented at 90 degrees to the original rectangle) is also a golden rectangle, as illustrated in Figure 1.55.

GOLDEN RECTANGLES

Figure 1.55 This panel is a golden rectangle. If we cut off the red square, as in the second panel, the vertical residual rectangle is also golden. Continuing to cut off squares as in the third to fifth panels leaves ever smaller residual golden rectangles. This leaves a smaller rectangle which again is cut and so on infinitum. The inset curve is the logarithmic or equiangular spiral.

A spiral can be constructed passing through the corners of all embedded squares of the preceding construction in a such way that the spiral is *equiangular*—also known as the *logarithmic spiral*, which has the form shown in Figure 1.56.

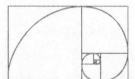

Figure 1.56 If we inset quarter circles into the squares obtained by repeatedly reducing golden rectangles as illustrated in this construction, we obtain a very good approximation of a true logarithmic or equiangular spiral, which is much more difficult to construct accurately.

Leonardo da Vinci (1452–1519), one of the greatest painters of all time, so valued the aesthetic proportions of the golden rectangle that aspects of figures and forms in many of his paintings conform to golden rectangle proportions. In the twentieth century, the noted American architect Frank Lloyd Wright (1867–1959) used the logarithmic spiral in designing the Guggenheim Museum in New York City.

1. List five paintings that art historians regard as compositions containing golden rectangles.

2. The shell of the nautilus mollusk, *Nautilus pompilius*, has the shape of a logarithmic spiral. Find a list of at least five other natural objects that contain shapes conforming to logarithmic spirals.

3. Define, using the concept of a tangent to a curve, what is meant by an *equiangular spiral*.

4. From Euclid's statement regarding the extreme and mean ratio, commonly denoted by the Greek letter phi (ϕ), show that $\phi = \dfrac{1 + \sqrt{5}}{2}$.

5. If
$$\phi_1 = \sqrt{1} = 1,$$
$$\phi_2 = \sqrt{1 + \sqrt{1}} = \sqrt{2} = 1.141421\ldots.$$
$$\phi_3 = \sqrt{1 + \sqrt{1 + \sqrt{1}}} = \sqrt{1 + \sqrt{2}} = 1.553773\ldots.$$
$$\phi_4 = \sqrt{1 + \sqrt{1 + \sqrt{1 + \sqrt{1}}}} = 1.598053\ldots.$$
$$\vdots$$
$$\phi_n = \sqrt{1 + \sqrt{1 + \ldots 1 + \sqrt{1}}} \quad n \text{ square roots deep}$$
then use technology to calculate ϕ_i, $i = 5, \ldots, 10$. Use the definition of ϕ_n to generate a relationship of the form $\phi_{n+1} = f(\phi_n)$ and demonstrate that an equilibrium solution $\phi = f(\phi)$ is the golden ratio. To how many decimal places do the numerical values of ϕ and ϕ_{10} coincide?

6. If
$$\phi_0' = 1,$$
$$\phi_1' = 1 + \frac{1}{1} = \frac{2}{1} = 2,$$
$$\phi_2' = 1 + \frac{1}{1 + \frac{1}{1}} = \frac{3}{2} = 1.5$$
$$\phi_3' = 1 + \frac{1}{1 + \frac{1}{1 + \frac{1}{1}}} = \frac{5}{3} = 1.666\ldots$$
$$\phi_4' = 1 + \frac{1}{1 + \frac{1}{1 + \frac{1}{1 + \frac{1}{1}}}} = \frac{8}{5} = 1.666\ldots$$
$$\phi_5' = 1 + \frac{1}{1 + \frac{1}{1 + \frac{1}{1 + \frac{1}{1 + \frac{1}{1}}}}} = \frac{13}{8} = 1.625$$
$$\vdots$$
$$\phi_n' = 1 + \frac{1}{1 + \frac{1}{1 + \frac{1}{1 + \cdots 1 + \frac{1}{1}}}} \quad n \text{ denominators deep}$$
can you find a relationship of the form $\phi_{n+1}' = f(\phi_n')$? Demonstrate that an equilibrium solution $\phi' = f(\phi')$

is the golden ratio. Notice that the denominators and numerators of the consecutive fractions $\phi_1' = \frac{2}{1}$, $\phi_2' = \frac{3}{2}$, $\phi_3' = \frac{5}{3}$, ... are the Fibonacci sequence discussed in the $\mathfrak{Historical\ Quest}$, Problem 38 of Section 1.7. Use this fact to write the expression for ϕ_{10}'. Draw a conclusion.

7. Compare the value of ϕ_{10}' obtained in the preceding question with the golden ratio ϕ and ϕ_{10} obtained from the question before that. Which of ϕ_{10} and ϕ_{10}' provides the better approximation to ϕ? Can you generalize this statement to ϕ_n and ϕ_n' as an approximation to ϕ for any n?

ANSWERS TO SELECTED PROBLEMS

CHAPTER 1

Problem Set 1.1, Page 20

1. a. yes; D: $\{3, 4, 5, 6\}$; R: $\{4, 7, 9\}$ **b.** no **3. a.** no **b.** yes; D: $x \neq 0$; R: $\{-1, 1\}$ **5. a.** no **b.** yes; D: $\mathbb{R}$; R: $y \geq -4$
7. a. yes; D: $\mathbb{R}$; R: $y \geq 0$ **b.** yes; D: $\mathbb{R}$; R: $\mathbb{R}$
9. a. no; D: $-2 \leq x \leq 2$; R: $-4 \leq y \leq 4$ **b.** yes; D: $x \neq \pm 2$; R: $y \neq 1$ **11. a.** no; D: $x \geq -3$; R: $\mathbb{R}$ **b.** yes; D: $\mathbb{R}$; R: $y \geq -80$
13. $D = \mathbb{R}$; $f(0) = 3$; $f(1) = 4$; $f(-2) = -5$
15. $D = \mathbb{R}$, $x \neq 3$; $f(2) = 0$; $f(0) = -2$; $f(-3)$ not defined
17. $D = \mathbb{R}$; $f(3) = 4$; $f(1) = 2$; $f(0) = 4$ **19.** $F(x) = x^2$
21. 8; -7; -16; $M(x) = 3x - 7$ **23.** D: $-6 \leq x \leq 6$;
$-5 \leq y \leq 5$; decreasing on $[-6, 0)$; increasing on $(0, 6]$
25. D: $x \neq 2$; R: $y = 5$; constant on $(-\infty, 2)$, $(2, \infty)$
27. D: $x \geq -5$, $x \neq 3$; R: $y \geq -3$, $y \neq 6$; increasing on $[0, 3)$ and on $(3, \infty)$; decreasing on $[-2, 0)$; constant on $[-5, -2]$
29. $D = \mathbb{R}$; $y = 3x - 5$ **31.** D: $\{x \geq 5\}$; $y = \sqrt{5 - x}$

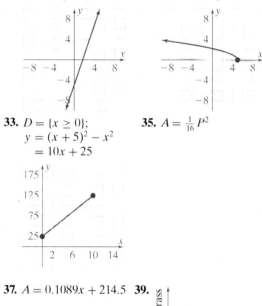

33. $D = \{x \geq 0\}$; **35.** $A = \frac{1}{16}P^2$
$y = (x + 5)^2 - x^2$
$= 10x + 25$

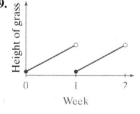

37. $A = 0.1089x + 214.5$ **39.**

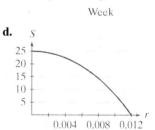
Height of grass — Week

41. a. 25.34 cm/s **d.**
b. 19.01 cm/s
c. $[0, 1.2 \times 10^{-2}]$

43. a. $n \neq 0$ **c.** **d.** It approaches
b. positive (but does not
integers reach) 3.

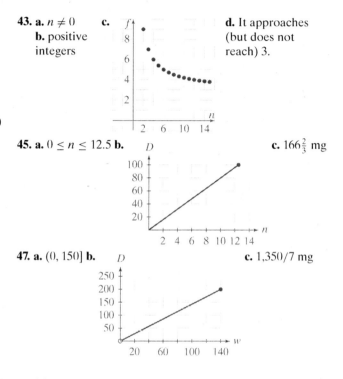

45. a. $0 \leq n \leq 12.5$ **b.** **c.** $166\frac{2}{3}$ mg

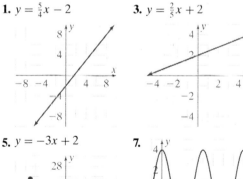

47. a. $(0, 150]$ **b.** **c.** $1{,}350/7$ mg

Problem Set 1.2, Page 33

1. $y = \frac{5}{4}x - 2$ **3.** $y = \frac{2}{5}x + 2$

5. $y = -3x + 2$ **7.**

9. **11.** $y = 3x$
13. $y = -x + 1$
15. $y = 4$

1

17. Given $y = mx + b$ with (h, k) a point on the line. That is,

$y = mx + b$	*Given*
$k = mh + b$	*Point (h, k) satisfies the equation.*
$k - mh = b$	*Solve for b.*
$y = mx + (k - mh)$	*Substitute the value for b in the given equation.*
$y - k = mx - mh$	*Subtract k from both sides.*
$y - k = m(x - h)$	*Factor.*

19. $m = 2$; $y = 2x - 4$ **21.** $p = 2\pi$; $a = 3$; $y = 3\cos x$
23. $p = 2$; $a = 2$; $y = 2\cos\pi(x - 1)$ **25.** D   **27.** A   **29.** C

31. $(h, k) = \left(-\dfrac{\pi}{6}, 0\right)$,   **33.** $(h, k) = (0, 0)$,

$a = \dfrac{1}{2}, b = 1, p = 2\pi$ $a = 2, b = 2\pi, p = 1$

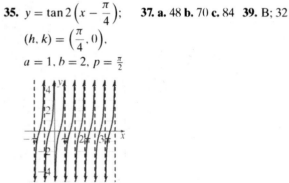

35. $y = \tan 2\left(x - \dfrac{\pi}{4}\right)$;   **37. a.** 48 **b.** 70 **c.** 84   **39.** B; 32

$(h, k) = \left(\dfrac{\pi}{4}, 0\right)$,

$a = 1, b = 2, p = \dfrac{\pi}{2}$

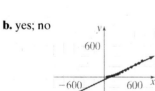

41. a. not quite linear,   **b.** yes; no
but close

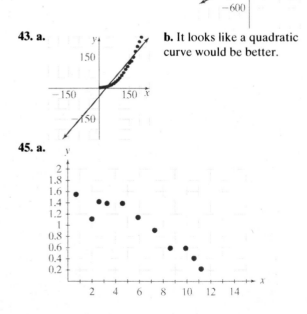

43. a.   **b.** It looks like a quadratic
curve would be better.

45. a.

b.

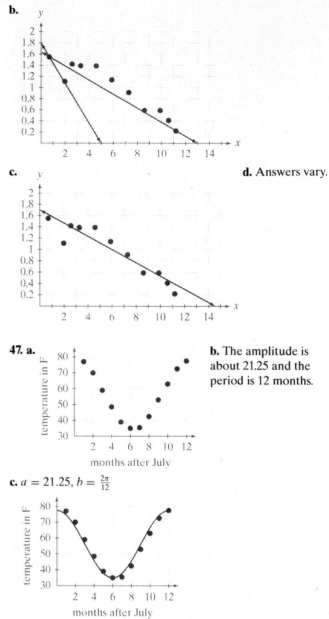

c.   **d.** Answers vary.

47. a.   **b.** The amplitude is
about 21.25 and the
period is 12 months.

c. $a = 21.25, b = \dfrac{2\pi}{12}$

Problem Set 1.3, Page 46

1. a. power function; $a = \frac{1}{3}$, $b = 1$ **b.** power function; $a = \frac{1}{3}$,
$b = -1$ **c.** not a power function   **3.** not a power function
5. $y = \frac{1}{4}x^{-3/2}$, power function; $a = \frac{1}{4}, b = -\frac{3}{2}$ **7.** $y = 90^x$, not
a power function   **9.** $y = 6x^{-1/2}$, power function; $a = 6$,
$b = -\frac{1}{2}$ **11.** It increases by a factor of 10^6.   **13.** y is
proportional to the cube of x.   **15.** x is proportional to the
sixth power of z.

17. 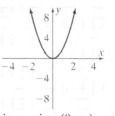   **19.**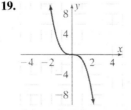

increasing: $(0, \infty)$ decreasing: $(-\infty, \infty)$
decreasing: $(-\infty, 0)$

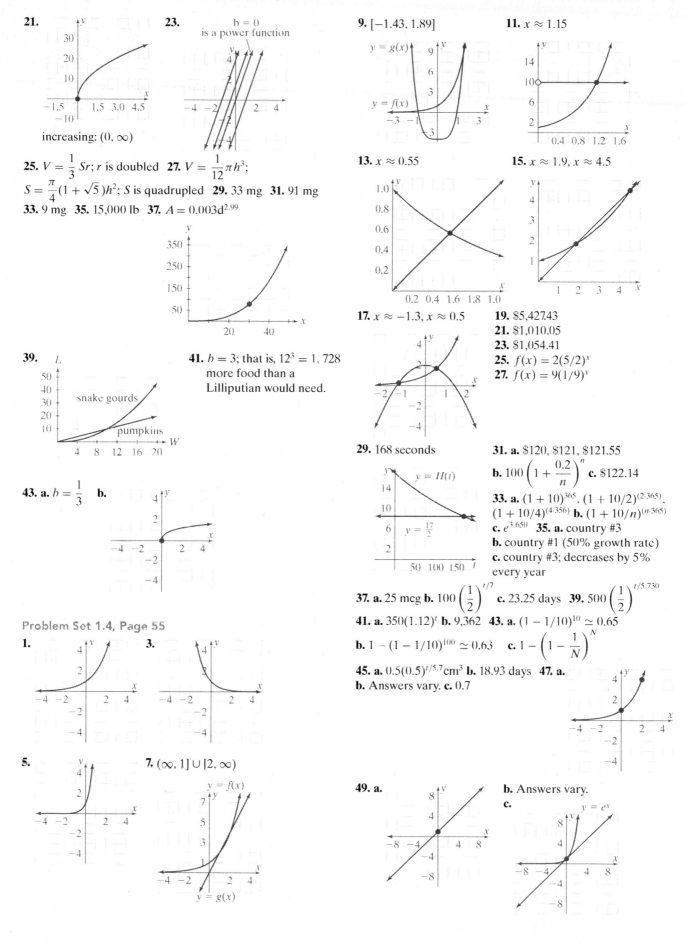

21.

increasing: $(0, \infty)$

23. $b = 0$ is a power function

25. $V = \dfrac{1}{3}Sr$; r is doubled **27.** $V = \dfrac{1}{12}\pi h^3$;
$S = \dfrac{\pi}{4}(1 + \sqrt{5})h^2$; S is quadrupled **29.** 33 mg **31.** 91 mg
33. 9 mg **35.** 15,000 lb **37.** $A = 0.003d^{2.99}$

39.

41. $b = 3$; that is, $12^3 = 1,728$ more food than a Lilliputian would need.

43. a. $b = \dfrac{1}{3}$ **b.**

Problem Set 1.4, Page 55

1.

3.

5.

7. $(\infty, 1] \cup [2, \infty)$

9. $[-1.43, 1.89]$

11. $x \approx 1.15$

13. $x \approx 0.55$

15. $x \approx 1.9$, $x \approx 4.5$

17. $x \approx -1.3$, $x \approx 0.5$

19. \$5,427.43
21. \$1,010.05
23. \$1,054.41
25. $f(x) = 2(5/2)^x$
27. $f(x) = 9(1/9)^x$

29. 168 seconds

31. a. \$120, \$121, \$121.55
b. $100\left(1 + \dfrac{0.2}{n}\right)^n$ **c.** \$122.14

33. a. $(1 + 10)^{365}$, $(1 + 10/2)^{(2 \cdot 365)}$, $(1 + 10/4)^{(4 \cdot 356)}$ **b.** $(1 + 10/n)^{(n \cdot 365)}$
c. $e^{3.650}$ **35. a.** country #3
b. country #1 (50% growth rate)
c. country #3; decreases by 5% every year

37. a. 25 mcg **b.** $100\left(\dfrac{1}{2}\right)^{t/7}$ **c.** 23.25 days **39.** $500\left(\dfrac{1}{2}\right)^{t/5.730}$
41. a. $350(1.12)^t$ **b.** 9,362 **43. a.** $(1 - 1/10)^{10} \simeq 0.65$
b. $1 - (1 - 1/10)^{100} \simeq 0.63$ **c.** $1 - \left(1 - \dfrac{1}{N}\right)^N$

45. a. $0.5(0.5)^{t/5.7}\,\text{cm}^3$ **b.** 18.93 days **47. a.**
b. Answers vary. **c.** 0.7

49. a.
b. Answers vary.
c.

Problem Set 1.5, Page 67

1.

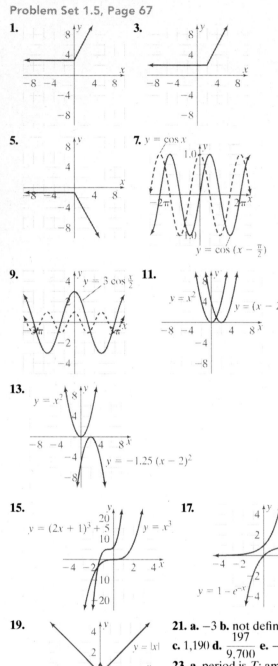

3.

5.

7. $y = \cos x$

9. $y = 3\cos\frac{x}{2}$

11. $y = x^2$; $y = (x - 2)^2$

13. $y = x^2$; $y = -1.25(x - 2)^2$

15. $y = (2x + 1)^3 + 5$; $y = x^3$

17. $y = e^x$; $y = 1 - e^{-x}$

19. $y = |x|$; $y = 1 - 2|x|$

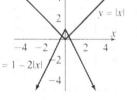

21. a. -3 **b.** not defined **c.** 1,190 **d.** $\dfrac{197}{9{,}700}$ **e.** -5

23. a. period is T; amplitude is A **b.** period is T; amplitude is $4A$ **c.** period is $\dfrac{T}{3}$; amplitude is $2A$ **d.** period is T; amplitude is $2A$

25. $g(x) = 1 - \sin x$; $f(x) = \sqrt{x}$ **27.** $g(x) = e^x$; $f(x) = 1 - x^2$

29. $g(x) = x^2 - 1$; $f(x) = x^3 + \sqrt{x} + 5$

31.

$f + g$; domain	fg; domain	f/g; domain
$x^2 + x - 5$	$2x^3 - 5x^2 - x + 6$	$\dfrac{2x - 3}{(x - 2)(x + 1)}$
D: $x \neq -1$	D: $x \neq -1$	D: $x \neq -1, 2$

33.

$\sqrt{4 - x^2} + \sin(\pi x)$	$\sqrt{4 - x^2}\,\sin(\pi x)$	$\dfrac{\sqrt{4 - x^2}}{\sin(\pi x)}$
D: $-2 \leq x \leq 2$	D: $-2 \leq x \leq 2$	D: $-2 < x < 2$, $x \neq -1$, $x \neq 0$, $x \neq 1$

35. $A = 3.1$, $B = \dfrac{\pi}{6}$, $C = -11$, and $D = 2.7$ **37. a.** $z = \dfrac{t + a}{b}$

b. $a = -\dfrac{1}{2}$, $b = \dfrac{1}{2}$ **39. a.** $V = \dfrac{16}{3}\pi$ **b.** $\dfrac{2\pi}{3}t^3$ **c.** $[0, 3]$

41.

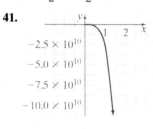

43. May 1, 2011 and August 24, 2011. The sunrise-sunset tables for Los Angeles, indicate the actual dates are April 14, 2011, and August 28, 2011. This offers a good jump-off point for a discussion of mathematical modeling.

45. Between 1844 and 1997, a 153-year period, sunspot intensity went though fourteen cycles. Hence, the period is $\dfrac{153}{14} \approx 10.9$. The minimum number is always around 0 and the black curve indicates an average amplitude of around 70 sunspots. A reasonable fitting sunspot curve is $y = 70 - \dfrac{70\cos 2\pi x - \pi}{10.9}$, which implies $a = 70$, $b = -70$, $c = \dfrac{2\pi}{10.9} \approx 0.576$, $d = -\dfrac{\pi}{10.9} \approx 0.288$.

Problem Set 1.6, Page 81

1. not one-to-one **3.** one-to-one;

$f^{-1}(x)$	x
0	11.9
1	17
4	-2
2	4
6	5

5. one-to-one **7.** one-to-one

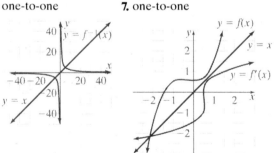

9. $y = \dfrac{x}{1 - x}$; D: $x \neq -1$; R: $x \neq 1$ **11.** $y = \sqrt[3]{x + 2} - 1$; D: $\mathbb{R}$;

R: $\mathbb{R}$ **13.** $y = -\sqrt{\ln x}$; D: $[-\infty, 0)$, R: $[0, \infty)$ **15. a.** $x = 1$

b. $x = -3$ **17. a.** $x = 3$ **b.** $x = 2$ **19. a.** $x = e^3$ **b.** $x = 10^{4.5}$

21. a. $3x$ **b.** $4x$ **c.** $3x$ **d.** $-5x$ **e.** $-2x$ **23. a.** $e^{x \ln 5}$

b. $e^{-x \ln 2}$ **c.** $e^{\ln 5/x}$ **d.** $e^{x^2 \ln 4}$ **e.** $e^{x^e \ln 3}$ **25. a.** $\dfrac{\ln(x + 1)}{\ln 10}$

b. $\dfrac{1 + \ln(x + 1)}{\ln 10}$ **c.** $\dfrac{\ln(x^2 - 2)}{\ln 2}$ **d.** $\dfrac{\ln(2x - 3)}{\ln 7}$ **27.** 543 **29.** 0.5

31.

33.

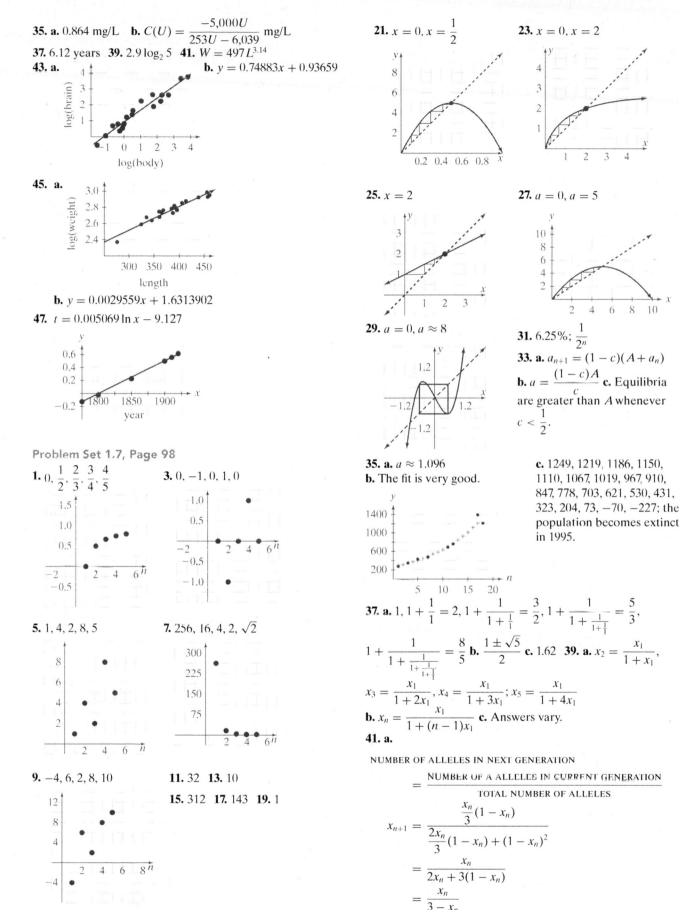

35. a. 0.864 mg/L **b.** $C(U) = \dfrac{-5,000U}{253U - 6,039}$ mg/L

37. 6.12 years **39.** $2.9 \log_2 5$ **41.** $W = 497L^{3.14}$

43. a.

b. $y = 0.74883x + 0.93659$

log(brain) vs log(body)

45. a.

log(weight) vs length

b. $y = 0.0029559x + 1.6313902$

47. $t = 0.005069 \ln x - 9.127$

year vs x

Problem Set 1.7, Page 98

1. $0, \dfrac{1}{2}, \dfrac{2}{3}, \dfrac{3}{4}, \dfrac{4}{5}$

3. $0, -1, 0, 1, 0$

5. 1, 4, 2, 8, 5

7. 256, 16, 4, 2, $\sqrt{2}$

9. $-4, 6, 2, 8, 10$

11. 32 **13.** 10

15. 312 **17.** 143 **19.** 1

21. $x = 0, x = \dfrac{1}{2}$

23. $x = 0, x = 2$

25. $x = 2$

27. $a = 0, a = 5$

29. $a = 0, a \approx 8$

31. $6.25\%; \dfrac{1}{2^n}$

33. a. $a_{n+1} = (1 - c)(A + a_n)$

b. $a = \dfrac{(1 - c)A}{c}$ **c.** Equilibria are greater than A whenever $c < \dfrac{1}{2}$.

35. a. $a \approx 1.096$
b. The fit is very good.

c. 1249, 1219, 1186, 1150, 1110, 1067, 1019, 967, 910, 847, 778, 703, 621, 530, 431, 323, 204, 73, -70, -227; the population becomes extinct in 1995.

37. a. $1, 1 + \dfrac{1}{1} = 2, 1 + \dfrac{1}{1 + \frac{1}{1}} = \dfrac{3}{2}, 1 + \dfrac{1}{1 + \frac{1}{1 + \frac{1}{1}}} = \dfrac{5}{3},$

$1 + \dfrac{1}{1 + \frac{1}{1 + \frac{1}{1 + \frac{1}{1}}}} = \dfrac{8}{5}$ **b.** $\dfrac{1 \pm \sqrt{5}}{2}$ **c.** 1.62 **39. a.** $x_2 = \dfrac{x_1}{1 + x_1},$

$x_3 = \dfrac{x_1}{1 + 2x_1}, x_4 = \dfrac{x_1}{1 + 3x_1}; x_5 = \dfrac{x_1}{1 + 4x_1}$

b. $x_n = \dfrac{x_1}{1 + (n - 1)x_1}$ **c.** Answers vary.

41. a.

NUMBER OF ALLELES IN NEXT GENERATION

$= \dfrac{\text{NUMBER OF A ALLELES IN CURRENT GENERATION}}{\text{TOTAL NUMBER OF ALLELES}}$

$x_{n+1} = \dfrac{\dfrac{x_n}{3}(1 - x_n)}{\dfrac{2x_n}{3}(1 - x_n) + (1 - x_n)^2}$

$= \dfrac{x_n}{2x_n + 3(1 - x_n)}$

$= \dfrac{x_n}{3 - x_n}$

b. $\dfrac{1}{2}, \dfrac{1}{3}, \dfrac{1}{14}, \dfrac{1}{41}, \dfrac{1}{122}, \dfrac{1}{365}, \dfrac{1}{1,074}, \dfrac{1}{3,281}, \dfrac{1}{9,842}, \dfrac{1}{29,525}$ **c.** $0, 2$

d.

n:	1	2	3	4	5	6	7	8	9	10
$x_{n+1} = \dfrac{x_n}{3 - x_n}$	$\dfrac{1}{2}$	$\dfrac{1}{3}$	$\dfrac{1}{14}$	$\dfrac{1}{41}$	$\dfrac{1}{122}$	$\dfrac{1}{365}$	$\dfrac{1}{1,074}$	$\dfrac{1}{3,281}$	$\dfrac{1}{9,842}$	$\dfrac{1}{29,525}$
$x_{n+1} = \dfrac{x_n}{1 + x_n}$	$\dfrac{1}{2}$	$\dfrac{1}{3}$	$\dfrac{1}{4}$	$\dfrac{1}{5}$	$\dfrac{1}{6}$	$\dfrac{1}{7}$	$\dfrac{1}{8}$	$\dfrac{1}{9}$	$\dfrac{1}{10}$	$\dfrac{1}{11}$

43. Answers vary.

n:	1	2	3	4	5	6	7	8	9	10
$x_{n+1} = \dfrac{x_n}{3 + x_n}$	0.50	0.29	0.18	0.11	0.07	0.05	0.03	0.02	0.01	0.01
all Aa survive	0.50	0.33	0.25	0.20	0.17	0.14	0.13	0.11	0.10	0.09
$\dfrac{2}{3}$ of Aa survive	0.50	0.29	0.18	0.11	0.07	0.05	0.03	0.02	0.01	0.01
$\dfrac{1}{2}$ of Aa survive	0.5	0.25	0.13	0.06	0.03	0.02	0.01	0.00	0.00	0.00
$\dfrac{1}{3}$ of Aa survive	0.5	0.20	0.07	0.02	0.01	0.00	0.00	0.00	0.00	0.00

We conclude that as a diminishing proportion of Aa survive, so the sequences approach zero more rapidly, and if there is no Aa, then the proportion of a immediately goes to zero in the next generation.

Chapter 1 Review Questions, Page 101

1. a. D: $[0.1, \infty)$; R: $[0, \infty)$
b. $f^{-1}(x) = 10^{x^2-1}$; D: $[0, \infty)$; R: $[0.1, \infty)$
3. $a = 1.4$

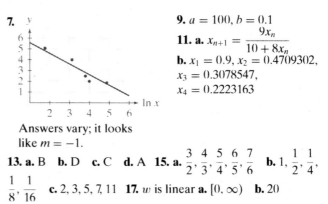

5. The residuals for $y = x$ are 0.7, 0.1, and 0.2 with the sum of squares 0.54;

the residuals for $y = \dfrac{1}{2}x + 1$ are 0.3, 0.4, and 0.2 with the sum of squares 0.29. Thus, $y = \dfrac{1}{2}x + 1$ is the better-fitting line.

7.

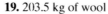

Answers vary; it looks like $m = -1$.

9. $a = 100$, $b = 0.1$
11. a. $x_{n+1} = \dfrac{9x_n}{10 + 8x_n}$
b. $x_1 = 0.9$, $x_2 = 0.4709302$, $x_3 = 0.3078547$, $x_4 = 0.2223163$

13. a. B   **b.** D   **c.** C   **d.** A   **15. a.** $\dfrac{3}{2}, \dfrac{4}{3}, \dfrac{5}{4}, \dfrac{6}{5}, \dfrac{7}{6}$ **b.** $1, \dfrac{1}{2}, \dfrac{1}{4}, \dfrac{1}{8}, \dfrac{1}{16}$ **c.** $2, 3, 5, 7, 11$ **17.** w is linear   **a.** $[0, \infty)$ **b.** 20
19. 203.5 kg of wool

CHAPTER 2

Limits and Derivatives

Figure 2.1 Biologists count spawning adult sockeye salmon to obtain a stock-recruitment relationship (see Figure 2.43).

© Darryl Leniuk/Age Fotostock America, Inc.

Preview

"Mathematics, in one view, is the science of infinity."

Philip Davis and Reuben Hersh,
The Mathematical Experience, Birkhäuser
Boston, 1981, p. 152.

Calculus, one of the great intellectual achievements of humankind, came to fruition through the work of Sir Isaac Newton (1642–1727) and Gottfried Wilhelm Leibniz (1646–1716). It consists of two parts, *differential calculus* and *integral calculus*, both of which hinge on the concept of a *limit* in which the behavior of a function is described as its argument approaches a selected *limiting value*. In this chapter, we first discuss some of the basic properties of a limit and the associated concept of *continuity*. Using limits, we then introduce the main concept in differential calculus: the *derivative*. This concept is one of the fundamental ideas in mathematics and a cornerstone of modern scientific thought. It allows us to come to grips with the phenomenon of change in the value of variables over increasingly small intervals of time or space (or any other independent variable—variables representing such things as the velocity of a stooping falcon or the density of a population of fish). By finding the derivative of functions, we calculate the slopes of tangent lines to these functions and examine rates of change defined by these functions. Applications considered in this chapter include enzyme kinetics, biodiversity, foraging of hummingbirds, wolf predation, and population dynamics of the sockeye salmon depicted in Figure 2.1.

2.1   Rates of Change and Tangent Lines

One of the fundamental concepts in calculus is that of the limit. Intuitively, "taking a limit" corresponds to investigating the value of a function as you get closer and closer to a specified point without actually reaching that point. To "motivate limits," we begin by showing how they arise when we consider rates of change and the tangent lines to graphs of functions's.

Rates of change

Rates of change describe how quantities change with respect to a variable such as time or body mass. For instance, in countries where overpopulation is an issue, projections are constantly made about the population growth rate. For a patient receiving drug treatment, physicians perform experiments to estimate the clearance rate of the drug (i.e., the rate at which the drug leaves the blood stream). To define a rate of change for a given function, we can specify an interval over which we find the average rate of change.

Average Rate of Change

The **average rate of change** of f over the interval $[a, b]$ is
$$\frac{f(b) - f(a)}{b - a}$$

Example 1 Mexico population growth

The (estimated) population size of Mexico (in millions) in the early 1980s is reported in the following table.

Year	Time lapsed t	Population $N(t)$
1980	0	67.38
1981	1	69.13
1982	2	70.93
1983	3	72.77
1984	4	74.66
1985	5	76.60

From this table, we see that $N(t)$ denotes the population size in millions t years after 1980.

a. Compute the population's average rate of change (i.e., the average population growth rate) for the time-lapse interval $[3, 5]$. Identify the units for this average rate of change and interpret this rate of change.

b. Compute the average population growth rate for the interval $[1, 3]$. How does this compare to your answer in **a**? What does this imply about the population growth?

c. Compute the average population growth rates for the intervals $[0, 5], [0, 4], [0, 3], [0, 2]$, and $[0, 1]$. Discuss the trend of these growth rates.

Solution

a. The average growth rate for $N(t)$ over $[3, 5]$ is given by
$$\frac{N(5) - N(3)}{5 - 3} = \frac{76.6 - 72.77}{2} = 1.915$$

The units of this growth rate are millions per year. Hence, between the years 1983 and 1985, the population increases on average by 1.915 million individuals per year.

b. The average growth rate for $N(t)$ over $[1, 3]$ is given by
$$\frac{N(3) - N(1)}{3 - 1} = \frac{72.77 - 69.13}{2} = 1.82$$

The population is growing on average of approximately 1.8 million per year. Thus, the average growth rate from 1981 to 1983 is less than the average growth rate from 1983 to 1985. The population growth rate in Mexico appears to be increasing over the time period 1983 to 1985.

c. Computing the average growth rates over the requested time intervals yields

Time interval	Average growth rate
[0, 5]	1.84
[0, 4]	1.82
[0, 3]	1.80
[0, 2]	1.78
[0, 1]	1.75

The average population growth rate is decreasing over the smaller time intervals and appears to converge to a value close to but a little below 1.75 million per year.   ◼

The *instantaneous rate of change* of $f(x)$ at $x = a$ (if it exists) is defined to be the limiting value of the average rate of change of f on smaller and smaller intervals starting at $x = a$. For instance, in Example 1, we would estimate the instantaneous rate of change of the population in Mexico in 1980 to be 1.75 million per year. In other words, the population is growing at a rate of 1.75 million per year in 1980. More precisely, we get the following definition.

> **Instantaneous Rate of Change**
>
> The **instantaneous rate of change** of f at $x = a$ is given by
> $$\lim_{b \to a} \frac{f(b) - f(a)}{b - a}$$
> where the symbol "$\lim_{b \to a}$" is interpreted as taking b arbitrarily close but not equal to a.

How to calculate such limits is one of the challenges of differential calculus, a problem that we will tackle further in Sections 2.2 and 2.3.

Example 2   Rate of change of carbon dioxide

In Example 4 in Section 1.1, we initially approximated the concentration of CO_2 in parts per million at the Mauna Loa Observatory of Hawaii with the linear function

$$L(t) = 329.3 + 0.1225\,t$$

where t is measured in months after April 1974. We then refined our approximation with the function

$$F(t) = 329.3 + 0.1225\,t + 3\cos\left(\frac{\pi t}{6}\right)$$

Using the definition introduced in this section, estimate the instantaneous rate of change of the functions $L(t)$ and $F(t)$ at $t = 3$.

Solution   To estimate the instantaneous rate of change of L at $t = 3$, we can look at the average rate of change over the interval $[3, b]$ for values of b progressively closer to 3. From our definition for the average rate of change, we have

$$\frac{L(b) - L(3)}{b - 3} = \frac{329.3 + 0.1225b - (329.3 + 0.1225 \cdot 3)}{b - 3}$$

$$= \frac{0.1225(b - 3)}{b - 3}$$

$$= 0.1225$$

Since L is a linear function of b, the average rate of change of L is independent of b, as the above algebra reveals, and equals the slope of $L(t)$ for all $b \neq 3$. Hence, we find that the instantaneous rate of change of $L(t)$ at $t = 3$ is 0.1225 ppm/month.

On the other hand, the function $F(b)$ is nonlinear in the variable t. To estimate the instantaneous rate of change of $F(t)$ at $t = 3$, we look at the average rate of change

$$\frac{F(b) - F(3)}{b - 3}$$

over intervals $[3, b]$ for values of b values progressively closer to 3, but satisfying $b > 3$. Carrying out a sequence of such calculations yields the following table:

Interval	$b - 3$	Average rate of change of $F(t)$
[3, 4]	1	−1.3775
[3, 3.5]	0.5	−1.43041
[3, 3.1]	0.1	−1.44758
[3, 3.01]	0.01	−1.44829
[3, 3.001]	0.001	−1.44830

This table suggests the instantaneous rate of change of $F(t)$ is a little less than −1.45 ppm/month.

You might ask why there is a difference in the signs between the answers for $L(t)$ and $F(t)$. Recall that $L(t)$ only described the linear trend of the CO_2 data that was increasing. On the other hand, $F(t)$ captured the seasonal fluctuations of the CO_2 levels, which are sometimes increasing and sometimes decreasing. Turning back to Figure 1.5 in Section 1.1, we see that, indeed, in the third month of the data, the level of CO_2 was decreasing. ∎

This example indicates that a linear fit to an oscillating function may provide a reasonable estimate of rates of change averaged over several oscillations; however, it is a poor estimate of the instantaneous rate of change because that depends on the particular stage of each oscillation.

Velocity

Now we consider one of the most important concepts in the history of calculus, one that motivated much of the work of Newton: the *velocity* (considered here) and the *acceleration* (considered in Sections 3.6 and 5.1) of an object moving along a line. For example, the object may be an athlete running along a racing track, or a coffee mug falling straight down.

Average and Instantaneous Velocity

Let $f(t)$ be the position of an object at time t. The **average velocity** of an object from time t to time $t + h$ is given by the formula

$$\text{AVERAGE VELOCITY} = \frac{\text{displacement}}{\text{time elapsed}} = \frac{f(t + h) - f(t)}{h}$$

while the **instantaneous velocity** of an object at time t is given by the formula

$$\text{INSTANTANEOUS VELOCITY} = \lim_{h \to 0} \frac{\text{displacement}}{\text{time elapsed}} = \lim_{h \to 0} \frac{f(t + h) - f(t)}{h}$$

If we define $b = t + h$ and $a = t$, then our definitions of average velocity and instantaneous velocity are equivalent to the average rate of change of the object's position and instantaneous rate of change of the object's position.

If you have ever watched a track meet, you may have wondered how fast the winners ran during their races. In the next example, we find out exactly how fast the world's best 100-meter sprinters are and how their velocities change during the race.

Figure 2.2 Usian Bolt is widely regarded as the fastest person ever, earning him the nickname "Lightning Bolt."

Example 3   **The fastest humans**

Among the fastest 100-meter races ever run are the performances of Ben Johnson at the 1988 Seoul Olympics and Usain Bolt at the 2008 Beijing Olympics. The reaction times at the start of the race and the times taken to run each 10-meter split (the first split is the time to reach 10 meters minus the reaction time) are given in Table 2.1. Ben Johnson was disqualified three days after the event when the steroid Stanozolol was found in his urine.

a. From these data, estimate Usain Bolt's velocities at the end of each of the 10-meter splits during the course of the race. (For calculation of Ben Johnson's velocities, see Problem 51 in Problem Set 2.1.)

Table 2.1 Reaction times to start running (RT) and times (in seconds) take to run each of the 10-meter splits in the 1998 and 2008 Olympic 100-meter races

Split time	Ben Johnson 1988 (s)	Usain Bolt 2008 (s)
RT	0.13	0.17
0–10 m	1.70	1.68
10–20 m	1.04	1.02
20–30 m	0.93	0.91
30–40 m	0.86	0.87
40–50 m	0.84	0.85
50–60 m	0.83	0.82
60–70 m	0.84	0.82
70–80 m	0.85	0.82
80–90 m	0.87	0.83
90–100 m	0.90	0.90
Total time	9.79	9.69

b. From the data calculated in part **a**, discuss how Usain Bolt's velocities changed through the course of the race.

Solution

a. From Table 2.1 and the definition of average velocity given above, Usain Bolt's average velocities (m/s, that is, meters per second) at the end of each split can be shown to be

Velocity (m/s) at	0 m	10 m	20 m	30 m	40 m	50 m	60 m	70 m	80 m	90 m	100 m
Usain Bolt	0	5.9	9.8	11.0	11.5	11.8	12.2	12.2	12.2	12.0	11.1

b. From Figure 2.3, we see that Bolt's velocity keeps increasing until the end of the sixth 10-meter split, since all the segments making up this graph have positive slopes until this point. His velocity then remains constant for the next two 10-meter splits but declines noticeably over the final 10-meter split.

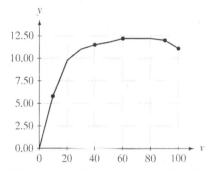

Figure 2.3 Usain Bolt's average velocities at the end of all the 10-meter splits are plotted here with values at each split joined by the solid blue line.

We have all seen objects fall for different periods of time, whether it be a coffee mug falling off a table or a peregrine falcon stooping from high altitudes. The next example uses a basic physical principle (developed in greater detail in Section 5.1) to determine how the distance traveled by a falling object changes in time.

Example 4   Instantaneous velocity of a falling object

Consider a coffee mug falling off a 32-foot ladder. Ignoring air resistance, the height of this coffee mug from the ground at time t seconds can be shown to be

$$f(t) = 32 - 16t^2 \text{ feet}$$

Determine what time the mug is halfway to the ground and its instantaneous velocity at this time.

Solution   The coffee mug is halfway to the ground when the height above the ground is 16 feet. Therefore, we need to solve $16 = f(t) = 32 - 16t^2$. Equivalently, $t^2 = 1$, which has solutions $t = -1, +1$. The only solution that is relevant physically is $t = 1$ seconds.

To find the instantaneous velocity of $f(t)$ at $t = 1$, we need the displacement over the time interval $t = 1$ to $t = 1 + h$. This displacement is given by

$$f(1 + h) - f(1) = 32 - 16(1 + h)^2 - (32 - 16)$$

$$= -16(1 + h)^2 + 16$$

$$= -16 - 32h - 16h^2 + 16 = -32h - 16h^2$$

Therefore,

$$\frac{\text{displacement}}{\text{elapsed time}} = \frac{-32h - 16h^2}{h} = -32 - 16h$$

Letting the elapsed time h go to zero yields an instantaneous velocity of $-32 - 16(0) = -32$ feet/second. This velocity is approximately -22 miles per hour! The negative sign on the velocity corresponds to the fact that the mug is falling downward. ∎

Tangent lines

A linear function is a function with constant slope, which raises this question: What is the slope of a nonlinear function at a point? To answer this question, we need to solve the *tangent problem*, and the solution resides in the following words of Leibniz quoted by David Berlinski (*Infinite Ascent: A Short History of Mathematics* (2008) Random House, NY):

We have only to keep in mind that to find a tangent means to draw the line that connects two points of the curve at an infinitely small distance

As illustrated in Figure 2.4 and stated by Leibniz, the tangent line of $y = f(x)$ at a point $(a, f(a))$ (in blue) can be approximated by secant lines (in red) passing through the points $(a, f(a))$ and $(a + h, f(a + h))$ as $h \neq 0$ gets closer and closer to 0. The slope of this secant line is given by

$$\text{SLOPE OF SECANT LINE} = \frac{f(a + h) - f(a)}{h}$$

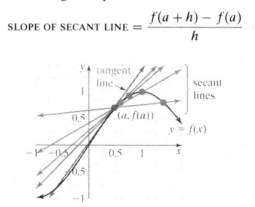

Figure 2.4 Approximating the tangent line with a secant line.

By letting h get arbitrarily close to 0, we get the

$$\text{SLOPE OF TANGENT LINE} = \lim_{h \to 0} \frac{f(a + h) - f(a)}{h}$$

where the symbol "$\lim_{h \to 0}$" can be interpreted as taking $h > 0$ arbitrarily close to, but not equal to 0. This limit may or may not exist, so not every curve will have a tangent line at every point.

Example 5   Approximating a tangent line

Approximate the tangent line of $y = \ln x$ at the point $x = 1$ using the method of secants with decreasing values of $h = 1, 0.5, 0.1, 0.01,$ and 0.001.

Solution   As a first approximation to the tangent line, for the case $h = 1$, we consider the secant line passing through the point $(1, \ln 1) = (1, 0)$ and $(2, \ln 2)$. The slope of this secant line is given by

$$\text{SLOPE OF SECANT LINE} = \frac{\ln 2 - 0}{2 - 1} = \ln 2 \approx 0.693$$

Using the point slope formula for a line, the equation of the secant line is

$$y = (\ln 2)(x - 1)$$

Graphing $y = \ln x$ and $y = \ln 2(x - 1)$ yields the plots depicted in Figure 2.5.

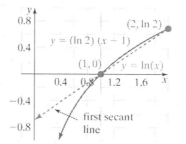

Figure 2.5 Plots of the functions $y = \ln x$ and $y = \ln 2(x - 1)$.

To obtain a better approximation, we now move closer to $(1, 0)$ by letting $h = 0.5$. This secant line passes through $(1, 0)$ and $(1.5, \ln 1.5)$. The slope of this secant line is

$$\frac{\ln 1.5 - 0}{1.5 - 1} = 2 \ln 1.5 \approx 0.811$$

and the secant line is

$$y = 2(\ln 1.5)(x - 1)$$

This secant looks like a better approximation to a tangent line, as illustrated in Figure 2.6.

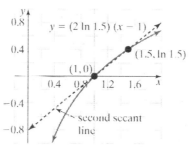

Figure 2.6 Plots of the functions $y = \ln x$, $y = \ln 2(x - 1)$, and $y = 2 \ln 1.5(x - 1)$.

To obtain better approximations, repeat the exercise of finding the slope of the secant line passing through $(1, 0)$ and $(1 + h, \ln(1 + h))$ for $h = 0.1, 0.01$, and 0.001 to obtain the values reported to three decimal places (3 dp) in the following table:

h	Slope of secant line (to 3 dp)
1	0.693
0.5	0.811
0.1	0.953
0.01	0.995
0.001	1.000

This table suggests that as h gets closer to 0, the slope of the corresponding secant line approaches 1. Hence, it seems reasonable to approximate the tangent line by $y = x - 1$, as shown in Figure 2.7.

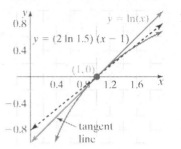

Figure 2.7 Plots of the functions $y = \ln x$, $y = (\ln 2)(x - 1)$, $y = 2(\ln 1.5)(x - 1)$ and $y = x - 1$.

We will see later that this is actually the tangent line.

Sometimes it is possible to algebraically determine the slope of the tangent line.

Example 6   Tangent line for a parabola

Find the equation of the tangent line passing through the point $(1, 1)$ on the curve $y = x^2$.

Solution   To find the tangent line, we first need its slope. The slope of the secant line passing through the point $(1, 1)$ and $(1 + h, (1 + h)^2)$ is given by

$$\frac{(1 + h)^2 - 1}{1 + h - 1} = \frac{1 + 2h + h^2 - 1}{h}$$
$$= \frac{2h + h^2}{h}$$
$$= 2 + h \quad \text{for } h \neq 0$$

The slope of the tangent line is $\lim_{h \to 0}(2 + h)$. Since $2 + h$ gets arbitrarily close to 2 as h gets close to 0, the slope of the tangent line is 2. Using the point-slope formula, we find the equation of the tangent line:

$$y = 2(x - 1) + 1 = 2x - 1$$

Plotting this line against $y = x^2$ in Figure 2.8 shows that the tangent line just "kisses" the parabola at $(1, 1)$, touching it in a single point in this case.

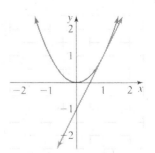

Figure 2.8 Graph of the tangent to $y = x^2$ at $(1, 1)$.

PROBLEM SET 2.1

Level 1 DRILL PROBLEMS

Find the average rate of change for the functions in Problems 1 to 6 on the specified intervals.

1. $f(x) = 4 - 3x$ on $[-3, 2]$
2. $f(x) = 5$ on $[-3, 3]$
3. $f(x) = 3x^2$ on $[1, 3]$
4. $f(x) = -2x^2 + x + 4$ on $[1, 4]$
5. $f(x) = \sqrt{x}$ on $[4, 9]$
6. $f(x) = \dfrac{-2}{x+1}$ on $[1, 5]$

Approximate the instantaneous rate of change for the functions in Problems 7 to 12 at the indicated point. These are the same functions as those given in Problems 1 to 6.

7. $f(x) = 4 - 3x$ at $x = -3$
8. $f(x) = 5$ at $x = 3$
9. $f(x) = 3x^2$ at $x = 1$
10. $f(x) = -2x^2 + x + 4$ at $x = 4$
11. $f(x) = \sqrt{x}$ at $x = 4$
12. $f(x) = \dfrac{-2}{x+1}$ at $x = 1$

Find the instantaneous velocity of a cup falling from the specified height h feet and time t second in Problems 13 to 16. Use the fact that the height of the cup as a function of time t is given by $f(t) = h - 16t^2$ feet.

13. $h = 64$ feet; $t = 1$ seconds
14. $h = 64$ feet; $t = 2$ seconds
15. $h = 4$ feet; $t = 1/2$ seconds
16. $h = 1,600$ feet; $t = 10$ seconds

Trace the curves in Problems 17 to 22 onto your own paper and draw the secant line passing through P and Q. Next, imagine $h \to 0$ and draw the tangent line at P, assuming that Q moves along the curve to the point P. Finally, estimate the slope of the curve at P using the slope of the tangent line you have drawn.

17.
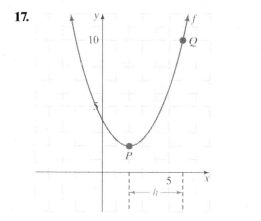

18.
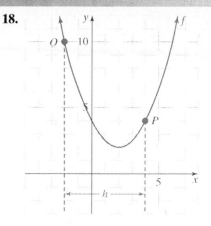

19.
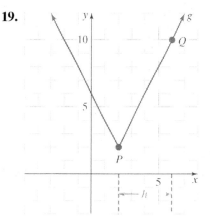

20.
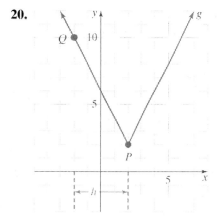

21.
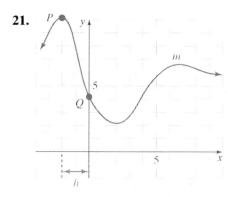

22.

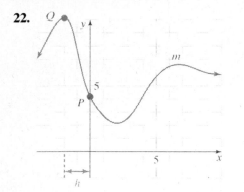

Estimate the tangent line for $y = f(x)$ *in Problems 23 to 36 by approximating secant slopes to estimate the limiting value. Graph both the function and the tangent line on the same plot.*

23. $f(x) = x^2 - x + 1$ at $x = -1$

24. $f(x) = 4 - x^2$ at $x = 0$

25. $f(x) = \sin \dfrac{\pi x}{2}$ at $x = 0.5$

26. $f(x) = \cos \dfrac{\pi x}{2}$ at $x = 0.5$

27. $f(x) = \tan \dfrac{\pi x}{2}$ at $x = 0.5$

28. $f(x) = \sin \dfrac{\pi x}{2}$ at $x = 1$

29. $f(x) = \dfrac{1}{x + 3}$ at $x = 3$

30. $f(x) = e^x$ at $x = 0$

31. $f(x) = \ln x$ at $x = 9$

32. $f(x) = \tan x$ at $x = 0$

33. $f(x) = \tan \dfrac{\pi x}{2}$ at $x = 0.95$

34. $f(x) = \ln \dfrac{1}{x}$ at $x = 1$

35. $f(x) = \ln \dfrac{1}{x}$ at $x = 0.1$

36. $f(x) = e^{-x}$ at $x = 0$

Algebraically determine the tangent line for $y = f(x)$ *at the point specified in Problems 37 to 42. Graph both* $y = f(x)$ *and the tangent line on the same plot.*

37. $f(x) = 3x - 7$ at $x = 3$

38. $f(x) = x^2$ at $x = -1$

39. $f(x) = 3x^2$ at $x = -2$

40. $f(x) = x^3$ at $x = 1$

41. $\sqrt{x}$ at $x = 9$. Hint: Multiply by $\dfrac{\sqrt{x + h} + \sqrt{x}}{\sqrt{x + h} + \sqrt{x}}$

42. $\sqrt{5x}$ at $x = 5$

Level 2 APPLIED AND THEORY PROBLEMS

Find the average rate of change of the given functions over the specified intervals in Problems 43 to 46. Be sure to specify units and briefly state the meaning of the average rate of change.

43. $P(t) = 8.3 \times 1.33^t$ is the number (in millions) of people living in the United States t decades after 1815 over intervals $[0, 2]$ and $[2, 4]$.

44. $L(x) = 20.15 \, x^{2/3}$ is the number of kilograms lifted by Olympic Gold Medal weightlifters weighing x kilograms over intervals $[56, 75]$ and $[100, 110]$.

45. The height $H(t)$ of beer froth after t seconds over intervals $[0, 30]$ and $[60, 90]$. Use the data in Table 2.2.

Table 2.2 Height of beer froth as a function of time after pouring

Time t (seconds)	Froth height H (centimeters)
0	17.0
15	16.1
30	14.9
45	14.0
60	13.2
75	12.5
90	11.9
105	11.2
120	10.7

Data Source: Arnd Leike, "Demonstration of the Exponential Decay Law Using Beer Froth," *European Journal Physics* 23 (2002): 21–26.

46. The height $f(x)$, in feet, of the tide at time x hours, where the graph of $y = f(x)$ is provided in Figure 2.9, over intervals $[0.25, 0.50]$ and $[1, 2]$

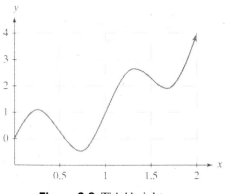

Figure 2.9 Tidal height.

Approximate the instantaneous rates of change of the given functions at the points specified in Problems 47 to 50. These are the same functions as those in Problems 43 to 46.

47. $P(t) = 8.3(1.33)^t$ is the number (in millions) of people living in the United States t decades after 1815 at the points $t = 0$ and $t = 2$.

48. $L(x) = 20.15\, x^{2/3}$ is the number of kilograms lifted by Olympic Gold Medal weightlifters weighing x kilograms at the points $x = 56$ and $x = 100$.

49. Use the data in Table 2.2 to estimate the instantaneous rate of change of height $H(t)$ of beer froth after 0 and 60 seconds respectively.

50. The height $f(x)$, in feet, of the tide at time x hours where the graph of $y = f(x)$ is in given in Figure 2.9 at the points $x = 0.25$ and $x = 1$.

51. From the data presented in Table 2.1 in Example 3, calculate Ben Johnson's velocities at the end of each of the 10-meter splits during the course of his race and discuss how his velocity changes over the course of the race.

52. The population of a particular bacterial colony was determined to be given by the function

$$P(t) = 84 + 61t + 3t^2$$

thousand individuals t hours after observation began. Find the rate at which the colony was growing after exactly five hours.

53. The biomass of a particular bush growing in a field is given by the function $B(t) = 1 + 10t^{1/2}$ kg, where t is years. Find the rate at which the bush is increasing in biomass after exactly sixteen years.

54. An environmental study of a certain suburban community suggests that t years from now, the average level of CO_2 in the air can be modeled by the formula

$$q(t) = 0.05t^2 + 0.1t + 3.4$$

parts per million.

a. By how much will the CO_2 level change in the first year?

b. By how much will the CO_2 level change over the next (second) year?

c. At what rate will the CO_2 level be changing with respect to time exactly one year from now?

2.2   Limits

In defining the instantaneous rate of change and the slope of a tangent line, we use the notation for a limit first introduced in Section 2.1. The concept of a *limit* is one of the foundations of both differential and integral calculus. Thus, we devote this subsection to exploring the concept of limits in the context of functions before proceeding to the calculus itself.

Introduction to Limits

We begin our study of limits with the following mathematically "informal" definition.

Limit (Informal)

Let f be a function. The notation

$$\lim_{x \to a} f(x) = L$$

is read as "the **limit** of $f(x)$ as x approaches a is L" and means that the functional values $f(x)$ can be made arbitrarily close to L by requiring that x be sufficiently close to, but not equal to, a.

Note that sometimes $f(x)$ may not be defined at $x = a$ but may be defined for all x as close as you like to the value of a.

This definition is made mathematically precise at the end of this section. At several other places in this book we favor informal over formal definitions, using the following statement of the historian E. T. Bell as our justification (see *Men of Mathematics*, New York: Simon & Schuster, 1937, p. 98):

To the early developers of the calculus the notions of variables and limits were intuitive; to us they are extremely subtle concepts hedged about with thickets of semi-metaphysical mysteries concerning the nature of numbers ....

Our goal is to provide definitions that make the concepts usable without getting caught up in the technicalities of formal definitions.

Example 1   **Finding limits**

Find the following limits using the informal definition provided above.

a. Graph the function $y = x^2$ to find $\lim\limits_{x \to 2} x^2$ for $x > 2$.

b. Numerically evaluate the function $y = \dfrac{x - 2}{x^2 - 4}$ to find $\lim\limits_{x \to 2} \dfrac{x - 2}{x^2 - 4}$.

c. Use the informal definition of a limit to find $\lim\limits_{x \to 0} e^{-1/x^2}$.

Solution

a. Graph $y = x^2$. Choose several values of x (getting closer to 2, but not equal to 2) and then corresponding y values. As illustrated in Figure 2.10, we can see that as x gets closer to 2 from above, the value of the function gets closer to 4.

　In fact, if we zoom in around the point $x = 2$, we obtain the plot illustrated in Figure 2.11.

　These graphs (correctly) suggest that $\lim\limits_{x \to 2} x^2 = 4$. This limit corresponds to simply evaluating x^2 at $x = 2$. This is the idea of *continuity*, which is described in the next section.

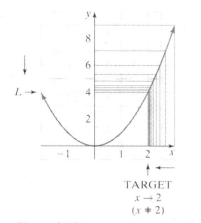

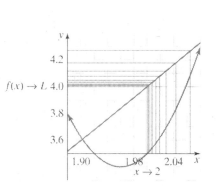

Figure 2.10 Illustration of the process of finding $\lim\limits_{x \to 2} x^2$.

Figure 2.11 Illustration of the process of finding $\lim\limits_{x \to 2} x^2$ when zooming in around the point $x = 2$.

b. The function $f(x) = \dfrac{x - 2}{x^2 - 4}$ is not defined at $x = 2$ (division by zero), so we cannot simply evaluate this function at $x = 2$ as suggested at the end of part **a**. Instead, we can only consider values near (but not equal to) 2. Since $x^2 - 4 = (x - 2)(x + 2)$, we have

$$f(x) = \frac{x - 2}{(x - 2)(x + 2)} = \frac{1}{x + 2} \quad \text{for } x \neq 2$$

Evaluating f at x values near 2 yields the following table:

x	$f(x)$	x	$f(x)$
1.0	0.333333	3.0	0.200000
1.5	0.285714	2.5	0.222222
1.9	0.256410	2.1	0.243902
1.99	0.250627	2.01	0.249377
1.999	0.250063	2.001	0.249938
1.9999	0.250006	2.0001	0.249994

This table suggests that $\lim\limits_{x \to 2} \dfrac{x - 2}{x^2 - 4} = 0.25$, which corresponds to evaluating $\dfrac{1}{x + 2}$ at $x = 2$.

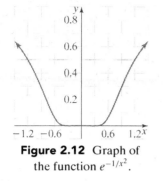

Figure 2.12 Graph of the function e^{-1/x^2}.

c. The function $f(x) = e^{-1/x^2}$ is not defined at $x = 0$. However, if x is close to zero, then $-\dfrac{1}{x^2}$ is very large and negative. Consequently, if x is close to zero, e^{-1/x^2} is close to zero. This suggests that $\lim\limits_{x \to 0} e^{-1/x^2} = 0$. We can reinforce this conclusion by looking at the graph of f, as shown in Figure 2.12.

The existence of a limit $\lim\limits_{x \to a} f(x) = L$ can be interpreted in terms of choosing the appropriate window for viewing a function.

Example 2   Choosing the correct viewing window

For the following limits $\lim\limits_{x \to a} f(x) = L$, determine how close x needs to be to a to ensure that $f(x)$ is within 0.01 and 0.00001 of L. In each case plot the function in the appropriate window to illustrate your findings.

a. $\lim\limits_{x \to 4}(2x - 1) = 7$ **b.** $\lim\limits_{x \to 0} e^{-1/x^2}$

Solution

a. To have $2x - 1$ within 0.01 of 7, we need

$$6.99 \le 2x - 1 \le 7.01$$
$$7.99 \le 2x \le 8.01 \qquad \textit{adding 1 to all sides of the inequality.}$$
$$3.995 \le x \le 4.4005 \qquad \textit{dividing all sides of the inequality by 2.}$$

Plotting $y = 2x - 1$ in the window $[3.995, 4.005] \times [6.99, 7.01]$, yields the graph illustrated in Figure 2.13. Notice that the graph of the function plotted in Figure 2.13 just fits in this window!

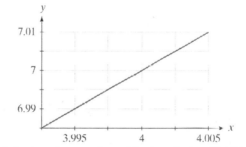

Figure 2.13 Plot of the function $y = 2x - 1$ in the window $[3.995, 4.005] \times [6.99, 7.01]$.

To have $2x - 1$ within 0.00001 of 7, we need

$$6.99999 \le 2x - 1 \le 7.00001$$
$$7.99999 \le 2x \le 8.00001$$
$$3.999995 \le x \le 4.000005$$

Plotting $y = 2x - 1$ in the window $[3.999995, 4.000005] \times [6.99999, 7.00001]$ yields Figure 2.14. Again, notice that the graph of the function plotted in Figure 2.14 just fits in this window.

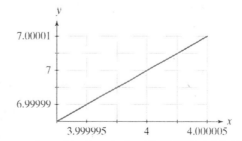

Figure 2.14 Plot of the function $y = 2x - 1$ in the window $[3.999995, 4.000005] \times [6.99999, 7.00001]$.

b. To ensure that e^{-1/x^2} is within 0.01 of 0, we need

$$-0.01 \leq e^{-1/x^2} \leq 0.01$$

Since the left-hand inequality is always true, we can ignore it. Also, since the natural logarithm is an increasing function, we have

$$\ln e^{-1/x^2} \leq \ln 0.01$$

$$\frac{-1}{x^2} \leq -\ln 100$$

$$\frac{1}{x^2} \geq \ln 100$$

$$\frac{1}{\ln 100} \geq x^2 \qquad \textit{since } x^2 > 0 \textit{ for } x \neq 0$$

$$0.46599 \approx \sqrt{\frac{1}{\ln 100}} \geq |x| \qquad \textit{since } \sqrt{x} \textit{ is increasing}$$

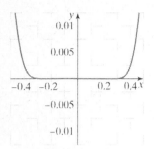

Figure 2.15 Plot of the function $y = e^{-1/x^2}$ in the window $[-0.46599, 0.46599] \times [-0.01, 0.01]$.

Thus, if we plot $y = e^{-1/x^2}$ in the window $[-0.46599, 0.46599] \times [-0.01, 0.01]$, we obtain the graph illustrated in Figure 2.15. In this case, the upper half of the function just fits the window.

To ensure that e^{-1/x^2} is within 0.00001 of 0, we need

$$-0.00001 \leq e^{-1/x^2} \leq 0.00001$$

Since the left-hand inequality is always true, we can ignore it. Also, since the natural logarithm is an increasing function, we have

$$\ln e^{-1/x^2} \leq \ln 0.00001$$

$$\frac{-1}{x^2} \leq -\ln 100,000$$

$$\frac{1}{\ln 100,000} \geq x^2 \qquad \textit{since } x^2 > 0 \textit{ for } x \neq 0$$

$$0.294718 \approx \sqrt{\frac{1}{\ln 100,000}} \geq |x| \qquad \textit{since } \sqrt{x} \textit{ is increasing}$$

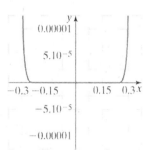

Figure 2.16 Plot of the function $y = e^{-1/x^2}$ in the window $[-0.294718, 0.294718] \times [-0.00001, 0.00001]$.

Thus, if we plot e^{-1/x^2} in the window $[-0.294718, 0.294718] \times [-0.00001, 0.00001]$ we obtain the graph illustrated in Figure 2.16, whose upper half also just fits the window.

The statement $\lim_{x \to a} f(x) = L$ can fail in two ways. First, $\lim_{x \to a} f(x)$ exists but does not equal L. Second, the $\lim_{x \to a} f(x)$ does not exist. In other words, no matter what L we choose, the statement $\lim_{x \to a} f(x) = L$ is false. You typically encounter the first failure when someone is testing you on this material or when someone has defined a function such that $f(a) \neq \lim_{x \to a} f(x)$. The second failure is more interesting.

Example 3   Limit failures

Determine whether the following limits exist.

a. $\lim_{x \to 0} \cos \dfrac{2\pi}{x}$

b. $\lim_{x \to 0} x \cos \dfrac{2\pi}{x}$

Solution

a. To understand $\lim_{x \to 0} \cos \dfrac{2\pi}{x}$, we might begin by evaluating $\cos \dfrac{2\pi}{x}$ at smaller and smaller x values. But we need to be careful!

- If we evaluate at $x = 1, x = 0.1, x = 0.01, x = 0.001, \ldots$, we obtain $\cos 2\pi = 1$, $\cos 20\pi = 1$, $\cos 200\pi = 1, \ldots$. This suggests $\lim\limits_{x \to 0} \cos \dfrac{2\pi}{x} = 1$.

- If we evaluate at $x = 2$, $x = 2/3$, $x = 2/5 \ldots$, we obtain $\cos \pi = -1$, $\cos 3\pi = -1$, $\cos 5\pi = -1, \ldots$. This suggests that $\lim\limits_{x \to 0} \cos \dfrac{2\pi}{x} = -1$.

Both of these statements cannot be true simultaneously. Lets consider the statement $\lim\limits_{x \to 0} \cos \dfrac{2\pi}{x} = 1$; this requires that $\cos \dfrac{2\pi}{x}$ can be made *arbitrarily close to* 1 *for all x sufficiently close (but not equal to)* 0. However, there are x's arbitrarily close but not equal to 0 (namely, $x = 2/3, 2/5, 2/7, \cdots$) such that $\cos \dfrac{2\pi}{x} = -1$, which is 2 units away from 1. Hence, $\lim\limits_{x \to a} \cos \dfrac{2\pi}{x} \neq 1$. This argument can be refined to show that $\lim\limits_{x \to 0} \cos \dfrac{2\pi}{x} \neq L$ for any choice of L. Therefore, the limit does not exist.

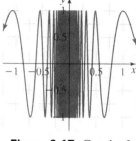

Figure 2.17 Graph of $f(x) = \cos \dfrac{2\pi}{x}$.

Graphing this function in Figure 2.17 illustrates the dramatic nature of this nonexisting limit.

b. To understand $\lim\limits_{x \to 0} x \cos \dfrac{2\pi}{x}$, we begin by noticing that cosine takes on values between -1 and 1. Hence, for $x \neq 0, -1 \leq \cos \left(\dfrac{2\pi}{x} \right) \leq 1$ and thus

$$-|x| \leq x \cos \dfrac{2\pi}{x} \leq |x|$$

for all $x \neq 0$. Therefore, by choosing x sufficiently close to 0 but not equal to 0, we can make $|x|$ as close to 0 as we want, so that $x \cos \dfrac{2\pi}{x}$ becomes arbitrarily close to 0. Therefore,

$$\lim_{x \to 0} x \cos \dfrac{2\pi}{x} = 0$$

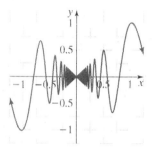

Figure 2.18 Graph of $f(x) = \cos \dfrac{2\pi}{x}$.

as the graph of $y = x \cos \dfrac{2\pi}{x}$ in Figure 2.18 illustrates. In the next section, we will see that this example is an application of the squeeze theorem.

We occasionally rely on technology to compute limits. Although technology almost always steers us in the right direction, cases exist where it drives us to incorrect conclusions.

Example 4 A computational dilemma

Consider the function

$$f(x) = \frac{\sqrt{1 + x^2} - 1}{x^2}$$

a. Use technology to evaluate $f(x)$ at $x = \pm 0.1, \pm 0.01, \pm 0.001, \pm 0.0001$. Based on these evaluations, formulate a conclusion about $\lim\limits_{x \to 0} f(x)$.

b. Use technology to evaluate $f(x)$ at $x = \pm 10^{-5}, \pm 10^{-6}, \pm 10^{-7}, \pm 10^{-8} \pm 10^{-9}$. Based on these evaluations, formulate a conclusion about $\lim\limits_{x \to 0} f(x)$. Compare your results to those of part **a**.

Solution

a. We begin with a table of values.

x	$f(x)$
± 0.1	0.498756
± 0.01	0.499988
± 0.001	0.500000
± 0.0001	0.500000

This table suggests that the limit is 0.5. Moreover, plotting this function in Figure 2.19 over the interval $-1 \leq x \leq 1$ reaffirms this conclusion.

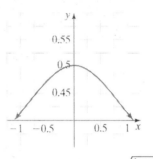

Figure 2.19 Graph of numerical solution to $f(x) = \dfrac{\sqrt{1 + x^2} - 1}{x^2}$ over the range $[-1, 1]$.

b. Next, we evaluate f for even smaller values of x.

x	$f(x)$
$\pm 10^{-5}$	0.500000
$\pm 10^{-6}$	0.500044
$\pm 10^{-7}$	0.488498
$\pm 10^{-8}$	0.000000
$\pm 10^{-9}$	0.000000

It appears that f is approaching the value 0, not 0.5. Plotting the graph of $y = f(x)$ over this smaller range of x values yields Figure 2.20, which suggests that the limiting value is 0—very strange indeed!

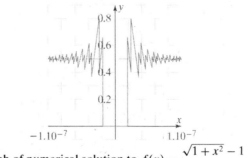

Figure 2.20 Graph of numerical solution to $f(x) = \dfrac{\sqrt{1 + x^2} - 1}{x^2}$ over the range $[-10^{-7}, 10^{-7}]$.

So we have a dilemma. Should the answer be 0 or 0.5? Later, we will develop more reliable methods that will show this limit is 0.5. Hence, when you use technology, always be aware that technology may mislead you.

One-sided limits

The definition of the limit of $f(x)$ as x approaches a requires that $f(x)$ approach the same value independent of whether x approaches a from the right or the left. In this sense, $\lim\limits_{x \to a} f(x)$ is a "two-sided" limit. One-sided limits, on the other hand, only require that $f(x)$ approach a value as x approaches a from the left or the right.

One-sided Limits (Informal)

Right-hand limit: We write

$$\lim_{x \to a^+} f(x) = L$$

if we can make $f(x)$ as close to L as we please by choosing x sufficiently close to a and *to the right of a*.

Left-hand limit: We write

$$\lim_{x \to a^-} f(x) = L$$

if we can make $f(x)$ as close to L as we please by choosing x sufficiently close to a and *to the left of a*.

A two-sided limit cannot exist if the corresponding pair of one-sided limits is different. Conversely, it can be shown that if the two one-sided limits of a given function f as $x \to a^-$ and $x \to a^+$ both exist and are equal, then the two-sided limit, $\lim\limits_{x \to a} f(x)$, exists. These observations are so important that we restate them as follows:

Matching Limits

Let f be a function. Then

$$\lim_{x \to a} f(x) = L \text{ if and only if } \lim_{x \to a^+} f(x) = \lim_{x \to a^-} f(x) = L$$

Example 5 Finding one-sided limits

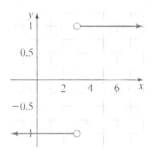

Figure 2.21 Graph of $f(x) = \dfrac{x-3}{|x-3|}$.

Consider the function $f(x) = \dfrac{x-3}{|x-3|}$. Find the right-hand limit as $x \to 3^+$ and the left-hand limit as $x \to 3^-$; discuss whether $\lim\limits_{x \to 3} f(x)$ exists.

Solution   Since $f(x) = \dfrac{x-3}{|x-3|} = 1$ whenever $x > 3$, we have

$$\lim_{x \to 3^+} f(x) = 1$$

Since $f(x) = \dfrac{x-3}{|x-3|} = -1$ whenever $x < 3$, we have

$$\lim_{x \to 3^-} f(x) = -1$$

A graph of this function is given in Figure 2.21.

Since the right-hand and left-hand limits are not the same, $\lim\limits_{x \to 3} f(x)$ does not exist.

Example 6 The floor function

The **floor function**, sometimes called the **step-function**, is the function that returns the largest integer less than or equal to x. The function is typically denoted by $\lfloor x \rfloor$. For instance, $\lfloor 3 \rfloor = 3$, $\lfloor \pi \rfloor = 3$, $\lfloor \frac{1}{3} \rfloor = 0$, and $\lfloor -1.1 \rfloor = -2$.

a. Graph the $y = \lfloor x \rfloor$ over the interval $[-\pi, \pi]$.

b. Determine at what values of a, $\lim\limits_{x \to a} \lfloor x \rfloor$ does not exist.

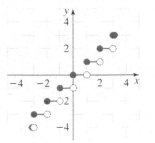

Figure 2.22 Graph of $\lfloor x \rfloor$ on $\lfloor -\pi, \pi \rfloor$.

Solution

a. The graph of $y = \lfloor x \rfloor$ is shown in Figure 2.22. Notice that the closed circles include the end point and the open circles exclude the end point.

b. From Figure 2.22, we see that the limit will not exist at integer values. That is, at the points $a = -3, -2, -1, 0, 1, 2, 3$, we have

$$\lim_{x \to a^+} \lfloor x \rfloor = \lim_{x \to a^-} \lfloor x \rfloor + 1$$

Therefore, by the matching limits property, the limit does not exist at $a = -3, -2, -1, 0, 1, 2, 3$.

One-sided limits are particularly useful when considering piece-wise defined function (see Section 1.1 for a definition).

The following piece-wise defined function describes the feeding behavior of the copepod *Calanus pacificus*, illustrated in Figure 2.23.

Courtesy Dr. David Pond, Scottish Marine Institute

Figure 2.23 The planktonic copepod *Calanus pacificus* as seen under an electron microscope. Copepods such as this are believed by some scientists to form the largest animal biomass on Earth.

Planktonic copepods are small crustaceans found in the sea. These organisms play an important role in global ecology as they are a major food source for small fish, whales, and sea birds. It is believed that they form the largest animal biomass on Earth. Given their importance, scientists are interested in understanding how their feeding rate depends on availability of resources. In a classic ecology paper, C. S. Holling classified feeding rates into three types. (See his article, "The Functional Response of Invertebrate Predators to Prey Density," *Memoirs of the Entomological Society of Canada* 48 (1966): 1–86.) The first type, so-called type I, assumes that organisms consume at a rate proportional to the amount of food available until they achieve a maximal feeding rate. The type II feeding rate was studied in Example 6 of Section 1.6.

Example 7 Type I functional response

In the 1970s, B. W. Frost, a scientist at the Department of Oceanography at the University of Washington, measured feeding rates of the planktonic copepod *Calanus pacificus* in the lab. In one of his experiments, *C. pacificus* were offered different concentrations of the diatom species *Coscinodiscus anstii*. Frost found that *C. pacificus* reached its maximal feeding rate of 1,250 cells/hour when the concentration of *C. anstii* was approximately 200 cells/milliliter (see Figure 2.24). If you assume that the feeding rate is proportional to the concentration x of *C. anstii* until they achieve their maximal feeding rate, then the feeding rate as a function of x is of the form

$$f(x) = \begin{cases} ax \text{ cells/hour} & \text{if } x \leq 200 \\ 1{,}250 \text{ cells/hour} & \text{if } x > 200 \end{cases}$$

where $a > 0$ is a proportionality constant.

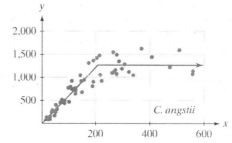

Figure 2.24 Feeding rate I (cells/hour) of a copepod as a function of the density of the diatoms (cells/milliliter) upon which it feeds.

Data Source: B. W. Frost, 1972. "Effects of Size and Concentration of Food Particles on the Feeding Behavior of the Marine Planktonic Copepod *Calanus pacificus.*" *Limnology and Oceanography* 17(6): 805–815.

a. Find $\lim_{x \to 200^+} f(x)$ and $\lim_{x \to 200^-} f(x)$.

b. Determine for what choice of a, $\lim_{x \to 200} f(x)$ exists.

Solution

a. Since $f(x) = 1{,}250$ for all $x > 200$, we find

$$\lim_{x \to 200^+} f(x) = 1{,}250$$

On the other hand, $f(x) = ax$ for all $x \le 200$. Hence, as x increases to 200, $f(x)$ approaches $200a$ and

$$\lim_{x \to 200^-} f(x) = 200a,$$

b. By the matching limit property, $\lim_{x \to 200} f(x)$ exists if and only if the left- and right-hand limits are equal. Therefore, we need to ensure that $1{,}250 = 200a$ or $a = 6.25$. In which case, $\lim_{x \to 200} f(x) = 1{,}250$. The graph of this function, along with the data as plotted in Figure 2.24, illustrates that by choosing $a = 6.25$, the linear function and constant function are pasted together in such a way that their values agree at $x = 200$.

Limits: A formal perspective (optional)

This section can be omitted by those not going on to major in mathematics at the undergraduate level. Our informal definition of the limit provides valuable intuition that allows you to develop a working knowledge of this fundamental concept. For theoretical work, however, the intuitive definition will not suffice, because it gives no precise, quantifiable meaning to the terms "arbitrarily close to L" and "sufficiently close to a." In the nineteenth century, leading mathematicians, including Augustin-Louis Cauchy (1789–1857) and Karl Weierstrass (1815–1897), sought to put calculus on a sound logical foundation by giving precise definitions for the foundational ideas of calculus. The following definition, derived from the work of Cauchy and Weierstrass, gives precision to the **definition of a limit**.

**Limit
(Formal Definition)**

Let f be a real-valued function.

$$\lim_{x \to a} f(x) = L$$

if for every $\epsilon > 0$ there is some $\delta > 0$ such that $|f(x) - L| \le \epsilon$ whenever $0 < |x - a| < \delta$.

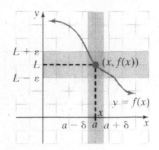

Figure 2.25 The epsilon-delta definition of limit.

Behind the formal language is a fairly straightforward idea. Given any $\epsilon > 0$ specifying a desired degree of proximity to L, a number $\delta > 0$ is found that determines how close x must be to a to ensure that $f(x)$ is within ϵ of L. This is shown in Figure 2.25.

Because the Greek letters ϵ (epsilon) and δ (delta) are traditionally used in this context, the formal definition of limit is sometimes called the epsilon-delta definition of the limit. The goal of this subsection is to show how it can be used rigorously to establish a variety of results.

One can view this definition as setting up an adversarial relationship between two individuals. One person shouts out a value of $\epsilon > 0$. The opponent has to come up with a $\delta > 0$ such that $f(x)$ is within ϵ of L whenever x is within δ of a. This relationship is illustrated in Figure 2.26.

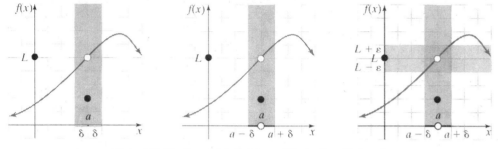

Figure 2.26 Formal definition of limit: $\lim_{x \to c} f(x) = L$.

Notice that whenever x is within δ units of a (but not equal to a), the point $(x, f(x))$ on the graph of f must lie in the rectangle (shaded region) formed by the intersection of the horizontal band of width 2ϵ centered at L and the vertical band of width 2δ centered at a. The smaller the ϵ interval around the proposed limit L, generally the smaller the δ interval will need to be for $f(x)$ to lie in the ϵ interval. If such a δ can be found no matter how small ϵ is, then $f(x)$ and L are arbitrarily close, so L must be the limit. The following examples illustrate epsilon-delta proofs, one in which the limit exists and one in which it does not.

Example 8   An epsilon-delta proof of a limit statement

Show that $\lim_{x \to 2}(4x - 3) = 5$.

Solution   The object is to prove that the limit is 5. We have

$$|f(x) - L| = |4x - 3 - 5|$$
$$= |4x - 8|$$
$$= 4|x - 2| \quad \textit{this must be less than } \epsilon \textit{ whenever } |x - 2| < \delta$$

For a given $\epsilon > 0$ choose $\delta = \dfrac{\epsilon}{4}$. Then

$$|f(x) - L| = 4|x - 2| < 4\delta = 4\left(\frac{\epsilon}{4}\right) = \epsilon$$

This process is illustrated in Figure 2.27.

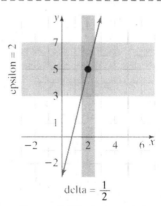

Figure 2.27 Illustration of the epsilon-delta proof of a limit statement.

Example 9   Limit of a constant

Use an epsilon-delta proof to show that the limit of a constant is a constant; that is, show $\lim_{x \to a} c = c$.

Solution   Let $f(x) = c$

$$|f(x) - c| = |c - c|$$
$$= 0$$

Thus, for any given $\epsilon > 0$, pick any $\delta > 0$. Then, if $|x - a| < \delta$, we have

$$|f(x) - c| = 0 < \epsilon$$

Example 10   An epsilon-delta proof to show that a limit does not exist

Show that $\lim_{x \to 0} \dfrac{1}{x}$ does not exist.

Solution   Let $f(x) = \dfrac{1}{x}$ and L be any number. Suppose that $\lim_{x \to 0} f(x) = L$. Consider the graph of f plotted in Figure 2.28.

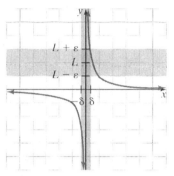

Figure 2.28 Illustration of the epsilon-delta proof that the limit $\lim_{x \to 0} f(x) = L$ exists.

It would seem that no matter what value $\epsilon > 0$ is chosen, it would be impossible to find a corresponding $\delta > 0$. Indeed, suppose that

$$\left| \frac{1}{x} - L \right| < \epsilon$$

Then

$$\epsilon < \frac{1}{x} - L < \epsilon$$

and

$$L - \epsilon < \frac{1}{x} < L + \epsilon$$

This inequality holds whenever

$$\frac{1}{|x|} < |L| + \epsilon$$

and hence will be violated whenever

$$|x| < \frac{1}{|L| + \epsilon}$$

Thus, no matter what value of $\epsilon > 0$ we choose, we cannot find a $\delta > 0$ such that $|1/x - L| < \epsilon$ for all $0 < |x - 0| < \delta$. Since this statement is true for any L we chose, it follows that the limit does not exist.

PROBLEM SET 2.2

Level 1 DRILL PROBLEMS

Given the functions f and g defined by the graphs in Figure 2.29, find the limits in Problems 1 to 4.

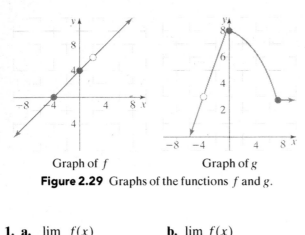

Graph of *f*   Graph of *g*

Figure 2.29 Graphs of the functions *f* and *g*.

1. a. $\lim\limits_{x \to -4} f(x)$ **b.** $\lim\limits_{x \to 0} f(x)$

2. a. $\lim\limits_{x \to 7} g(x)$ **b.** $\lim\limits_{x \to 0} g(x)$

3. a. $\lim\limits_{x \to 2} f(x)$ **b.** $\lim\limits_{x \to -4} g(x)$

4. a. $\lim\limits_{x \to 2^-} f(x)$ **b.** $\lim\limits_{x \to -4^+} g(x)$

Given the functions defined by the graphs in Figure 2.30, find the limits, if they exist, in Problems 5 to 8. If the limits do not exist, discuss why.

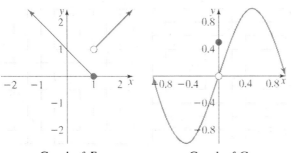

Graph of *F*   Graph of *G*

Figure 2.30 Graphs of the functions *F* and *G*.

5. a. $\lim\limits_{x \to 1^-} F(x)$ **b.** $\lim\limits_{x \to 1^+} F(x)$ **c.** $\lim\limits_{x \to 1} F(x)$

6. a. $\lim\limits_{x \to -1^-} F(x)$ **b.** $\lim\limits_{x \to -1^+} F(x)$ **c.** $\lim\limits_{x \to -1} F(x)$

7. a. $\lim\limits_{x \to 0^-} G(x)$ **b.** $\lim\limits_{x \to 0^+} G(x)$ **c.** $\lim\limits_{x \to 0} G(x)$

8. a. $\lim\limits_{x \to 0.5^-} G(x)$ **b.** $\lim\limits_{x \to 0.5^+} G(x)$ **c.** $\lim\limits_{x \to 0.5} G(x)$

Describe each figure in Problems 9 to 12 with a one-sided limit statement. For example, for Problem 9, the answer is $\lim\limits_{x \to 1^+} f(x) = 2$.

9.   **10.**

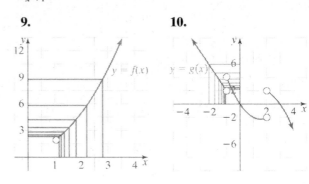

11.   **12.**

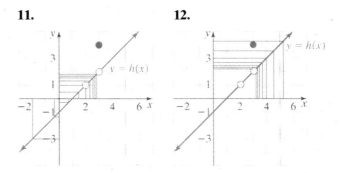

Approximate the limits by filling in the appropriate values in the tables in Problems 13 to 15 using a one-sided statement.

13. $\lim\limits_{x \to 5^-} f(x)$ where $f(x) = (3x - 2)$

x	2	3	4	4.5	4.9	4.99
$f(x)$	4					

14. $\lim\limits_{x \to 2^-} g(x)$ where $g(x) = \dfrac{x^3 - 8}{x^2 + 2x + 4}$

x	1	1.5	1.9	1.99	1.999	1.9999
$g(x)$	-1					

15. $\lim\limits_{x \to 2} h(x)$ where $h(x) = \dfrac{3x^2 - 2x - 8}{x - 2}$

x	1	1.5	1.9	1.99	1.999	1.9999
$h(x)$	7					

x	3	2.5	2.1	2.01	2.001	2.0001
$h(x)$	13					

Determine the limits in Problems 16 to 24. If the limit exists, explain how you found the limit. If the limit does not exist, explain why.

16. $\lim\limits_{x\to5} \dfrac{1}{x}$

17. $\lim\limits_{x\to-3^+} \dfrac{|x+3|}{x+3}$

18. $\lim\limits_{x\to-1} \cos x$

19. $\lim\limits_{x\to-1} \cos(\pi x)$

20. $\lim\limits_{x\to1} \dfrac{\ln x}{x-1}$

21. $\lim\limits_{x\to2} \dfrac{\sqrt{x+2}-2}{x-2}$

22. $\lim\limits_{x\to0} \dfrac{x}{|x|}$

23. $\lim\limits_{x\to0} \dfrac{x^2}{|x|}$

24. $\lim\limits_{x\to4} \dfrac{(x-4)^2}{|x-4|}$

25. Consider the function

$$f(x) = \sqrt{x}\cos\left(\frac{1}{x}\right)$$

whose graph is given Figure 2.31. Does $\lim\limits_{x\to0^+} f(x)$ exist? If so, what is it? If not, why not?

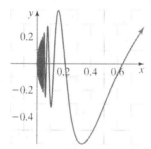

Figure 2.31 Graph of the function $f(x) = \sqrt{x}\cos\left(\dfrac{1}{x}\right)$.

26. Consider the function

$$f(x) = |x|\sin\left(\frac{1}{x}\right)$$

whose graph is given Figure 2.32. Does $\lim\limits_{x\to0} f(x)$ exist? If so, what is it? If not, why not?

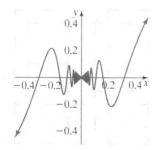

Figure 2.32 Graph of the function $f(x) = |x|\sin\left(\dfrac{1}{x}\right)$.

27. Consider the statement $\lim\limits_{x\to1}(4+x) = 5$. How close does x need to be to 1 to ensure that $4+x$ is within the given distance of 5?

   a. 0.1   **b.** 0.01   **c.** 0.001

28. Consider the statement $\lim\limits_{x\to2} x^2 = 4$. How close does x need to be to 2 to ensure that x^2 is within the given distance of 4?

   a. 0.1   **b.** 0.01   **c.** 0.001

29. Consider the statement $\lim\limits_{x\to0^+} \sqrt{x} = 0$. How close does x need to be to 0 to ensure that $\sqrt{x}$ is within the given distance of 0?

   a. 0.1   **b.** 0.01   **c.** 0.001

30. Consider the statement $\lim\limits_{x\to e} \ln x = 1$. How close does x need to be to e to ensure that $\ln x = 1$ is within the given distance of 1?

   a. 0.1   **b.** 0.01   **c.** 0.001

31. Consider the function

$$f(x) = \frac{\sqrt{4-x^2}-2}{x^2}$$

   a. Use technology to graph $y = f(x)$ over the interval $[-2, 2]$.

   b. Use technology to graph $y = f(x)$ over the interval $[-0.1, 0.1]$. Based on your graph, guess the value of $\lim\limits_{x\to0} f(x)$.

   c. Use technology to graph $y = f(x)$ over the interval $[-10^{-7}, 10^{-7}]$. Based on your graph, guess the value of $\lim\limits_{x\to0} f(x)$.

   d. Most technologies can keep track of sixteen or fewer digits. In light of this observation, discuss what might be happening in parts **b** and **c**.

32. Consider the function $f(x) = \dfrac{\ln(1+x^2)}{x^2}$.

   a. Use technology to graph $y = f(x)$ over the interval $[-2, 2]$.

   b. Use technology to graph $y = f(x)$ over the interval $[-0.1, 0.1]$. Based on your graph, guess the value of $\lim\limits_{x\to0} f(x)$.

   c. Use technology to graph $y = f(x)$ over the interval $[-10^{-7}, 10^{-7}]$. Based on your graph, guess the value of $\lim\limits_{x\to0} f(x)$.

   d. Most technologies can keep track of sixteen or fewer digits. In light of this observation, discuss what might be happening in parts **b** and **c**.

In Problems 33 to 38, prove the limit exists using the formal definition of the limit.

33. $\lim\limits_{x\to5}(x+1) = 6$

34. $\lim\limits_{x\to5}(1-3x) = -14$

35. $\lim\limits_{x\to2} \dfrac{1}{x} = \dfrac{1}{2}$

36. $\lim\limits_{x\to1}(x^2-3x+2) = 0$

37. $\lim\limits_{x \to 2}(x^2 + 2) = 6$

38. $\lim\limits_{x \to 1}(x^2 + 1) = 2$

Level 2 APPLIED AND THEORY PROBLEMS

39. The federal income tax rates for singles in 2010 is shown in Table 2.3.

Table 2.3 Schedule X—Single

If taxable income is over	But not over	The tax is
$ 0	$ 8,350	10% of the amount over $0
$ 8,350	$ 33,950	$835 plus 15% of the amount over $8,350
$ 33,950	$ 82,250	$4,675 plus 25% of the amount over $33,950
$ 82,250	$171,550	$16,750 plus 28% of the amount over $82,250
$171,550	$372,950	$41,754 plus 33% of the amount over $171,550
$372,950	no limit	$108,216 plus 35% of the amount over $372,950

Express the income tax $f(x)$ for an individual in 2010 with adjusted income x dollars as a piecewise defined function.

a. Graph $y = f(x)$ over the interval $[0, 500,000]$.

b. Determine at what values of a, $\lim\limits_{x \to a} f(x)$ does not exist.

40. In 2011, the U. S. postal rates were 44 cents for the first ounce or fraction of an ounce, and 17 cents for each additional ounce or fraction of an ounce up to 3.5 ounces. Let p represent the total amount of postage (in cents) for a letter weighing x ounces.

a. Graph $y = p(x)$ over the interval $[0, 3.5]$ ounces.

b. Determine at what values of a, $\lim\limits_{x \to a} f(x)$ does not exist.

41. A wildlife ecologist who studied the rate at which wolves kill moose in Yellowstone National Park found that when moose were plentiful, wolves killed moose at the rate of one moose per wolf every twenty-five days. (Note this doesn't mean that wolves only eat every twenty-five days, because they hunt in packs and share kills.) However, when the density of moose drops below $x = 3$ per km^2, then the rate at which wolves kill moose is proportional to the density. Construct a type I functional response $f(x)$ (see Example 7) such that $f(x)$ has a limit at $x = 3$.

42. A student looking at Figure 2.24 decided that the following function might provide a better fit to the data:

$$f(x) = \begin{cases} 6.25x \text{ cells/hour} & \text{if } x \leq 150 \\ ax + b \text{ cells/hour} & \text{if } 150 < x < 300 \\ 1{,}300 \text{ cells/hour} & \text{if } x \geq 300 \end{cases}$$

Find values for the parameters a and b that ensure $f(x)$ has limits at $x = 150$ and $x = 300$.

2.3   Limit Laws and Continuity

Having defined limits, we are ready to develop some tools to verify their existence and to compute them more readily. In some cases, taking the limit of a function reduces to evaluating the function at the limit point, and in other cases we cannot find the limit by evaluation. In this section, we find when evaluation is acceptable and when it is not.

Properties of limits

With a definition of a limit in hand, it is important to understand how the definition acts under functional arithmetic. For instance, if $\lim\limits_{x \to a} f(x) = L$ and $\lim\limits_{x \to a} g(x) = M$, then $f(x)$ and $g(x)$ can be made arbitrarily close to L and M, respectively, for all x sufficiently close but not equal to a. Hence, $f(x)g(x)$ must be arbitrarily close to LM for all x sufficiently close but not equal to a. Therefore, it is reasonable to conjecture that the limit of the product $f \cdot g$ is the product LM of the limits. Indeed, this is true and can be proved using the formal definition of the limit. In fact, limits satisfy all the arithmetic properties that you would think they should, as summarized in the following box of limit laws.

Limit Laws

Let f and g be functions such that $\lim\limits_{x \to a} f(x) = L$ and $\lim\limits_{x \to a} g(x) = M$. Then

Sums $\lim\limits_{x \to a} (f(x) + g(x)) = L + M$

Differences $\lim\limits_{x \to a} (f(x) - g(x)) = L - M$

Products $\lim\limits_{x \to a} f(x)g(x) = LM$

Quotients $\lim\limits_{x \to a} \dfrac{f(x)}{g(x)} = \dfrac{L}{M}$ provided that $M \neq 0$

Example 1   Using limit laws

Using the limit laws, find the following limits. You may assume that $\lim\limits_{x \to 4} x = 4$ and $\lim\limits_{x \to 4} 1 = 1$.

a. $\lim\limits_{x \to 4} x^2$ **b.** $\lim\limits_{x \to 4}(x^2 + x)$ **c.** $\lim\limits_{x \to 4} \left(\dfrac{1}{x} - \dfrac{1}{x^2} \right)$

Solution

a.
$$\lim_{x \to 4} x^2 = (\lim_{x \to 4} x)(\lim_{x \to 4} x) \quad product\ law$$
$$= 4 \times 4 \quad given\ value$$
$$= 16$$

b.
$$\lim_{x \to 4}(x^2 + x) = \lim_{x \to 4} x^2 + \lim_{x \to 4} x \quad sum\ law$$
$$= \left[\lim_{x \to 4} x \right]^2 + \lim_{x \to 4} x \quad product\ law$$
$$= [4]^2 + 4 \quad given\ value$$
$$= 20$$

c.
$$\lim_{x \to 4} \left(\frac{1}{x} - \frac{1}{x^2} \right) = \lim_{x \to 4} \frac{1}{x} - \lim_{x \to 4} \frac{1}{x^2} \quad difference\ law$$
$$= \lim_{x \to 4} \frac{1}{x} - \left[\lim_{x \to 4} \frac{1}{x} \right]^2 \quad product\ law$$
$$= \frac{1}{4} + \left[\frac{1}{4} \right]^2 \quad quotient\ law$$
$$= \frac{3}{16}$$

The preceding example illustrates that applying the product and sum limit laws repeatedly allows us to quickly compute limits of polynomials and rational functions as x approaches a by evaluating them at the value a, provided a is in the domain.

Limits of Polynomials and Rational Functions

Let f be either a polynomial or a rational function. If a is in the domain of f, then

$$\lim_{x \to a} f(x) = f(a)$$

Proof. We have previously shown that $\lim\limits_{x \to a} c = c$ (the limit of a constant is a constant) and $\lim\limits_{x \to a} x = a$. By applying the limit law for products repeatedly, we have $\lim\limits_{x \to a} x^n = a^n$ for $n = 1, 2, 3, \ldots$. Let $p(x) = b_0 + b_1 x + b_2 x^2 + \ldots b_n x^n$ be a polynomial. Then

$$\lim_{x \to a} p(x) = \lim_{x \to a} b_0 + \lim_{x \to a} b_1 x + \cdots + \lim_{x \to a} b_n x^n \qquad \textit{limit law for sums}$$

$$= b_0 \lim_{x \to a} 1 + b_1 \lim_{x \to a} x + \cdots + b_n \lim_{x \to a} x^n \qquad \textit{limit law for products}$$

$$= b_0 + b_1 a + \ldots b_n a^n$$

$$= p(a)$$

Thus, we have shown $\lim\limits_{x \to a} p(x) = p(a)$ for any polynomial. You will be asked to prove the result for a rational function in problem 34 in Problem Set 2.3. ◼

Example 2   Finding limits algebraically

Find the limits and show each step of your derivation.

a. $\lim\limits_{x \to 2} (2x^4 - 5x^3 + 2x^2 - 5)$

b. $\lim\limits_{x \to 2} \dfrac{x^2 - 4}{x + 2}$

c. $\lim\limits_{x \to -2} \dfrac{x^2 - 4}{x + 2}$

Solution

a. Since $2x^4 - 5x^3 + 2x^2 - 5$ is a polynomial, it is sufficient to evaluate the polynomial at $x = 2$:

$$\lim_{x \to 2} (2x^4 - 5x^3 + 2x^2 + 5) = 2(2)^4 - 5(2)^3 + 2(2)^2 - 5$$

$$= 32 - 40 + 8 - 5$$

$$= -5$$

b. Since $\dfrac{x^2 - 4}{x + 2}$ is a rational function and $x = 2$ is in the domain, it is sufficient to evaluate the rational function at $x = 2$:

$$\lim_{x \to 2} \frac{x^2 - 4}{x + 2} = \frac{(2)^2 - 4}{2 + 2}$$

$$= \frac{0}{4}$$

$$= 0$$

c. Since $x = -2$ is not in the domain, we cannot simply evaluate the function at $x = -2$ to determine the limit. However, we can factor and then evaluate at $x = -2$:

$$\lim_{x \to -2} \frac{x^2 - 4}{x + 2} = \lim_{x \to -2} \frac{(x - 2)(x + 2)}{x + 2}$$

$$= \lim_{x \to -2} (x - 2) \qquad \textit{now it is a polynomial}$$

$$= -4$$
◼

In Example **3b** of Section 2.2, we computed a limit by "squeezing" a function for an unknown limit between functions whose limits we understand. The squeeze theorem provides a general approach for computing limits in this manner. This theorem, stated below, is sometimes called the *sandwich theorem* or *pinching theorem*.

Theorem 2.1   Squeeze theorem

Let f, g, and h be functions such that

$$f(x) \leq g(x) \leq h(x) \quad \text{for all } x \text{ near but not equal to } a$$

If $\lim_{x \to a} f(x) = L$ and $\lim_{x \to a} h(x) = L$, then $\lim_{x \to a} g(x) = L$.

Example 3   Using the squeeze theorem

Find $\lim_{x \to 5} \dfrac{x^2 + (x-5)^2 \sin\left(\dfrac{1}{x-5}\right)}{x+1}$

Solution   Since $-1 \leq \sin\left(\dfrac{1}{x-5}\right) \leq 1$ for $x \neq 5$, we have

$$-(x-5)^2 \leq (x-5)^2 \sin\left(\frac{1}{x-5}\right) \leq (x-5)^2$$

for $x \neq 5$. Therefore,

$$\frac{x^2 - (x-5)^2}{x+1} \leq \frac{x^2 + (x-5)^2 \sin\left(\dfrac{1}{x-5}\right)}{x+1} \leq \frac{x^2 + (x-5)^2}{x+1}$$

for all $x > -1$ and $x \neq 5$. Define

$$f(x) = \frac{x^2 - (x-5)^2}{x+1}$$

$$g(x) = \frac{x^2 + (x-5)^2 \sin\dfrac{1}{x-5}}{x+1}$$

$$h(x) = \frac{x^2 + (x-5)^2}{x+1}$$

Since f and h are rational functions with $x = 5$ in their domain,

$$\lim_{x \to 5} f(x) = f(5) = 25/6 \quad \text{and} \quad \lim_{x \to 5} h(x) = h(5) = 25/6$$

Since $f(x) \leq g(x) \leq h(x)$ for x near 5, the squeeze theorem implies

$$\lim_{x \to 5} g(x) = 25/6$$

Continuity at a point

Example 2 illustrated how easy it is to find limits $\lim_{x \to a} f(x)$ when f is a polynomial or rational function and $x = a$ is in the domain of f. One simply evaluates f at $x = a$. When one is able to evaluate a limit so easily, a function is *continuous* at $x = a$. The idea of *continuity* corresponds to the intuitive notion of a curve "without breaks or jumps".

Continuity at a Point

A function f is **continuous at the point** $x = a$ if f is defined at $x = a$ and $\lim_{x \to a} f(x) = f(a)$.

A function f is **discontinuous at the point** $x = a$ if it is not continuous at the point $x = a$.

Example 4   **Checking continuity**

Test the continuity of each of the following functions at $x = 0$ and $x = 1$. If the function is not continuous at the point, explain. Discuss whether the function can be redefined at points of discontinuity to make it continuous.

a. The function f is defined by the graph $y = f(x)$:

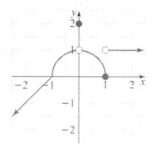

b. $g(x) = \dfrac{x^2 + 2x - 3}{x - 1}$ if $x \neq 1$, $g(x) = 6$ if $x = 1$

Solution

a. Since $f(x)$ approaches 1 from both sides of $x = 0$, we see $\lim\limits_{x \to 0} f(x) = 1$. However, as $f(0) = 2$, we see that

$$\lim\limits_{x \to 0} f(x) \neq f(0)$$

and f is not continuous at $x = 0$. However, this discontinuity can be fixed by redefining $f(0)$ to be 1.

At $x = 1$, we see

$$\lim\limits_{x \to 1^-} f(x) = 0 \quad \text{and} \quad \lim\limits_{x \to 1^+} f(x) = 1$$

Thus the limit does not exist, so f is not continuous at $x = 1$. Since the left- and right-hand side limits do not agree, there is no way redefine f at $x = 1$ to repair this discontinuity.

b. At $x = 0$ we use the limit law for quotients

$$\lim\limits_{x \to 0} \frac{x^2 + 2x - 3}{x - 1} = \frac{0^2 + 2(0) - 3}{0 - 1} = 3$$

and $g(0) = 3$, so g is continuous at $x = 0$. At $x = 1$ we see $g(1) = 6$. We cannot use the limit of a quotient law because of division by zero at $x = 1$. However, if we factor the numerator and then take the limit, we get

$$\begin{aligned} \lim\limits_{x \to 1} \frac{x^2 + 2x - 3}{x - 1} &= \lim\limits_{x \to 1} \frac{(x - 1)(x + 3)}{x - 1} \\ &= \lim\limits_{x \to 1}(x + 3) \\ &= 4 \end{aligned}$$

Since $\lim\limits_{x \to 1} g(x) \neq g(1)$, g is not continuous at $x = 1$. However, this discontinuity is reparable by redefining $g(1) = 4$.

In general, continuity of a function $f(x)$ at $x = a$ can fail in three ways. First, the limit $\lim_{x \to a} f(x) = L$ may be well defined, but either $f(a)$ is not defined or $f(a) \neq L$. When this occurs, f has a **point discontinuity at** $x = a$. These discontinuities can be repaired by redefining f at $x = a$ by $f(a) = L$. For example, in Example **4a**, we repaired a point discontinuity at $x = 0$. The second type of discontinuity is a **jump discontinuity** where $\lim_{x \to a^+} f(x) = L$ and $\lim_{x \to a^-} f(x) = M$ with $L \neq M$. The left and right limits don't agree, there is no way to repair the discontinuity. Example **4a** illustrates this type of discontinuity at $x = 1$. The final type of discontinuity is an **essential discontinuity**, which occurs when one or both of the one-sided limits, $\lim_{x \to a^+} f(x)$ or $\lim_{x \to a^-} f(x)$, do not exist or are infinite. In Example **3a** and Figure 2.17 in Section 2.2, we showed that $f(x) = x \cos \dfrac{2\pi}{x}$ exhibits an essential discontinuity at $x = 0$.

With the concept of continuity, we are able to get a limit law for a composition of functions.

Composition Limit Law

Let f and g be functions such that $\lim_{x \to a} f(x) = L$ and g is continuous at $x = L$. Then

$$\lim_{x \to a} g[f(x)] = g[f(a)]$$

The next examples illustrate why $\lim_{x \to L} g(x)$ existing does not suffice for $\lim_{x \to a} g[f(x)]$ to exist.

Example 5   Compositional limits

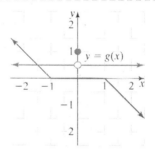

Consider the functions f and g, whose graphs are shown on the left in blue and red, respectively.

a. Find $\lim_{x \to 1} f(x)$ and $\lim_{x \to 0} g(x)$.

b. Does $\lim_{x \to 1} g[f(x)]$ exist? If it doesn't exist, determine whether you can redefine one of the functions at a point to ensure the limit exists.

Solution

a. In the graph $f(x)$ approaches 0 as x approaches 1. Hence, $\lim_{x \to 1} f(x) = 0$. Since $g(x) = 0.5$ for all $x \neq 0$, $\lim_{x \to 0} g(x) = 0$.

b. Consider the right-sided limit, $\lim_{x \to 1^+} g[f(x)]$. Since $f(x) < 0$ for $x > 1$ and $g(x) = 0.5$ for $x \neq 0$, we have $g[f(x)] = 0.5$ for all $x > 1$. Therefore, $\lim_{x \to 1^+} g[f(x)] = 0.5$.

Now, consider the left-sided limit, $\lim_{x \to 1^-} g[f(x)]$. Since $f(x) = 0$ for x in $[-1, 1]$, $g[f(x)] = 1$ for x in $[-1, 1]$. Therefore, $\lim_{x \to 1^-} g[f(x)] = 1$.

Since the right-sided and left-sided limits are not equal, the limit $\lim_{x \to 1} g[f(x)]$ does not exist. However, if we redefine, $g(0) = 0.5$. Then,

$$\lim_{x \to 1^-} g[f(x)] = 1/2 = \lim_{x \to 1^+} g[f(x)]$$

and the limit does exist. Notice that by redefining g to be 0.5 at $x = 0$, we made g continuous at $x = 0$ and, consequently, resulted in the limit of the composition becoming well defined.

Using the limit laws, we can derive some laws of continuity.

Continuity Laws

Let f and g be functions that are continuous at $x = a$. Then

Sums $f + g$ is continuous at $x = a$

Differences $f - g$ is continuous at $x = a$

Products $f \cdot g$ is continuous at $x = a$

Quotients f/g is continuous at a provided that $g(a) \neq 0$

Composition $g \circ f$ is continuous at $x = a$, provided g is continuous at $x = f(a)$

Proof.   We will illustrate the proof of the continuity property for products. All other parts follow in a similar manner. Assume that f and g are continuous at a. Then $\lim_{x \to a} f(x) = f(a)$ and $\lim_{x \to a} g(x) = g(a)$. Hence

$$\lim_{x \to a}(fg)(x) = \lim_{x \to a} f(x)\, g(x)$$

$$= \lim_{x \to a} f(x) \lim_{x \to a} g(x) \qquad \textit{limit law for products}$$

$$= f(a)g(a) \qquad \textit{continuity of } f \textit{ and } g \textit{ at } x = a$$

$$= (fg)(a)$$

Therefore, fg is continuous at $x = a$.

Since we have shown that $\lim_{x \to a} f(x) = f(a)$ for polynomial and rational functions at points in their domain, these functions are continuous at all points on their domain. As it turns out, this statement holds for all elementary functions.

Theorem 2.2   Continuity of elementary functions theorem

Let f be a polynomial, a rational function, a trigonometric function, a power function, an exponential function, or a logarithmic function. Then f is continuous at all points in its domain.

Armed with the tools of continuity, we can readily calculate many limits.

Example 6   Quick limits

Use the results of this section to find the given limits, and justify each step of your derivation.

a. $\lim_{x \to 1}(\ln x - \sin(\pi x) + x^3)$ **b.** $\lim_{x \to 4} \dfrac{\ln \sqrt{x}}{1 + x}$

Solution

a. $\lim_{x \to 1}(\ln x - \sin(\pi x) + x^3) = \lim_{x \to 1} \ln x - \lim_{x \to 1} \sin(\pi x) + \lim_{x \to 1} x^3$ *sum and difference*
limit laws

$$= \ln 1 - \sin \pi + 1^3 \quad \textit{continuity of elementary functions}$$

$$= 0 - 0 + 1$$

$$= 1$$

b. $\lim\limits_{x \to 4} \dfrac{\ln \sqrt{x}}{1 + x} = \dfrac{\lim\limits_{x \to 4} \ln \sqrt{x}}{\lim\limits_{x \to 4}(1 + x)}$ *quotient limit law*

$= \dfrac{\ln \sqrt{4}}{1 + 4}$ *composition limit law and continuity*
of elementary functions

$= \dfrac{1}{5} \ln 2$

Combining continuity theorems with the limit laws, we can compute limits that we could not otherwise find.

Example 7   Technology vanquished

Recall in Example 4 of Section 2.2, we used technology to study the limit

$$\lim_{x \to 0} \frac{\sqrt{1 + x^2} - 1}{x^2}$$

and this study was inconclusive. Now find this limit using algebra and the results of this section.

Solution   To work with the expression $f(x) = \dfrac{\sqrt{1 + x^2} - 1}{x^2}$, we need to simplify it. One way to simplify is to multiply the numerator and denominator by $\sqrt{1 + x^2} + 1$.

$$\frac{\sqrt{1 + x^2} - 1}{x^2} = \frac{\sqrt{1 + x^2} - 1}{x^2} \cdot \frac{\sqrt{1 + x^2} + 1}{\sqrt{1 + x^2} + 1}$$

$$= \frac{1 + x^2 - 1}{x^2(\sqrt{1 + x^2} + 1)}$$

$$= \frac{1}{\sqrt{1 + x^2} + 1}$$

We now turn to evaluating the limit.

$$\lim_{x \to 0} \frac{\sqrt{1 + x^2} - 1}{x^2} = \lim_{x \to 0} \frac{1}{\sqrt{1 + x^2} + 1} \quad \text{\textit{from the above simplification}}$$

$$= \frac{\lim\limits_{x \to 0} 1}{\lim\limits_{x \to 0}(\sqrt{1 + x^2} + 1)} \quad \text{\textit{limit law for quotients}}$$

$$= \frac{1}{\sqrt{1 + 0^2} + 1} \quad \sqrt{x} \text{ \textit{is continuous}}$$

$$= \frac{1}{2}$$

Notice that this value of $\frac{1}{2}$ corresponds to our initial guess of 0.5 in Example 4 of Section 2.2, based on using technology with $x = 10^{-5}$ but not when using technology with $x \le 10^{-8}$.

Intermediate Value Theorem

The function f is said to be **continuous on the open interval** (a, b) if it is continuous for each number (i.e., at each point) in this interval. Note that the end points are not part of open intervals. If f is also continuous from the right at a, we say it is *continuous on the half-open interval* $[a, b)$. Similarly, f is continuous on the half-open interval $(a, b]$ if it is continuous at each number between a and b and is continuous from the left at the end point b. Finally, f is **continuous on the closed interval** $[a, b]$ if it is continuous at each number between a and b and is both continuous from the right at a and continuous from the left at b.

Example 8 Intervals of continuity

For the following functions, determine on which intervals the function is continuous.

a. $\dfrac{1}{1 - x^2}$ b. $\dfrac{x + 3}{|x + 3|}$ c. $\tan x$

Solution

a. Since $\dfrac{1}{1 - x^2}$ is a rational function, it is continuous on its domain, that is, when-ever its denominator is nonzero. Since $1 - x^2 = 0$ if and only if $x = \pm 1$, $\dfrac{1}{1 - x^2}$ is continuous on the open intervals $(-\infty, -1)$, $(-1, 1)$, and $(1, \infty)$.

b. Since $\dfrac{x + 3}{|x + 3|}$ equals 1 for all $x > -3$ and equals -1 for all $x < -3$, $\dfrac{x + 3}{|x + 3|}$ is continuous on the open intervals $(-\infty, -3)$ and $(3, \infty)$.

c. Since $\tan x = \dfrac{\sin x}{\cos x}$ is a quotient of the elementary functions $\sin x$ and $\cos x$, it is continuous at all points where $\cos x \neq 0$. Therefore, $\tan x$ is continuous on all intervals of the form $(\pi/2 + k\pi, 3\pi/2 + k\pi)$ where k is an integer. ◾

The graphs of functions that are continuous on an interval cannot have any breaks or gaps. Because of this, the following theorem applies.

Theorem 2.3 Intermediate value theorem

Let f be continuous on the closed interval $[a, b]$. If L lies strictly between $f(a)$ and $f(b)$, then there exists at least one number c on the open interval (a, b) such that $f(c) = L$.

This theorem says that if f is a continuous function on some *closed* interval $[a, b]$, then $f(x)$ must take on all values between $f(a)$ and $f(b)$. The intermediate value theorem is extremely useful in ensuring that we can solve certain nonlinear equations. Consider the following example.

Example 9 Proving the existence of roots

Use the intermediate value theorem to prove that there exists a solution to

$$x^5 - x^2 + 1 = 0$$

Use technology to estimate one of the solutions.

Solution   Let $f(x) = x^5 - x^2 + 1$. Since f is a polynomial, it is continuous at all points on the real number line. To use the intermediate value theorem, we need to find an interval $[a, b]$ such that $f(a)$ and $f(b)$ have opposite signs (since 0 is a value between a positive number and a negative one). A little experimentation reveals that $f(-1) = -1 < 0$ and $f(1) = 1 > 0$. Hence, there must be a c in $(-1, 1)$ such that $f(x) = 0$. Using technology, we see that there is a solution around $x = -0.8$. ◾

While the intermediate value theorem allows us to prove when a function has a root, sometimes we need to solve for these roots numerically. One numerical approach is the bisection method.

The Bisection Method

Let $f(x)$ be a continuous function on $[a, b]$ where $f(a)$ and $f(b)$ have opposite signs. By the intermediate value theorem, there is a root in $[a, b]$. To find the root,

Step 1. Calculate $f\left(\dfrac{a+b}{2}\right)$.

Step 2. If $f\left(\dfrac{a+b}{2}\right)$ has the same sign as $f(a)$, then by the intermediate value theorem, the root lies between $f\left(\dfrac{a+b}{2}\right)$ and $f(b)$. In this case, rename the interval $\left[\dfrac{a+b}{2}, b\right]$ as $[a, b]$ and repeat the process.

Step 3. If $f\left(\dfrac{a+b}{2}\right)$ has the same sign as $f(b)$, then by the intermediate value theorem, the root lies between $f(a)$ and $f\left(\dfrac{a+b}{2}\right)$. In this case, rename the interval $\left[a, \dfrac{a+b}{2}\right]$ as $[a, b]$ and repeat the process.

Step 4. Keep repeating until the width $b - a$ of the interval is smaller than the desired accuracy for the root.

Example 10 Bisection method for solving equations

Given a plot of the polynomial

$$x^5 - 10x^3 + 21x + 4 = 0$$

and a calculator use the bisection method to find the largest root of this equation correct to two decimal places (two decimal places).

Solution We see from a plot of this polynomial in Figure 2.33 that it has five roots, one each, respectively, on the integer intervals $[-3, -2]$, $[-2, -1]$, $[-1, 0]$, $[1, 2]$, and $[2, 3]$. Table 2.4 presents the calculations for the bisection method for the interval $[2, 3]$, which contains the largest root. After ten iterations of the method, Table 2.4 implies that the root lies in the interval $[2.5615, 2.5621]$. Thus, to two decimal places, the root is $x = 2.56$. If we wanted to find the root to more than two decimal places, we could keep going, as illustrated in Table 2.4, until the desired accuracy is obtained.

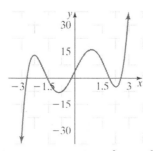

Figure 2.33 Graph of $f(x) = x^5 - 10x^3 + 21x + 4$.

Table 2.4 Bisection method for finding roots of a nonlinear function

Iteration	a	$\dfrac{a+b}{2}$	b	$f(a)$	$f\left(\dfrac{a+b}{2}\right)$	$f(b)$
0	2	2.5	3	−2	−2.09375	40
1	2.5	2.75	3	−2.09375	11.05761	40
2	2.5	2.625	2.75	−2.09375	2.882965	11.05761
3	2.5	2.5625	2.625	−2.09375	0.037423	2.882965
4	2.5	2.53125	2.5625	−2.09375	−1.112400	0.037423
5	2.53125	2.546875	2.5625	−1.112400	−0.559168	0.037423
6	2.546875	2.5546875	2.5625	−0.559168	−0.266371	0.037423
7	2.5546875	2.55859375	2.5625	−0.266371	−0.115859	0.037423
8	2.55859375	2.560546875	2.5625	−0.115859	−0.039565	0.037423
9	2.560546875	2.5615234375	2.5625	−0.039565	−0.001158	0.037423
10	2.5615234375	2.56201171875	2.5625	−0.001158	0.018111	0.037423

Equations that take the form of finding the roots of polynomials, such as the problem in the previous example of finding the largest root of a fifth-order polynomial, are known as *algebraic equations*. Equations that involve exponential or trigonometric functions, such as $x \sin x - 1/2 = 0$ or $e^{\sqrt{x}} - \pi = 0$, are known as *transcendental equations* and generally have nonanalytical solutions but need to be solved numerically.

Example 11 Limiting global warming

According to an article in the *New Scientist*,* recent research suggests that stabilizing carbon dioxide concentrations in the atmosphere at 450 parts per million (ppm) could limit global warming to 2°C. In Section 1.2, we modeled carbon dioxide concentrations in the atmosphere with the function (which we now present to higher precision to make more transparent the numerical details of the convergence process)

$$f(x) = 0.122463x + 329.253 + 3\cos\frac{\pi x}{6} \text{ ppm}$$

where x is months after April 1974. Use the bisection method to find the first time that the model predicts carbon dioxide levels of 450 ppm. Get a prediction that is accurate to 2 decimal places.

Solution Solving $f(x) = 450$ is equivalent to solving $g(x) = 0$ where $g(x) = f(x) - 450$. Using technology to plot $g(x)$, we see from the left panel in Figure 2.34 that $g(x)$ first equals zero around $t = 970$ months.

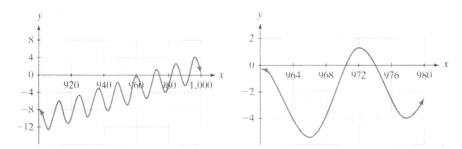

Figure 2.34 Plots of the function $g(x) = f(x) - 450$ on relatively large and small intervals containing $x = 970$ ppm, where $f(x)$ is defined in Example 11.

*Catherine Brahic, "Carbon Emissions Rising Faster than Ever," New Scientist.com news service 17 (November 10, 2006): 29.

There appear to be several zeros in the interval [900, 1000]. Zooming into the interval [960, 980], we get the right panel in Figure 2.34. Since the first zero appears to be between 965 and 972, we can set $a = 965$ and $b = 972$ and apply the bisection method, which yields the following table of values (where all the values have all been rounded to 4 decimal places throughout the calculations):

Iteration	a	$\dfrac{a+b}{2}$	b	$f(a)$	$f\left(\dfrac{a+b}{2}\right)$	$f(b)$
0	965	968.5	972	−5.1683	−2.9180	1.2870
1	968.5	970.25	972	−2.9180	−0.1010	1.2870
2	970.25	971.125	972	−0.1010	0.8705	1.2870
3	970.25	970.6875	971.125	−0.1010	0.4453	0.8705
4	970.25	970.4688	970.6875	−0.1010	0.1859	0.4453
5	970.25	970.3594	970.4688	−0.1010	0.0457	0.1859
6	970.25	970.3047	970.3594	−0.1010	−0.0269	0.0457
7	970.3047	970.3320	970.3594	−0.0269	0.0095	0.0457
8	970.3047	970.3184	970.3320	−0.0269	−0.0086	0.0095
9	970.3184	970.3252	970.3320	−0.0086	0.0005	0.0095
10	970.3184	970.3218	970.3252	−0.0086	−0.0041	0.0005
11	970.3218	970.3235	970.3252	−0.0041	−0.0018	0.0005

Hence, the model predicts that carbon dioxide concentrations will reach 450 ppm in 970.32 months, which is 80 years and 10 months, after April 1974. In other words, in February 2055.

PROBLEM SET 2.3

Level 1 DRILL PROBLEMS

Determine the limits $\lim\limits_{x \to a^-} f(x)$, $\lim\limits_{x \to a^+} f(x)$ *and* $\lim\limits_{x \to a} f(x)$ *in Problems 1 to 6. If they do not exist, discuss why.*

1. $f(x) = \begin{cases} x^2 - 2 & \text{if } x > 1 \\ 2x - 3 & \text{if } x \leq 1 \end{cases}$ with $a = 1$

2. $f(x) = \begin{cases} 3x + 2 & \text{if } x \leq 1 \\ 5 & \text{if } 1 < x \leq 3 \\ 3x^2 - 1 & \text{if } x > 3 \end{cases}$ with $a = 1$

3. $f(x) = x/|x|$ with $a = 0$.

4. $f(x) = x^2/|x|$ with $a = 0$.

5. $f(x)$ defined by the graph with $a = 1$.

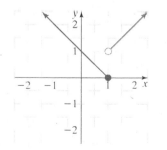

6. $f(x)$ defined by the graph with $a = 0$.

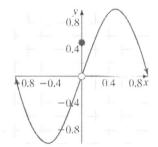

Find the limits in Problems 7 to 14. Justify each step with limit laws and the appropriate results from this section.

7. $\lim\limits_{x \to 3} \dfrac{x^2 + 3x - 10}{3x^2 + 5x - 7}$

8. $\lim\limits_{x \to 0} \dfrac{(x + 1)^2 - 1}{x}$

9. $\lim\limits_{t \to -3} \dfrac{t^2 + 5t + 6}{t + 3}$

10. $\lim\limits_{t \to 0} \dfrac{\sqrt{4 - t^2} - 2}{t^2}$

11. $\lim\limits_{s \to 3} \dfrac{s - 2}{s + 2} + \sin s$

12. $\lim\limits_{s \to 1} s + \sin(\ln s)$

13. $\lim\limits_{x \to \pi} \dfrac{1 + \tan x}{2 - \cos x}$

14. $\lim\limits_{x \to 1/3} \dfrac{x \sin(\pi x)}{1 + \cos(\pi x)}$

The graph of a function f is shown in Problems 15 to 18. Determine at what points f is not continuous and whether f can be redefined at these points to make it continuous. Explain briefly.

15.   **16.**

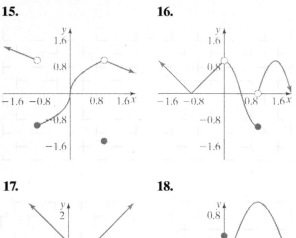

17.   **18.**

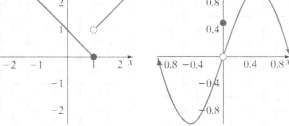

Each function in Problems 19 to 22 is defined for all x > 0, except at x = 2. In each case, find the value that should be assigned to f(2), if any, to guarantee that f will be continuous at 2. Explain briefly.

19. $f(x) = \dfrac{x^2 - x - 2}{x - 2}$

20. $f(x) = \sqrt{\dfrac{x^2 - 4}{x - 2}}$

21. $f(x) = \begin{cases} 2x + 5 & \text{if } x > 2 \\ 15 - x^2 & \text{if } x < 2 \end{cases}$

22. $f(x) = \dfrac{\frac{1}{x} - 1}{x - 2}$

In Problems 23 to 28, use the intermediate value theorem to prove the following equations have at least one solution.

23. $-x^7 + x^2 + 4 = 0$

24. $\dfrac{1}{x + 1} = x^2 - x - 1$

25. $\sqrt[3]{x} = x^2 + 2x - 1$

26. $\sqrt[3]{x - 8} + 9x^{2/3} = 29$

27. $x2^x = \pi$

28. $1 + \sin x + x^3 = 0$

29. Use the bisection method explicated in Example 10 to find the following roots of the polynomial

$$x^5 - 10x^3 + 21x + 4 = 0$$

to an accuracy of 3 decimal places.

  a. smallest root

  b. second smallest root

  c. largest negative root

  d. smallest positive root

In Problems 30 to 33, use the squeeze theorem, limit laws, and continuity of elementary functions to find the limit.

30. $\lim\limits_{x \to 1} (x - 1) \sin \dfrac{1}{x - 1}$

31. $\lim\limits_{x \to 0} \dfrac{5 + x^2 - x\cos(1/x)}{2 + x}$

32. $\lim\limits_{x \to 1} \ln x \sin(\ln x) + 3$

33. $\lim\limits_{x \to \pi/2} \dfrac{x}{8 + \cos x \sin(\cos x)}$

Level 2 APPLIED AND THEORY PROBLEMS

34. Prove that if p and q are polynomial functions with $q(a) \neq 0$, then

$$\lim\limits_{x \to a} \frac{p(x)}{q(x)} = \frac{p(a)}{q(a)}$$

35. Use limit laws to prove if f and g are continuous at $x = a$, then $f + g$ is continuous at $x = a$.

36. Use limit laws to prove if f and g are continuous at $x = a$, then $f - g$ is continuous at $x = a$.

37. Use limit laws to prove if f and g are continuous at $x = a$ and $g(a) \neq 0$, then $\dfrac{f}{g}$ is continuous at $x = a$.

38. Use limit laws to prove if f is continuous at $x = a$ and g is continuous at $x = f(a)$, then $g \circ f$ is continuous at $x = a$.

39. Why does the cubic equation $x^3 + ax^2 + bx + c = 0$ have at least one root for any values of $a, b,$ and c?

40. For any constants a, b, why does the equation $x^n = a + b\cos(x)$ always have at least one real root when n is an odd integer but not necessarily when n is an even integer?

41. Consider an organism that can move freely between two spatial locations. In one location, call it patch 1, the number of progeny produced per individual is

$$f(N) = \frac{100}{1 + N}$$

where N is the population size. In the other location, call it patch 2, the number of progeny produced per individual is always 5. Assume that all individuals in the population move to the patch that allows them to produce the greatest number of progeny. Let $g(N)$ represent the number of progeny produced per individual for such a population.

a. Write an explicit expression for $g(N)$ such that $g(N) = f(N)$ whenever $N < c$ for some constant $c > 0$ and $g(N) = 5$ whenever $N \geq c$.

b. Determine the value of c that ensures $g(N)$ is continuous for $N \geq 0$.

42. As discussed in Example 11, recent research suggests that stabilizing carbon dioxide concentrations in the atmosphere at 450 parts per million (ppm) could limit global warming to $2°C$. Use the bisection method and the carbon dioxide concentration model

$$f(x) = 0.122463x + 329.253 + 3\cos\frac{\pi x}{6} \text{ ppm}$$

where x is months after December 1973, to find the *second* time that this model predicts carbon dioxide levels of 450 ppm. Get a prediction that is accurate to 2 decimal places.

43. Use the bisection method to find the *last* time that the model in Problem 42 predicts carbon dioxide levels of 450 ppm. Get a prediction that is accurate to 2 decimal places.

44. Scientists believe that it will be extremely difficult to rein in carbon emissions enough to stabilize the atmospheric CO_2 concentration at 450 parts per million, as discussed in Example 11, and think that even 550 ppm will be a challenge. Use the bisection method to find the *first* time that the model in Problem 42 predicts carbon dioxide levels of 550 ppm. Get a prediction that is accurate to 2 decimal places.

45. Fisheries scientists often use data to establish a *stock-recruitment* relationship of the general form $y = f(x)$, where x is the number of adult fish participating in the *spawning* process (i.e., the laying and fertilizing of eggs) that occurs on a seasonal basis each year and y is the number of young fish *recruited* to the fishery as a result of hatching from the eggs and surviving through to the life stage at which they become part of the fishery (i.e., available for harvesting). Two fisheries scientists found that the following stock-recruitment function provides a good fit to data pertaining to the southeast Alaska pink salmon fishery:

$$y = 0.12x^{1.5}e^{-0.00014x}$$

Use the bisection method to find the spawning stock level x that is expected to recruit 10,000 individuals to the fishery. (Hint: For the value of y in question, find the root of the equation $y - f(x) = 0$.) For more information on the research study, see T. J. Quinn and R. B. Deriso, *Quantitative Fish Dynamics* (New York: Oxford University Press, 1977).

46. Use the bisection method to find the spawning stock level x that is expected to recruit 20,000 individuals to the fishery modeled by the stock-recruitment function given in Problem 45.

47. Use the bisection method to find the spawning stock level x that is expected to recruit 5,000 individuals to the fishery modeled by the stock-recruitment function given in Problem 45.

2.4   Asymptotes and Infinity

In Chapter 1, we introduced the notion of *infinity* and represented it with the symbols ∞ and $-\infty$. This symbol was used by the Romans to represent the number 1,000 (a *big* number to them). It was not until 1650, however, that it was first used by John Wallis (1616–1703) to represent an uncountably large number. From childhood many of us come to think of infinity as endlessness, which in a sense it is since infinity is a not a number. To mathematicians, however, infinity is a much more complicated idea than simply endlessness. As the famous mathematician David Hilbert (1862–1943) said, "The infinite! No other question has ever moved so profoundly the spirit of man" (in J. R. Newman, ed., *The World of Mathematics*, New York: Simon & Schuster, 1956, 1593).

In this section, we tackle limits involving the infinite in two ways. First, we determine under what conditions functions approach a limiting value as their argument becomes arbitrarily positive or arbitrarily negative. Second, we study functions whose value becomes arbitrarily large as their arguments approach a finite value where the function is not well defined.

Horizontal asymptotes

To understand the behavior of functions as their argument becomes very positive or negative (i.e., further from the origin in either direction), we introduce horizontal asymptotes.

Let f be a function. We write

$$\lim_{x \to \infty} f(x) = L$$

if $f(x)$ can be made arbitrarily close to L for all x sufficiently large. We write

$$\lim_{x \to -\infty} f(x) = L$$

if $f(x)$ can be made arbitrarily close to L for all x sufficiently negative. Whenever one of these limits occurs, we say that $f(x)$ has a **horizontal asymptote** at $y = L$.

Example 1   Finding horizontal asymptotes

Find the following limits involving a given function f. In each, indicate how positive or negative x needs to be to ensure that $f(x)$ is within one ten-millionth of the limiting value L.

a. $\displaystyle\lim_{x \to \infty} \left(2 + \frac{1}{x}\right)$ **b.** $\displaystyle\lim_{x \to -\infty} e^x$ **c.** $\displaystyle\lim_{x \to \infty} \frac{10x}{1 + 5x}$

Solution   To help visualize the solutions, plots of these three functions are given in Figure 2.35 over domains of x that illustrate the asymptotic behavior of these functions.

a. For x sufficiently large, $\dfrac{1}{x}$ is arbitrarily close to 0. Hence

$$\lim_{x \to \infty} 2 + \frac{1}{x} = 2$$

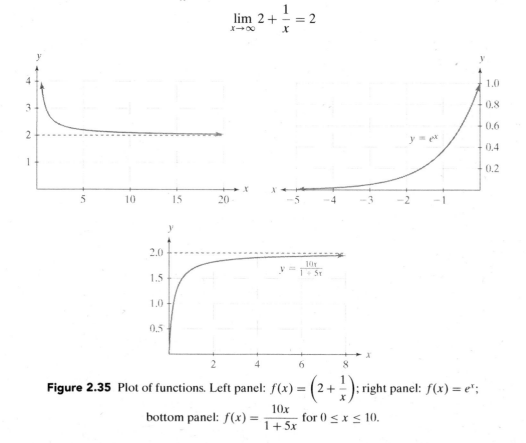

Figure 2.35 Plot of functions. Left panel: $f(x) = \left(2 + \dfrac{1}{x}\right)$; right panel: $f(x) = e^x$; bottom panel: $f(x) = \dfrac{10x}{1 + 5x}$ for $0 \le x \le 10$.

To say that $f(x)$ is within one ten-millionth of the limiting value, L, is to say that

$$|f(x) - L| < \frac{1}{10,000,000}$$

For positive x, we need

$$\left|\left(2 + \frac{1}{x}\right) - 2\right| < \frac{1}{10,000,000}$$

$$\frac{1}{x} < \frac{1}{10,000,000}$$

$$x > 10,000,000$$

Thus, if x is greater than 10,000,000, then $f(x)$ will be within one ten-millionth of $x = 2$.

b. For x sufficiently negative, e^x is arbitrarily small. Hence, we would expect that

$$\lim_{x \to -\infty} e^x = 0$$

To see how negative x needs to be to ensure that e^x is less than one ten-millionth, we have

$$|e^x - 0| < \frac{1}{10,000,000}$$

$$e^x < \frac{1}{10,000,000}$$

$$x < \ln \frac{1}{10,000,000}$$

$$< -16.2$$

Thus, if x is less than -16.2, then $f(x)$ will be within one ten-millionth of zero.

c. To find the limiting value of this function, we can divide the numerator and denominator of $f(x)$ by x:

$$\lim_{x \to \infty} \frac{10x}{1 + 5x} = \lim_{x \to \infty} \frac{10}{\frac{1}{x} + 5}$$

$$= \frac{10}{5} \quad \textit{since } 1/x \textit{ approaches } 0 \textit{ as } x \textit{ gets very positive}$$

$$= 2$$

In order to be within one ten-millionth of the limiting value of 2, we need

$$\left|\frac{10x}{1 + 5x} - 2\right| < \frac{1}{10,000,000}$$

$$\left|\frac{10x}{1 + 5x} - \frac{2 + 10x}{1 + 5x}\right| < \frac{1}{10,000,000}$$

$$\left|\frac{-2}{1 + 5x}\right| < \frac{1}{10,000,000}$$

$$\frac{2}{1 + 5x} < \frac{1}{10,000,000} \quad \textit{for } x > 0$$

$$20,000,000 < 1 + 5x$$

$$19,999,999 < 5x$$

$$x > \frac{19,999,999}{5}$$

Thus, if x is greater than about 4,000,000, then $f(x)$ will be within one ten-millionth of two.

Understanding the asymptotic behavior of a function can help us graph and interpret it. The next example involves dose–response curves that arise in many kinds of biological experiments. For example, the x axis of a dose–response curve may represent concentration of a drug or hormone delivered at various "doses." The y axis represents the response, which could be many things, depending on the experiment. For example, the response might be the activity of an enzyme, accumulation of an intracellular messenger, voltage drop across a cell membrane, secretion of a hormone, increase in heart rate, or contraction of a muscle. In the next example, dose is the amount of a histamine (measured in millimoles) administered to a patient, and response is the percentage of patients exhibiting above-normal temperatures.

Example 2   Dose–response curves

The percentage of patients exhibiting an above-normal temperature response to a specified dose of a histamine is given by the function

$$R(x) = \frac{100e^x}{e^x + e^{-5}}$$

where x is the natural logarithm of the dose in millimoles (mmol or mM).

a. Find the horizontal asymptotes of $R(x)$.

b. Show that $R(x)$ is increasing and sketch $y = R(x)$.

c. Calculate how large x needs to be to ensure that it is within 1% of its asymptotic value.

Solution

a. To find the horizontal asymptotes, we find

$$\lim_{x \to \infty} \frac{100\,e^x}{e^x + e^{-5}} = \lim_{x \to \infty} \frac{100\,e^x}{e^x + e^{-5}} \cdot \frac{e^{-x}}{e^{-x}}$$

$$= \lim_{x \to \infty} \frac{100}{1 + e^{-x-5}}$$

$$= \frac{100}{1 + 0} \qquad \textit{since the value } e^{-x} \textit{ approaches zero as } x \textit{ becomes very positive}$$

$$= 100$$

and

$$\lim_{x \to -\infty} \frac{100\,e^x}{e^x + e^{-5}} = \frac{0}{e^{-5} + 0} \qquad \textit{since the value } e^x \textit{ approaches zero as } x \textit{ becomes very negative}$$

$$= 0$$

Thus, the horizontal asymptotes are $y = 100$ and $y = 0$.

b. To show $R(x)$ is increasing, notice that

$$R(x) = \frac{100\,e^x}{e^x + e^{-5}} \frac{e^{-x}}{e^{-x}} \qquad \textit{multiply by one in the form } \frac{e^{-x}}{e^{-x}}$$

$$= \frac{100}{1 + e^{-5-x}}$$

Since $1 + e^{-5-x}$ is a decreasing function, $R(x)$ is an increasing function of x. The y-intercept of $R(x)$ is $R(0) = \dfrac{100e^0}{e^{-5} + e^0} \approx 100$. Thus, the graph of the function $R(x)$ has the form illustrated in Figure 2.36. Notice that this curve fits the data fairly well.

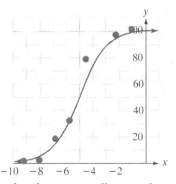

Figure 2.36 Percentage of patients responding to a dose of histamine. The x axis corresponds to the natural logarithm of the doses in millimeters.

Data Source: K. A. Skau, "Teaching Pharmacodynamics: An Introductory Module on Learning Dose–Response Relationships," *American Journal of Pharmaceutical Education* 68 (2004), article 73.

c. To find when $R(x)$ is within 1% of 100, that is when it reaches the value 99, we first note that $R(x) < 100$ for all x. Hence, we only need to solve

$$99 < \frac{100e^x}{e^x + e^{-5}}$$

$$99(e^x + e^{-5}) < 100e^x \quad \textit{after multiplying both sides by } e^x + e^{-5}$$

$$99e^{-5} < e^x \quad \textit{after subtracting } 99e^x \textit{ from both sides}$$

$$\ln 99 - 5 < x$$

$$-0.40 < x \quad \textit{evaluating on a calculator}$$

Limits at infinity can be very nonintuitive, as the following example shows.

Example 3   A difference of infinities

Find

$$\lim_{x \to \infty} \sqrt{x^2 + x + 1} - x$$

Solution   To deal with this limit, it is useful to multiply and divide by the conjugate $\sqrt{x^2 + 1} + x$ of $\sqrt{x^2 + 1} - x$.

$$\left(\sqrt{x^2 + 1} - x\right)\frac{\sqrt{x^2 + 1} + x}{\sqrt{x^2 + 1} + x} = \frac{x^2 + 1 - x^2}{\sqrt{x^2 + 1} + x}$$

$$= \frac{1}{\sqrt{x^2 + 1} + x}$$

Since $\sqrt{x^2 + 1} + x$ gets arbitrarily large as x gets arbitrarily large,

$$\lim_{x \to \infty} \sqrt{x^2 + 1} - x = \lim_{x \to \infty} \frac{1}{\sqrt{x^2 + 1} + x} = 0$$

This asymptote is somewhat surprising, as one might first guess that $\sqrt{x^2 + x}$ is much bigger than x for large x and therefore the limit is arbitrarily large. However, our calculations show that this initial guess is wrong.

Vertical asymptotes

Many functions, such as rational functions, logarithms, and certain power functions, are not defined at isolated values. As the argument of the function gets close to these isolated values, the function may become arbitrarily large or arbitrarily negative and exhibit a vertical asymptote.

Vertical Asymptotes (Informal Definition)

Let f be a function. We write

$$\lim_{x \to a^-} f(x) = \infty$$

if $f(x)$ can be made arbitrarily large for all x sufficiently close to a and to the left of a. We write

$$\lim_{x \to a^+} f(x) = \infty$$

if $f(x)$ can be made arbitrarily large for all x sufficiently close to a and to the right of a. We write

$$\lim_{x \to a^-} f(x) = -\infty$$

if $f(x)$ can be made arbitrarily negative for all x sufficiently close to a and to the left of a. We write

$$\lim_{x \to a^+} f(x) = -\infty$$

if $f(x)$ can be made arbitrarily negative for all x sufficiently close to a and to the right of a.

Whenever any one of these limits occurs, we say that $f(x)$ has a **vertical asymptote** at $x = a$.

Example 4   Finding vertical asymptotes

Find $\lim\limits_{x \to a^-} f(x)$ and $\lim\limits_{x \to a^+} f(x)$ for the given functions, then sketch the graph of $y = f(x)$ near $x = a$.

a. $f(x) = \dfrac{1}{x}$ with $a = 0$

b. $f(x) = \dfrac{1}{(x - 2)^2}$ with $a = 2$

c. $f(x) = \tan x$ with $a = \dfrac{\pi}{2}$

Solution

a. $\lim\limits_{x \to 0^-} f(x) = -\infty$ since for $x < 0$ sufficiently close to 0, $\dfrac{1}{x}$ is arbitrarily negative.

$\lim\limits_{x \to 0^+} f(x) = \infty$ since for $x > 0$ sufficiently near 0, $\dfrac{1}{x}$ is arbitrarily positive.

Since $y = \dfrac{1}{x}$ is decreasing for all $x \neq 0$, the graph of $y = \dfrac{1}{x}$ near $x = 0$ is as shown in Figure 2.37.

b. $\lim\limits_{x \to 2^-} \dfrac{1}{(x - 2)^2} = \infty$ since for $x < 2$ and sufficiently close to 2, $\dfrac{1}{(x - 2)^2}$ is arbitrarily large.

$\lim\limits_{x \to 2^+} \dfrac{1}{(x - 2)^2} = \infty$ since for $x > 2$ and sufficiently close to 2, $\dfrac{1}{(x - 2)^2}$ is arbitrarily large.* The graph of $y = \dfrac{1}{(x - 2)^2}$ close to the vertical asymptote $y = 2$ is illustrated in Figure 2.38.

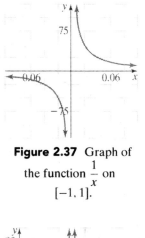

Figure 2.37 Graph of the function $\dfrac{1}{x}$ on $[-1, 1]$.

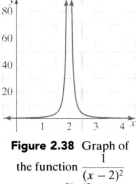

Figure 2.38 Graph of the function $\dfrac{1}{(x - 2)^2}$ on $[0, 4]$.

---

*If you want to support this statement with a technical argument, suppose you want $\dfrac{1}{(x - 2)^2} \geq 1{,}000{,}000$. Taking the square root of both sides and cross-multiplying yields $\dfrac{1}{1{,}000} \geq |x - 2|$. Hence, $f(x) \geq 1{,}000{,}000$ whenever $0 < |x - 2| < \dfrac{1}{1{,}000}$.

c. $\displaystyle\lim_{x\to\frac{\pi}{2}^-} \tan x = \lim_{x\to\frac{\pi}{2}^-} \frac{\sin x}{\cos x} = \infty$ since for $x < \dfrac{\pi}{2}$ and arbitrarily close to $\dfrac{\pi}{2}$, $\sin x$ is arbitrarily close to 1 and $\cos x$ is positive and arbitrarily close to 0, so the quotient of sine and cosine is arbitrarily large.

$\displaystyle\lim_{x\to\frac{\pi}{2}^+} \frac{\sin x}{\cos x} = -\infty$ since for $x > \dfrac{\pi}{2}$ and arbitrarily close to $\dfrac{\pi}{2}$, $\sin x$ is arbitrarily close to 1 and $\cos x$ is negative and arbitrarily close to 0, so the quotient of sine and cosine is arbitrarily negative. The graph of $y = \tan x$ close to the vertical asymptote $x = \pi/2$ is illustrated in Figure 2.39.

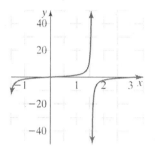

Figure 2.39 Graph of the function $\tan x$ on $[-1, 4]$.

Combining the information about horizontal and vertical asymptotes can provide a relatively complete sense of the graph of a function, as illustrated in the next example. This example, described by Francois Messier ("Ungulate Population Models with Predation: A Case Study with the North American Moose." *Ecology* 75 (1994): 478–488), examines wolf-moose interactions over a broad spectrum of moose densities throughout North America. One of his primary objectives was to determine how the predation rate of moose by wolves depends on moose density. Messier found that a Michaelis-Menton function provides a good fit to moose-killing rates by wolves as a function of moose density. Recall that we encountered the Michaelis-Menton function in Example 6 of Section 1.5 for modeling bacterial nutrient-uptake rates.

Example 5   Wolves eating moose

The rate $f(x)$ at which wolves kill moose, as a function of moose density x (numbers per square kilometer), can be described by the function

$$f(x) = \frac{3.36x}{0.46 + x} \text{ moose killed per wolf per hundred days}$$

Here, we examine the shape of the function $f(x)$ over the biologically relevant range of values $x \geq 0$, as well as the biologically irrelevant range $x < 0$.

a. Find all horizontal and vertical asymptotes for $y = f(x)$. Discuss the biological meaning of the horizontal asymptote.

b. Sketch its graph $y = f(x)$ for all x and discuss the biological meaning of the graph for nonnegative x.

c. Relate the graph to the following statement of Sir Winston Churchill (1874–1965) (quoted in H. Eves, *Return to Mathematical Circles*, Boston: Prindle, Weber & Schmidt, 1988):

I had a feeling once about Mathematics—that I saw it all. Depth beyond depth was revealed to me—the Byss and Abyss. I saw—as one might see the transit of Venus or even the Lord Mayor's Show—a quantity passing through infinity and changing its sign from plus to minus. I saw exactly why it happened and why the tergiversation was inevitable but it was after dinner and I let it go.

Solution

a. First, let us find the horizontal asymptotes.

$$\lim_{x\to\infty} \frac{3.36x}{0.46+x} = \lim_{x\to\infty} \frac{3.36x}{0.46+x} \cdot \frac{\dfrac{1}{x}}{\dfrac{1}{x}}$$

$$= \lim_{x\to\infty} \frac{3.36}{\dfrac{0.46}{x}+1}$$

$$= \frac{3.36}{0+1}$$

$$= 3.36$$

Thus, $f(x)$ has a horizontal asymptote $y \approx 3.36$, which $f(x)$ approaches as x approaches ∞; this means that when the moose density is very large, the wolf killing rate stabilizes around 3.36 moose per wolf per 100 days. Similarly (without the corresponding biological meaning) for $x < 0$, we obtain

$$\lim_{x\to-\infty} \frac{3.36x}{0.46+x} = 3.36$$

Next, let us find the vertical asymptotes. Since $f(x)$ is not defined at $x = -0.46$, there is a possible vertical asymptote at $x = -0.46$. We have $\lim\limits_{x\to-0.46^-} f(x) = \infty$ because when $x < -0.46$, but close to -0.46, x is negative and $0.46 + x$ is arbitrarily small and also negative. Alternatively, we have $\lim\limits_{x\to-0.46^+} f(x) = -\infty$ because when $x > -0.46$, but close to -0.46, x is negative and $0.46 + x$ is arbitrarily small and positive.

b. We begin by drawing the asymptotes: $y = 3.36$ and $x = -0.46$. The y-intercept is found at $x = 0$ as $f(0) = 0$. Our observation that $\dfrac{3.36x}{0.46+x} = \dfrac{3.36}{0.46/x+1}$ for $x \neq 0$ implies that this function is increasing for all $x \neq 0$. Using this information, we draw the graph shown in Figure 2.40.

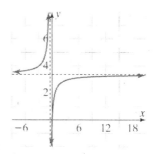

Figure 2.40 Graph of the function $\dfrac{3.36x}{0.46}$.

Looking at the nonnegative portion of this graph, we see that the killing rate is zero at $x = 0$ (i.e., moose cannot be killed if they are not around) and that this rate increases monotonically with increasing moose density. The rate, however, saturates at approximately $x = 3.36$ moose per wolf per 100 days. Biologists refer to this saturation rate as the killing rate when moose are "not limiting."

c. As viewed from left to right, the function passes from positive infinity to negative infinity as it passes through the value $x = -0.46$, which is Churchill's "quantity passing through infinity and changing its sign from plus to minus." Perhaps Churchill saw a wolf after his dinner and that's why he let it go.

Infinite limits at infinity

As x gets larger and larger without bound, the value of f might also get larger and larger without bound. In such a case, it is natural to say that $f(x)$ approaches infinity as x approaches infinity.

Infinity at Infinity (Informal Definition)	Let f be a function. We write $$\lim_{x \to \infty} f(x) = \infty$$ if $f(x)$ can be made arbitrarily large for all x sufficiently large. We write $$\lim_{x \to -\infty} f(x) = \infty$$ if $f(x)$ can be made arbitrarily large for all x sufficiently negative. We write $$\lim_{x \to \infty} f(x) = -\infty$$ if $f(x)$ can be made arbitrarily negative for all x sufficiently large. We write $$\lim_{x \to -\infty} f(x) = -\infty$$ if $f(x)$ can be made arbitrarily negative for all x sufficiently negative.

Example 6 Limits to infinity

Find the following limits.

a. $\lim\limits_{x \to \infty} x^2$ **b.** $\lim\limits_{x \to \infty} (x - x^2)$ **c.** $\lim\limits_{x \to \infty} \dfrac{x^2}{1{,}000{,}000 + 10x}$

Solution

a. For large x the number x^2 can be made arbitrarily large for all sufficiently large x, so we say $\lim\limits_{x \to \infty} x^2 = \infty$.

b. It is tempting to use a limit law here and write

$$\lim_{x \to \infty} (x - x^2) = \lim_{x \to \infty} x - \lim_{x \to \infty} x^2$$
$$= \infty - \infty$$
$$= 0$$

However, this is incorrect! Limit laws do not apply to infinite limits. Indeed, $\infty - \infty$ is not a meaningful statement as ∞ is not a real number. Luckily, we can deal with this by noticing that for large x, $x - x^2 = x(1 - x)$ is the product of two numbers such that for large x, one of these numbers is large and positive and the other can be made arbitrarily negative. Thus, for sufficiently large x, $x(1 - x)$ is arbitrarily negative. Hence, $\lim\limits_{x \to \infty} (x - x^2) = -\infty$.

c. Again, it is tempting to use a limit law to conclude the limit is $\dfrac{\infty}{\infty}$. This is meaningless. However, if we divide the numerator and denominator by x, we find (for $x \neq 0$)

$$\frac{x^2}{1{,}000{,}000 + 10x} = \frac{x}{\dfrac{1{,}000{,}000}{x} + 10}$$

Since $\dfrac{1,000,000}{x} + 10$ approaches $0 + 10 = 10$ as x approaches ∞, we find

$$\dfrac{x^2}{1,000,000 + 10\,x} \approx \dfrac{x}{10} \text{ for } x \text{ sufficiently large. Therefore}$$

$$\lim_{x \to \infty} \dfrac{x^2}{1,000,000 + 10x} = \infty$$

Part **b** of the previous example and Example 3 illustrate the subtlety of taking the limits of the form $\lim\limits_{x \to \infty} f(x) - g(x)$ when $\lim\limits_{x \to \infty} f(x) = \infty$ and $\lim\limits_{x \to \infty} g(x) = \infty$. In the previous example with $f(x) = x$ and $g(x) = x^2$, the limit of the difference was $-\infty$. In Example 3 with $f(x) = \sqrt{x^2 + 1}$ and $g(x) = x$, the limit of the difference was 0. The following example illustrates that any limiting value is possible.

Example 7   Another limit of an infinite difference

Find $\lim\limits_{x \to \infty} \sqrt{x^2 + 2ax + 1} - x$ where is a constant.

Solution   Multiplying and dividing by the conjugate $\sqrt{x^2 + 2ax + 1} + x$ yields

$$(\sqrt{x^2 + 2ax + 1} - x) \dfrac{\sqrt{x^2 + 2ax + 1} + x}{\sqrt{x^2 + 2ax + 1} + x} = \dfrac{x^2 + 2ax + 1 - x^2}{\sqrt{x^2 + 2ax + 1} + x}$$

$$= \dfrac{2ax + 1}{\sqrt{x^2 + 2ax + 1} + x} \dfrac{1/x}{1/x}$$

multiplying and dividing by $\dfrac{1}{x}$

$$= \dfrac{2a + 1/x}{\sqrt{1 + 2a/x + 1/x^2} + 1}$$

Since $\dfrac{1}{x}$ and $\dfrac{1}{x^2}$ go to zero as x gets very positive, we have

$$\lim_{x \to \infty} \sqrt{x^2 + 2ax + 1} - x = \lim_{x \to \infty} \dfrac{2a + 1/x}{\sqrt{1 + 2a/x + 1/x^2} + 1}$$

$$= \dfrac{2a + 0}{\sqrt{1 + 0 + 0} + 1} = a$$

We have shown that the limit of a difference of terms can take on any value!

Example 8   Unabated population growth

At the beginning of Section 1.4, we modeled population growth in the United States with the function

$$N(t) = 8.3(1.33)^t \text{ millions}$$

where t represents the number of decades after 1815.

a. Find $\lim\limits_{t \to \infty} N(t)$.

b. Determine how large t has to be to ensure that $N(t)$ is greater than 300,000,000. Discuss how your answer relates to the current U.S. population size.

Solution

a. Since $8.3(1.33)^t$ gets arbitrarily large for large t, we have that $\lim\limits_{t \to \infty} 8.33(1.33)^t = \infty$.

b. We want $N(t) \geq 300,000,000$. Solving for t in this inequality yields

$$8.3(1.33)^t \geq 300,000,000$$

$$1.33^t \geq \frac{300,000,000}{8.3} \approx 36,145,000$$

$$t \ln 1.33 \geq \ln \left(\frac{300,000,000}{8.3} \right)$$

$$t \geq \frac{17.4}{\ln 1.33} \approx 61$$

Therefore, the model predicts that $t = 61$ decades after 1815, in other words in the year 2425, there will be approximately $N(t) = 300$ million people in the United States. Given that the population size in January 2007 was over 300 million, we can see that the model from the 1800s considerably underestimated the future growth of the U.S. population.

PROBLEM SET 2.4

Level 1 DRILL PROBLEMS

In Problems 1 to 24, find the specified limits.

1. $\lim\limits_{x \to -\infty} e^x$

2. $\lim\limits_{x \to 0^+} \ln x$

3. $\lim\limits_{x \to 2^+} \dfrac{1}{x - 2}$

4. $\lim\limits_{x \to 2^-} \dfrac{1}{x - 2}$

5. $\lim\limits_{x \to 3^-} \left(3 + \dfrac{2x}{x - 3} \right)$

6. $\lim\limits_{x \to \infty} \sin x$

7. $\lim\limits_{x \to 3^+} \left(3 + \dfrac{2x}{x - 3} \right)$

8. $\lim\limits_{x \to 1^-} \dfrac{x - 1}{|x^2 - 1|}$

9. $\lim\limits_{x \to 3^+} \dfrac{x^2 - 4x + 3}{x^2 - 6x + 9}$

10. $\lim\limits_{x \to \infty} \dfrac{x^3}{1 + x^3}$

11. $\lim\limits_{x \to \infty} \cos x^2$

12. $\lim\limits_{x \to -\infty} \dfrac{x^3}{1 + x^3}$

13. $\lim\limits_{x \to \infty} \dfrac{(2x + 5)(x - 2)}{(7x - 2)(3x + 1)}$

14. $\lim\limits_{x \to \infty} \dfrac{(2x^2 - 5x + 7)}{x^2 - 9}$

15. $\lim\limits_{x \to \infty} \dfrac{\sin x}{1 + x}$

16. $\lim\limits_{Q \to \infty} \dfrac{aQ^2 + Q}{1 - Q^2}$ where a is a constant.

17. $\lim\limits_{x \to \infty} \dfrac{Ae^x + 3}{Be^{2x} + 4}$ where $A > 0$ and $B > 0$ are constants.

18. $\lim\limits_{x \to -\infty} \dfrac{1 + ax + 3x^3}{1 + 5x - 5x^3}$ where a is a constant.

19. $\lim\limits_{x \to \infty} \dfrac{1 + 5e^{ax}}{7 + 2e^{ax}}$ where $a > 0$ is a constant.

20. $\lim\limits_{x \to \infty} \dfrac{1 + 5e^{ax}}{7 + 2e^{ax}}$ where $a < 0$ is a constant.

21. $\lim\limits_{x \to \infty} \sqrt{x + 1} - \sqrt{x}$

22. $\lim\limits_{x \to \infty} x - \sqrt{x}$

23. $\lim\limits_{x \to \infty} \sqrt{x^4 + ax^2 + x + 1} - x^2$

24. $\lim\limits_{x \to -\infty} \sqrt{x^2 + 1} + x$

For $\lim\limits_{x \to a^+} f(x)$ in Problems 25 to 30, determine how close $x > a$ needs to be to a to ensure that $f(x) \geq 1,000,000.$

25. $\lim\limits_{x \to 2^+} \dfrac{1}{x - 2}$

26. $\lim\limits_{x \to 0^+} \ln \dfrac{1}{x}$

27. $\lim\limits_{x \to 1^-} \dfrac{1}{1 - x}$

28. $\lim\limits_{x \to 3^+} \dfrac{1}{(x - 3)^2}$

29. $\lim\limits_{x \to 1^-} \dfrac{-1}{\sin x}$

30. $\lim\limits_{x \to 1^-} \ln \dfrac{1}{x - 1}$

For $\lim\limits_{x \to -\infty} f(x) = L$ in Problems 31 to 34, determine how negative x needs to be to ensure that $|f(x) - L| \le 0.05$.

31. $\lim\limits_{x \to -\infty} \dfrac{1}{x^2} = 0$

32. $\lim\limits_{x \to -\infty} (e^x + 5) = 5$

33. $\lim\limits_{x \to -\infty} \dfrac{x}{1+x} = 1$

34. $\lim\limits_{x \to -\infty} \dfrac{1}{\ln x^2} = 0$

For the limit $\lim\limits_{x \to \infty} f(x) = \infty$ in Problems 35 to 38, determine how large x needs to be to ensure that $f(x) > 1{,}000{,}000$.

35. $\lim\limits_{x \to \infty} x^2$

36. $\lim\limits_{x \to \infty} (e^x + 5)$

37. $\lim\limits_{x \to \infty} \dfrac{x^2}{1+x}$

38. $\lim\limits_{x \to \infty} \ln x$

Level 2 APPLIED AND THEORY PROBLEMS

39. In Example 8, we showed that $\lim\limits_{t \to \infty} N(t) = \infty$ where $N(t) = 8.3(1.33)^t$ represents U.S. population size in millions t decades after 1815. To see that $N(t)$ can get arbitrarily large for x sufficiently large, do the following:

    a. Determine how large t needs to be to ensure that $N(t) \ge 500{,}000{,}000$.

    b. Determine how large t needs to be to ensure that $N(t) \ge 1{,}000{,}000{,}000$.

40. In Example 5 of Section 1.4, we modeled the height of beer froth with the function $H(t) = 17(0.99588)^t$ cm where t is measured in seconds.

    a. Determine L such that $\lim\limits_{t \to \infty} H(t) = L$.

    b. Determine how large t needs to be to ensure that $H(t)$ is within 0.1 of L.

    c. Determine how large t needs to be to ensure that $H(t)$ is within 0.01 of L.

41. In Example 6 of Section 1.5, we modeled the uptake rate of glucose by bacterial populations with the function $f(x) = \dfrac{1.2708x}{1 + 0.0506x}$ mg per hour where x is measured in milligrams per liter.

    a. Find the horizontal and vertical asymptotes of $f(x)$. Interpret the horizontal asymptote(s).

    b. Graph $f(x)$ for all values of x.

42. In Example 5, we examined how the predation rate of wolves depended on moose density. Messier also studied how wolf densities in North America depend on moose densities. He found that the

following function provides a good fit to the data:

$$f(x) = \frac{58.7(x - 0.03)}{0.76 + x} \text{ wolves per } 1{,}000 \text{ km}^2$$

where x is number of moose per square kilometer.

    a. Find the horizontal and vertical asymptotes of $f(x)$. Interpret the horizontal asymptotes.

    b. Graph $f(x)$ for all values of $x > 0$.

43. In Problem 42, you were asked to find L such that $\lim\limits_{x \to \infty} f(x) = L$.

    a. Determine how large x needs to be to ensure that $f(x)$ is within 0.1 of L.

    b. Determine how large x needs to be to ensure that $f(x)$ is within 0.01 of L.

44. The von Bertalanffy growth curve is used to describe how the size L (usually in terms of length) of an animal changes with time. The curve is given by

$$L(t) = a(1 - e^{-b(t - t_0)})$$

where t measures time after birth and a, b, and t_0 are positive parameters. We will derive this curve in Chapter 6. To better understand the meaning of the parameters t_0 and b, carry out these steps.

    a. Evaluate $L(t_0)$. What does this imply about the meaning of t_0?

    b. Find $\lim\limits_{t \to \infty} L(t)$. What does this limit say about the biological meaning of a?

    c. Graph $L(t)$ and discuss how an organism grows according to this curve.

45. At the beginning of the twentieth century, several notable biologists, including G. F. Gause and T. Carlson, studied the population dynamics of yeast. For example, Carlson grew yeast under constant environmental conditions in a flask; he regularly monitored their population densities.* In Chapter 6, we will show that the following function describes the growth of the population:

$$N(t) = \frac{9.7417e^{0.53t}}{1 + 0.01476e^{0.53t}}$$

where $N(t)$ is the population density and t is time in hours. Find $\lim\limits_{t \to \infty} N(t)$ and discuss the meaning of this limit.

46. The following equation is used to calculate the average firing rate f of a neuron (in spikes per second) as a function of the concentration x of neurotransmitters perfusing its synapses.

$$f(x) = \frac{20e^{3x}}{2.1 + e^{3x}}$$

*T. Carlson, "Über Geschwindigkeit und Größe der Hefevermehrung in Würze," *Biochem* Z57 (1913): 313–334.

Find the horizontal asymptote; then find the values of x such that $f(x)$ is within 0.5% of its asymptotic values.

47. The following equation is used to calculate the average firing rate f of a neuron (in spikes per second) as a function of the concentration x of neurotransmitters perfusing its synapses.

$$f(x) = \frac{16e^{5x}}{3.2 + e^{5x}}$$

Find the values of x such that $f(x)$ is within 0.5% of its asymptotic values.

48. Compare the solutions obtained to Problems 46 and 47 and decide which of these represents a tighter on-off switch of the neuron, that is, from firing at its maximum rate to being inactive. What do you conclude in terms of which of the parameters a, b, and c in the function

$$f(x) = \frac{ae^{cx}}{b + e^{cx}}$$

controls the narrowness of the range of x over which on-off switching occurs? Note that this function is called the *logistic function* and will be encountered in many different examples in upcoming chapters.

2.5   Sequential Limits

In Section 1.7, we considered sequences $a_1, a_2, \ldots$ of real numbers, which can be used to model drug concentrations, population dynamics, and population genetics. In some cases, these sequences converged to a limiting value as n got very large. In this section, we study the limits of sequences, their relationship to continuity, and a convergence theorem, as well as how these concepts can be used to understand the asymptotic behavior of difference equations. While limits of functions form the basis of differentiation as we shall soon see, limits of sequences form the basis of integration (as we will discuss in Chapter 5).

Sequential limits and continuity

For sequences, there is only one type of limit to consider: the **sequential limit**, defined as the limiting value of a_n as $n \to \infty$.

Sequential Limits (Informal Definition)

Let $a_1, a_2, a_3, \ldots$ be a sequence. We write

$$\lim_{n \to \infty} a_n = L$$

provided that we can make a_n arbitrarily close to L for all n sufficiently large. In this case, we say the sequence converges to L.

We write

$$\lim_{n \to \infty} a_n = \infty$$

provided that we can make $a_n > 0$ arbitrarily large for all n sufficiently large.

We write

$$\lim_{n \to \infty} a_n = -\infty$$

provided that we can make a_n arbitrarily negative for all n sufficiently large.

Example 1   **Finding sequential limits**

In each of the following, if it exists, calculate $\lim_{n \to \infty} a_n$ where

a. $a_n = 2^n$ **b.** $a_n = 1 + \dfrac{1}{n}$ **c.** $a_n = \dfrac{2n^2 + 3n - 1}{5n^2 - n + 8}$

d. $a_n = \cos\dfrac{n\pi}{2}$ **e.** $a_n = \dfrac{1}{n}\cos\dfrac{n\pi}{2}$

Solution

a. Since 2^n gets arbitrarily large as n gets arbitrarily large, $\lim\limits_{n\to\infty} 2^n = \infty$.

b. Since $\dfrac{1}{n}$ approaches zero as n gets arbitrarily large, $\lim\limits_{n\to\infty} 1 + \dfrac{1}{n} = 1$.

c. Since the numerator and denominator are polynomials in n, we divide the numerator and denominator by the term with largest exponent, namely, n^2.

$$\lim\limits_{n\to\infty} \frac{2n^2 + 3n - 1}{5n^2 - n + 8} = \lim\limits_{n\to\infty} \frac{2n^2 + 3n - 1}{5n^2 - n + 8} \times \frac{\frac{1}{n^2}}{\frac{1}{n^2}}$$

$$= \lim\limits_{n\to\infty} \frac{2 + \frac{3}{n} - \frac{1}{n^2}}{5 - \frac{1}{n} + \frac{8}{n^2}}$$

$$= \frac{2}{5}$$

d. Since $\cos\dfrac{n\pi}{2}$ alternates between the values 0, 1, and -1, this sequence does not have a limit. There is no unique value that the sequence approaches.

e. Since $\left|\dfrac{1}{n}\cos\dfrac{n\pi}{2}\right| \le \dfrac{1}{n}$ and we can make $\dfrac{1}{n}$ arbitrarily close to 0 for n sufficiently large,

$$\lim\limits_{n\to\infty} \frac{1}{n}\cos\frac{n\pi}{2} = 0$$

Graphing this sequence, illustrated in the figure below, confirms this convergence to zero.

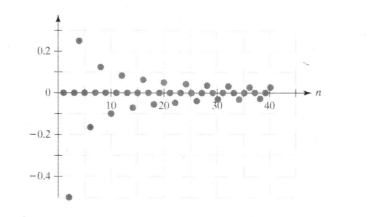

As in our previous limit definitions, the existence of a sequential limit implies that we can make a_n as close to L as we like, provided that n is sufficiently large. But how do we verify this statement? What is meant by *sufficiently large?* The following example illustrates the answer to this question.

Example 2   **Finding sufficiently large n**

Consider $a_n = \dfrac{n}{2 + n}$.

a. Find $\lim\limits_{n\to\infty} a_n = L$.

b. Determine how large n needs to be to ensure that $|a_n - L| < 0.002$.

Solution

a. Dividing the numerator and denominator by n yields

$$\lim_{n\to\infty} \frac{n}{2+n} = \lim_{n\to\infty} \frac{1}{2/n+1}$$
$$= 1$$

Hence, $L = 1$.

b. We want that

$$\left|\frac{n}{2+n} - 1\right| < 0.002 \qquad \textit{this is } |a_n - L| < 0.002$$

$$\left|\frac{n}{2+n} - \frac{2+n}{2+n}\right| < 0.002$$

$$\left|\frac{-2}{2+n}\right| < 0.002$$

$$\frac{2}{2+n} < 0.002 \qquad \textit{absolute value of a negative divided by a positive number}$$

$$\frac{2}{0.002} < 2+n \qquad \textit{multiply both sides by } 2+n, \textit{ and divide both sides by 0.002}$$

$$998 < n \qquad \textit{simplify and subtract 2 from both sides}$$

The number n must be greater than 998.   ▪

There is an important relationship between limits of sequences and limits of functions. This relationship is most useful for proving discontinuity of a function.

Theorem 2.4   **Sequential continuity theorem**

Let f be a function. Then $\lim_{x\to a} f(x) = L$ if and only if $\lim_{n\to\infty} f(a_n) = L$ for any sequence satisfying $\lim_{n\to\infty} a_n = a$.

One direction of this theorem is clear. If $\lim_{n\to\infty} a_n = a$, then a_n can be made arbitrarily close to a for n sufficiently large. Therefore, if $\lim_{x\to a} f(x) = L$, then $f(a_n)$ is arbitrarily close to L for n sufficiently large. Hence, if $\lim_{x\to a} f(x) = L$, then $\lim_{n\to\infty} f(a_n) = L$. If you are feeling sufficiently adventuresome, try proving this direction using formal definitions of limits. To do so, you will have to come up with a formal definition of sequential limits. The other direction of the sequential continuity theorem is more subtle, and the ideas of the proof are beyond the scope of this text.

Example 3   **Proving nonexistence of limits**

Show that $\lim_{x\to 0} \sin \frac{1}{x}$ does not exist.

Solution   Let $f(x) = \sin\frac{1}{x}$. Our goal is to find two sequences a_n and b_n satisfying $\lim_{n\to\infty} a_n = a$ and $\lim_{n\to\infty} b_n = a$, but $\lim_{n\to\infty} f(a_n) = L$ and $\lim_{n\to\infty} f(b_n) = M$ with $L \neq M$. Then, we can apply the sequential continuity theorem to conclude that the limit $\lim_{x\to a} f(x)$ does not exist. For this example, we let $a_n = \frac{1}{\pi n}$ and $b_n = \frac{2}{\pi(4n+1)}$. Then,

$$\lim_{n\to\infty} \frac{1}{\pi n} = 0 \qquad \text{and} \qquad \lim_{n\to\infty} \frac{2}{\pi(4n+1)} = 0$$

We now find the limits of $f(a_n)$ and $f(b_n)$:

$$\lim_{n\to\infty} f(a_n) = \lim_{n\to\infty} \sin\frac{1}{a_n} = \lim_{n\to\infty} \sin(\pi n) = 0$$

and

$$\lim_{n\to\infty} f(b_n) = \lim_{n\to\infty} \sin\frac{1}{b_n} = \lim_{n\to\infty} \sin\left[\frac{\pi(4n+1)}{2}\right] = 1$$

Since $\lim_{n\to\infty} f(a_n) \neq \lim_{n\to\infty} f(b_n)$, it follows (from the sequential continuity theorem) that $\lim_{x\to 0} \sin\frac{1}{x}$ does not exist because it cannot be equal to both 0 and 1 at the same time. ∎

Asymptotic behavior of difference equations

When we introduced sequences in Section 1.7, we considered a special class of sequences that arises through a difference equation

$$a_{n+1} = f(a_n)$$

where a_1 is specified and f is a function. In some instances, we can actually find explicit expressions for the sequence defined by the difference equation and take the limit.

Example 4   Finding the limit of a sequence

Find an explicit expression for the sequences defined by the following difference equations and find the limit as n becomes large.

a. $a_{n+1} = 0.1a_n$ with $a_1 = 0.1$ **b.** $a_{n+1} = \sqrt{a_n}$ with $a_1 = 2$

Solution

a. We have $a_1 = 0.1$, $a_2 = 0.1a_1 = 0.1^2$, and $a_3 = 0.1a_2 = 0.1^3$. Hence, we can see inductively that $a_n = 0.1^n$. Since a_n gets arbitrarily small as n gets sufficiently large, we obtain $\lim_{n\to\infty} a_n = 0$.

b. We have, $a_1 = \sqrt{2} = 2^{1/2}$, $a_2 = a_1^{1/2} = 2^{1/4}$, $a_3 = a_2^{1/2} = 2^{1/8}$, $\ldots$, $a_n = a_{n-1}^{1/2} = 2^{1/2^n}$. To find this limit, consider the logarithm of this sequence, that is,

$$\ln a_n = \frac{\ln 2}{2^n}$$

Clearly, $\lim_{n\to\infty} \ln a_n = 0$. Thus, by the continuity of e^x and the sequential continuity theorem, we get that

$$\lim_{n\to\infty} a_n = \lim_{n\to\infty} e^{\ln a_n} = e^{\lim_{n\to\infty} \ln a_n} = e^0 = 1$$ ∎

In part **b** of Example 4, we saw that sometimes it is useful to find $\lim_{n\to\infty} a_n$ by finding $\lim_{n\to\infty} f(a_n)$ for an appropriate choice of a continuous one-to-one function f.

Example 5   Lethal recessives revisited

In Example 5 of Section 1.7, we modeled the proportion x_n of a lethal recessive allele in a population at time n with the difference equation:

$$x_{n+1} = \frac{x_n}{1 + x_n}$$

Keeping with the notation x_n rather than a_n, assume that the initial proportion of the lethal allele is $x_1 = 0.5$.

a. Verify that $x_n = \dfrac{1}{1 + n}$ satisfies the difference equation.

b. Determine $\lim\limits_{n \to \infty} x_n$. Discuss the implication for the proportion of the lethal recessive allele in the long term.

c. Determine how large n needs to be to ensure that $x_n \leq 0.1$.

d. Determine how large n needs to be to ensure that $x_n \leq 0.01$. Discuss the implications.

Solution

a. First we verify that the formula holds for $n = 1$, namely, $x_1 = \dfrac{1}{1 + 1} = 0.5$. To verify that $x_n = \dfrac{1}{1 + n}$ satisfies the difference equation for any $n > 1$, we substitute our expression for x_n into both sides of the difference equation and show that they are equal. Evaluating the proposed solution on the left-hand side of the difference equation $x_{n+1} = \dfrac{x_n}{1 + x_n}$ gives us

$$x_{n+1} = \frac{1}{1 + (n + 1)} = \frac{1}{n + 2}$$

Evaluating the proposed solution on the left-hand side of the difference equation equation give us

$$\frac{x_n}{1 + x_n} = \frac{\dfrac{1}{1 + n}}{1 + \dfrac{1}{1 + n}}$$

$$= \frac{1}{(n + 1) + 1} \quad \textit{after multiplying by } 1 = \frac{\frac{1}{n+1}}{\frac{1}{n+1}}$$

$$= \frac{1}{n + 2}$$

Hence, we have shown that the formula $x_n = \dfrac{1}{1 + n}$ satisfies the difference equation $x_{n+1} = \dfrac{1}{1 + x_n}$ for all n.

b. Since $\dfrac{1}{1 + n}$ gets arbitrarily small as n gets arbitrarily large, $\lim\limits_{n \to \infty} x_n = 0$. Hence, in the long term, we expect the lethal recessive genes to vanish from the population.

c. We want

$$\frac{1}{1 + n} \leq \frac{1}{10}$$

$$10 \leq 1 + n$$

$$9 \leq n$$

Hence, after nine generations the proportion of lethal recessives is less than 0.1.

d. We want

$$\frac{1}{1 + n} \leq \frac{1}{100}$$

$$100 \leq 1 + n$$

$$99 \leq n$$

Hence, after ninety-nine generations the proportion of lethal recessives is less than 0.01. These calculations suggest that initially the proportion of lethal recessives decreases rapidly, but further decreases in the proportion occur more and more slowly.

Returning to our a_n notation, recall from Section 1.7, that a point a is an equilibrium of a difference equation $a_{n+1} = f(a_n)$ if $f(a) = a$. In Example 4a and Example 5, the only solution to the equation $f(a) = a$ is $a = 0$, and the sequences generated by these difference equations converge to this equilibrium. In Example 4b, the equation $\sqrt{a} = a$ has two solutions: $a = 0$ and $a = 1$, and the sequence we examined converged to the latter rather than former equilibrium.

To see why this convergence to equilibria occurs, consider a sequence a_n that satisfies the difference equation

$$a_{n+1} = f(a_n)$$

where f is a continuous function. Assume that $\lim_{n\to\infty} a_n = a$. By the sequential continuity theorem, we have

$$
\begin{aligned}
a &= \lim_{n\to\infty} a_n \\
&= \lim_{n\to\infty} a_{n+1} \qquad n+1 \to \infty \text{ if and only if } n \to \infty \\
&= \lim_{n\to\infty} f(a_n) \\
&= f\left(\lim_{n\to\infty} a_n \right) \qquad \text{by sequential continuity} \\
&= f(a)
\end{aligned}
$$

Hence, the limiting value a is an equilibrium for this difference equation.

Limits of Difference Equations

Let f be a continuous function and a_n be a sequence that satisfies

$$a_{n+1} = f(a_n)$$

If $\lim_{n\to\infty} a_n = a$, then $f(a) = a$. In other words, a is an equilibrium.

Example 6   To converge or not to converge

Find the equilibria of the following difference equations and use technology to determine whether the specified sequence converges to one of the equilibria.

a. $a_{n+1} = \dfrac{1}{1 + a_n}$ with $a_1 = 1$

b. $a_{n+1} = 2a_n(1 - a_n)$ with $a_1 = 0.1$

c. $a_{n+1} = 3.5a_n(1 - a_n)$ with $a_1 = 0.1$

Solution

a. To find the equilibria, we solve

$$
\begin{aligned}
a &= \frac{1}{1+a} \\
a(1+a) &= 1 \qquad \text{after multiplying by } 1 + a \\
a^2 + a - 1 &= 0 \\
a &= -\frac{1}{2} \pm \frac{\sqrt{5}}{2} \qquad \text{by the quadratic formula}
\end{aligned}
$$

Hence, if the sequences determined by this difference equation have well-defined limits, then these limits are either $-\dfrac{1}{2} + \dfrac{\sqrt{5}}{2} \approx 0.6180$ or $-\dfrac{1}{2} - \dfrac{\sqrt{5}}{2} \approx -1.6180$. Computing the first twenty terms of the difference equation with $a_1 = 1$ and plotting yields the following graph.

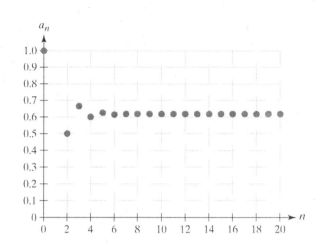

It appears that the sequence is converging to the positive equilibrium.

b. To find the equilibrium, we solve

$$a = 2a(1 - a)$$
$$2a^2 - a = 0$$
$$a(2a - 1) = 0 \qquad \textit{by factoring the common term } a$$
$$a = 0 \quad \text{and} \quad a = \frac{1}{2}$$

Computing and plotting the first twenty terms of the difference equation with $a_1 = 0.1$ and plotting yields the following graph.

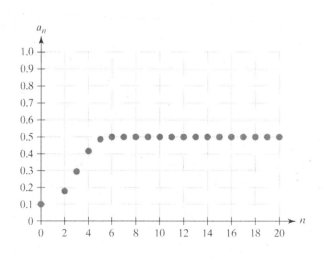

It appears that the sequence is converging to $\dfrac{1}{2}$.

c. To find the equilibrium, we solve

$$a = 3.5a(1 - a)$$
$$3.5a^2 - 2.5a = 0$$
$$a(3.5a - 2.5) = 0 \qquad \textit{by factoring the common term } a$$
$$a = 0 \quad \text{or} \quad a = \frac{5}{7}$$

Computing and plotting the first one hundred terms of the difference equation with $a_1 = 0.1$ and plotting yields the following graph.

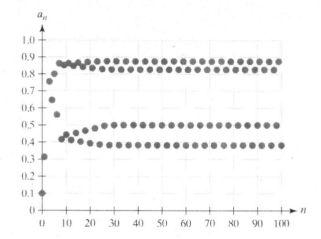

It appears that the sequence does not converge; rather, it seems to eventually oscillate between four values.

One of the most important models in population biology is the discrete logistic model:

$$a_{n+1} = a_n + ra_n\left(1 - \frac{a_n}{K}\right)$$

where the parameter $r > 0$ is called the *intrinsic rate of growth* and $K > 0$ is called the *environmental carrying capacity*.

Example 7   Dynamics of the discrete logistic model

a. Find the equilibrium solutions associated with the discrete logistic equation. What do you observe about the roles of the parameters r and K in determining this equilibrium?

b. Calculate the first twenty points of the sequence $a_{n+1} = a_n + 0.3a_n(1 - a_n)$ with $a_1 = 0.1$.

c. Repeat part **b** with $a_1 = 1.5$.

d. Calculate the first twenty points of the sequence $a_{n+1} = a_n + 1.9a_n(1 - a_n)$ with $a_1 = 0.6$.

e. Calculate the first twenty points of the sequence $a_{n+1} = a_n + 2.2a_n(1 - a_n)$ with $a_1 = 0.6$.

Solution

a. The equilibria are solutions to the equation

$$a = a + ra\left(1 - \frac{a}{K}\right)$$
$$ra\left(1 - \frac{a}{K}\right) = 0$$
$$a = 0 \quad \text{and} \quad a = K.$$

From this it is clear that the value of r does not influence the value of the equilibria, one of which is equal to K.

b. The values in this sequence are plotted in the left-hand side of Figure 2.41. The sequence appears to be converging to the positive equilibrium $K = 1$.

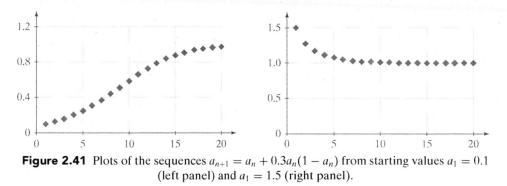

Figure 2.41 Plots of the sequences $a_{n+1} = a_n + 0.3a_n(1 - a_n)$ from starting values $a_1 = 0.1$ (left panel) and $a_1 = 1.5$ (right panel).

c. The values in this sequence are plotted in the right-hand side of Figure 2.41. The sequence appears to be converging to the equilibrium $K = 1$.

d. The values in this sequence are plotted in the left-hand side of Figure 2.42. The sequence exhibits dampened oscillations around the equilibrium $K = 1$. It still appears to be converging to $K = 1$.

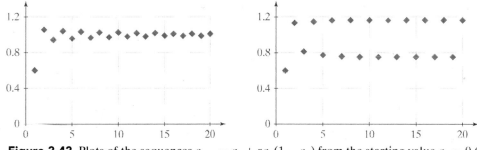

Figure 2.42 Plots of the sequences $a_{n+1} = a_n + ra_n(1 - a_n)$ from the starting value $a_1 = 0.6$ for the cases $r = 1.9$ (left panel) and $r = 2.2$ (right panel).

e. The values in this sequence are plotted in the right-hand side of Figure 2.42. The sequence oscillates between a lower and higher population density. The oscillations are not dampened and the sequence does not appear to be converging to the equilibrium $K = 1$.

Examples 6 and 7 illustrate that the existence of equilibria for a difference equation does not ensure the convergence of the sequences generated by it. This raises the question, when do the sequences generated by a difference equation converge to an equilibrium? In general, this is a hard question. The following theorem provides a criterion that ensures convergence of solutions of a difference equation. Later, when we have covered the basics of derivatives of functions, we will present another criterion that ensures convergence of a sequence to an equilibrium. We make two definitions before stating this theorem. We say that a sequence is **increasing** (respectively, **decreasing**) if $a_1 \leq a_2 \leq a_3 \leq \ldots$ (respectively, $a_1 \geq a_2 \geq a_3 \ldots$).

Theorem 2.5   Monotone convergence theorem

Let f be a continuous, increasing function on an interval $I = [a, b]$ such that the image of f lies in I (i.e., if x is in I, then $f(x)$ is a value that also lies within I). If $a_1, a_2, a_3, \ldots,$ is a sequence that satisfies $a_{n+1} = f(a_n)$, then the sequence is either increasing or decreasing. Moreover, $\lim_{n \to \infty} a_n = a$ exists and satisfies $f(a) = a$.

The next example illustrates the application of the monotone convergence theorem to the Beverton-Holt stock-recruitment model. This model has been used extensively by fisheries scientists to formulate models of fish, such as Pacific salmon, that breed once and then die. *Stock-recruitment curves* describe how a spawning stock of N individuals in one generation contributes recruits R (i.e., new individuals) to the next generation. An example of a Beverton-Holt function fitted to data obtained for sockeye salmon spawning in Karluk Lake, Alaska, is shown in Figure 2.43.

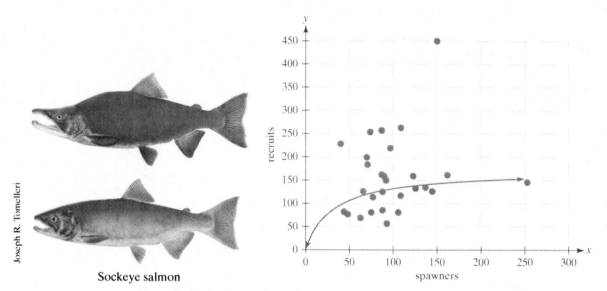

Sockeye salmon

Figure 2.43 Sockeye salmon (*Oncorhynchus nerka*) on the left, and on the right, the relationship between recruits and stock for sockeye salmon in Karluk Lake, Alaska.

Data Source: John A. Gulland, *Fish Stock Assessment: A Manual of Basic Methods* (New York: Wiley, 1983).

Example 8   Beverton-Holt sockeye salmon dynamics

The function plotted in the right panel of Figure 2.43 is given by

$$R(N) = \frac{N}{0.006\,N + 0.2}$$

Note that it is more natural for us to continue using N_n rather then the sequence notation a_n, since N is the symbol most commonly used to denote population size in the ecology literature.

where N is the stock size (spawners) in a particular generation and $R(N)$ is the number of recruits produced for the next generation. Since the number of recruits determines the size of the stock that will be spawners in the next generation, it follows that the salmon dynamics can be modeled by the difference equation

$$N_{n+1} = R(N_n)$$

where N_n is the stock size of the nth generation.

a. Find the equilibria of this difference equation.

b. Graph $R(N)$ and $y = N$.

c. Apply the monotone convergence theorem to determine what happens to N_n when $N_1 = 10$ and when $N_1 = 200$. Use cobwebbing to illustrate your results.

(Note that it is possible to find an explicit solution of this difference equation. This is explored in Problem Set 2.5.)

Solution

a. To find the equilibria, we solve

$$N = \frac{N}{0.006\,N + 0.2}$$

$$N(0.006\,N + 0.2) = N$$

$$N(0.006\,N - 0.8) = 0$$

$$N = 0, \frac{0.8}{0.006}$$

Hence, the equilibria are given by 0 and $\dfrac{0.8}{0.006} = 133\dfrac{1}{3}$.

It may seem strange for population size to have a fractional value, but not if size is measured as a density—that is, numbers per unit area—or is in units of millions of individuals.

b. Plotting the two functions yields the following graph.

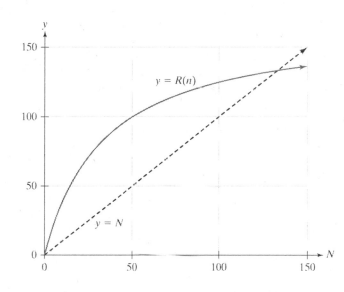

The equilibria correspond to the points where the functions intersect.

c. Since $R(N)$ is increasing on $I = [0, \infty)$ and the image of I under f is I, we can apply the monotone convergence theorem.

Assume $N_1 = 10$. Since $N_2 = \dfrac{10}{0.06 + 0.2} \approx 38.46 \geq N_1$, the monotone convergence theorem implies that N_n is increasing. On the other hand, since the graph of $R(N)$ is saturating at $166\dfrac{2}{3}$, we have $10 \leq N_{n+1} = R(N_n) \leq 166\dfrac{2}{3}$ for all $n \geq 1$. Therefore, by the monotone convergence theorem $\lim_{n \to \infty} N_n$ must equal the equilibrium $133\dfrac{1}{3}$. Cobwebbing with $N_1 = 10$ illustrates this convergence in Figure 2.44 (left).

Assume $N_1 = 200$. Since $N_2 = \dfrac{200}{0.006 \cdot 200 + 0.2} \approx 142.85 \leq N_1$, the monotone convergence theorem implies that N_n is a decreasing sequence. On the other hand, $200 \geq N_n \geq 133\dfrac{1}{3}$ for all $n \geq 1$. Therefore, by the monotone convergence theorem, $\lim_{n \to \infty} N_n$ must equal the equilibrium $133\dfrac{1}{3}$ (from part **a**). Cobwebbing with $N_1 = 200$ illustrates this convergence in Figure 2.44 (right).

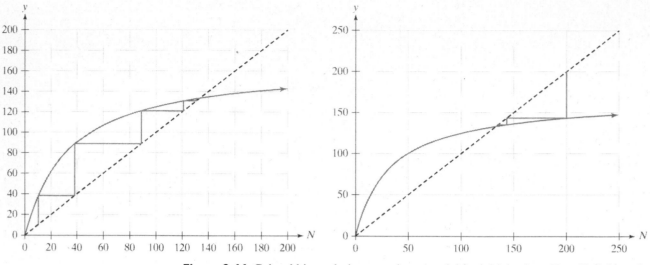

Figure 2.44 Cobwebbing solutions to salmon model for initial values $N_1 = 10$ (left) and $N_1 = 200$ (right).

In Example 5 of Section 1.7, we developed a population genetics model under the assumption that individuals could carry and pass on a recessive lethal allele. In formulating this model, we assumed that two alleles, A and a, exist and determine three possible genotypes: AA, Aa, and aa. If the allele a is the recessive lethal, then this implies that genotype aa is the least viable since, by definition, aa individuals all die before they are able to reproduce. In the next example, we assume that all three genotypes are viable, but that the so-called *heterozygous* genotype Aa is the least viable. Extreme instances of heterozygous inviability arise when different genotypes can mate but produce infertile offspring, such as mules, which are produced when horses mate with donkeys.

Example 9   Disruptive selection

If two *homozygous* genotypes AA and aa produce equal numbers of progeny that exceed the number of progeny produced by the *heterozygous* Aa genotype, then the proportion x_n of allele a at time n can be shown to be modeled by $x_{n+1} = f(x_n)$, where the graph of $f(x)$ has the S-shaped curve depicted in Figure 2.45. Curves of this shape are said to depict *disruptive selection*.

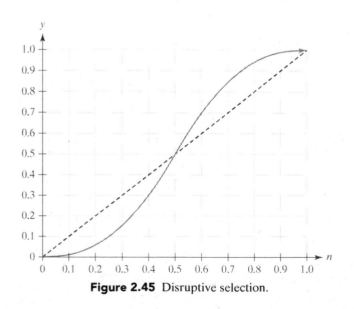

Figure 2.45 Disruptive selection.

Using cobwebbing methods, determine from this graph what happens to x_n in the long term for the two cases given in parts **a** and **b** below.

a. $x_1 = 0.6$ **b.** $x_1 = 0.4$

c. As reported in a 1972 *Science* article, Foster and others experimentally examined changes in two chromosomal proportions in *Drosophila melanogaster*. Data from a set of experiments is graphed in Figure 2.46.

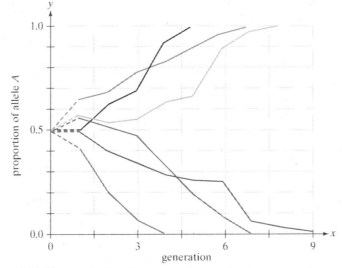

Figure 2.46 Time series for disruptive selection in chromosomal proportions for a species of fruit fly.

Source: G. G. Foster, M. J. Whitten, T. Prout, and R. Gill, "Chromosome Rearrangements for the Control of Insect Pests," *Science* 176: 875–880. Reprinted with permission.

These experimentally determined graphs show how the proportion of an allele changes over generations for initial conditions that through a small amount of random variation lead to different population levels at time 1 on the *x*-axis. Discuss whether these experiments are consistent with the model predictions.

Solution

a. Since the graph of f is increasing, we can apply the monotone convergence theorem. Since $f(0.6) > 0.6$, the sequence x_n is increasing if $x_1 = 0.6$. Since $x_n \leq 1$ for all n and $f(1) = 1$ is the only equilibrium greater than 0.6, x_n converges to 1 as n increases. In other words, the proportion of a alleles approaches one. Cobwebbing reaffirms this prediction, as shown in the following graph.

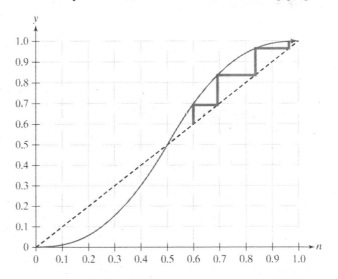

b. Since the graph of f is increasing, we can apply the monotone convergence theorem. Since $f(0.4) < 0.4$, the sequence x_n is decreasing if $x_1 = 0.4$. Since $x_n \geq 0$ for all n and $f(0) = 0$ is the only equilibrium less than 0.4, x_n converges to 0 as n increases. In other words, the proportion of a alleles approaches zero. Cobwebbing reaffirms this prediction, as shown in this graph.

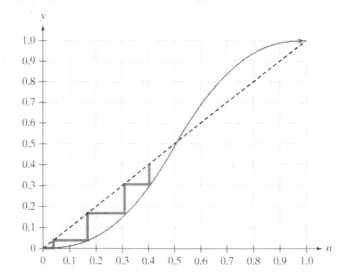

c. The experiments of Foster and others are consistent with the model predictions, if we look at the proportion of allele a at the start of the second generation (i.e., at 1 rather than 0 on the horizontal axis). Specifically, within the limits of a small amount of random variation, the data show that if the proportion of allele a is greater or less than one-half, then the proportion of allele a, respectively, approaches one or goes extinct. ◼

Fibonacci famously posed the following problem (reworded here) over 800 years ago. Suppose a newly born pair of rabbits, one male and one female, are put in an enclosed, but very large, field. Further, suppose all rabbits are able to mate at the age of one month and that the impregnated female gives birth to a male-female pair one month later. Ignoring questions relating to inbreeding, assuming that rabbits never die and there is always enough food for them to eat, what is the asymptotic annual rate of increase of the rabbits in the enclosed field? This is the problem we address in the next example.

Example 10 Fibonacci and the growth rate of rabbits

Fibonacci's rabbit model (see 𝔥istorical 𝔔uest, Problem 38 of Section 1.7) has the form

$$R_n = R_{n-1} + R_{n-2}.$$

where R_n is the number of rabbit pairs in month n.

a. What is the asymptotic behavior of R_n as $n \to \infty$?

b. What is the annual rate of increase in the population? Calculate the population produced by one pair at the end of the first year (i.e., calculate R_{12} when $R_0 = 1$).

Solution

a. To find the asymptotic behavior of R_n, we can transform the model into a familiar sequence model problem by dividing both sides of the above equation by R_{n-1} to obtain

$$\frac{R_n}{R_{n-1}} = 1 + \frac{R_{n-2}}{R_{n-1}}$$

and then define $a_n = R_n/R_{n-1}$. In this case a_n, the ratio of the number of rabbits in month n to those in month $n - 1$, satisfies the equation

$$a_n = 1 + \frac{1}{a_{n-1}}$$

The equilibrium solution to this equation is

$$a = 1 + 1/a$$
$$a^2 = a + 1 \qquad \text{multiplying both sides by } a$$
$$a^2 - a - 1 = 0$$
$$a = \frac{1}{2} \pm \frac{\sqrt{5}}{2}. \qquad \text{by the quadratic formula}$$

Only the positive solution $a \approx 1.6180$ applies here, and it can be shown that the sequence converges to this value as the number of months increases (see Problem 44 in Problem Set 2.5). Thus, although R_n increases without bound, the ratio $a_n = R_n/R_{n-1}$ approaches a constant.

b. To get the annual rate of increase we need to calculate $(1.618)^{12} \approx 322$, a really stunning rate of growth. In Table 2.5, we list the first 13 terms and note that the rate of increase over the first 12 iterations is not exactly 322, because the equilibrium value represents an asymptotic rate rather than an actual rate for any 12 iterations. ∎

Table 2.5 Fibonacci rabbit growth

Month	Number of pairs
0	1
1	1
2	2
3	3
4	5
5	8
6	13
7	21
8	34
9	55
10	89
11	144
12	233

PROBLEM SET 2.5

Level 1 DRILL PROBLEMS

Determine whether the sequential limits in Problems 1 to 8 exist. If they exist, find the limit. If they do not exist, explain briefly why.

1. $\lim\limits_{n\to\infty} a_n$ where $a_n = \dfrac{n^2 - n}{1 + 3n^2}$

2. $\lim\limits_{n\to\infty} a_n$ where $a_n = \dfrac{5 - 2n}{6 + 3n}$

3. $\lim\limits_{n\to\infty} a_n$ where $a_n = \dfrac{e^n}{1 + e^n}$

4. $\lim\limits_{n\to\infty} a_n$ where $a_n = 2^{3/n}$

5. $\lim\limits_{n\to\infty} a_n$ where $a_{n+1} = -a_n$ and $a_1 = 2$

6. $\lim\limits_{n\to\infty} a_n$ where $a_{n+1} = -a_n^{-1}$ and $a_1 = 3$

7. $\lim\limits_{n\to\infty} a_n$ where $a_n = \cos n$

8. $\lim\limits_{n\to\infty} a_n$ where $a_n = [1 + (-1)^n]$

Consider the sequences defined in Problems 9 to 14.

a. Find $\lim\limits_{n\to\infty} a_n$.

b. Determine how large n needs to be to ensure that $|a_n - L| < 0.001$.

9. $\lim\limits_{n\to\infty} a_n$ where $a_n = \dfrac{n}{3 + n}$

10. $\lim\limits_{n\to\infty} a_n$ where $a_n = \dfrac{2n}{n - 1}$

11. $\lim\limits_{n\to\infty} a_n$ where $a_n = \dfrac{1,000}{n}$

12. $\lim\limits_{n\to\infty} a_n$ where $a_n = \dfrac{n + 1}{1,000n}$

13. $\lim\limits_{n\to\infty} a_n$ where $a_n = \dfrac{n^2 + 1}{n^3}$

14. $\lim\limits_{n\to\infty} a_n$ where $a_n = e^{-n}$

All the sequences in Problems 15 to 18 satisfy $\lim\limits_{n\to\infty} a_n = \infty$. Determine how large n has to be to ensure that $a_n \geq 1,000,000$.

15. $a_n = 2n$

16. $u_n = n^2$

17. $a_n = 2^n - 10,000$

18. $a_n = \dfrac{n^2}{1 + n}$

Find the sequences determined by the difference equation $x_{n+1} = f(x_n)$ with the initial condition x_1 specified in Problems 19 to 24. Determine $\lim\limits_{n\to\infty} a_n$. Justify your answer.

19. $f(x) = x + 2$ with $x_1 = 0$

20. $f(x) = \dfrac{x}{3}$ with $x_1 = 27$

21. $f(x) = \sqrt{x}$ with $x_1 = 100$

22. $f(x) = x^2$ with $x_1 = 1.00001$

23. $f(x) = x^2$ with $x_1 = 0.99999$

24. $f(x) = 4x^2$ with $x_1 = 1$

Find the equilibrium of the difference equations in Problems 25 to 28 and use technology to determine which of the specified sequences converge to one of the equilibria.

25. $a_{n+1} = \dfrac{3}{2 + a_n}$ with $a_1 = 1$

26. $a_{n+1} = \dfrac{1}{5 - a_n}$ with $a_1 = 1$

27. $a_{n+1} = 3a_n(1 - a_n)$ with $a_1 = 0.1$

28. $a_{n+1} = 5.5(1 - a_n)$ with $a_1 = 0.2$

Use the monotone convergence theorem in Problems 29 to 34 to determine the limits of the following specified sequences.

29. $a_{n+1} = \dfrac{2a_n}{1 + a_n}$ with $a_1 = 0.5$

30. $a_{n+1} = \dfrac{2a_n}{1 + a_n}$ with $a_1 = 2$

31. $a_{n+1} = 2\ln a_n$ with $a_1 = 1$

32. $a_{n+1} = 2\ln a_n$ with $a_1 = 100$

33. $a_{n+1} = \sqrt{5 + a_n}$ with $a_1 = 0$

34. $a_{n+1} = \sqrt{5 + a_n}$ with $a_1 = 20$

Level 2 APPLIED AND THEORY PROBLEMS

35. In Example 5 of Section 2.5 we introduced a model for the frequency of lethal recessive alleles in a population. The model is given by

$$x_{n+1} = \frac{x_n}{1 + x_n}$$

where x_n is the frequency of the recessive allele in the population.

a. If $x_1 = 0.25$, then verify that $x_n = \dfrac{1}{n + 3}$ satisfies the difference equation.

b. Find $\lim\limits_{n \to \infty} x_n$.

c. Determine how large n needs to be to ensure that $x_n \le 0.1$.

d. Determine how large n needs to be to ensure that $x_n \le 0.001$.

36. Let us consider the lethal recessive allele model in greater generality.

a. Verify that $x_n = \dfrac{x_1}{1 + (n-1)x_1}$ satisfies the difference equation $x_{n+1} = \dfrac{x_n}{1 + x_n}$ for any choice of x_1.

b. For any x_1, find $\lim\limits_{n \to \infty} x_n$.

c. Assuming that x_1 lies in $(0, 1)$, determine how large n needs to be to ensure that $x_n \le 0.01$.

37. In Example 5 of Section 1.7, we discussed a population genetics model under the assumption that there

were two alleles, A and a, that determined three possible genetic types, AA, Aa, and aa. We assume that genetic type Aa (so called heterozygote) is the least viable. If the genotype aa produces nine times more progeny than genotype AA progeny, then the frequency x_n of allele a at time n can be modeled by $x_{n+1} = f(x_n)$ where the graph of f is given by

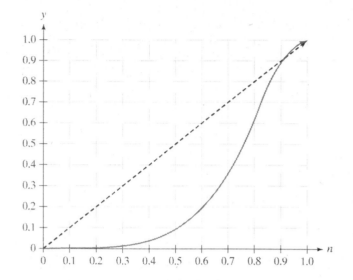

a. Determine what happens to x_n in the long term if $x_1 = 0.91$.

b. Determine what happens to x_n in the long term if $x_1 = 0.89$.

c. As reported in a 1972 *Science* article, Foster and others experimentally examined changes in two chromosomal frequencies in *Drosophila melanogaster*. Data from a set of experiments are graphed next:

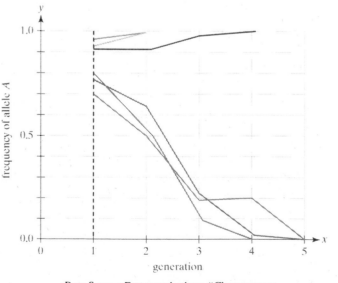

Data Source: Foster and others, "Chromosome Rearrangements," 875–880.

These experimentally determined graphs show how the frequency of an allele changes over generations for different initial conditions. Discuss whether these experiments are consistent with the model predictions.

38. The Beverton-Holt model has been used extensively by fisheries. This model assumes that populations are competing for a single limiting resource and reproduce at discrete moments in time. If we let N_n denote the population abundance in the nth year (or generation), $r > 0$ the maximal per capita growth rate, and $a > 0$ as a competition coefficient, then the model is given by

$$N_{n+1} = \frac{r N_n}{1 + a N_n}$$

with $r > 0$ and $a > 0$.

a. Assume $N_1 = 1$ and find the first four terms of the sequence.

b. Guess the explicit expression for the sequence and verify that your guess is correct.

c. Find the equilibria of this difference equation.

d. By considering the $\lim_{n \to \infty} N_n$, determine under what conditions the population goes extinct (i.e., converges to 0) versus under what conditions it is able to persist (i.e., converge to a positive equilibrium $N > 0$) if it is initially at $N_1 = 1$.

In the Fibonacci rabbit problem laid out in Example 10, suppose only a proportion p of the females that could become pregnant actually do become pregnant each month. (We assume the population starts with a large number of pairs so that when we refer to proportions, we are actually thinking of whole numbers of pairs rather than, say one-third of two pairs, which makes no biological sense.) What is the annual rate of increase in Problems 39 to 43 if p equals the specified value?

39. 3/4   40. 2/3   41. 1/2   42. 1/3   43. 1/4

44. Consider the Fibonacci sequence in Example 10. Show that

$$a_{n+2} = 1 + \frac{1}{a_{n+1}} = 1 + \frac{a_n}{1 + a_n}$$

and hence apply the monotone convergence theorem to find out what happens to the sequences of even elements of a_n.

45. Use technology to calculate the first twenty points of the sequence $a_{n+1} = a_n + r a_n (1 - a_n)$ with $a_1 = 0.5$ for the cases $r = 0.9, r = 1.5$ and $r = 2.1$. How does this fit in with the discussion in the solution to part **e** of Example 7.

46. Revisiting the sockeye salmon stock-recruitment relationship considered in Example 8, we see from Figure 2.43 that we could just as credibly fit the Ricker function

$$y = f(x) = 3.7xe^{-0.01x}$$

If x is the stock in one generation and y is the stock recruited in the next generation, then this relationship is actually a population model of the form

$$x_{n+1} = 3.7x_n e^{-0.01x_n}$$

If the population is now at the level $x_1 = 100$ individuals, use technology to generate the number of individuals that you expect in the next ten generations. Deduce the equilibrium value and check this value by using technology or the bisection method to solve the equation $x = 3.7xe^{-0.01x}$. In Figure 2.47, the solid line is fit to the data using a Ricker functional form that is similar to the Beverton-Holt form considered in Example 8.

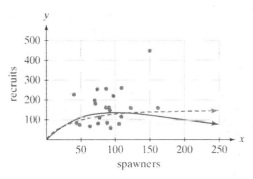

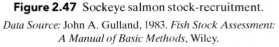

Figure 2.47 Sockeye salmon stock-recruitment.

Data Source: John A. Gulland, 1983. *Fish Stock Assessment: A Manual of Basic Methods*, Wiley.

2.6   **Derivative at a Point**

In this section, we introduce one of the major concepts in calculus, the idea of a *derivative*. Although functions are fundamental and limits are essential, they simply laid the foundation for the excitement to come. To motivate the idea of the derivative at a point, let us recast Example 1 of Section 2.1 using different notation. If we let $f(x)$ represent the population of Mexico in year x, then the average population between the years 1980 and 1985 can be found by

$$\frac{f(a+h) - f(a)}{h} = \frac{f(1980 + 5) - f(1980)}{5} = \frac{76.6 - 67.38}{5} = 1.844 \text{ million per year}$$

where $a = 1980$ (the base year) and $h = 5$ (the duration of the time interval). We also found the average rate of change over smaller and smaller intervals to guess that the instantaneous rate of change of the Mexico population in 1980 to be 1.75 million per year. This idea can be written as

$$\lim_{h \to 0} \frac{f(1980 + h) - f(1980)}{h} \approx 1.75 \text{ million per year}$$

In Chapter 1 and Section 2.1, we previewed the notion of the derivative at a point by defining the tangent line for $f(x)$ at a point $x = a$ to be the limit of the slope of the secant lines

$$\lim_{h \to 0} \frac{f(a+h) - f(a)}{h}$$

Slopes of tangent lines and instantaneous rates of changes have the same formula, and it is this limiting process that is the basis for the concept of the derivative.

Derivative at a Point

The **derivative** of function f at a point $x = a$, denoted by $f'(a)$, is

$$f'(a) = \lim_{h \to 0} \frac{f(a+h) - f(a)}{h}$$

provided this limit exists. If the limit exists, we say that f is **differentiable at** $x = a$.

Example 1   Finding derivatives using the definition

Use the definition of a derivative to find the following derivatives.

a. $f'(3)$ where $f(x) = 1$

b. $f'(2)$ where $f(x) = 3x$

c. $f'(1)$ where $f(x) = 1 + 3x^2$

Solution

a. Let $f(x) = 1$ and $a = 3$.

$$\begin{aligned}
f'(3) &= \lim_{h \to 0} \frac{f(3+h) - f(3)}{h} \\
&= \lim_{h \to 0} \frac{1 - 1}{h} \\
&= \lim_{h \to 0} \frac{0}{h} \\
&= 0
\end{aligned}$$

b. Let $f(x) = 3x$ and $a = 2$.

$$\begin{aligned}
f'(2) &= \lim_{h \to 0} \frac{f(2+h) - f(2)}{h} \\
&= \lim_{h \to 0} \frac{3(2+h) - 6}{h} \\
&= \lim_{h \to 0} \frac{6 + 3h - 6}{h} \\
&= \lim_{h \to 0} \frac{3h}{h} \\
&= 3
\end{aligned}$$

c. Let $f(x) = 1 + 3x^2$ and $a = 1$.

$$f'(1) = \lim_{h \to 0} \frac{f(1+h) - f(1)}{h}$$

$$= \lim_{h \to 0} \frac{[1 + 3(1+h)^2] - [1 + 3(1)^2]}{h}$$

$$= \lim_{h \to 0} \frac{1 + 3 + 6h + 3h^2 - 4}{h}$$

$$= \lim_{h \to 0} \frac{6h + 3h^2}{h}$$

$$= \lim_{h \to 0} (6 + 3h)$$

$$= 6$$

Example 1 illustrates two facts. First, the derivative of a constant function is zero. Intuitively this makes sense, as a constant function by definition does not change and, consequently, its rate of change should be zero. Second, the derivative of a linear function is the slope of the linear function. Intuitively, this makes sense as the rate at which the function is increasing is given by the slope of the function. More interestingly, Example 1 illustrates that we can explicitly compute the slope (equivalently, the instantaneous rate of change) of a quadratic function.

The derivatives in Example 1 were pretty straightforward to compute, but other derivatives require certain algebraic procedures to compute, as illustrated by the next example.

Example 2 Algebraic steps to find a derivative

Find the following derivatives algebraically.

a. $f'(4)$ where $f(x) = \sqrt{x}$ **b.** $f'(5)$ where $f(x) = \dfrac{1}{1+x}$

Solution

a. To find this derivative, we multiply the numerator and denominator of the quotient by the "conjugate" of the original numerator.

$$\frac{f(4+h) - f(4)}{h} = \frac{\sqrt{4+h} - \sqrt{4}}{h}$$

$$= \frac{\sqrt{4+h} - \sqrt{4}}{h} \times \frac{\sqrt{4+h} + \sqrt{4}}{\sqrt{4+h} + \sqrt{4}} \qquad \textit{multiplying by 1}$$

$$= \frac{4 + h - 4}{h(\sqrt{4+h} + \sqrt{4})} \qquad \textit{multiplying out the numerator}$$

$$= \frac{h}{h(\sqrt{4+h} + 2)} \qquad \textit{simplifying}$$

$$= \frac{1}{\sqrt{4+h} + 2} \qquad \textit{since } h \neq 0 \textit{ in the limit}$$

Hence, taking the limit as h goes to 0 yields $f'(4) = \dfrac{1}{\sqrt{4} + 2} = \dfrac{1}{4}$.

b. To find this derivative, we can multiply by the common denominator in the numerator.

$$\frac{f(5+h) - f(5)}{h} = \frac{1/(1 + (5+h)) - 1/6}{h}$$

$$= \frac{1/(6+h) - 1/6}{h} \qquad simplifying$$

$$= \frac{1/(6+h) - 1/6}{h} \times \frac{(6+h)6}{(6+h)6} \qquad multiplying\ by\ 1$$

$$= \frac{6 - (6+h)}{h(6+h)6} \qquad simplifying$$

$$= \frac{-h}{h(6+h)6} \qquad simplifying\ more$$

$$= \frac{-1}{(6+h)6} \qquad since\ h \neq 0\ in\ the\ limit$$

Taking the limit as h goes to 0 yields $f'(5) = -\dfrac{1}{36}$.

Slopes of tangent lines

The definition of the derivative was inspired directly by the slope of the tangent line. Using derivatives, we can find the tangent line.

> **Tangent Line**
>
> Let f be a function that is differentiable at the point $x = a$. The **tangent line of** f **at** $x = a$ is the line with slope $f'(a)$ that passes through the point $(a, f(a))$.

Example 3   Tangent line to a parabola

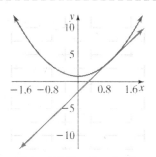

Figure 2.48 Graph of the parabola $y = 1 + 3x^2$ with tangent line at $(1, 4)$.

Find the tangent line to $f(x) = 1 + 3x^2$ at $x = 1$. Sketch the parabola and the tangent line.

Solution   In Example 1 we found that the slope of the tangent line is $f'(1) = 6$. Since the tangent line passes through $(1, f(1)) = (1, 4)$, we can use the point-slope formula to find the equation of the tangent line:

$$y - 4 = 6(x - 1)$$
$$y = 6x - 2$$

The graph of the parabola, along with the tangent line at $(1, 4)$ is shown in Figure 2.48.

In Example 3, the tangent line intersects the graph of the function in exactly one point. This unique intersection is not typical, as illustrated in the next example.

Example 4   Multiple intersections

Find the tangent line to the cubic $f(x) = x^3$ at $x = 1$. Sketch the cubic and the tangent line.

Solution   We first find the slope of the tangent line:

$$f'(1) = \lim_{h \to 0} \frac{f(1+h) - f(1)}{h}$$

$$= \lim_{h \to 0} \frac{(1+h)^3 - 1}{h}$$

$$= \lim_{h \to 0} \frac{1 + 3h + 3h^2 + h^3 - 1}{h}$$

$$= \lim_{h \to 0} (3 + 3h + h^2)$$

$$= 3$$

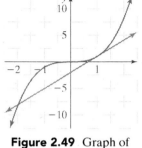

Figure 2.49 Graph of the cubic $y = x^3$ and its tangent line at $(1, 1)$.

The tangent line passes through $(1, f(1)) = (1, 1)$, so the equation of the tangent line is

$$y - 1 = 3(x - 1)$$

Equivalently, $y = 3x - 2$. The graph of $y = x^3$ and the tangent line at $(1, 1)$ is shown in Figure 2.49.

Instantaneous rates of change

In Section 2.1, we defined

$$\frac{f(b) - f(a)}{b - a}$$

to be the average rate of change of f over the interval $[a, b]$. Taking the limit as b approaches a yields the instantaneous rate of change

$$\lim_{b \to a} \frac{f(b) - f(a)}{b - a}$$

In the next example, we relate this definition of the instantaneous rate of change to the derivative.

Example 5   Instantaneous rates of change

Show that

$$\lim_{b \to a} \frac{f(b) - f(a)}{b - a} = f'(a)$$

provided that the limits exist.

Solution   Let $h = b - a$. Then $b = a + h$ so that

$$\frac{f(b) - f(a)}{b - a} = \frac{f(a + h) - f(a)}{h}$$

Since b approaching a is equivalent to h approaching 0, we have

$$\lim_{b \to a} \frac{f(b) - f(a)}{b - a} = \lim_{h \to 0} \frac{f(a + h) - f(a)}{h}$$

provided the limits exist. By the definition of a derivative, we get

$$f'(a) = \lim_{b \to a} \frac{f(b) - f(a)}{b - a}$$

The solution to Example 5 allows us to equate the derivative with an instantaneous rate of change.

Instantaneous Rate of Change as a Derivative Let f be a function that is differentiable at $x = a$. The **instantaneous rate of change of f at $x = a$** is $f'(a)$.

Example 6   Instantaneous velocity

On a calm day, a seed cone of a coastal California redwood tree drops from one of its high branches 305 feet above the ground. From physics, we know that the distance s in feet an object falls after t seconds, when air resistance is negligible, is given by the formula

$$s(t) = 16t^2$$

a. Find $s'(1)$ and interpret this quantity.

b. Find the velocity (instantaneous rate of change) of the cone at the moment it hits the ground.

Solution

a.
$$
\begin{aligned}
s'(1) &= \lim_{h \to 0} \frac{s(1+h) - s(1)}{h} \\
&= \lim_{h \to 0} \frac{16(1+h)^2 - 16(1)^2}{h} \\
&= \lim_{h \to 0} \frac{16 + 32h + 16h^2 - 16}{h} \\
&= \lim_{h \to 0} \frac{32h + 16h^2}{h} \\
&= \lim_{h \to 0} (32 + 16h) \\
&= 32
\end{aligned}
$$

After one second, the cone is falling at a velocity of 32 feet per second (or 32 ft/s).

b. First, we need to find how long it takes the cone to fall to the ground. When the cone hits the ground, it has fallen 305 feet. Hence, we need to solve $305 = s(t) = 16t^2$, which yields $t = \dfrac{\sqrt{305}}{4}$. To find $s'\left(\dfrac{\sqrt{305}}{4}\right)$, we use the definition of a derivative

$$
\begin{aligned}
s'\left(\frac{\sqrt{305}}{4}\right) &= \lim_{h \to 0} \frac{s\left(\frac{\sqrt{305}}{4} + h\right) - s\left(\frac{\sqrt{305}}{4}\right)}{h} \\
&= \lim_{h \to 0} \frac{16\left(\frac{\sqrt{305}}{4} + h\right)^2 - 16\left(\frac{\sqrt{305}}{4}\right)^2}{h} \\
&= \lim_{h \to 0} \frac{8\sqrt{305}\, h + 16h^2}{h} \\
&= \lim_{h \to 0} (8\sqrt{305} + 16h) \\
&= 8\sqrt{305} \approx 139.7
\end{aligned}
$$

Hence, at the moment the cone hits the ground it is falling at a velocity of 139.7 ft/s. This is equivalent to 95.3 miles per hour (mi/h). Of course, if the effects of air resistance are taken into account, velocity will be less.

Example 7   Melting Arctic sea ice

One of the important consequences of increasing temperature on Earth is that sea ice is melting at both the North and South poles. In 2012, the extent of Arctic sea ice was approximately 3.61 million square kilometers, the lowest in the past thirty years. Figure 2.50 contains the plot of the average Arctic sea ice extent for the past thirty years. These data can be approximated by a quadratic function of the form

$$S(t) = 7.292 + 0.023t - 0.004t^2 \text{ million square kilometers}$$

where t is years after 1980.

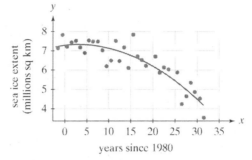

Figure 2.50 Sea ice extent as a function of years since 1980.

a. Find $S'(32)$.

b. Determine the units of this derivative and discuss their meaning.

Solution

a. Using the definition of a derivative, we get

$$S'(32) = \lim_{h \to 0} \frac{S(32+h) - S(32)}{h}$$

$$= \lim_{h \to 0} \frac{[7.292 + 0.023(32+h) - 0.004(32+h)^2] - [7.292 + 0.023 \cdot 32 - 0.004 \cdot 32^2]}{h}$$

$$= \lim_{h \to 0} \frac{0.023h - 0.004(64h + h^2)}{h}$$

$$= \lim_{h \to 0} \frac{-0.233h - 0.004h^2}{h}$$

$$= \lim_{h \to 0} -0.233 - 0.004h = -0.233$$

b. The units of $S'(32)$ are millions of square kilometers per year. Since $S'(32) = -0.233$, we conclude that we are losing 233 thousands of square kilometers of Arctic sea ice per year.

Differentiability and continuity

If a function $f(x)$ is differentiable at a point a, then it is also continuous at a point a, as stated in the following theorem.

Theorem 2.6   Differentiability implies continuity theorem

If f is differentiable at the point $x = a$, then f is continuous at $x = a$.

Proof.   To prove this theorem, assume that f is differentiable at $x = a$. Then

$$\lim_{x \to a}[f(x) - f(a)] = \lim_{h \to 0}[f(a+h) - f(a)]$$

$$= \lim_{h \to 0} \frac{h}{h}[f(a+h) - f(a)] \qquad multiplying\ by\ one$$

$$= \lim_{h \to 0} h\left[\frac{f(a+h) - f(a)}{h}\right]$$

$$= \lim_{h \to 0} h \cdot \lim_{h \to 0} \frac{f(a+h) - f(a)}{h} \qquad limit\ law\ for\ product$$

$$= 0 \cdot f'(a) \qquad definition\ of\ derivative$$

$$= 0$$

Therefore, by the limit law for sums,

$$\lim_{x \to a} f(x) - \lim_{x \to a} f(a) = 0$$

Hence,

$$\lim_{x \to a} f(x) = \lim_{x \to a} f(a)$$

and thus f is continuous at $x = a$. ■

The reverse of this theorem, however, is not true. To fully appreciate differentiability, it is useful to understand examples of where continuity holds but the function is not differentiable.

Example 8   Absolute value functions have nondifferentiable corners

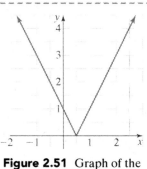

Figure 2.51 Graph of the function $f(x) = |ax - b|$ for the case $a = 2$ and $b = 1$.

The absolute value function $f(x) = |ax - b|$, for positive values of a and b, is defined to be

$$f(x) = \begin{cases} ax - b & \text{if } x \geq b/a \\ b - ax & \text{if } x < b/a \end{cases}$$

Show that $f(x)$, which is illustrated in Figure 2.51 for the case $a = 2$ and $b = 1$, is continuous but not differentiable at $x = b/a$.

Solution   Since $\lim_{x \to b/a^+}(ax - b) = \lim_{x \to b/a^-}(b - ax) = 0$, $f(x)$ is continuous at $x = b/a$.

Now consider the limit from the left in the definition of a derivative applied to the given function:

$$\lim_{h \to 0^-} \frac{f(b/a + h) - f(b/a)}{h} = \lim_{h \to 0^-} \frac{b - a(b/a + h) - 0}{h} = \lim_{h \to 0^-} \frac{-h}{h} = -1$$

Similarly consider the limit from the right in the definition of a derivative applied to the given function:

$$\lim_{h \to 0^+} \frac{f(b/a + h) - f(b/a)}{h} = \lim_{h \to 0^+} \frac{a(b/a + h) - b - 0}{h} = \lim_{h \to 0^+} \frac{h}{h} = 1$$

Since these two limits are not equal, the function is not differentiable at $x = a$. ■

A biological model where we have continuity but nondifferentiability at a point is illustrated in the following example.

Example 9 **Continuous but not differentiable**

Examine the continuity and differentiability of $f(x)$ at $x = a$ for the following two functions.

a.
$$f(x) = \begin{cases} 6.25\,x \text{ cells/hour} & \text{if } x \leq 200 \\ 1{,}250 \text{ cells/hour} & \text{if } x > 200, \end{cases} \quad a = 200$$

where we recall from Example 7 in Section 2.2 that this function models the feeding rate of planktonic copepods and x is the concentration of planktonic cells per liter.

b. $f(x) = x^{1/3}$ and $a = 0$.

Solution

a. Since

$$\lim_{x \to 200^+} f(x) = \lim_{x \to 200^+} 1250 = 1250$$

and

$$\lim_{x \to 200^-} f(x) = \lim_{x \to 200^-} 6.25x = 1250$$

we see f is continuous at $x = 200$.
On the other hand, for $h < 0$,

$$\lim_{h \to 0^-} \frac{f(200 + h) - f(200)}{h} = \lim_{h \to 0^-} \frac{6.25(200 + h) - 6.25(200)}{h}$$
$$- \lim_{h \to 0^-} \frac{6.25\,h}{h}$$
$$= 6.25$$

and for $h > 0$,

$$\lim_{h \to 0^+} \frac{f(200 + h) - f(200)}{h} = \lim_{h \to 0^+} \frac{1250 - 1250}{h}$$
$$= \lim_{h \to 0^+} \frac{0}{h}$$
$$= 0$$

Since the left- and right-hand limits are not equal, the limit does not exist, so f is not differentiable at $x = 200$. As you can see in Figure 2.52, the function is continuous but is still not differentiable at $x = 200$.

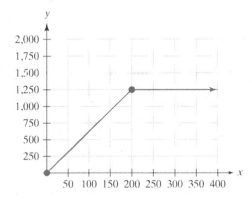

Figure 2.52 Feeding rate of planktonic copepods.

b. Since $f(x) = x^{1/3}$ is arbitrarily close to 0 for all x sufficiently close to 0, $\lim\limits_{x \to 0} f(x) = 0$. Since $f(0) = 0$, f is continuous at $x = 0$. To determine the derivative of $x^{1/3}$ at $x = 0$, we need to consider

$$\lim_{h \to 0} \frac{f(0 + h) - f(0)}{h} = \frac{(0 + h)^{1/3} - 0^{1/3}}{h}$$

$$= \lim_{h \to 0} h^{-2/3}$$

$$= \infty$$

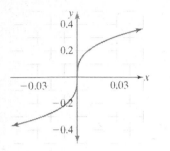

Hence, the derivative is not defined, as the limit is not finite. Graphing $y = x^{1/3}$ reveals that the slope of the tangent line at $x = 0$ is infinite; that is, it is vertical, as illustrated on the left.

Example 9 illustrates that continuity does not ensure differentiability and that differentiability can fail in at least two ways. The limit of the slopes of the secant lines might not converge or this limit may become infinitely large. While continuity does not imply differentiability, the opposite is true; that is, differentiability ensures continuity. Hence, differentiability can be viewed as an improvement over continuity in what mathematicians refer to as the smoothness of a function.

PROBLEM SET 2.6

Level 1 DRILL PROBLEMS

Using the definition of a derivative, find the derivatives specified in Problems 1 to 10.

1. $f'(-2)$ where $f(x) = 3x - 2$
2. $f'(3)$ where $f(x) = 5 - 2x$
3. $f'(1)$ where $f(x) = -x^2$
4. $f'(0)$ where $f(x) = x + x^2$
5. $f'(-4)$ where $f(x) = \dfrac{1}{2x}$
6. $f'(2)$ where $f(x) = \dfrac{1}{x + 1}$
7. $f'(-1)$ where $f(x) = x^3$
8. $f'(2)$ where $f(x) = x^3 + 1$
9. $f'(9)$ where $f(x) = \sqrt{x}$. Hint: Multiply by 1 (think conjugate).
10. $f'(5)$ where $f(x) = \sqrt{5x}$. Hint: Multiply by 1 (think conjugate).

Find the tangent line at the specified point and graph the tangent line and the corresponding function in Problems 11 to 20. Notice these functions are the same as those given in Problems 1 to 10.

11. $f(x) = 3x - 2$ at $x = -2$
12. $f(x) = 5 - 2x$ at $x = 3$
13. $f(x) = -x^2$ at $x = 1$
14. $f(x) = x + x^2$ at $x = 0$
15. $f(x) = \dfrac{1}{2x}$ at $x = -4$
16. $f(x) = \dfrac{1}{x + 1}$ at $x = 2$
17. $f(x) = x^3$ at $x = -1$
18. $f(x) = x^3 + 1$ at $x = 2$
19. $f(x) = \sqrt{x}$ at $x = 9$
20. $f(x) = \sqrt{5x}$ at $x = 5$

Determine at which values of x in Problems 21 to 26 that f is not differentiable. Explain briefly.

21.

22.

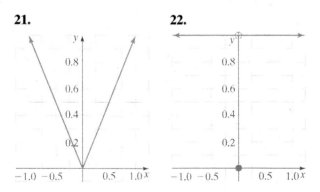

23.

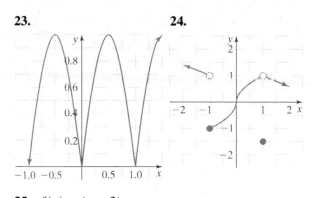

24.

25. $f(x) = |x - 2|$

26. $f(x) = 2|x + 1|$

27. Let $f(x) = \begin{cases} -2x & \text{if } x < 1 \\ \sqrt{x} - 3 & \text{if } x \geq 1 \end{cases}$

   a. Sketch the graph of f.

   b. Show that f is continuous, but not differentiable, at $x = 1$.

28. Give an example of a function that is continuous on $(-\infty, \infty)$ but is not differentiable at $x = 5$.

29. Consider the function defined by

$$f(x) = \begin{cases} \dfrac{1}{-x + 1} & \text{if } x \leq 0 \\ \dfrac{1}{x + 1} & \text{if } x > 0 \end{cases}$$

Sketch this graph and find all points where the graph is continuous but not differentiable.

30. Consider the function defined by

$$f(x) = \begin{cases} 0 & \text{if } x \leq 0 \\ x & \text{if } 0 < x < 1 \\ \dfrac{1}{x} & \text{if } x \geq 1 \end{cases}$$

Sketch this graph and find all points where the graph is continuous but not differentiable.

Level 2 APPLIED AND THEORY PROBLEMS

31. A baseball is thrown upward and its height at time t in seconds is given by

$$H(t) = 10t - 16t^2 \text{ meters}$$

   a. Find the velocity of the baseball after two seconds.

   b. Find the time at which the baseball hits the ground.

   c. Find the velocity of the baseball when it hits the ground.

32. A ball is thrown directly upward from the edge of a cliff and travels in such a way that t seconds later, its height above the ground at the base of the cliff is

$$H(t) = -16t^2 + 40t + 24$$

feet.

   a. Find the velocity of the ball after two seconds.

   b. When does the ball hit the ground, and what is its impact velocity?

   c. When does the ball have a velocity of zero? What physical interpretation should be given to this time?

33. If the data in Figure 2.53 represents a set of measurements relating enzyme activity to temperature in degrees Celsius, and the quadratic equation

$$A(x) = 11.8 + 19.1\,x - 0.2\,x^2$$

provides a good fit to this data, then find $A'(50)$ and discuss its meaning.

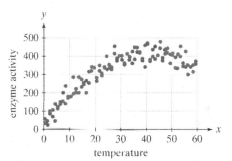

Figure 2.53 Enzyme activity as a function of temperature.

34. In Example 7 we discussed how the extent of Arctic sea ice is modeled by the function

$$S(t) = 7.292 + 0.023t - 0.004t^2 \text{ million square kilometers}$$

where t is years after 1980. Use the definition of the derivative to compute $S'(20)$. How does this value compare to $S'(30)$ found in Example 7? What does this comparison suggest about the rate at which arctic ice is being lost?

35. In 2010, W. B. Grant published an article about the prevalence of multiple sclerosis in three U.S. communities and the role of vitamin D. The best-fitting quadratic relationship to the data published in this article, relating prevalence of multiple sclerosis (MS) to latitude (exposure to sunlight, hence vitamin D synthesis decreases with latitude) is shown in Figure 2.54. This quadratic function is given by

$$P(x) = 499 - 30.8x + 0.5x^2 \text{ cases per 100,000}$$

where x is latitude.

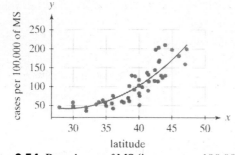

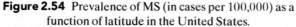

Figure 2.54 Prevalence of MS (in cases per 100,000) as a function of latitude in the United States.

Data Source: W. B. Grant, "The Prevalence of Multiple Sclerosis in 3 US Communities: The Role of Vitamin D" [letter]. *Prevention of Chronic Diseases* 7 (2010): A89.

a. Find $P'(40)$.

b. Find $P'(45)$.

c. Interpret and compare the numbers that you found in **a** and **b**.

36. An environmental study of a certain suburban community suggests that t years from now, the average level of carbon monoxide in the air can be modeled by the formula

$$f(t) = 0.05t^2 + 0.1t + 3.4$$

parts per million.

a. At what rate will the carbon monoxide level be changing with respect to time one year from now?

b. By how much will the carbon monoxide level change during the first year?

37. Perelson and colleagues studied the viral load of HIV patients during antiviral drug treatment.* They estimated the viral load of the typical patient to be

$$V(t) = 216e^{-0.2t}$$

particles per milliliter on day t after the drug treatment.

a. Estimate $V'(2)$.

b. Describe the units of $V'(2)$ and interpret this quantity.

38. Stock-recruitment data and a fitted Beverton-Holt function for sockeye salmon in Karluk Lake, Alaska,

were was shown in Figure 2.43. The fitted function was

$$y = f(x) = \frac{x}{0.006\,x + 0.2}$$

where x is the current stock size and y is the number of recruits for the next year. To determine the number of recruits produced per individual, consider the function

$$y = g(x) = \frac{f(x)}{x} = \frac{1}{0.006\,x + 0.2}$$

a. Algebraically find $g'(10)$.

b. Describe the units of $g'(10)$, and discuss the meaning of this quantity.

39. In Example 6 of Section 1.5, we developed the Michaelis-Menton model for the rate at which an organism consumes its resource. For bacterial populations in the ocean, this model was given by

$$f(x) = \frac{1.2078x}{1 + 0.0506x} \text{ micrograms of glucose per hour}$$

where x is the concentration of glucose (micrograms per liter) in the environment. To determine the rate of glucose consumption per microgram of glucose in the environment, consider the function

$$y = g(x) = \frac{f(x)}{x} = \frac{1.2078}{1 + 0.0506x}$$

a. Algebraically compute $g'(0)$ and $g'(20)$.

b. Describe the meaning of the derivatives that you computed.

40. In Example 5 of Section 2.4, we found that the rate at which wolves kill moose can be modeled by

$$f(x) = \frac{3.36x}{0.42 + x} \quad \begin{array}{l} \text{moose killed per wolf} \\ \text{per hundred days} \end{array}$$

where x is measured in number of moose per square kilometer. To determine the per capita killing rate of moose, consider the function

$$y = g(x) = \frac{f(x)}{x} = \frac{3.36}{0.42 + x}$$

a. Algebraically compute $g'(1)$ and $g'(2)$.

b. Describe the meaning of the derivatives that you computed.

2.7   Derivatives as Functions

Our notion $f'(a)$ for the derivative at the point $x = a$ suggests that we can think of f' as a function. Indeed this is true.

---

*A. S. Perelson, A. U. Neumann, M. Markowitz, J. M. Leonard, D. D. Ho, "HIV-1 Dynamics in Vivo: Virion Clearance Rate, Infected Cell Lifespan, and Viral Generation Time," *Science* 271 (1996): 1582–1586; and A. S. Perelson and P. W. Nelson "Mathematical Analysis of HIV-1 Dynamics in Vivo," *SIAM Review* 41 (1999): 3–44.

Derivative as a Function

Let f be a function. The **derivative of** f is defined by

$$f'(x) = \lim_{h \to 0} \frac{f(x+h) - f(x)}{h}$$

for all x for which this limit exists.

Example 1   Finding Derivatives

Find the derivatives f' of the following functions f.

a. $f(x) = 1$ **b.** $f(x) = x$ **c.** $f(x) = x^2$ **d.** $f(x) = x^3$

e. Guess the derivative of $f(x) = x^n$ for n a whole number.

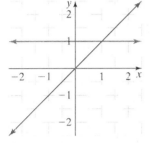

Figure 2.55 The function $f(x) = x$ (blue) and its derivative $f'(x) = 1$ (red) are plotted on the interval $[-2, 2]$.

Solution

a. If $f(x) = 1$, then $f'(x) = 0$ for every x (see Example 1 of Section 2.6). The derivative of a constant is 0.

b. Use the definition of the derivative of a function.

$$\begin{aligned}
f'(x) &= \lim_{h \to 0} \frac{f(x+h) - f(x)}{h} \\
&= \lim_{h \to 0} \frac{x + h - x}{h} \\
&= \lim_{h \to 0} \frac{h}{h} \\
&= 1
\end{aligned}$$

The function and its derivative are illustrated in Figure 2.55.

c. For $f(x) = x^2$ and a fixed value of x, the definition of a derivative implies

$$\begin{aligned}
f'(x) &= \lim_{h \to 0} \frac{f(x+h) - f(x)}{h} \\
&= \lim_{h \to 0} \frac{(x+h)^2 - x^2}{h} \\
&= \lim_{h \to 0} \frac{x^2 + 2hx + h^2 - x^2}{h} \\
&= \lim_{h \to 0} \frac{2hx + h^2}{h} \\
&= \lim_{h \to 0} (2x + h) \\
&= 2x
\end{aligned}$$

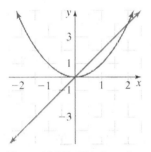

Figure 2.56 The function $f(x) = x^2$ (blue) and its derivative $f'(x) = 2x$ (red).

The function x^2 and its derivative $2x$ are illustrated in Figure 2.56.

d. Again, we use the definition. For a fixed number x

$$\begin{aligned}
f'(x) &= \lim_{h \to 0} \frac{f(x+h) - f(x)}{h} \\
&= \lim_{h \to 0} \frac{(x+h)^3 - x^3}{h} \\
&= \lim_{h \to 0} \frac{x^3 + 3hx^2 + 3h^2x + h^3 - x^3}{h} \\
&= \lim_{h \to 0} \frac{3hx^2 + 3h^2x + h^3}{h} \\
&= \lim_{h \to 0} (3x^2 + 3hx + h^2) \\
&= 3x^2
\end{aligned}$$

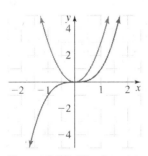

Figure 2.57 The function $f(x) = x^3$ (blue) and its derivative $f'(x) = 3x^2$ (red).

The function x^3 and its derivative $3x^2$ are illustrated in Figure 2.57.

e. The above parts suggest that $f'(x) = nx^{n-1}$ for n a whole number. Indeed, this turns out to be true, as we will show in Chapter 3. ■

When given numerical data, we can estimate the derivative of the data using the definition of the derivative with the smallest possible h value.

Example 2 **Estimating the derivative using a table**

In Example 1 of Section 2.1, we considered the population size of Mexico (in millions) in the early 1980s as reported in the following table:

Year	Population (millions)
1980	67.38
1981	69.13
1982	70.93
1983	72.77
1984	74.66
1985	76.60

Let $P(t)$ denote the population size t year after 1980. That is, $t = 0$ corresponds to 1980. For example, we found the average population growth rate in 1980 to be about 1.75 million/year, so we would write this as $P'(0) \approx 1.75$.

a. Estimate $P'(t)$ at $t = 0, 1, 2, 3, 4$ using $h = 1$ in the definition of a derivative.

b. In Problem 28 of Section 1.4, you may have found the population size could be represented by the exponential function $P(t) = 67.37(1.026)^t$. Approximate the derivative with an exponential function and compare it with $P(t)$. What do you notice?

Solution

a. The estimates of $P'(t)$ are calculated from the data as indicated in the third column in Table 2.6.

Table 2.6 Estimates of the rate of population growth in Mexico

Year	t	Estimates of $P'(t)$ from data	$0.26 P(t)$
1980	0	$\dfrac{P(1) - P(0)}{1} = 69.13 - 67.38 = 1.75$	1.75
1981	1	$\dfrac{P(2) - P(1)}{1} = 70.93 - 69.13 = 1.80$	1.80
1982	2	$\dfrac{P(3) - P(2)}{1} = 72.77 - 70.93 = 1.84$	1.84
1983	3	$\dfrac{P(4) - P(3)}{1} = 74.66 - 72.77 = 1.89$	1.89
1984	4	$\dfrac{P(5) - P(4)}{1} = 76.60 - 74.66 = 1.96$	1.94
1985	5	calculation not possible	–

b. To approximate $P'(t)$ by an exponential function, we can look at these ratios:

$$\frac{P'(1)}{P'(0)} = \frac{1.80}{1.75} \approx 1.029$$

$$\frac{P'(2)}{P'(1)} = \frac{1.84}{1.80} \approx 1.022$$

$$\frac{P'(3)}{P'(2)} = \frac{1.89}{1.84} \approx 1.027$$

$$\frac{P'(4)}{P'(3)} = \frac{1.94}{1.89} \approx 1.026$$

These ratios are all about the same. In fact, the average is 1.026, which is the ratio for the population function itself! We approximate $P'(t)$ by

$$P'(t) \approx 1.75(1.026)^t$$

Comparing this function with the function for the population growth, we see that

$$\frac{P'(t)}{P(t)} \approx \frac{1.75(1.026)^t}{67.37(1.026)^t} \approx 0.026$$

Thus

$$P'(t) \approx 0.026 P(t)$$

If we use this formula to calculate the derivative at times $t = 0, 1, \ldots, 5$ we see in Table 2.6 that values obtained are very close to the estimates obtained directly from the data, with only the $t = 4$ differing by an amount of 0.02. The advantage of having the formula is that we can calculate the derivative at any t value.

The solution to part **b** of Example 2 suggests that whenever $P(t)$ has the general exponential form $P(t) = ab^t$, then the derivative has the same form but differing by some constant; that is, $P'(t) = cP(t)$, where for Example 3 we obtained $c = 0.026$. This equation is an example of what is known as a *differential equation*, as it relates a function to its derivative. You will learn more about differential equations in Chapters 6 and 8. In Chapter 3, we will verify that the derivative of an exponential function is a constant multiple of the exponential function.

Notational alternatives

The primed-function notation f' that we have been using to denote derivatives is but one of several used in various texts. Newton used a "dot" notation, which we will not consider here. The notation that mathematicians prefer was developed by Leibniz. This notation is inspired by the following presentation of the derivative.

Let Δx represent a small change in x. The change of $y = f(x)$ over the interval $[x, x + \Delta x]$ is given by

$$\Delta y = f(x + \Delta x) - f(x)$$

The average rate of change of $y = f(x)$ over the interval $[x, x + \Delta x]$ is given by

$$\frac{\Delta y}{\Delta x}$$

Hence, the derivative of f at x is

$$\lim_{\Delta x \to 0} \frac{\Delta y}{\Delta x}$$

Leibniz represented this limit as

$$\frac{dy}{dx} = \lim_{\Delta x \to 0} \frac{\Delta y}{\Delta x}$$

where in some sense dy corresponds to an "infinitesimal" change in y and dx represents an "infinitesimal" change in x. Commonly used variations in notation that you will find in this and other calculus texts include

$$f'(x) = \frac{dy}{dx} = \frac{df}{dx} = \frac{d}{dx} f(x)$$

To indicate the derivative at the point $x = a$ using Leibniz notation, we use the cumbersome expression

$$\left. \frac{dy}{dx} \right|_{x=a} = f'(a)$$

Example 3   **Using alternative derivative notations**

Find the following derivatives.

a. $\dfrac{dy}{dx}\Big|_{x=-1}$ where $y = x^3$

b. $\dfrac{df}{dx}$ where $f(x) = x^5$

Solution

a. In Example 1, we found that the derivative of x^3 is $3x^2$. Since $\dfrac{dy}{dx}\Big|_{x=-1}$ is the derivative of $y = x^3$ evaluated at $x = -1$, we have

$$\frac{dy}{dx}\Big|_{x=-1} = 3x^2\Big|_{x=-1} = 3$$

b. In Example 1, we guessed that the derivative of x^n is nx^{n-1}; in which case, for $n = 5$ we have

$$\frac{df}{dx} = \frac{d}{dx}(x^5) = 5x^4$$

The next example draws upon research undertaken by ecologist Nathan Sanders and colleagues, who assessed the number of local ant species along an elevational gradient, Kyle Canyon, in the Spring Mountains of Nevada to obtain a measure called *species richness*. These data, illustrated in Figure 2.58, are plotted in terms of number of species of ants as a function of elevation (in kilometers).

Example 4   **Ant biodiversity**

Ecologists, noting that the number of ant species declines at both low (close to sea level) and high (at the tops of mountains) levels, fitted a parabola to the data plotted in Figure 2.58. The fit they obtained is given by

$$S = -10.3 + 24.9\,x - 7.7\,x^2 \text{ species}$$

where x is elevation measures in kilometers.

a. Find $\dfrac{dS}{dx}$.

b. Identify the units of $\dfrac{dS}{dx}$ and interpret $\dfrac{dS}{dx}$.

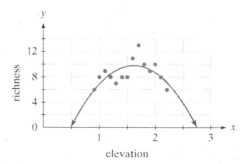

Figure 2.58 Number of species of ants as a function of elevation.

Data Source: N. Sanders, J. Moss, and D. Wagner, "Patterns of Ant Species Richness along Elevational Gradients in an Arid Ecosystem," *Global Ecology and Biogeography,* 12 (2003): 93–102.

Solution

a.
$$\frac{dS}{dx} = \lim_{h \to 0} \frac{S(x+h) - S(x)}{h}$$

$$= \lim_{h \to 0} \frac{[-10.3 + 24.9(x+h) \quad 7.7(x+h)^2] - [-10.3 + 24.9x - 7.7x^2]}{h}$$

$$= \lim_{h \to 0} \frac{24.9\,h - 15.4\,xh - 7.7h^2}{h}$$

$$= \lim_{h \to 0} (24.9 - 15.4\,x - 7.7\,h)$$

$$= 24.9 - 15.4x.$$

b. The units of $\dfrac{dS}{dx}$ are species per kilometer elevation. $\dfrac{dS}{dx}$ represents the rate of change of species richness with respect to elevation. For elevations less than $24.9/15.4 \approx 1.6$ kilometers, $\dfrac{dS}{dx} > 0$. Consequently, for elevations of less than 1.6 kilometers, an ant-loving entomologist would encounter more species of ants by hiking higher up. However, for elevations greater than 1.6 kilometers, an ant-loving entomologist would encounter more species of ants by walking downward.

Mean Value Theorem

To understand what the derivative tells us about the shape of a function, we need the mean value theorem (MVT). The proof of this theorem is given as a series of challenging exercises in Problem set 2.7.

Theorem 2.7   Mean value theorem

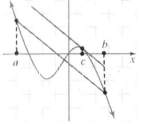

Figure 2.59 Mean value theorem in action. The slope of the tangent line at $x = c$ equals the slope of the secant line from $x = a$ to $x = b$.

Let f be a function that is continuous on the closed interval $[a, b]$ and differentiable on the open interval (a, b). Then there exists c in (a, b) such that

$$f'(c) = \frac{f(b) - f(a)}{b - a}$$

Notice that the right-hand side of this equation is the average rate of change of f over the interval $[a, b]$. Hence, the MVT states that for a differentiable function on an interval $[a, b]$, there is a point in the interval where the instantaneous rate of change equals the average rate of change. Alternatively, we can think of the MVT in geometric terms. Recall that the right-hand side of the MVT equation is the slope of the secant line passing through the points $(a, f(a))$ and $(b, f(b))$. Hence, the MVT asserts that there is a point in the interval such that the slope of the tangent line at this point equals the slope of the secant line. A graphical representation of this interpretation is given in Figure 2.59.

Example 5   Mean value theorem in action

Determine whether the MVT applies for the following functions f on the specified intervals $[a, b]$. If the MVT applies, then find c in (a, b) such that the statement of the MVT holds.

a. $f(x) = x^2$ on the interval $[0, 2]$

b. $f(x) = |x|$ on the interval $[-1, 1]$

Solution

a. Recall that $f'(x) = 2x$ for all x. Hence, f is differentiable on the interval $[0, 2]$. Consequently, the MVT applies and we should be able to find the desired value c. The average rate of change of f on $[0, 2]$ is given by

$$\frac{f(2) - f(0)}{2 - 0} = \frac{2^2 - 0}{2} = 2$$

Solving $f'(x) = 2x = 2$ yields $x = 1$. Hence, the instantaneous rate of change at $x = 1$ equals the average rate of change over the interval $[0, 2]$. The following plot with $y = x^2$ in red, the tangent line in blue, and the black line connecting $(0, f(0))$ to $(2, f(2))$ illustrates our calculations.

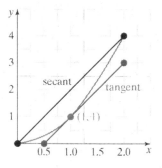

b. We need to find the derivative of $f(x) = |x|$. Since $f(x) = x$ for $x > 0$, we get

$$\frac{f(x + h) - f(x)}{h} = \frac{x + h - x}{h}$$

$$= \frac{h}{h} = 1$$

whenever every h is sufficiently small but not equal to zero. Hence, $f'(x) = 1$ for $x > 0$. On the other hand, since $f(x) = -x$ for $x < 0$, we get

$$\frac{f(x + h) - f(x)}{h} = \frac{-x - h - (-x)}{h}$$

$$= \frac{-h}{h} = -1$$

whenever h is sufficiently small but not equal to zero. Hence, $f'(x) = -1$ for $x < 0$.

What happens at the point $x = 0$? Our calculations imply that $\lim\limits_{h \to 0^+} \dfrac{f(h) - f(0)}{h} = 1$ but $\lim\limits_{h \to 0^-} \dfrac{f(h) - f(0)}{h} = -1$. Since the one-sided limits do not agree, f is not differentiable at $x = 0$ and the MVT need not apply. In fact, since the average rate of change over the interval $[-1, 1]$ equals $\dfrac{|-1| - |1|}{1 - (-1)} = 0$, there is no instantaneous rate of change of f that equals the average rate of change.

Example 6   Foraging for food

Hummingbirds (Figure 2.60) are small birds that weigh as little as three grams and have an energetically demanding lifestyle. With their wings beating at rates of eighty to a hundred beats per second, the hummingbird can lose 10% to 20% of its body weight in one to two hours. To survive, hummingbirds require relatively large amounts of nectar from flowers. Therefore, they spend much of the day flying

Figure 2.60 Ruby-throated hummingbird (*Archilochus colubris*).

between patches of flowers extracting nectar. As a hummingbird extracts nectar in a patch, its energetic gains $E(t)$ in calories increase with time t (in seconds). Figure 2.61 shows a hypothetical graph of energetic gains $E(t)$, in calories, in one patch.

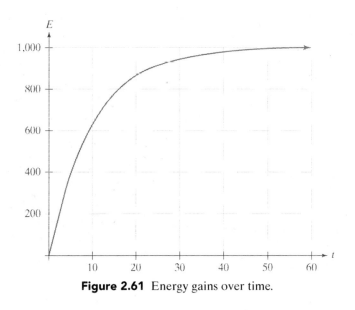

Figure 2.61 Energy gains over time.

a. Approximate the average rate of energy intake over the interval [0, 60].

b. Use the geometric interpretation of the mean value theorem to estimate the time when the instantaneous rate of energy intake equals the average rate of energy intake.

Solution

a. Since $E(0) = 0$ and $E(60) \approx 1000$, we obtain

$$\text{AVERAGE RATE OF ENERGY INTAKE} \approx \frac{1000}{60} \approx 16.7$$

calories per second.

b. Graphing the line connecting the points $(0, 0)$ and $(60, 1000)$ yields this result:

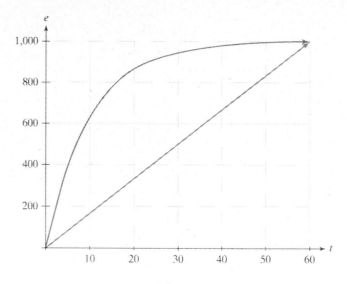

The slope of this line is approximately 16.7. To estimate the time at which $E'(t) = \dfrac{1{,}000}{60}$, we can place a straightedge on top of the red line segment and slowly slide it upward keeping it parallel to the red segment. If we slide it upward until the straightedge is tangent to the curve $y = E(t)$, then we obtain the following graph:

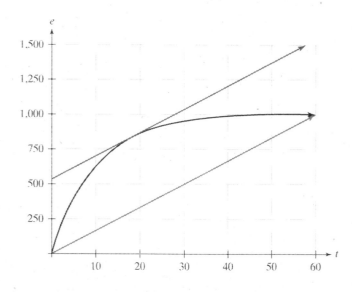

The blue segment shows the location of the tangent line at $t \approx 20$ seconds. Hence, the instantaneous rate of energy intake rate equals the average energy intake rate at $t \approx 20$.

It is worth noting from Figure 2.61 that $E'(t)$ is above the average rate of energy intake for $t < 20$ and below the average for $t > 20$. Hence, as we explore in more detail in Chapter 4, the hummingbird may consider leaving the patch after 20 seconds.

Derivatives and graphs

Using the mean value theorem, we can prove the following two facts about the relationship of the sign of the derivative f' to the graph of $y = f(x)$.

Increasing-Decreasing

Let f be a function that is differentiable on the interval (a, b). If $f'(x) > 0$ for all x in (a, b), then f is increasing on (a, b). If $f'(x) < 0$ for all x in (a, b), then f is decreasing on (a, b).

To prove these properties, assume that $f' > 0$ on (a, b). Take any two points $x_2 > x_1$ in the interval (a, b). By the mean value theorem, there exists a point c in the interval $[x_1, x_2]$ such that

$$f'(c) = \frac{f(x_2) - f(x_1)}{x_2 - x_1}$$

Since $f'(c) > 0$, we have

$$\frac{f(x_2) - f(x_1)}{x_2 - x_1} > 0$$

Since $x_2 - x_1 > 0$, we have $f(x_2) - f(x_1) > 0$. Equivalently, $f(x_2) > f(x_1)$. Therefore, f is increasing on the interval $[a, b]$. The case of $f' < 0$ on $[a, b]$ can be proved similarly, and it appears as an exercise in Problem Set 2.7.

Example 7 Identifying signs of f′

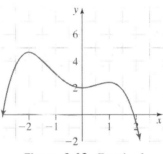

Figure 2.62 Graph of $y = f(x)$.

Let the graph of $y = f(x)$ be given by Figure 2.62. For the interval $[-3, 2]$, determine where the derivative of f is positive and where the derivative of f is negative.

Solution   Since the graph is increasing on the intervals $(-3, -2)$ and $(0, 1)$, $f' > 0$ on these intervals. Since the graph is decreasing on the intervals $(-2, 0)$ and $(1, 3)$, $f' < 0$ on these intervals.

For a function $y = f(x)$, a **turning point** is an x value where the function switches from increasing to decreasing, or vice versa. More precisely, if f is continuous on (a, b), then c in (a, b) is a turning point provided that either (i) f is increasing on (a, c) and decreasing on (c, b), or (ii) f is decreasing on (a, c) and increasing on (c, b). When f is differentiable on (a, b), turning points correspond to where the derivative f' changes sign. For example, if $f'(x) > 0$ on (a, c) and $f'(x) < 0$ on (c, b), then c is a turning point as the function switches from increasing to decreasing at $x = c$.

Example 8 Mix and match

Match the graphs of $y = f(x)$

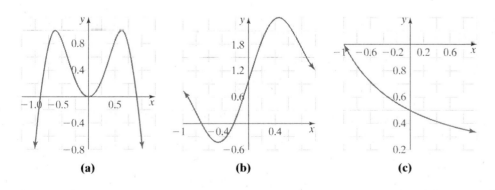

(a)   (b)   (c)

with the graph of their derivatives $y = f'(x)$

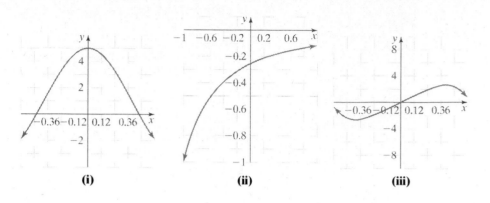

(i)   (ii)   (iii)

Solution

a. Looking at graph (a), we see three turning points at approximately $-0.6, 0,$ and 0.6. Turning points corresponds to x values where the derivative of function equals zero. Since only graph (iii) of the graphs (i)–(iii) intersects the x axis in three points, the derivative graph for (a) must be (iii).

b. The turning points for graph (b) are at approximately -0.4 and 0.4; the graph of (i) shows the derivative to be 0 at those points. Hence, graph (i) must be the derivative of the graph of (b).

c. There are no turning points on graph (c), so the derivative graph should not cross the x axis. Therefore, the derivative graph is (ii).

Example 9   Reconstructing f from f'

Let the graph of $y = f'(x)$ be given by the graph in Figure 2.63. Sketch a possible graph for $y = f(x)$.

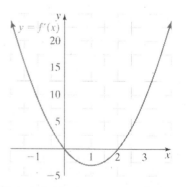

Figure 2.63 Graph of a derivative.

Solution   We can sketch the graph of f by looking at the intervals for which the graph of $f'(x)$ is positive or negative, as shown in Figure 2.64. On intervals where $f'(x)$ is positive, we sketch a curve that is increasing, and on intervals where $f'(x)$ is negative, we sketch a curve that is decreasing.

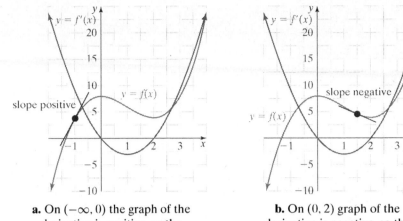

a. On $(-\infty, 0)$ the graph of the derivative is positive, so the graph of f is rising (slope positive).

b. On $(0, 2)$ graph of the derivative is negative, so the graph of f is falling.

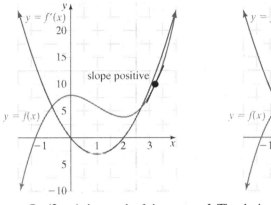

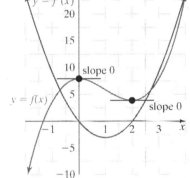

c. On $(2, \infty)$ the graph of the derivative is positive, so the graph of f is rising.

d. The derivative crosses the x-axis at $x = 0$ and $x = 2$, so the graph of f reaches a high point at $x = 0$ and a low point at $x = 2$.

Figure 2.64 Construction of the graph of a function f given its derivative f'.

A possible graph of $y = f(x)$ is shown here:

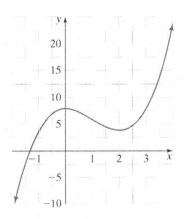

PROBLEM SET 2.7

Level 1 DRILL PROBLEMS

Use the definition of a derivative to find $f'(x)$ *for the functions in Problems 1 to 8.*

1. $f(x) = 8$

2. $f(x) = 3x - 2$

3. $f(x) = -x^2$

4. $f(x) = x + x^2$

5. $f(x) = x^4$

6. $f(x) = x^3 - x$

7. $f(x) = \dfrac{1}{x}$

8. $f(x) = \dfrac{1}{2x}$

Use the derivatives found in Problems 1 to 8 to find the values requested in Problems 9 to 16.

9. $\dfrac{dy}{dx}\Big|_{x=-2}$ where $y = 8$

10. $\dfrac{dy}{dx}\Big|_{x=-2}$ where $y = 3x - 2$

11. $\dfrac{dy}{dx}\Big|_{x=4}$ where $y = -x^2$

12. $\dfrac{dy}{dx}\Big|_{x=4}$ where $y = x + x^2$

13. $\dfrac{dy}{dx}\Big|_{x=2}$ where $y = x^4$

14. $\dfrac{dy}{dx}\Big|_{x=2}$ where $y = x^3 - x$

15. $\dfrac{dy}{dx}\Big|_{x=10}$ where $y = \dfrac{1}{x}$

16. $\dfrac{dy}{dx}\Big|_{x=10}$ where $y = \dfrac{1}{2x}$

Find at what point the slope of the instantaneous rate of change equals the average rate of change over the specified intervals in Problems 17 to 22. Also, provide a sketch that illustrates this relationship.

17. $f(x) = 8$ over the interval $[-5, 5]$

18. $f(x) = 3x - 2$ over the interval $[3, 4]$

19. $f(x) = -x^2$ over the interval $[-1, 1]$

20. $f(x) = x + x^2$ over the interval $[0, 1]$

21. $f(x) = \dfrac{1}{x}$ over the interval $[1, 2]$

22. $f(x) = \dfrac{1}{2x}$ over the interval $[1, 4]$.

Mix and match the graphs in Problems 23 to 28 with the graphs labeled (A) to (F), which are the derivative graphs.

23.

24.

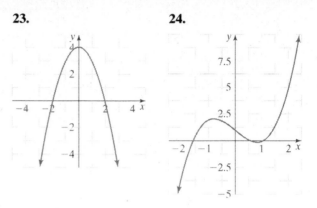

25.

26.

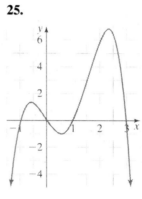 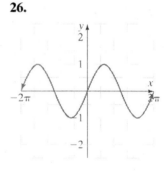

27.

28.

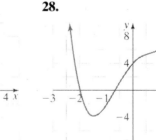

A

B

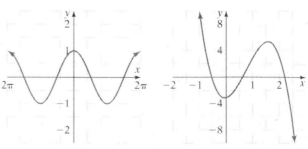

C   **D**

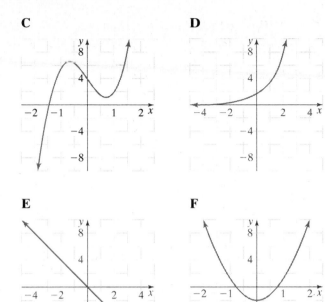

E   **F**

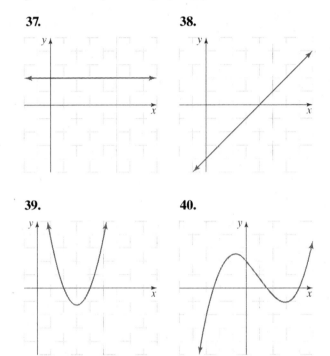

For each of the functions given in Problems 29 to 34, find intervals for which f is increasing and intervals for which f is decreasing.

29. $f(x) = x^2 - x + 1$

30. $f(x) = 5 - x^2$

31. $f(x) = x^3 + x$

32. $f(x) = 8 - x^3$

33. Let f be the function for which the graph of the derivative $y = f'(x) = g(x)$ is given by

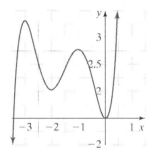

34. Let f be the function for which the graph of the derivative $y = f'(x) = g(x)$ is given by

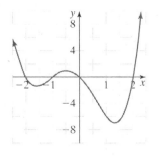

35. For the graph $y = g(x)$ given in Problem 33, estimate all values of c in $[-3, 0]$ such that

$$\frac{g(-3) - g(0)}{3} = g'(c)$$

36. For the graph $y = g(x)$ given in Problem 34, estimate all values of c in $[-2, 2]$ such that

$$\frac{g(-2) - g(2)}{4} = g'(c)$$

In each of Problems 37 to 40, the graph of a function f' is given. Draw a possible graph of f.

37.   **38.**

39.   **40.**

Level 2 **APPLIED AND THEORY PROBLEMS**

41. Let f be differentiable on the interval (a, b). Use the mean value theorem to prove if $f' < 0$ on $[a, b]$, then f is decreasing on (a, b).

42. **Rolle's theorem**: Let f be differentiable on (a, b) and continuous on $[a, b]$. Assume $f(a) = f(b) = 0$. Without using the mean value theorem, argue that there exists a c in (a, b) such that $f'(c) = 0$.

43. Use Rolle's theorem to prove the mean value theorem.

44. A baseball is thrown upward and its height at time t in seconds is given by

$$H(t) = 100t - 16t^2 \text{ meters}$$

  a. Find the velocity of the baseball after t seconds.

  b. Find the time at which the velocity of the ball is 0.

  c. Find the height of the ball at which the velocity is 0.

45. To study the response of nerve fibers to a stimulus, a biologist models the sensitivity, S, of a particular group of fibers by the function

$$f(t) = \begin{cases} t & \text{for } 0 \le t \le 3 \\ \dfrac{9}{t} & \text{for } t > 3 \end{cases}$$

where t is the number of days since the excitation began.

a. Over what time period is sensitivity increasing? When is it decreasing?

b. Graph $S'(t)$.

46. During the time period 1905–1940, hunters virtually wiped out all large predators on the Kaibab Plateau near the Grand Canyon in northern Arizona. The data for the deer population, P, over this period of time are as follows:

Year	Deer population	Year	Deer population
1905	4,000	1927	37,000
1910	9,000	1928	35,000
1915	25,000	1929	30,000
1920	65,000	1930	25,000
1924	100,000	1931	20,000
1925	60,000	1935	18,000
1926	40,000	1939	10,000

Source: www.biologycorner.com/worksheets/kaibab.html

a. Estimate $P'(t)$ for $1905 \le t \le 1939$.

b. Graph and interpret $P'(t)$.

47. In 1913, Carlson studied a growing culture of yeast (see Problem 45 in Problem Set 2.4 and Section 6.1). The table of population densities $N(t)$ at one-hour intervals is shown here:

Time	Population	Time	Population	Time	Population
0	9.6	6	174.6	12	594.8
1	18.3	7	257.3	13	629.4
2	29.0	8	350.7	14	640.8
3	47.2	9	441.0	15	651.1
4	71.1	10	513.3	16	655.9
5	119.1	11	559.7	17	659.6

a. Estimate $N'(t)$ for $0 \le t \le 17$.

b. Graph $N'(t)$ and briefly interpret this graph.

48. Our ruby-throated hummingbird has entered another patch of flowers, and the energy she is getting as a function of time in the patch is plotted below.

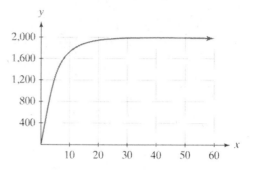

a. Find the average energy intake rate.

b. Estimate at what time the instantaneous energy intake rate equals the average intake rate.

49. Two radar patrol cars are located at fixed positions 6 miles apart on a long, straight road where the speed limit is 65 miles per hour. A sports car passes the first patrol car traveling at 60 miles per hour; then 5 minutes later, it passes the second patrol car going 65 miles per hour. Analyze this situation to show that at some time between the two clockings, the sports car exceeded the speed limit. Hint: Use the MVT.

50. Suppose two race cars begin at the same time and finish at the same time. Analyze this situation to show that at some point in the race they had the same speed.

CHAPTER 2 REVIEW QUESTIONS

1. Find at what point the instantaneous rate of change of the function $f(x) = x^3 - x$ equals the average rate of change over the interval $[-1, 2]$. Provide a sketch that illustrates this relationship.

2. In the 2012 Summer Olympics in London, swimmer Ye Shiwen swam the last 50 meters of her 400-meter individual medley final quicker than the winner of the men's race, Ryan Lochte. The 50-meter split times for both swimmers are shown in the following table:

Distance (meters)	Split time (seconds) for Shiwen	Split time (seconds) for Lochte
50	28.85	25.82
100	33.34	30.06
150	35.34	31.32
200	34.20	31.00
250	38.80	34.68
300	39.22	35.65
350	29.75	29.31
400	28.93	29.22

Data Source: http://www.guardian.co.uk/sport/datablog/2012/aug/02/olympics-2012-ye-shiwen-400-medley-statistics-data#data

a. Find the average velocity of both swimmers in the last split of the race.

b. Find the average velocity of both swimmers over the entire race.

3. Use the definition of derivative to find $f'(x)$ for
$$f(x) = \frac{1}{x^2}.$$

4. Find the average rate of change of $f(x) = x^2 - 2x + 1$ on $[1, 3]$ and the instantaneous rate of change at $x = 1$.

5. Consider $f(x) = 9 - x^2$ and $g(x) = \ln x$.

a. Graph $y = f(x)$ and $y = g(x)$ on the same coordinate axes.

b. Plot the point $P(2, \ln 2)$ on the graph of g. Graphically, estimate the position of the line tangent to g at the point P.

c. Plot the point $Q(2, 5)$ on the graph of f. Algebraically find the line tangent to f at the point Q. Use the equation of this tangent line to show that it "kisses" the graph of f at the point Q.

6. Find $\lim\limits_{x \to 4} \dfrac{16 - x^2}{x - 4}$ with the suggested methods.

a. Graphically

b. Using a table of values

c. By algebraic simplification

d. By using the informal definition of limit

e. Using technology

7. Let $f(x) = \begin{cases} 2 - 2x & \text{if } x < 2, x \neq 1 \\ \dfrac{-1}{x - 4} & \text{if } x > 2 \text{ and } x \neq 7 \end{cases}$

Find the requested limits.

a. $\lim\limits_{x \to 1} f(x)$ **b.** $\lim\limits_{x \to 2^-} f(x)$

c. $\lim\limits_{x \to 2^+} f(x)$ **d.** $\lim\limits_{x \to 7} f(x)$

e. Is f continuous at $x = 7$? If not, is this reparable?

8. Evaluate the sequential limits, if they exist.

a. $\lim\limits_{n \to \infty} \dfrac{2n^3 + 4n}{1 - 2n^2 - 5n^3}$

b. $\lim\limits_{n \to \infty} a_n$ where $a_1 = 1$, and $a_{n+1} = \dfrac{1}{a_n}$

c. $\lim\limits_{n \to \infty} a_n$ where $a_1 = 14$, and $a_{n+1} = a_n/2$

9. The graph of a function f' is given. Draw a possible graph of f.

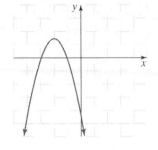

10. An environmental study of a certain suburban community suggests that t years from now, the average level of carbon dioxide in the air can be modeled by the formula
$$q(t) = 0.05t^2 + 0.1t + 3.4$$
parts per million.

a. At what rate will the CO_2 level be changing with respect to time one year from now?

b. By how much will the CO_2 level change in the first year?

c. By how much will the CO_2 level change over the next (second) year?

11. Consider the function $y = \dfrac{2x^2 + 1}{x(x - 2)}$.

a. Find the horizontal asymptote(s) of this function.

b. Find the right-hand side and left-hand side limits of this function at all of its vertical asymptotes.

12. The canopy height (in meters) of a tropical elephant grass (*Pennisetum purpureum*) is modeled by
$$h(t) = -3.14 + 0.142t - 0.0016t^2$$
$$+ 0.0000079t^3 - 0.000000133t^4$$
where t is the number of days after mowing.

a. Sketch the graph of $h(t)$.

b. Sketch the graph of $h'(t)$.

c. Approximately when was the canopy height growing most rapidly? Least rapidly?

13. The concentration $C(t)$ of a drug in a patient's blood stream is given by

t in minutes	0	0.1	0.2	0.3	0.4	0.5	0.6	0.7	0.8	0.9	1.0
C in milligrams/ milliliter	0	0.2	0.4	0.6	0.8	0.9	1.0	0.9	1.0	0.9	0.7

a. Estimate $C'(t)$ for $t = 0, 0.1, \ldots 0.9$.

b. Sketch $C'(t)$ and interpret it.

14. Suppose that systolic blood pressure of a patient t years old is modeled by
$$P(t) = 39.73 + 23.5 \ln(0.97t + 1)$$
for $0 \leq t \leq 65$, where $P(t)$ is measured in millimeters of mercury.

a. Sketch the graph of $y = P(t)$.

b. Using the graph in part **a**, sketch the graph of $y = P'(t)$.

15. Find the limit $\lim_{x \to \infty} \dfrac{e^x}{2 + 2e^x}$ and determine how positive x needs to be to ensure that $\dfrac{e^x}{2 + 2e^x}$ is within one millionth of the limiting value L.

16. Whales have difficulty finding mates in the vast oceans of the world when their population numbers drop below a critical value. Thus, a model of the growth of whale populations from one whale generation to the next is going to be relatively more robust at intermediate whale densities than at low densities when finding mates is a problem, or at high densities when competition for food is a problem. The form of a hypothetical function f in the difference equation

$$a_{n+1} = f(a_n)$$

that reflects the above properties is illustrated in Figure 2.65, where a_n is the density of the whales in generation n (units are whales per 1000 sq km).

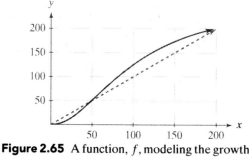

Figure 2.65 A function, f, modeling the growth of a hypothetical whale population.

Determine $\lim_{n \to \infty} a_n$ when $a_1 = 55$. Justify your answer.

17. Give a proof that the function $f(x) = xe^{-x} - 0.1$ has at least one positive root.

18. Sketch a graph of a function $y = f(x)$ on the interval $[-2, 2]$ such that $f(-2) = f(0) = f(2) = 0$, $\dfrac{dy}{dx} > 0$ on $[-2, -1]$ and $(1, 2]$, and $\dfrac{dy}{dx} < 0$ on $(-1, 1)$.

19. The average population growth rate of Mexico from 1981 to 1983 was 1.82 million per year and from 1983 to 1985 was 1.915 million per year. Assume the population size $N(t)$ as a function of time and $N'(t)$ are continuous. Prove that at some point in time between 1981 and 1985, the instantaneous rate of population growth was 1.85 million per year.

20. Consider the graph of f shown in Figure 2.66. On the interval $[-3, 4]$ find the points of discontinuity as well as places where the derivative does not exist. Explain your reasoning.

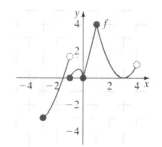

Figure 2.66 A function, f, on the interval $[-3, 4]$.

GROUP PROJECTS

Seeing a project through on your own, or working in a small group to complete a project, teaches important skills. The following projects provide opportunities to develop such skills.

Project 2A A simple model of gene selection

One of the simplest problems in population genetics is to consider what happens to a particular version of a gene, where each version is referred to as an *allele*, that is being selected for or against because it confers some advantage or disadvantage to carriers of that allele. Examples of disadvantageous or *deleterious alleles* are those associated with genetic diseases such as sickle cell anemia, hemophilia, and Tay-Sachs disease. Most of our genes come in pairs of alleles, and if one allele in the pair is deleterious, then the effect of that allele may often be partially or fully masked by the other allele in the pair.

If a person has a double dose of the deleterious allele, the disease is expressed in its severest form. If a person has a single dose of the deleterious allele (i.e., one normal and one deleterious allele) then, depending on the disease, a milder version of the disease may be expressed (partial masking), or the individual is completely healthy (full masking). In the latter case, the individual is said to be a *carrier* for the disease (e.g., hemophilia).

On the other hand, alleles may confer a strong advantage to an organism that carries them. For example, if an insect carries an allele of a particular gene that allows it to detoxify a pesticide or a virus carries an allele that allows it to neutralize an otherwise effective drug, then we say that these pests and pathogens carry alleles of genes that *confer resistance* to the chemicals that would otherwise control or kill them.

Sometimes individuals who carry two different alleles of a particular gene are better off than individuals who have two copies of the same allele, regardless of which allele it is Biologist call this condition *heterozygous superiority*, and it is associated with the phenomenon called *hybrid vigor*. For example, an individual human is going to be better at fighting disease if he or she has two different alleles at an immune system gene responsible for the production of antibodies that protect against invading pathogens, such as the influenza virus.

Population geneticists have devised a simple model that allows them to assess what happens to such alleles. The form of this model is $p_{n+1} = f(p_n)$, where p_n represents the proportion of the allele in question in the population in the nth generation: If $p_n = 1$, then every individual in the population has a double dose of the allele in question. If $p_n = 0$, then no one has even a single dose of this allele. If $p_n = 0.5$, some individuals do not have the allele, some have a single dose, and some a double dose of the allele, but the total proportion in the population of this allele is 1/2.

In this simple allele proportion model, the specific form of $f(p)$ is

$$f(p) = \frac{p(ap + (1 - p))}{ap^2 + 2p(1 - p) + b(1 - p)^2}$$

where $a \geq 0$ and $b \geq 0$ are constants that determine whether the allele in question confers an overall advantage or disadvantage or is associated with heterozygote superiority.

In this project, investigate the value of the equilibria that arise for various combinations of a and b, paying particular attention to whether a or b is greater than or less than 1. Interpret the various cases in terms of the limiting values of several sequences of proportions p_n that start at different values p_1 satisfying $0 < p_1 < 1$. Also, describe how these cases correspond to classification of the alleles as advantageous, deleterious, or associated with heterozygote superiority. Find specific cases in the literature, or by searching the Web, to illustrate these three phenomena.

Project 2B Fibonacci rabbit growth when death is included

In the rabbit population growth process proposed by Fibonacci (Example 10 of Section 2.5), the assumption was that all the rabbits live forever. As an alternative, let's assume that only a proportion s of rabbits alive each month survive to the next month (independent of how old they are or what gender they are) and, of those that survive, only a proportion p of the females from the month before produce a litter that always consists of r male-female pairs. Investigate the growth of this population by carrying out the following tasks.

a. Derive an equation for the rate at which the proportion of pairs increases from month to month as a function of the three population parameters $0 < s \leq 1$, $0 < p \leq 1$, and r a positive integer. Note that getting the correct equation can be a little tricky, so use a diagram similar to the one outlined in Chapter 1: see the Fibonacci $\mathfrak{H}$istorical $\mathfrak{Q}$uest, that is, Problem 38 in Section 1.7. In particular, starting out with a suitable number of new-born pairs, draw diagrams for the cases $(s, p, r) = (1/2, 1, 1)$, $(1, 1/2, 1)$, and $(1, 1, 2)$ and use these to construct a general expression for $a_n = f(a_{n-1}, a_{n-2})$ that contains the three parameters in question.

b. What must hold true for the parameters s, r, and p to ensure the population size remains constant for all time for any initial population size? For the case $r = 1$, express s as a function of p such that the population is neither growing nor declining. Hence, in the square of the positive quadrant of the p-s plane defined by $0 \leq p \leq 1$ and $0 \leq s \leq 1$, shade all points where the rabbit population is growing and all points where it is declining. *Hint:* Write a difference equation for $x_n = a_n/a_{n-1}$.

c. Repeat exercise **b** for the case $r = 2$ and make a general statement about how the two shaded areas change as r increases.

CHAPTER 2

Problem Set 2.1, Page 117

1. -3 **3.** 12 **5.** $\frac{1}{5}$ **7.** -3 **9.** 6 **11.** $\frac{1}{4}$ **13.** -32 feet/second
15. -16 feet/second

17.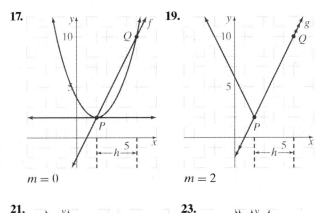

$m = 0$

19.

$m = 2$

21.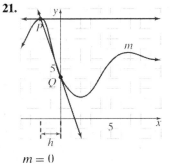

$m = 0$

23.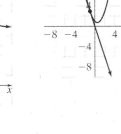

25.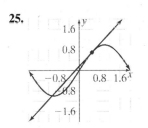

27.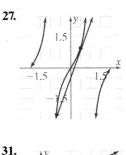

29.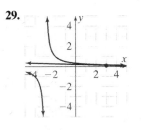

31.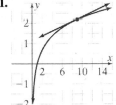

33.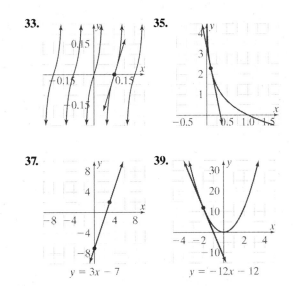

35.

37.

$y = 3x - 7$

39.

$y = -12x - 12$

41.

$y = 1/6\, x + 3/2$

43. on $[0, 2]$: increase of 3.19 million people per decade; on $[2, 4]$: increase of 5.64 million people per decade
45. on $[0, 30]$: 0.07 cm of froth is evaporating per second; on $[60, 90]$: 0.0433 cm of froth is evaporating per second

47. at $t = 0$: increase of 2.37 million people per decade; at $t = 2$: increase of 4.18 million people per decade
49. at $x = 0$: estimate 0.06 cm of froth evaporating per second; at $x = 60$: estimate 0.05 cm of froth evaporating per second **51.** velocities for Ben Johnson:

Distance (in meters)	0	10	20	30	40	50
Velocity (meters per second)	0	5.9	9.6	10.8	11.6	11.9
Distance (in meters)	60	70	80	90	100	
Velocity (meters per second)	12.0	11.9	11.8	11.5	11.1	

53. 1.25 kg/yr

Problem Set 2.2, Page 130

1. a. 0 **b.** 4 **3. a.** 6 **b.** 3 **5. a.** 0 **b.** 1 **c.** does not exist
7. a. 0 **b.** 0 **c.** 0 **9.** $\lim\limits_{x \to 1^+} f(x) = 2$ **11.** $\lim\limits_{x \to 3^-} h(x) = 2$
13. $\lim\limits_{x \to 5^-} f(x) = 13$ **15.** $\lim\limits_{x \to 2} h(x) = 10$ **17.** 1 **19.** -1 **21.** $\frac{1}{4}$
23. 0 **25.** 0 **27. a.** 0.1 **b.** 0.01 **c.** 0.001 **29. a.** 0.01
b. 0.0001 **c.** 0.000001

1

31. a.

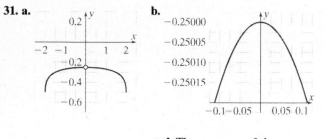

b.

c.

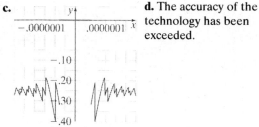

d. The accuracy of the technology has been exceeded.

33. Given $\epsilon > 0$, choose $\delta = \epsilon$. Then,

$$|f(x) - L| = |(x + 1) - 6|$$
$$= |x - 5|$$
$$< \delta = \epsilon$$

35. Given $\epsilon > 0$, choose δ to be the smaller of 1 or $\dfrac{\epsilon}{2}$. Then,

$$|f(x) - L| = \left|\frac{1}{x} - \frac{1}{2}\right|$$
$$= \left|\frac{2 - x}{2x}\right|$$
$$= \frac{|x - 2|}{2|x|}$$
$$< \frac{\delta}{2} < \epsilon$$

37. Given $\epsilon > 0$, choose δ to be the smaller of 1 or $\dfrac{\epsilon}{5}$. Then,

$$|f(x) - L| = |(x^2 + 2) - 6|$$
$$= |x^2 - 4|$$
$$= |(x + 2)(x - 2)|$$
$$= |x + 2||x - 2|$$
$$< 5\delta = 5\left(\frac{\epsilon}{5}\right) = \epsilon$$

39. a.

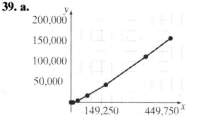

b. Limit exists for all values of a.

41. $f(x) = \begin{cases} \dfrac{x}{75}, & \text{if } 0 \le x \le 3 \\ \dfrac{1}{25} & \text{if } x > 3 \end{cases}$

Problem Set 2.3, Page 143

1. $\lim\limits_{x \to 1} f(x) = -1$ **3.** $\lim\limits_{x \to 0^-} f(x) = -1$; $\lim\limits_{x \to 0^+} f(x) = 1$; $\lim\limits_{x \to 0} f(x)$ does not exist **5.** $\lim\limits_{x \to 1^-} f(x) = 0$; $\lim\limits_{x \to 1^+} f(x) = 1$; $\lim\limits_{x \to 1} f(x)$ does not exist **7.** $\dfrac{8}{35}$ **9.** -1 **11.** $\sin 3 + \dfrac{1}{5}$ **13.** $\dfrac{1}{3}$
15. $x = -1$ (jump), $x = 1$ (removable) **17.** $x = 1$ (jump)
19. $f(2) = 3$ **21.** not possible (jump) **23.** Let
$f(x) = -x^7 + x^2 + 4$; $f(1) > 0$, $f(2) < 0$; root for $1 < x < 2$
25. Let $f(x) = \sqrt[3]{x} - x^2 - 2x + 1$; $f(0) > 1$, $f(1) < 0$; root for
$0 < x < 1$ **27.** Let $f(x) = x2^x - \pi$; $f(1) < 0$, $f(2) > 0$; root
for $1 < x < 2$ **29. a.** -2.709 **b.** -1.562 **c.** -0.194 **d.** 1.903
31. $\dfrac{5}{2}$ **33.** $\dfrac{\pi}{16}$ **39.** Let a, b, and c be chosen. If x is large
enough in the positive direction, we have
$x^3 + ax^2 + bx + c > 0$. Also, if x is large enough in the
negative direction, we have $x^3 + ax^2 + bx + c < 0$. These
follow from the fact that x^3 dominates the quadratic
$ax^2 + bx + c$. Then by the intermediate value theorem, there
must be at least one part of the graph that crosses the x axis;
hence it must have at least one real root.

41. a. $g(N) = \begin{cases} 5 & \text{if } N \ge c \\ \dfrac{100}{1 + N} & \text{if } N < c \end{cases}$ **b.** $c = 19$

43. It will happen in 2056. **45.** 2,383; 29,248 **47.** 1,365; 36,603

Problem Set 2.4, Page 155

1. 0 **3.** ∞ **5.** $-\infty$ **7.** ∞ **9.** ∞ **11.** limit does not exist
13. $\dfrac{2}{21}$ **15.** 0 **17.** 0 **19.** $\dfrac{5}{2}$ **21.** 0 **23.** $\dfrac{a}{2}$
25. $2 < x \le 2 + 10^{(-6)}$ **27.** $1 - 10^{(-6)} \le x < 1$
29. $\sin^{-1}(10^{-6}) \le x < 0$ **31.** $x \le -2\sqrt{5}$ **33.** $x \le -21$
35. $x > 1,000$ **37.** $x > 10^6$ **39. a.** $t > 62$ **b.** $t > 65$
41. a. $y = 25.11$, $x = -19.76$; the horizontal asymptote is the
maximum uptake rate

b.

43. $x > 463$ **b.** $x > 4,637$
45. the limit is 660, which is
the maximum size the
population will approach as
$t \to \infty$
47. $y = 16$; $x > 1.291$

Problem Set 2.5, Page 171

1. $\dfrac{1}{3}$ **3.** 1 **5.** no limit because of oscillation **7.** no limit
because of oscillation **9. a.** $L = 1$ **b.** $n > 2,997$ **11. a.** $L = 0$
b. $n > 1,000,000$ **13. a.** $L = 0$ **b.** $n > 1,000$ **15.** 500,000
17. 20 **19.** ∞ **21.** 1 **23.** 0 **25.** 1 **27.** $\dfrac{2}{3}$ **29.** 1 **31.** no limit;
function not defined after a_2 **33.** $\dfrac{1 + \sqrt{21}}{2}$ **35. b.** 0 **c.** $n \ge 7$
d. $n \ge 997$ **37. a.** frequency approaches 1 **b.** frequency
approaches 0 **39.** 50.0% **41.** 36.6% **43.** 20.7%
45. $r = 0.9$: 0.5, 0.725, 0.904438, 0.982225, 0.997938, 0.99979,
0.999979, 0.999998, 1, 1, $\cdots$; converges to 1
$r = 1.5$: 0.5, 0.875, 1.039063, 0.97818, 1.010196, 0.994746,
1.002586, 0.998697, 1.000649, 0.999675, 1.000162, 0.999919,
1.000041, 0.99998, 1.00001, $\cdots$; converges to 1

$r = 2.1$: 0.5, 1.025, 0.971188, 1.02995, 0.965171, 1.035765, 0.957973, 1.042521, $\cdots$; diverges by oscillation

Problem Set 2.6, Page 182

1. 3 **3.** -2 **5.** $-\dfrac{1}{32}$ **7.** 3 **9.** $\dfrac{1}{6}$ **11.** $3x - y - 2 = 0$
13. $2x + y - 1 = 0$ **15.** $x + 32y + 8 = 0$ **17.** $3x - y + 2 = 0$
19. $x - 6y + 9 = 0$ **21.** not differentiable at $x = 0$. **23.** not differentiable at $x = \pm 1, x = 0$ **25.** not differentiable at $x = 2$
27. a. **29.**

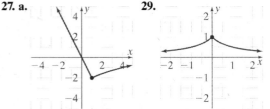

The graph (Problem 29) is continuous but not differentiable at $x = 0$. **31. a.** -54 m/s **b.** 0.625 s **c.** it is falling at 10 m/s
33. $A'(50) = -0.9$ **35. a.** 9.2 **b.** 14.2 **c.** the prevalence is increasing more rapidly at higher latitude **37. a.** -28.96
b. the units are particles per milliliter/day. **39. a.** -0.061; -0.015 **b.** The derivatives are the rate of change of the amount of glucose consumed per microgram of glucose in the environment per hour.

Problem Set 2.7, Page 196

1. 0 **3.** $-2x$ **5.** $4x^3$ **7.** $-\dfrac{1}{x^2}$ **9.** 0 **11.** -8 **13.** 32 **15.** -0.01
17. everywhere   **19.** $c = 0$

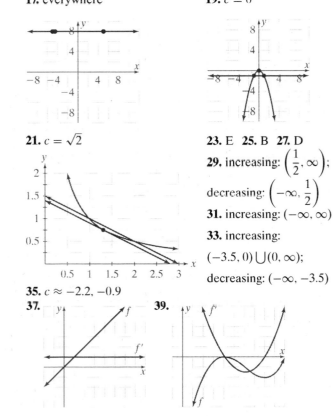

21. $c = \sqrt{2}$

35. $c \approx -2.2, -0.9$
37.   **39.**

23. E **25.** B **27.** D
29. increasing: $\left(\dfrac{1}{2}, \infty\right)$; decreasing: $\left(-\infty, \dfrac{1}{2}\right)$
31. increasing: $(-\infty, \infty)$
33. increasing: $(-3.5, 0) \cup (0, \infty)$; decreasing: $(-\infty, -3.5)$

45. a. increasing for $0 \le t \le 3$; decreasing for $t > 3$

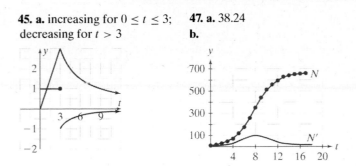

47. a. 38.24
b.

49. From the MVT, there must be some time that the car travels at 72 mph.

Chapter 2 Review Questions, Page 198

1. instantaneous   **3.** $-\dfrac{2}{x^3}$

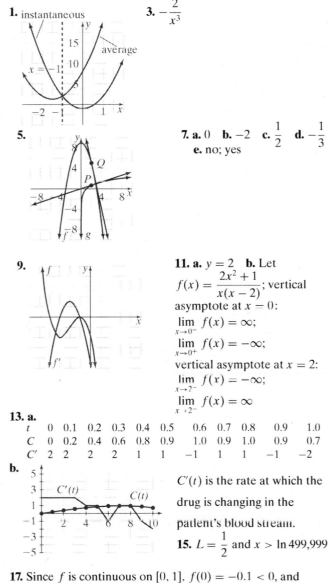

5.

7. a. 0 **b.** -2 **c.** $\dfrac{1}{2}$ **d.** $-\dfrac{1}{3}$
e. no; yes

9.

11. a. $y = 2$ **b.** Let $f(x) = \dfrac{2x^2 + 1}{x(x-2)}$; vertical asymptote at $x = 0$:
$\lim_{x \to 0^-} f(x) = \infty$;
$\lim_{x \to 0^+} f(x) = -\infty$;
vertical asymptote at $x = 2$:
$\lim_{x \to 2^-} f(x) = -\infty$;
$\lim_{x \to 2^-} f(x) = \infty$

13. a.

t	0	0.1	0.2	0.3	0.4	0.5	0.6	0.7	0.8	0.9	1.0
C	0	0.2	0.4	0.6	0.8	0.9	1.0	0.9	1.0	0.9	0.7
C'	2	2	2	2	1	1	-1	1	1	-1	-2

b.

$C'(t)$ is the rate at which the drug is changing in the patient's blood stream.
15. $L = \dfrac{1}{2}$ and $x > \ln 499{,}999$

17. Since f is continuous on $[0, 1]$, $f(0) = -0.1 < 0$, and $f(1) = \dfrac{1}{e} - 0.1 > 0$, the intermediate value theorem implies there exists a root of f on the interval $(0, 1)$.

19. Since the average population growth rate from 1981 to 1983 is 1.82 million per year, the mean value theorem implies there is a year t_1 between 1981 and 1983 such that $N'(t_1) = 1.82$. Similarly, there is a year t_2 between 1983 and 1985 such that $N'(t_2) = 1.915$. Since $N'(t)$ is continuous on the interval $[t_1, t_2]$, the intermediate value theorem implies there is a time t between t_1 and t_2 such that $N'(t) = 1.85$.

CHAPTER 3

Derivative Rules and Tools

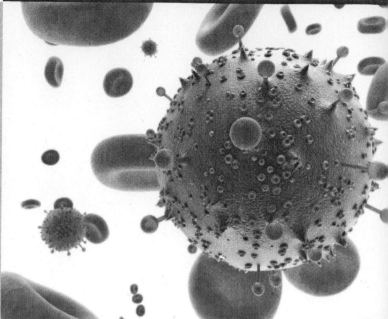

Figure 3.1 Differential calculus is used in Section 3.1 to model the rate at which HIV virions (as depicted) is cleared from the body during drug therapy.

© Muzon/iStockphoto

Preview

"I loved history, but still loved science, and thought maybe you don't need quite as much calculus to be a biology major."

Elizabeth Moon, science fiction writer (b. 1945)
Part 2 of an interview with Jayme Lynn Blaschke
November 1999; http://www.sfsite.com/02b/em75.htm

In the previous chapters we have only been able to compute derivatives by directly appealing to the definition of the derivative. As you may have noticed, computing derivatives in this manner quickly becomes tedious. In this chapter we consider the rules and tools that allow us to quickly compute the derivative of any imaginable function. Learning these rules is critical, as expressed in the following admonition (from Colin Adams, Joel Hass, and Abigail Thompson, *How to Ace Calculus: The Streetwise Guide*, New York: W. H. Freeman, 1998):

"Know these backwards and forwards. They are to calculus what 'Don't go through a red light' and 'Don't run over a pedestrian' are to driving."

The first three sections of this chapter provide essential basic rules for calculating derivatives, and the fourth section focuses on the important trigonometric functions. The last three sections expand these tools so that we can apply them to a variety of applications in biology and the life sciences. Applications in this chapter include predicting the growth of a fetal heart and of the Yellowstone bison population. Also, we use differential calculus to investigate the clearance rate of HIV viral particles (see Figure 3.1) from infected humans, how Northwestern crows break whelk shells, dose-response curves in the context of administering drugs and into rates of mortality due to airborne diseases, and Usain Bolt's record-breaking, 100-meter run in the Olympic Games in Beijing.

3.1   Derivatives of Polynomials and Exponentials

As we have seen in Chapters 1 and 2, we can use polynomial and exponential functions to model natural phenomena ranging from the melting of Arctic sea ice to the decay of a drug in the body. To facilitate finding the instantaneous rates of change of these processes, we now derive general rules for computing the derivatives of polynomials and exponentials.

Derivatives of $y = x^n$

In Example 1 of Section 2.7, we proved that

$$\frac{d}{dx}x = 1$$

$$\frac{d}{dx}x^2 = 2x$$

$$\frac{d}{dx}x^3 = 3x^2$$

and we guessed that $\frac{d}{dx}x^n = nx^{n-1}$. This powerful result is known as the **power rule**.

Power Rule

For any real number $n \neq 0$,

$$\frac{d}{dx}x^n = nx^{n-1}$$

At this point, we are only equipped to prove the power rule for any natural number n. Later, we shall prove the general power rule. The proof when n is a natural number involves the binomial expansion of $(a + b)^n$ (if you don't remember this expansion, look it up on the world wide Web):

$$(a + b)^n = a^n + na^{n-1}b + \frac{n(n-1)}{2}a^{n-2}n^2 + \cdots + b^n$$

Now to the proof of the power rule for n a natural number:

Proof. If $f(x) = x^n$, then from the binomial theorem

$$f(x + h) = (x + h)^n$$

$$= x^n + nx^{n-1}h + \frac{n(n-1)}{2}x^{n-2}h^2 + \cdots + h^n$$

From the definition of derivative we have

$$f'(x) = \lim_{h \to 0} \frac{f(x + h) - f(x)}{h}$$

$$= \lim_{h \to 0} \frac{\left[x^n + nx^{n-1}h + \frac{n(n-1)}{2}x^{n-2}h^2 + \cdots + h^n\right] - [x^n]}{h}$$

$$= \lim_{h \to 0} \frac{nx^{n-1}h + \frac{n(n-1)}{2}x^{n-2}h^2 + \cdots + h^n}{h}$$

$$= \lim_{h \to 0} \frac{h\left[nx^{n-1} + \frac{n(n-1)}{2}x^{n-2}h + \cdots + h^{n-1}\right]}{h}$$

$$= \lim_{h \to 0} \left[nx^{n-1} + \frac{n(n-1)}{2}x^{n-2}h + \cdots + h^{n-1}\right]$$

$$= nx^{n-1}$$

Note that if $n = 0$, then $f(x) = x^n = x^0 = 1$, so $f'(x) = 0$ as expected, since 1 is a constant.

Example 1   Using the power rule

Find

a. $\dfrac{d}{dx}x^5\Big|_{x=2}$

b. $\dfrac{d}{dQ}Q^{29}$

Solution

a. $\dfrac{d}{dx}x^5\Big|_{x=2} = 5x^4\Big|_{x=2} = 5 \cdot 2^4 = 80$

b. $\dfrac{d}{dQ}Q^{29} = 29Q^{28}$

Derivatives of sums, differences, and scalar multiples

The limit laws from Chapter 2 allow us to quickly compute the derivatives of a sum, difference, or scalar multiple whenever we know the derivatives for f and g. In stating these laws, it is more succinct to use the "prime" rather than full Leibnitz notation.

> **Elementary Differentiation Rules**
>
> Let f and g be differentiable at x. Let c be a constant. Then
>
> **Sum** $(f + g)'(x) = f'(x) + g'(x)$
>
> **Difference** $(f - g)'(x) = f'(x) - g'(x)$
>
> **Scalar multiple** $(cf)'(x) = cf'(x)$

In other words, the derivative of a sum is the sum of the derivatives, the derivative of a difference is the difference of the derivatives, and the derivative of a scalar multiple is the scalar multiple of the derivative.

Combining these elementary differentiation rules with the power rule allows us to differentiate any polynomial. Note that throughout this and subsequent chapters, we use the verb *differentiate* in a technical sense. To differentiate a function is to "take its derivative" using the methods of differential calculus presented in this book. It does not mean that we are trying to distinguish the function from some other function, unless we specifically say so!

Example 2   Using differentiation rules

Let $f(x) = x^3 + 3x^2 + 10$.

a. Find f'. Justify each step of your differentiation.

b. Determine on what intervals f is increasing and on what intervals f is decreasing.

Solution

a.
$$\frac{d}{dx}(x^3 + 3x^2 + 10) = \frac{d}{dx}x^3 + \frac{d}{dx}3x^2 + \frac{d}{dx}10 \qquad \textit{sum rule}$$

$$= \frac{d}{dx}x^3 + 3\frac{d}{dx}x^2 + \frac{d}{dx}10 \qquad \textit{scalar multiple rule}$$

$$= 3x^2 + 6x + 0 \qquad \textit{power rule}$$

Hence

$$f'(x) = 3x^2 + 6x$$

b. To determine where f is increasing and where f is decreasing, we need to find where $f' > 0$ and $f' < 0$, respectively. Since

$$f'(x) = 3x^2 + 6x = 3x(x + 2)$$

we look at the signs of the factors and the product by looking at a number line.

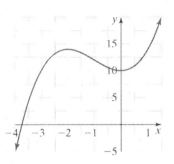

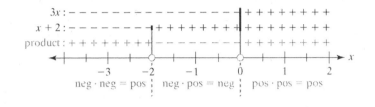

On the interval $(-\infty, -2)$, f is increasing since $f'(x) > 0$; on $(-2, 0)$, f is decreasing since $f'(x) < 0$, on $(0, \infty)$; f is increasing again since $f'(x) > 0$. Graphing $y = f(x)$ confirms these calculations.   ■

Example 3   Growth of a fetal heart (see Figure 3.2)

In 1992, a team of cardiologists determined how the left ventricular length L (in centimeters) of the heart in a fetus increases from eighteen weeks until birth. (See J. Tan, N. Silverman, J. Hoffman, M. Villegas, and K. Schmidt, "Cardiac Dimensions Determined by Cross-Sectional Echocardiography in the Normal Human Fetus from 18 Weeks to Term," *American Journal of Cardiology* 70(1992): 1459–1497.) The cardiologists used the following function to provide a continuous representation of the the data (i.e., model the data)

$$L(t) = -2.318 + 0.2356t - 0.002674t^2$$

where t is the age of the fetus (in weeks). Here $t = 18$ means at the end of week 18.

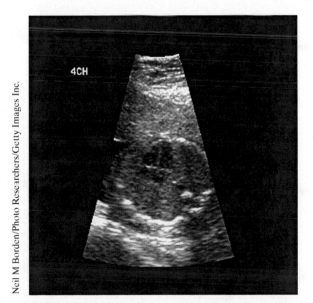

Figure 3.2 Fetal echocardiogram reveals a four-chamber heart correctly oriented in the left chest.

a. Find $L'(t)$ for $18 \le t \le 38$.

b. Discuss and interpret the units of $L'(t)$.

c. During which week between weeks 18 and 38 is the ventricular length growing most rapidly, and what is the associated rate? When is the ventricular length growing most slowly?

Solution

a.
$$\frac{dL}{dt} = \frac{d}{dt}(-2.318) + 0.2356\frac{d}{dt}(t) - 0.002674\frac{d}{dt}(t^2) \quad \textit{sum and scalar multiple laws}$$

$$= 0 + 0.2356 \cdot 1 - 0.002674 \cdot 2t \quad \textit{power law}$$

$$= 0.2356 - 0.005348\,t$$

b. The units of $L'(t)$ are centimeters per week. $L'(t)$ describes the rate at which the ventricular length is growing.

c. Since $L'(t)$ is a linear function with negative slope, its largest value on the interval $[18, 38]$ is at $t = 18$ and its smallest value on this interval is at $t = 38$. In particular,

$$L'(18) = 0.2356 - 0.005348 \times 18 = 0.139336 \quad \text{cm/week}$$

and

$$L'(38) = 0.2356 - 0.005348 \times 38 = 0.032376 \quad \text{cm/week}$$

Hence, the ventricular length in the last twenty weeks of pregnancy is increasing most rapidly at the beginning of this twenty week period and growing least rapidly at the time of birth.

∎

In addition to being used to finding derivatives of all polynomials, the power rule and the scalar multiplication rule can be used to find derivatives of all scaling laws.

Example 4   **Back to lifting weights**

In Example 6 of Section 1.3, we modeled the amount an Olympic weightlifter could lift as

$$L = 20.15 M^{2/3} \text{ kilograms}$$

where M is the body mass in kilograms of the weightlifter. Find and interpret $\dfrac{dL}{dM}$ at $M = 90$ kilograms.

Solution   To compute the derivative, we note that $n = 2/3$, and although n is not an integer, the power rule still applies with $n - 1 = -\dfrac{1}{3}$. Thus we obtain

$$\left.\frac{dL}{dM}\right|_{M=90} = 20.15\frac{d}{dM}M^{2/3}\bigg|_{M=90}$$

$$= 20.15 \cdot \frac{2}{3} \cdot M^{-1/3}\bigg|_{M=90}$$

$$\approx 2.998 \qquad \textit{correct to three decimal places}$$

Hence, for weightlifters weighing close to 90 kilograms, the rate at which the amount lifted increases with mass of the weightlifter is 2.998 kilograms per kilogram of body mass.

∎

Derivatives of exponentials

Consider the function $f(x) = a^x$ for some positive constant $a > 0$. To find the derivative, we use the definition of the derivative. Let x be a fixed number.

$$f'(x) = \lim_{h \to 0} \frac{f(x+h) - f(x)}{h} \qquad \textit{definition of derivative, provided the limits exist}$$

$$= \lim_{h \to 0} \frac{a^{x+h} - a^x}{h} \qquad \textit{since } f(x) = a^x$$

$$= \lim_{h \to 0} \frac{(a^h - 1)a^x}{h} \qquad \textit{common factor}$$

$$= \left[\lim_{h \to 0} \frac{a^h - 1}{h} \right] a^x \qquad \textit{property of limits provided } k = \lim_{h \to 0} \frac{a^h - 1}{h} \textit{ exists}$$

$$= ka^x$$

$$= kf(x)$$

Although it is beyond the scope of this book, it can be shown that $k = \lim_{h \to 0} \dfrac{a^h - 1}{h}$ exists whenever $a > 0$. In the following example, we estimate the value of k for the case $a = 2$.

Example 5   Derivative of 2^x

Find $\dfrac{d}{dx} 2^x$ by estimating $\lim_{h \to 0} \dfrac{2^h - 1}{h}$.

Solution   We showed that $\dfrac{d}{dx} 2^x = k 2^x$ where $k = \lim_{h \to 0} \dfrac{2^h - 1}{h}$. To estimate k, we can create the following table with a calculator:

h	$\dfrac{2^h - 1}{h}$	h	$\dfrac{2^h - 1}{h}$
0.1	0.717735	−0.1	0.66967
0.01	0.695555	−0.01	0.69075
0.001	0.693387	−0.001	0.692907
0.0001	0.693171	−0.0001	0.693123

Since $k \approx 0.693$, $\dfrac{d}{dx} 2^x \approx (0.693) 2^x$. In Example 6, we show that in fact $k = \ln 2 \approx 0.69315$. ∎

Since $f'(x) = kf(x)$ for an appropriate choice of k whenever $f(x) = a^x$, we can ask this question: Is there a value of a such that $k = 1$? It turns out that the number e, which we defined in Section 1.4 as $e = \lim_{n \to \infty} (1 + 1/n)^n$, is the appropriate choice of a. Namely,

$$\frac{d}{dx} e^x = e^x \text{ for all real } x$$

Except for multiplying by a constant, e^x is the only function that remains unchanged under the operation of differentiation; that is, if $f(x) = f'(x)$, then $f(x) = ae^x$ for some real number a. This fact inspired one mathematician to write: "Who has not been amazed to learn that the function $y = e^x$, like a phoenix rising again from its own ashes, is its own derivative?" (Francois l'Lionnais, *Great Currents of Mathematical Thought*, vol. 1, New York: Dover Publications, 1962). Armed with the derivative of e^x, we can use the rules of differentiation to find the derivative of more general exponential functions $f(x) = e^{ax}$.

Derivative of the Natural Exponential	For any real number a, $$\frac{d}{dx}e^{ax} = ae^{ax}$$ Further, for $b > 0$, $$\frac{d}{dx}b^x = (\ln b)b^x$$

Proof.   If $a = 0$, then

$$\frac{d}{dx}e^0 = 0$$

so the statement is true. If a is any nonzero real number, then $e^{ax} = (e^a)^x$ and

$$\frac{d}{dx}e^{ax} = \left(\lim_{h \to 0} \frac{e^{a(x+h)} - e^{ax}}{h}\right) \qquad \textit{definition of a derivative}$$

$$= \left(\lim_{h \to 0} \frac{(e^{ax}e^{ah} - e^{ax})}{h}\right) \qquad \textit{addition law of exponents}$$

$$= \left(\lim_{h \to 0} \frac{(e^{ah} - 1)e^{ax}}{h}\right) \qquad \textit{taking out a common factor}$$

$$= \left(\lim_{h \to 0} \frac{e^{ah} - 1}{h}\right)e^{ax} \qquad \textit{Taking constant out of the limit}$$

To find this limit, define $\Delta x = ah$. Since $h = \Delta x/a$ and $h \to 0$ whenever $\Delta x \to 0$,

$$\lim_{h \to 0} \frac{e^{ah} - 1}{h} = \lim_{\Delta x \to 0} \frac{e^{\Delta x} - 1}{\Delta x/a} \qquad \textit{substitute } \Delta x = ah$$

$$= a \lim_{\Delta x \to 0} \frac{e^{\Delta x} - 1}{\Delta x} \qquad \textit{limit law for products}$$

$$= a \cdot 1 \qquad \textit{derivative of } e^x \textit{ evaluated at } x = 0$$

Thus, we have shown that

$$\frac{d}{dx}e^{ax} = ae^{ax}$$

For the last part, find the value of a such that $b = e^a$ and finish the details on your own in Problem 27 in Problem Set 3.1. ■

Example 6   Déjà Vu

Find the exact value of $\frac{d}{dx}2^x$.

Solution $\frac{d}{dx}2^x = (\ln 2)2^x$. Since $\ln 2 \approx 0.693$, this agrees with the result obtained in Example 5. ■

Example 7   Clearance of HIV

Human immunodeficiency virus (shown in Figure 3.1) is a blood-borne pathogen that is typically transmitted through sexual contact or sharing of needles among drug users. HIV attacks the immune system. Understanding how the viral load in the blood of an HIV-infected individual changes with time is critical to treating HIV patients with a "cocktail" of several antiretroviral drugs. Theoretical immunologists have used data from various experiments to model observed changes in the viral load $V(t)$, in particles per milliliter, of an HIV patient undergoing antiretroviral drug therapy for t days.* If no new viral particles are generated by the host, they found that the viral load over time can be modeled by the equation

$$V(t) = 216{,}000\, e^{-0.2t}$$

Find $V'(t)$ and interpret it.

Solution

$$V'(t) = 216{,}000 \frac{d}{dt} e^{-0.2t} \qquad \textit{differentiation for scalar multiples}$$

$$= 216{,}000(-0.2)e^{-0.2t} \qquad \textit{derivative of an exponential}$$

$$= -43{,}200 e^{-0.2t}$$

The units of $V'(t)$ are particles per milliliter per day. $V'(t)$ describes the rate at which the viral load is changing whenever it is not replenished by new viral particles. Since $V'(t) < 0$ for all t, the viral load is decreasing.

Note that in HIV-infected patients, new viral particles are produced in the various cells found in the blood and in lymph tissue. In Chapter 6, we account for this second component of the infection process to obtain a more complete model of viral load dynamics within human hosts.

Example 8   Exponential depletion of resources

In Example 4 of Section 1.4, we projected that the U.S. population would contain $N(t) = 8.3(1.33)^t$ million individuals t decades after 1815. Suppose the amount of food produced each year, measured in terms of rations (i.e. the amount of food needed to sustain one individual for one year), grew linearly during this same period with the amount given by the equation

$$R(t) = 10 + 4t$$

The number of surplus rations $S(t)$ over this period can be found by taking the difference of the above two functions:

$$S(t) = R(t) - N(t)$$
$$= 10 + 4t - 8.3(1.33)^t$$

Determine at what point in time $S(t)$ starts decreasing.

Solution   To find where S changes from increasing to decreasing, we need to determine where $S'(t)$ changes sign from $S'(t) > 0$ to $S'(t) < 0$. In particular, we need to find where $S'(t) = 0$, provided the derivative exists at the point in question. We have

$$S'(t) = \frac{d}{dt}[10 + 4t - 8.3(1.33)^t] \qquad \textit{derivative of both sides of given equation}$$

$$= \frac{d}{dt}10 + 4\frac{d}{dt}t - 8.3\frac{d}{dt}(1.33)^t \qquad \textit{elementary rules of differentiation}$$

$$= 0 + 4 - 8.3(\ln 1.33)(1.33)^t \qquad \textit{power and exponential rules of differentiation}$$

$$= 4 - 8.3(\ln 1.33)(1.33)^t$$

---

*A. S. Perelson, A. U. Neumann, M. Markowitz, J. M. Leonard, D. D. Ho, "HIV-1 Dynamics In Vivo: Virion Clearance Rate, Infected Cell Lifespan, and Viral Generation Time," *Science* 271 (1996): 1582–1586. Also, A. S. Perelson and P. W. Nelson, "Mathematical Analysis of HIV-1 Dynamics In Vivo," *SIAM Review* 41(1999):3–44.

If we now solve for the values of t satisfying $S'(t) = 0$, we obtain

$$4 - 8.3(\ln 1.33)(1.33)^t = 0$$

$$(1.33)^t = \frac{4}{8.3 \ln 1.33} \qquad \textit{rearranging terms}$$

$$t \ln 1.33 = \ln\left(\frac{4}{8.3 \ln 1.33}\right) \qquad \textit{taking logarithms}$$

$$t = \frac{\ln\left(\dfrac{4}{8.3 \ln 1.33}\right)}{\ln 1.33} \qquad \textit{dividing by } \ln 1.33$$

$$\approx 1.84$$

Evaluating $S'(t)$ at values of t greater than and less than 1.84, we find that $S'(t) > 0$ for $t < 1.84$ and $S'(t) < 0$ for $t > 1.84$. Since the units of time are in decades, we see that in the year $1815 + 18.4 \approx 1833$ the surplus of resources will begin to decline. Plotting $y = S(t)$ reveals that at $t \approx 1.84$, $S(t)$ takes on its largest value and then begins to decrease, as shown in Figure 3.3.

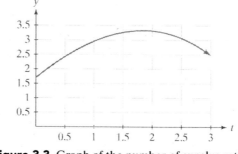

Figure 3.3 Graph of the number of surplus rations.

PROBLEM SET 3.1

Level 1 DRILL PROBLEMS

Differentiate the functions given in Problems 1 to 14. Assume that C is a constant.

1. a. $f(x) = x^7$ **b.** $g(x) = 7^x$

2. a. $f(x) = x^4$ **b.** $g(x) = 4^x$

3. a. $f(x) = 3x^5$ **b.** $g(x) = 3(7)^5$

4. a. $f(x) = x^3 + C$ **b.** $g(x) = C^2 + x$

5. a. $f(x) = x^2 + 3\pi + C$ **b.** $g(x) = \pi^2 - 2x - C$

6. $f(x) = 5x^3 - 5x^2 + 3x - 5$

7. $f(x) = x^5 - 3x^2 - 1$

8. $f(x) = 2x^2 - 5x^8 + 1$

9. $s(t) = 4e^t - 5t + 1$

10. $f(t) = 5 - e^{2t}$

11. $f(t) = 5.9(2.25)^t$

12. $f(t) = 82.1(1.85)^t$

13. $g(x) = Cx^2 + 5x + e^{-2x}$

14. $F(x) = 5e^{Cx} - 4x^2$

Determine on what intervals each function given in Problems 15 to 19 is increasing and on what intervals it is decreasing.

15. $f(x) = x^3 - x^2 + 1$

16. $g(x) = \dfrac{1}{3}x^3 - 9x + 2$

17. $f(x) = x^5 + 5x^4 - 550x^3 - 2{,}000x^2 + 60{,}000x$
(round to the nearest tenth)

18. $g(x) = x^3 + 35x^2 - 125x - 9{,}375$

19. $H(w) = 2w - e^w$

20. Let $f(x) = x^{1/2}$.

   a. Find the derivative using the definition of the derivative.

   b. Apply the power rule with $n = 1/2$.

21. Let $f(x) = x^{3/2}$.

   a. Find the derivative using the definition of derivative. Hint: Write $x^{3/2}$ as $x\sqrt{x}$ and rationalize the numerator.

   b. Apply the power rule with $n = 3/2$.

Simplify the functions in Problems 22 to 26 and find their derivative whenever it is well defined.

22. $g(x) = x^2(x^3 - 3x)$

23. $f(x) = \dfrac{x^{1/3}}{x^2}$

24. $f(x) = (e^x - 1)(e^x + 1)$

25. $h(t) = \dfrac{3^t + 3^{-t}}{2^t}$

26. $q(x) = \dfrac{x^2 - 4}{x + 2}$

Level 2 APPLIED AND THEORY PROBLEMS

27. Prove that for any real number $b > 0$

$$\frac{d}{dx}b^x = (\ln b)b^x$$

28. Use the limit laws to prove the sum rule for differentiation:

$$(f + g)' = f' + g'$$

29. Use the limit laws to prove the scalar multiple rule for differentiation:

$$(cf)' = cf'$$

for a constant c.

30. After pouring a mug full of the German beer Erdinger Weissbier (see Section 1.4), Leike ("Demonstration of Exponential Decay," pp. 21–26) measured the height of the beer froth at regular time intervals. He estimated the height (in centimeters) of the beer froth as

$$H(t) = 1.7(0.94)^t$$

where t is measured in seconds. Find

$$\left.\frac{dH}{dt}\right|_{t=25}$$

and interpret this quantity.

31. A drug that influences weight gain was tested on eight animals of the same size, age, and sex. Each animal was randomly assigned to a dose level. After two weeks, the difference W in the end and start weight (measured in decagrams) was calculated. The best-fitting quadratic equation to the data was found to be

$$W = 1.13 - 0.41\,D + 0.17\,D^2$$

where D is the dose level that ranges from 1 to 8.

a. Find $\dfrac{dW}{dD}$ and identify its units.

b. When does weight gain increase with dose level D?

32. Using data from 158 marine species, John Hoenig of the Virginia Institute of Marine Sciences studied how the natural mortality rate M of a species depends on the maximum T observed age ("Empirical Use of Longevity Data to Estimate Mortality

Rates," *Fisheries Bulletin* 82 (1983): 898–902). Using linear regression, he found

$$M(T) = e^{1.44 - 9.82\,T}$$

where T is measured in years. Find and interpret

$$\left.\frac{dM}{dT}\right|_{T=10}$$

33. During an outbreak of influenza at a school the number of students who became ill after t days is given by

$$N(t) = 50(1 - Ce^{-0.1t})$$

where C is a constant.

a. If ten people were ill at the beginning of the epidemic (when $t = 0$), what is C?

b. At what rate is $N(t)$ increasing when $t = 5$?

34. A glucose solution is administered intravenously into the blood stream of a patient at a constant rate of r milligrams/hour. As the glucose is being administered, it is converted into other substances and removed from the blood stream. Suppose the concentration of the glucose solution after t hours is given by

$$C(t) = r - (r - k)e^{-t}$$

where k is a constant.

a. If C_0 is the initial concentration of glucose (when $t = 0$), what is C_0 in terms of r and k?

b. What is the rate at which the concentration of glucose is changing at time t?

35. In Problem 39 in Problem Set 1.3, we found that the length L (cm) of a pumpkin is related to the width W (cm) of a pumpkin by the allometric equation

$$L = 1.12W^{0.95}$$

How rapidly is length changing with regard to width for pumpkins of size 5 cm compared with those of 50 cm?

36. At the beginning of Section 1.4, we saw that the population model $N(t) = 8.3(1.33)^t$, where N is in millions and t is in decades starting at $t = 0$ representing the year 1815, can be used to describe the size of the U.S. population during most of the nineteenth century. Use this relationship to compare the total rate of growth of the U.S. population in 1815 versus the growth rate in 1865 (i.e., five decades later).

37. In Section 1.3, we found that the amount lifted (in kilograms) by an Olympic weightlifter can be predicted by the scaling law

$$L = 20.15\,M^{2/3}$$

where M is the mass of the lifter in kilograms. Find and interpret $\left.\dfrac{dL}{dM}\right|_{M=100}$.

38. In Example 12 of Section 1.6 (changing the names of the variables from x and y to M and R), we found that the metabolic rate (in kilocalories/day) for animals ranging in size from mice to elephants is given by the function $\ln R = 0.75 \ln M + 4.2$ which yields the equation

$$R = e^{4.2} M^{3/4},$$

where M is the body mass of the animal in kilograms.

a. The average California Condor weighs about 10 kg. Find and interpret $\left. \dfrac{dR}{dM} \right|_{M=10}$.

b. The average football player weighs about 100 kg. Find and interpret $\left. \dfrac{dR}{dM} \right|_{M=100}$.

c. Compare and discuss the quantities that you found in parts **a** and **b**.

39. The number of children newly infected with a particular pathogen that is transmitted through contact with their mothers has been modeled by the function

$$N(t) = -0.21t^3 + 3.04t^2 + 44.05t + 200.29$$

where $N(t)$ is measured in thousands of individuals per year, and t is the number of years since 2000. In epidemiology, $N(t)$ is known as an *incidence function*.

a. At what rate is the incidence function N changing with respect to time in the year 2010?

b. When will the incidence start to decline?

3.2   Product and Quotient Rules

Previously, we saw that the derivative of a sum equals the sum of the derivatives, and the derivative of a difference equals the difference of the derivatives. Armed with these elementary differentiation rules, we might guess that the derivative of a product is the product of the derivatives. The following simple example, however, shows this not the case. Let $f(x) = x$ and $g(x) = x^2$, and consider their product

$$p(x) = f(x)g(x) = x^3$$

Because $f'(x) = 1$ and $g'(x) = 2x$, the product of the derivatives is

$$f'(x)g'(x) = (1)(2x) = 2x$$

whereas the actual derivative of $p(x) = x^3$ is $p'(x) = 3x^2$. Hence, our naïve guess is wrong! It is also easy to show that the derivative of a quotient is not the quotient of the derivatives. The goal of this section is to uncover the correct rules for differentiation for products and quotients of functions.

Product rule

To derive a rule for products, we appeal to our geometric intuition by considering areas where $\Delta x > 0$ and $f(x)$ and $g(x)$ are assumed to be increasing, positive differentiable functions of x. Note that the algebraic steps stand alone—without considering area or making the assumptions we made in the previous sentence.

Let

$$\underbrace{p(x)}_{area\ of\ rectangle} = \underbrace{f(x)}_{length} \underbrace{g(x)}_{width}$$

This product of p can be represented as the area of a rectangle:

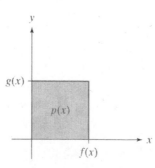

Next, we find

$$\underbrace{p(x + \Delta x)}_{\text{area of larger rectangle}} = \underbrace{f(x + \Delta x)}_{\text{length}} \underbrace{g(x + \Delta x)}_{\text{width}}$$

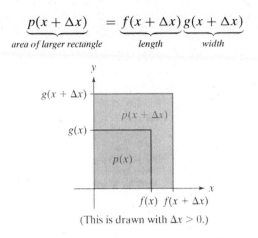

(This is drawn with $\Delta x > 0$.)

The next step gives us the area of the "inverted L-shaped" region:

$$p(x + \Delta x) - p(x) = f(x + \Delta x)g(x + \Delta x) - f(x)g(x)$$

The key to the proof of the product rule is to rewrite this difference. We can see how to do this by looking at the area of the inverted L-shaped region in another way:

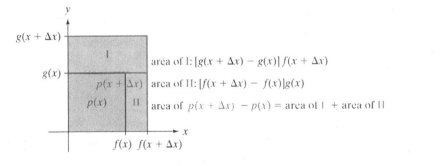

area of I: $[g(x + \Delta x) - g(x)]\, f(x + \Delta x)$

area of II: $[f(x + \Delta x) - f(x)]g(x)$

area of $p(x + \Delta x) - p(x) = $ area of I + area of II

$$\underbrace{p(x + \Delta x) - p(x)}_{\text{area of inverted L-shaped region}} = \underbrace{[g(x + \Delta x) - g(x)]\, f(x + \Delta x)}_{\text{area of region I}} + \underbrace{[f(x + \Delta x) - f(x)]g(x)}_{\text{area of region II}}$$

Divide both sides by Δx (where $\Delta x \neq 0$):

$$\frac{p(x + \Delta x) - p(x)}{\Delta x} - \frac{[g(x + \Delta x) - g(x)]}{\Delta x} f(x + \Delta x) + \frac{[f(x + \Delta x) - f(x)]}{\Delta x} g(x)$$

The last step in deriving the product rule is to take the limit as $\Delta x \to 0$:

$$p'(x) = \lim_{\Delta x \to 0} \frac{p(x + \Delta x) - p(x)}{\Delta x}$$

$$= \lim_{\Delta x \to 0} \left\{ f(x + \Delta x) \left[\frac{g(x + \Delta x) - g(x)}{\Delta x} \right] + g(x) \left[\frac{f(x + \Delta x) - f(x)}{\Delta x} \right] \right\}$$

$$= \lim_{\Delta x \to 0} f(x + \Delta x) \underbrace{\lim_{\Delta x \to 0} \left[\frac{g(x + \Delta x) - g(x)}{\Delta x} \right]}_{\text{This is the derivative of } g.} + g(x) \underbrace{\lim_{\Delta x \to 0} \left[\frac{f(x + \Delta x) - f(x)}{\Delta x} \right]}_{\text{This is the derivative of } f.}$$

$$= f(x)g'(x) + g(x)f'(x) \qquad \lim_{\Delta x \to 0} f(x + \Delta x) = f(x) \text{ because } f \text{ is continuous}$$

We have just proved the **product rule**.

Product Rule

Let f and g be differentiable at x. Then

$$(fg)'(x) = f'(x)g(x) + f(x)g'(x)$$

A simple way to remember the product rule is with this mnemonic: "The derivative of the product is the derivative of the first times the second plus the derivative of the second times the first." Or sing-song the words of the following ditty aloud or in your mind.

Sing the product rule in time,
One prime two plus one two prime.
Isn't mathematics fun,
One prime two plus two prime one.

Example 1   Computing with the product rule

Find $p'(x)$ and determine on what intervals p is increasing.

a. $p(x) = xe^x$ **b.** $p(x) = x^2 2^x$

Solution

a. Let $f(x) = x$ and $g(x) = e^x$. Then $p(x) = f(x)g(x)$. By the product rule,

$$p'(x) = f'(x)g(x) + f(x)g'(x)$$
$$= 1 \cdot e^x + x \cdot e^x$$
$$= (1 + x)e^x$$

Since $e^x > 0$ for all x, we have $p'(x) > 0$ if and only if $1 + x > 0$. Hence, p is increasing on the interval $(-1, \infty)$. Indeed, plotting $y = p(x)$ supports this conclusion:

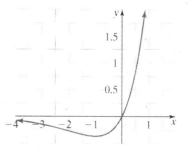

b. Let $f(x) = x^2$ and $g(x) = 2^x$. Then $p(x) = f(x)g(x)$. Recall that $f'(x) = 2x$ and $g'(x) = (\ln 2)2^x$. Hence, by the product rule,

$$p'(x) = f'(x)g(x) + f(x)g'(x)$$
$$= 2x2^x + x^2(\ln 2)2^x$$
$$= x2^x(2 + x \ln 2)$$

Since $p' > 0$ whenever $x > 0$ or $x < -\frac{2}{\ln 2}$, p is increasing on these intervals. Indeed, plotting $y = p(x)$ supports this conclusion:

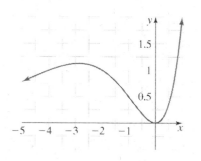

In the next problem, we encounter the notion that many events in biology are not certain but occur with a particular probability. Examples of this is an individual dying over a specified interval of time, a female giving birth to a particular number of individuals (e.g., the litter size of a mouse), or a molecule binding to a receptor site on a cell. You may have already learned, or will learn if you take a course in basic probability theory, that probabilities associated with independent events combine through multiplication. For example, if one flips a coin and the probability of getting heads is $p = 0.5$, then the probability of getting heads twice in a row is $p \times p = 1/2 \times 1/2 = 1/4$. Similarly, if one rolls a fair (honest or unbiased) six-sided die, then the probability of rolling a 3 is $p = 1/6$ and the probability of rolling an even number is $p = 3/6 = 1/2$. Thus the probability of getting a 3 on the first roll and an even number on the second roll is $1/6 \times 3/6 = 3/36 = 1/12$.

Although calculus and probability theory are generally taught as separate courses in college, probability is such an integral part of biological systems that it is useful for us to state and use the following fact in the examples we develop in this text.

Probability of two independent events. If p and q are the probabilities of the events 1 and 2 respectively occurring independent of one another, then pq is the probability that event 1 and event 2 both occur.

In Chapter 7, we revisit probability theory and explore how the integral calculus has become a central tool in the development of this theory.

Example 2   Survival rates

Over time, a zebra in Etosha National Park, Namibia, can die either because it is killed by a predator or because it succumbs to disease (primarily anthrax). Starting at the beginning of each year, suppose $f(t)$ and $g(t)$ respectively represent the probabilities of surviving predation and disease up to week t. Professor Getz's research group (see Figure 3.4) determined that at the height of a typical anthrax season, which occurs around the end of the eleventh week of a typical year (i.e., $t = 11$), $f(11) = 0.965$ and $g(11) = 0.981$. They also determined that the probability of surviving predation and disease at the end of the eleventh week is decreasing by 0.004 and 0.005 per week respectively.

Courtesy of Dr. Wayne Getz

Figure 3.4 Dr. Holly Ganz collecting blood from a zebra in Etosha National Park, Namibia, to test if it died of anthrax.

Assume that the events of dying from predation or disease are independent.

a. Find the probability of surviving to the end of week 11.

b. Find the rate at which this probability is changing at end of week 11.

c. Use your answers from parts **a** and **b** to estimate the probability of surviving to the end of week 12.

Solution

a. Since the events of being killed by a predator and dying from disease are assumed to be independent, then the probability $p(t)$ of surviving until week t is given, using the multiplication rule for independent probabilities, by the equation

$$p(t) = f(t)g(t)$$

Thus, the probability of surviving up to the end of week 11 is given by $p(11) = f(11)g(11) = 0.965 \times 0.981 = 0.9467$ (to 4 decimal places).

b. The problem statement implies that $f'(11) = -0.004$ and $g'(11) = -0.005$ (the negative values arise because the probabilities are decreasing). Using the product rule, we get

$$p'(11) = f'(11)g(11) + f(11)g'(11) = -0.965(0.004) - 0.981(0.005) = -0.0088$$

The probability of surviving is decreasing at rate of $0.0088 = 0.88\%$ per week at the end of week 11.

c. Since the probability of surviving is decreasing at a rate of 0.0088 per week at the end of week 11, we can estimate the probability surviving to the end of week 12 by

$$0.9467 - 0.0088 = 0.9379 = 93.79\%$$

Example 3   Per capita or intrinsic rate of growth

As we have seen in Section 3.1, single species population models can be of the form

$$N_{n+1} = N_n f(N_n) = g(N_n)$$

where N_n is the population abundance in the nth generation, $f(N)$ is the per capita growth rate of the population density as a function of population N, and $g(N)$ is the growth rate of the whole population as a function of N.

Find an expression in terms of f and N for $g'(0)$. Briefly explain what this expression represents.

Solution   Applying the product rule to the relationship $g(N) = Nf(N)$, we have

$$g'(N) = \left(\frac{d}{dN}N\right)f(N) + Nf'(N)$$
$$= f(N) + Nf'(N)$$

Evaluating at $N = 0$,

$$g'(0) = f(0) + 0 \times f'(0) = f(0)$$

Hence, the rate $g'(0)$ at which growth changes at low densities equals the per capita growth rate of the population at low densities.

Quotient rule

Before we derive a quotient rule, we begin with an example for finding the derivative of a reciprocal, which is a special case of a quotient that has 1 in the numerator.

Example 4   Reciprocal rule

Find the derivative of the reciprocal $\dfrac{1}{f(x)}$ of a differentiable function f by using the definition of derivative.

Solution   Let $r(x) = \dfrac{1}{f(x)}$. Then $r(x+h) = \dfrac{1}{f(x+h)}$, so using the definition of derivative we find:

$$r'(x) = \lim_{h \to 0} \frac{r(x+h) - r(x)}{h} \qquad \textit{definition of derivative}$$

$$= \lim_{h \to 0} \frac{\frac{1}{f(x+h)} - \frac{1}{f(x)}}{h}$$

$$= \lim_{h \to 0} \frac{\frac{f(x) - f(x+h)}{f(x)f(x+h)}}{h} \qquad \textit{common denominator for the numerator}$$

$$= \lim_{h \to 0} \frac{f(x) - f(x+h)}{hf(x)f(x+h)} \qquad \begin{array}{l} \textit{multiplying numerator and denominator by} \\ f(x)f(x+h) \end{array}$$

$$= \lim_{h \to 0} \frac{1}{f(x)f(x+h)} \lim_{h \to 0} \frac{f(x) - f(x+h)}{h} \qquad \textit{limit of a product}$$

$$= \frac{1}{[f(x)]^2} \lim_{h \to 0} \left[-\frac{f(x+h) - f(x)}{h} \right] \qquad \begin{array}{l} \textit{since } f \textit{ is continuous and factoring} \\ \textit{out } -1 \end{array}$$

$$= \frac{1}{[f(x)]^2} [-f'(x)] \qquad \textit{definition of derivative}$$

We restate the result of this example for easy reference.

Reciprocal Rule	Let f be differentiable at x. Then $$\frac{d}{dx}\left[\frac{1}{f(x)} \right] = -\frac{f'(x)}{[f(x)]^2}$$ provided that $f(x) \neq 0$.

Example 5   Using the reciprocal rule

Find the derivative of $g(x) = \dfrac{1}{x^2 + x + 1}$.

Solution   Let $f(x) = x^2 + x + 1$. Then $g(x) = \dfrac{1}{f(x)}$ and $f'(x) = 2x + 1$. By the reciprocal rule,

$$g'(x) = -\frac{f'(x)}{f(x)^2}$$

$$= -\frac{2x + 1}{(x^2 + x + 1)^2}$$

Example 6   **Breaking Whelks**

Crows feed on whelks by flying up and dropping the whelks (Figure 3.5) on a hard surface to break them.

Figure 3.5 Two types of whelks are pictured; lightning whelks (*Busycon sinistrum,* left) and turnip whelks (*Busycon contrarium,* right).

Biologists have noticed that Northwestern crows consistently drop whelks from about five meters. As a first step to understanding why this might be the case, we consider data collected by the Canadian scientist Reto Zach in which he repeatedly dropped whelks from various heights to determine how many drops were required to break the whelk. The data are shown in Figure 3.6.

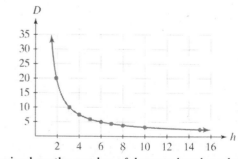

Figure 3.6 Data showing how the number of drops to break a whelk depends on the height of the drops.

Data Source: Reto Zach, 1979. Shell Dropping: Decision-Making and Optimal Foraging in Northwestern Crows. *Behaviour,* 68, pp. 106–117.

A best-fitting curve relating the number of drops, *D,* to the height, *h* (in meters), for these data is given by

$$D(h) = 1 + \frac{20.4}{h - 0.84}$$

a. Find $\dfrac{dD}{dh}$

b. Find $\dfrac{dD}{dh}\bigg|_{h=4}$ and interpret this quantity.

In Chapter 4, we shall use this function to determine the optimal height from which to drop whelks.

Solution

a. $\dfrac{dD}{dh} = \dfrac{d}{dh}(1) + 20.4\dfrac{d}{dh}\left[\dfrac{1}{h-0.84}\right]$ *elementary rules of differentiation*

$\qquad = 0 + 20.4\left[\dfrac{-1}{(h-0.84)^2}\right]$ *reciprocal rule*

$\qquad = \dfrac{-20.4}{(h-0.84)^2}$

b. $\dfrac{dD}{dh}\bigg|_{h=4} = \dfrac{-20.4}{(4-0.84)^2} \approx -2.04$

At $h = 4$ meters, the required number of drops decreases at a rate of -2.04 per meter. For instance, if we increased the height by approximately 1 meter, we should expect the number of drops to decrease by approximately 2. This can also be seen on the graph in Figure 3.6 from the fact that at $h = 4$, $D \approx 8$, while at $h = 5$, $D \approx 8 - 2 = 6$. ∎

Combining the reciprocal and product rule, we can find the derivative of a quotient of functions. Let f and g be differentiable functions, and assume that $g(x) \neq 0$.

$$\frac{d}{dx}\left[\frac{f(x)}{g(x)}\right] = \frac{d}{dx}\left[f(x)\cdot\frac{1}{g(x)}\right]$$

$$= f'(x)\cdot\frac{1}{g(x)} + f(x)\frac{d}{dx}\left[\frac{1}{g(x)}\right] \qquad \text{\textit{product rule}}$$

$$= \frac{f'(x)}{g(x)} + f(x)\left[\frac{-g'(x)}{g(x)^2}\right] \qquad \text{\textit{reciprocal rule}}$$

$$= \frac{f'(x)g(x) - f(x)g'(x)}{g(x)^2} \qquad \text{\textit{common denominator}}$$

Thus, we have derived what is known as the **quotient rule**.

Quotient Rule

Let f and g be differentiable at x. Then

$$(f/g)'(x) = \frac{f'(x)g(x) - f(x)g'(x)}{g(x)^2}$$

provided $g(x) \neq 0$.

There exist a variety of playful mnemonics that can be used to remember the quotient rule. For example, if we replace f by *hi* and g by *lo*, then we get the limmrick "lo-dee-hi less hi-dee-lo," draw the line and square below.

Example 7   Computing with the quotient rule

Find the following derivatives.

a. $\dfrac{d}{dt}\left[\dfrac{1+2t}{3+4t}\right]$

b. $\dfrac{d}{dx}\left[\dfrac{e^x}{1+x^2}\right]$

Solution

a. Let $f(t) = 1 + 2t$ and $g(t) = 3 + 4t$. By the quotient rule

$$\frac{d}{dt}\left[\frac{1+2t}{3+4t}\right] = \frac{d}{dt}\left[\frac{f(t)}{g(t)}\right]$$

$$= \frac{f'(t)g(t) - f(t)g'(t)}{g(t)^2}$$

$$= \frac{2(3+4t) - (1+2t)4}{(3+4t)^2}$$

$$= \frac{2}{(3+4t)^2}$$

b. Let $f(x) = e^x$ and $g(x) = 1 + x^2$. By the quotient rule

$$\frac{d}{dx}\left[\frac{e^x}{1+x^2}\right] = \frac{d}{dx}\left[\frac{f(x)}{g(x)}\right]$$

$$= \frac{f'(x)g(x) - f(x)g'(x)}{g(x)^2}$$

$$= \frac{e^x(1+x^2) - e^x 2x}{(1+x^2)^2}$$

$$= \frac{e^x(x^2 - 2x + 1)}{(1+x^2)^2}$$

$$= \frac{e^x(x - 1)^2}{(1+x^2)^2}$$

Example 8   Dose–response curves revisited

In Example 2 of Section 2.4, a dose–response curve for patients responding to a dose of histamine was given by

$$R = \frac{100e^x}{e^x + e^{-5}}$$

where x is the natural logarithm of the dosage in millimoles (mmol).

a. Find $\dfrac{dR}{dx}$.

b. Graph $\dfrac{dR}{dx}$ to determine at what logarithmic dosage the response is increasing most rapidly.

Solution

a.

$$\frac{d}{dx}\left[\frac{100e^x}{e^x + e^{-5}}\right] = \frac{100e^x(e^x + e^{-5}) - e^x 100e^x}{(e^x + e^{-5})^2}$$

$$= \frac{100e^{x-5}}{(e^x + e^{-5})^2}$$

b. Graphing $\dfrac{dR}{dx}$ yields

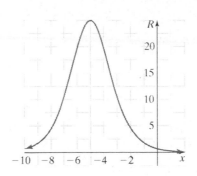

Hence, $\dfrac{dR}{dx}$ takes on its largest value at approximately $x = -5$, and the response increases most rapidly at this logarithmic dose. That is, the dose is $e^{-5} \approx 0.0067$ mmol.

PROBLEM SET 3.2

Level 1 DRILL PROBLEMS

Find the derivatives in Problems 1 to 18.

1. $p(x) = (3x^2 - 1)(7 + 2x^3)$

2. $p(x) = (x^2 + 4)(1 - 3x^3)$

3. $q(x) = \dfrac{4x - 7}{3 - x^2}$

4. $q(x) = \dfrac{x + 1}{1 + x^2}$

5. $f(x) = x2^x$

6. $f(x) = x^3 3^x$

7. $f(x) = (1 + x + x^2)e^x$

8. $f(x) = (e^3 + e^2 + e)x^2$

9. $F(L) = (1 + L + L^3 + L^4)(L - L^2)$

10. $G(M) = (M - M^3)(1 - 4M)$

11. $f(x) = (4x + 3)^2$ Hint: Think $(4x + 3)(4x + 3)$

12. $g(x) = (5 - 2x)^2$

13. $f(x) = \dfrac{e^x}{1 + e^x}$

14. $g(t) = \dfrac{1 + te^t}{1 + t}$

15. $f(p) = \dfrac{ap}{1 + 2^p}$ where a is a constant

16. $g(m) = \dfrac{bm}{1 - 3^m}$ where b is a constant

17. $F(x) = \dfrac{2}{3x^2} - \dfrac{x}{3} + \dfrac{4}{5} + \dfrac{x + 1}{x}$

18. $G(x) = x^2 - \dfrac{1}{x^2} + \dfrac{5}{x^4}$

Find the equation for the tangent line at the prescribed point for each function in Problems 19 to 24.

19. $f(x) = (x^3 - 2x^2)(x + 2)$ where $x = 1$

20. $G(x) = (x - 5)(x^3 - x)$ where $x = -1$

21. $F(x) = \dfrac{x + 1}{x - 1}$ where $x = 0$

22. $f(x) = e^x + e^{-x}$ where $x = 0$

23. $F(x) = \dfrac{3x^2 + 5}{2x^2 + x - 3}$ where $x = -1$

24. $g(x) = x \ln x$ where $x = 1$.

25. a. Differentiate the function
$$f(x) = 2x^2 - 5x - 3$$

b. Factor the function in part **a** and differentiate by using the product rule. Show that the two answers are the same.

26. a. Use the quotient rule to differentiate
$$f(x) = \dfrac{2x - 3}{x^3}$$

b. Rewrite the function in part **a** as $f(x) = x^{-3}(2x - 3)$ and differentiate by using the product rule.

c. Rewrite the function in part **a** as $f(x) = 2x^{-2} - 3x^{-3}$ and differentiate using the power rule.

d. Show that the answers to parts **a**, **b**, and **c** are all the same.

Level 2 APPLIED AND THEORY PROBLEMS

27. The body mass index (BMI) for an individual who weighs w pounds and is h inches tall is given by

$$B = \frac{703w}{h^2}$$

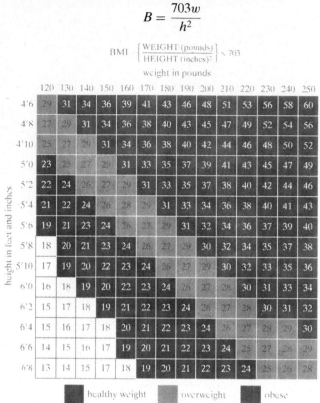

$$\text{BMI} \left[\frac{\text{WEIGHT (pounds)}}{\text{HEIGHT (inches)}^2} \right] \times 703$$

weight in pounds

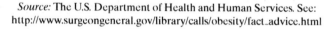

healthy weight   overweight   obese

Source: The U.S. Department of Health and Human Services. See:
http://www.surgeongeneral.gov/library/calls/obesity/fact_advice.html

A person with a body mass index greater than 30 is considered obese; see the BMI chart.

a. Consider all adults who are $h = 63$ inches tall. After setting $h = 63$ inches so that B is now a function of w only, find $\dfrac{dB}{dw}$ when $w = 130$ and interpret your results.

b. Consider all children who weigh 60 lb. After setting $w = 60$ lb so that B is now a function of h only, find $\dfrac{dB}{dh}$ when $h = 54$ and interpret your results.

28. In addition to zebra, Professor Getz's group studied springbok (a type of antelope) in Etosha National Park. In a study paralleling Example 2 of this section, they found that the probability of a springbok surviving predation and disease to the end of the eighth week of a typical year is given by, respectively, 94.9% and 98.8%. Suppose they also determined that at the end of this eight weeks the probability of dying from predation and disease is decreasing respectively by 0.6% and 0.25% per week. Assume the events of dying from predation or disease are independent.

a. Find the probability of surviving to the end of week 8.

b. Find the rate of change of probability of surviving at the end of week 8.

c. Estimate the probability of surviving to the end of week 9.

29. Suppose that Professor Getz's group found that the probability of zebra surviving both predation and disease to the end of week 4 was 98.4% and 99.6%, respectively. Suppose they also determined that at the end of week 4 the probability of a zebra dying from predation and disease is decreasing respectively by 0.4% and 0.1% per week (remember when converting percentages to numbers to shift the value by two decimal places). Assume the events of dying from predation or disease are independent.

a. Find the probability of surviving up to the end of week 4.

b. Find the rate of change of probability of surviving at the end of week 4.

c. Estimate the probability of surviving to end of week 5.

30. Consider the generalized Beverton-Holt model of population growth given by

$$N_{n+1} = g(N_n)$$

where

$$g(N) = \frac{N}{1 + (aN)^b}$$

and $a > 0, b > 0$.

a. Find $g'(N)$.

b. Determine what values of $b > 0$ cause g to be increasing for all $N > 0$.

c. When b is outside the range of values found in part **b**, determine on what interval g is increasing and on what interval g is decreasing.

31. A *ligand* is a molecule that binds to another molecule or other chemically active structure (*e.g.*, a receptor on a membrane) to form a larger complex. In a study of two ligands (I and II) competing for the same sites on a substrate, ligand II is added to a substrate solution that already contains ligand I. As the concentration of ligand II is increased, the concentration of ligand I bound to the substrate decreases. This one-site ligand competition process is characterized by this equation:

$$T = a + \frac{b - a}{1 + 10^{x - c}}$$

where T is the concentration of bound ligand I per milligram of tissue and x is the exponent of the concentration of ligand II in the solution. The constants

a and b arise from the relative binding rates of the two ligands and satisfy $a > 0$ and $b > a$.

a. Compute $\dfrac{dT}{dx}$

b. Interpret the quantities a, b, and c and sketch the graph.

32. In the 1960s, scientists at Woods Hole Oceanographic Institution measured the uptake rate of glucose by bacterial populations from the coast of Peru (R. R. Vaccaro and H. W. Jannasch, "Variations in Uptake Kinetics for Glucose by Natural Populations in Sea Water," *Limnol. Oceanogr.* (1967) 12, 540–542.). In one field experiment, they found that the uptake rate can be modeled by $f(x) = \dfrac{1.2078x}{1 + 0.0506x}$ micrograms per hour where x is micrograms of glucose per liter. Compute and interpret $f'(20)$ and $f'(100)$.

33. In Example 5 of Section 2.4, we found that the predation rate of wolves on moose in North America could be modeled by

$$f(x) = \frac{3.36x}{0.46 + x} \text{ moose killed per wolf per 100 days}$$

where x is measured in number of moose per square kilometer. Compute and interpret $f'(0.5)$ and $f'(2.0)$.

34. Cells often use receptors to transport nutrients from outside of the cell membrane to the inner cell. In Example 6 of Section 1.6, we determined that the rate, R, at which nutrients enter the cell depends on the concentration, N, of nutrients outside the cell. The function

$$R = \frac{aN}{b + N}$$

models the amount of nutrients absorbed in one hour where a and b are positive constants.

a. Find R when $N = b$. What does this tell you about b?

b. Compute and interpret $\dfrac{dR}{dN}$. When is R increasing? When is R decreasing?

35. In Problem 42 in Problem Set 2.4, we modeled how wolf densities in North America depend on moose densities with the following function

$$f(x) = \frac{58.7(x - 0.03)}{0.76 + x} \text{ wolves per 1000 km}^2$$

where x is number of moose per square kilometer. Determine for what x values $f(x)$ is increasing.

36. In Problem 45 in Problem Set 2.3, two fisheries scientists (T. J. Quinn and R. B. Deriso, "Stock and Recruitment," Chapter 3 (pp. 86–127) in *Quantitative Fish Dynamics*, 1999. Oxford University Press, New York, New York) found

that the following stock-recruitment function provides a good fit to data pertaining to the southeast Alaska pink salmon fishery:

$$y = 0.12x^{1.5}e^{-0.00014x}$$

where y is the number of young fish recruited, and x is the number of adult fish involved in recruitment.

a. Compute $\dfrac{dy}{dx}$.

b. Determine for what x values y is increasing and decreasing. Interpret your results.

37. This problem uses the hyperbolic secant function, denoted sech x, which is an important function in mathematics and is defined by the formula

$$\text{sech } x = \frac{2}{e^x + e^{-x}}$$

We will discuss further in Chapter 4 how two mathematicians, W. O. Kermack and A. G. McKendrick, showed that the weekly mortality rate during the outbreak of the plague in Bombay in 1905–1906 can be reasonably well described by the function

$$f(t) = 890 \text{ sech}^2(0.2t - 3.4) \text{ deaths/week}$$

where t is measured in weeks. Determine when the mortality rate is increasing and when the mortality rate is decreasing.

38. In a classic paper, V. A. Tucker and K. Schmidt-Koenig modeled the energy expended by a species of Australian parakeet during flight ("Flight of Birds in Relation to Energetics and Wind Directions," *The Auk* 88 (1971): 97–107). They used the following function:

$$E(v) = \frac{[0.074(v - 35)^2 + 22]}{v} \text{ calories per kilometer}$$

where v is the bird's velocity (km/h).

a. Find a formula for the rate of change of energy with respect to v.

b. At what velocity, v, is the energy expenditure neither increasing nor decreasing? Discuss the importance of this velocity.

© Juniors Bildarchiv GmbH/Alamy

Australian budgerigar (*Melopsittacus undulatus*)

3.3   Chain Rule and Implicit Differentiation

We now move to the next level in terms of developing tools to differentiate functions that can be regarded as the composite of more elementary functions (discussed in Section 1.5). These tools will give us the power to differentiate functions such as the bell-shaped curve $y = e^{-x^2}$, the polynomial $y = (1 + 2x + x^3)^{101}$, and the logarithm function $y = \ln x$.

Chain rule

Suppose we were asked to find the derivative of the function $y = (1 + 2x + x^3)^{101}$. It is not practical to expand this product in order to take the derivative of a polynomial. Instead, we can use a result known as the *chain rule*. In order to motivate this important rule, let us consider an application.

It is known that the carbon monoxide pollution in the air is changing at the rate of 0.02 ppm (parts per million) for each person in a town whose population is growing at the rate of 1000 people per year. To find the rate at which the level of pollution is increasing with respect to time, we must compute the product

$$(0.02 \text{ ppm/person})(1000 \text{ people/year}) = 20 \text{ppm/year}$$

We can generalize this commonsense calculation by noting that the pollution level, L, is a function of the population size, P, which itself is a function of time, t. Thus, L as a function of time is $(L \circ P)(t)$ or, equivalently, $L[P(t)]$. With this notation, the commonsense calculation becomes:

$$\begin{bmatrix} \text{RATE OF CHANGE OF } L \\ \text{WITH RESPECT TO } t \end{bmatrix} = \begin{bmatrix} \text{RATE OF CHANGE OF } L \\ \text{WITH RESPECT TO } P \end{bmatrix} \begin{bmatrix} \text{RATE OF CHANGE OF } P \\ \text{WITH RESPECT TO } t \end{bmatrix}$$

Expressing each of these rates in terms of an appropriate derivative of $L[P(t)]$ in Leibniz form, we obtain the following equation:

$$\frac{dL}{dt} = \frac{dL}{dP}\frac{dP}{dt}$$

These observations anticipate the following important result known as the **chain rule**.

Chain Rule

If $y = f(u)$ is a differentiable function of u, and u, in turn, is a differentiable function of x, then $y = f[u(x)]$ is a differentiable function of x, and its derivative is given by the product

$$\frac{dy}{dx} = \frac{dy}{du}\frac{du}{dx}$$

Equivalently,

$$(f \circ u)'(x) = f'[u(x)]u'(x)$$

Proof.   To prove the chain rule, define

$$G(h) = \begin{cases} \dfrac{f[u(x + h)] - f[u(x)]}{u(x + h) - u(x)} & \text{if } u(x + h) \neq u(x) \\ f'[u(x)] & \text{otherwise} \end{cases}$$

It should be intuitive that $G(h)$ is continuous at $h = 0$. (You will be asked to verify this statement in Problem Set 3.3). With this observation in hand, the proof of the chain rule becomes straightforward. By the definition of the derivative.

$$(f \circ u)'(x) = \lim_{h \to 0} \frac{f[u(x+h)] - f[u(x)]}{h} \qquad \textit{definition of derivative; note } h \neq 0$$

$$= \lim_{h \to 0} \left[G(h) \cdot \frac{u(x+h) - u(x)}{h} \right] \qquad \textit{definition of G}$$

$$= \lim_{h \to 0} G(h) \lim_{h \to 0} \frac{u(x+h) - u(x)}{h} \qquad \textit{limit law for products}$$

$$= G(0) u'(x) \qquad \textit{continuity of G at 0 and differentiability of u at a}$$

$$= f'[u(x)] u'(x) \qquad \textit{definition of G}$$

Example 1   Life made easier

Let $y = \dfrac{d}{dx}(1 + 2x + x^3)^{101}$. Find $\dfrac{dy}{dx}$.

Solution   View this as the composition of two functions: the "inner" function $u(x) = 1 + 2x + x^3$ and the "outer" function $f(u) = u^{101}$. Now use the chain rule:

$$\frac{dy}{dx} = \frac{dy}{du} \cdot \frac{du}{dx}$$

$$= 101 u(x)^{100}(0 + 2 + 3x^2)$$

$$= 101(1 + 2x + x^3)^{100}(2 + 3x^2)$$

In practice, we usually do not write down a function u, but carry out the above process mentally and write

$$y = (1 + 2x + x^3)^{101}$$

$$\frac{dy}{dx} = \underbrace{101(1 + 2x + x^3)^{100}}_{\substack{\text{derivative of} \\ \text{outer function}}} \underbrace{(2 + 3x^2)}_{\substack{\text{derivative of} \\ \text{inner function}}}$$

Example 2   Escaping parasitism

Parasitoids, usually wasps or flies, are insects whose young develop on and eventually kill their host, typically another insect. Parasitoids have been extremely successful in controlling insect pests, especially in agriculture. To better understand this success, theoreticians have extensively modeled host-parasitoid interactions. A key term in these models is the so-called *escape function* $f(x)$, which describes the fraction of hosts that escape parasitism when the parasitoid density is x individuals per unit area. If parasitoid attacks are randomly distributed among the hosts, then the escape function is the form $f(x) = e^{-ax}$ where a is the searching efficiency of the parasitoid.

Suppose that a population of parasitoids attacks alfalfa aphids with a searching efficiency of $a = 0.01$. If the density of parasitoids is currently 100 wasps per acre and is increasing at a rate of 20 wasps per acre per day, find the rate at which the fraction of aphids escaping parasitism is initially changing.

Solution   Let time in days be denoted by the independent variable t, starting with $t = 0$ at the current time. Since the density of wasps $x(t)$ is changing with time, the fraction of hosts that escape is a composition of two functions $f[x(t)]$. Hence, by the chain rule

$$\frac{df}{dt} = \frac{df}{dx} \cdot \frac{dx}{dt} \qquad \text{chain rule}$$

$$= (-0.01)e^{-0.01x} \cdot 20 \qquad \frac{dx}{dt} = 20 \text{ is given}$$

$$= -0.2e^{-0.01x}$$

In this example, we seek to find how f is changing over time, but initially at the current time $t = 0$; note that $x(0) = 100$ and evaluate

$$\frac{d}{dt}\bigg|_{t=0} f[x(t)] = -0.2e^{-0.01(100)} \approx -0.074.$$

Thus the fraction of hosts escaping is decreasing at a rate of 0.074 per day at $t = 0$.

In Example 2, we found the derivative of $f(x) = e^{-0.01x}$ by using the derivative of an exponential (Section 3.1), but we could also use the chain rule. It is worthwhile to restate an extended derivative rule for a natural exponential function:

$$\frac{d}{dx}e^{u(x)} = e^{u(x)}\frac{du}{dx}$$

We illustrate this idea with the following example.

Example 3   **The bell-shaped curve**

Consider the bell-shaped function

$$f(x) = e^{-x^2}$$

shown in Figure 3.7.

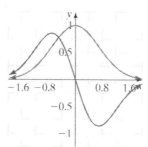

Figure 3.7 Graph of bell-shaped function (red) and its derivative (blue).

a. Find f' and determine where f is increasing and where it is decreasing.

b. Plot f and f' on the same coordinate axes and graphically verify the results from part **a**.

Solution

a. Using the extended derivative rule for a natural exponential function with $u = -x^2$, we find

$$f'(x) = e^{-x^2}(-2x) = -2xe^{-x^2}$$

Since $e^{-x^2} > 0$, the derivative is positive when $x < 0$, so the function f is increasing on $(-\infty, 0)$; and it is negative when $x > 0$, so the function is decreasing on $(0, \infty)$.

b. The graph of $y = f(x)$ is shown in red and $y = f'(x)$ in blue in Figure 3.7.

We see that the derivative function (blue) is positive where the bell-shaped curve (red) is rising, and the derivative function is negative where the bell-shaped curve is falling.

Example 4   Chain rule with graphs

Consider the functions $y = f(x)$ and $y = g(x)$ whose graphs in red and blue, respectively, are as shown here:

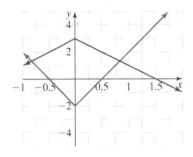

Find

$$(f \circ g)'(-0.5)$$

Solution   By the chain rule,

$$(f \circ g)'(-0.5) = f'[g(-0.5)]g'(-0.5)$$

By inspection, $g(-0.5) = 2$. To find the derivative of g at -0.5, we note that g is linear on the interval $[-1, 0]$, so the derivative is the slope of the line segment which we find by risc/run $= 2/1 = 2$, thus, $g'(-0.5) = 2$.

To find the derivative of f at $g(-0.5) = 2$, we note that f (red curve) is linear on $[0, 2]$ and has slope $m = $ risc/run $8/2 = 4$. Thus, $f'[g(-0.5)] = f'(2) = 4$.

We conclude that

$$\frac{d}{dx}\bigg|_{x=-0.5} f(g(x)) = f'(g(-0.5))g'(-0.5) = 4 \times 2 = 8$$

Implicit differentiation

The equation $y = \sqrt{25 - x^2}$ explicitly defines $f(x) = \sqrt{25 - x^2}$ as a function of x for $-5 \le x \le 5$. The same function can also be defined *implicitly* by the equation $x^2 + y^2 = 25$, as long as we restrict y by $0 \le y \le 5$ so the vertical line test is satisfied. To find the derivative of the explicit form, we use the chain rule:

$$\frac{d}{dx}\sqrt{25 - x^2} = \frac{d}{dx}(25 - x^2)^{1/2}$$

$$= \frac{1}{2}(25 - x^2)^{-1/2}(-2x) \qquad \textit{chain rule with } f(u) = u^{1/2} \textit{ and}$$
$$\hspace{8.5cm} u(x) = 25 - x^2$$

$$= \frac{-x}{\sqrt{25 - x^2}}$$

To obtain the derivative of the same function in its implicit form, we simply differentiate across the equation $x^2 + y^2 = 25$, remembering that y is a function of x and using the chain rule:

$$\frac{d}{dx}(x^2 + y^2) = \frac{d}{dx}(25) \qquad \textit{differentiate both sides}$$

$$2x + 2y\frac{dy}{dx} = 0 \qquad \textit{chain rule for the derivative of } y^2$$

$$\frac{dy}{dx} = -\frac{x}{y} \qquad \textit{solve for} \quad \frac{dy}{dx}$$

$$= -\frac{x}{\sqrt{25 - x^2}} \qquad \textit{write as a function of x, if desired}$$

The procedure we have just illustrated is called **implicit differentiation**.

Example 5   Circular tangents

Consider a circle of radius 5 centered at the origin. Find the equation of the tangent line of this circle at $(3, 4)$.

Solution   The equation of this circle is

$$x^2 + y^2 = 25$$

We recognize that this circle is not the graph of a function. However, if we look at a small neighborhood around the point $(3, 4)$, as shown in Figure 3.8, we see that this part of the graph does pass the vertical line test for functions. Thus, the required slope of the tangent line can be found by evaluating the derivative of dy/dx at $(3, 4)$. We have found that

$$\frac{dy}{dx} = -\frac{x}{y}$$

so the slope of the tangent at $(3, 4)$ is

$$\frac{dy}{dx} = -\frac{3}{4}$$

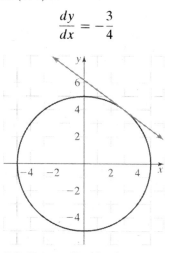

Figure 3.8 Tangent line (red) to a given circle.

Thus, the equation of the tangent line is

$$y - 4 = -\frac{3}{4}(x - 3)$$

$$y = -\frac{3}{4}x + \frac{9}{4} + \frac{16}{4}$$

$$y = -\frac{3}{4}x + \frac{25}{4}$$

More generally, given any equation involving x and y, we can differentiate both sides of the equation, use the chain rule, and solve for $\frac{dy}{dx}$. This becomes particularly important when one cannot (or not easily) express y in terms of x explicitly. The next example is of this type and is included because of its historical importance and aesthetic appeal. You may think that such curves have no application to biology; but, for example, the logarithmic spiral (see Figure 1.56) encountered in Project 1C: Golden Ratio (at the end of Chapter 1) describes the growth of the nautilus mollusk.

Example 6   Limaçon of Pascal

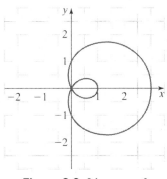

Figure 3.9 Limaçon of Pascal.

The limaçon of Pascal is a famous curve defined by the set of points satisfying

$$(x^2 + y^2 - 2x)^2 = x^2 + y^2$$

The graph is shown in Figure 3.9. This curve was discovered by Étienne Pascal, the father of the more famous Blaise Pascal. The name *limaçon* comes from the Latin *limax*, which means "a snail." Find the equation for the tangent line at the point $(0, 1)$.

Solution   To find the slope of the tangent line, we differentiate both sides implicitly and then evaluate at $(0, 1)$.

$$(x^2 + y^2 - 2x)^2 = x^2 + y^2 \qquad \textit{given equation}$$

$$\frac{d}{dx}(x^2 + y^2 - 2x)^2 = \frac{d}{dx}(x^2 + y^2) \qquad \begin{array}{l}\textit{differentiate both sides with} \\ \textit{respect to } x\end{array}$$

$$2(x^2 + y^2 - 2x)\frac{d}{dx}(x^2 + y^2 - 2x) = 2x + 2y\frac{dy}{dx} \qquad \textit{chain rule}$$

$$2(x^2 + y^2 - 2x)(2x + 2y\frac{dy}{dx} - 2) = 2x + 2y\frac{dy}{dx} \qquad \textit{chain rule again}$$

$$2(0^2 + 1^2 - 2 \cdot 0)(2 \cdot 0 + 2 \cdot 1\frac{dy}{dx} - 2) = 2(0) + 2(1)\frac{dy}{dx} \qquad \textit{evaluate at } (0, 1)$$

$$2(1)(2\frac{dy}{dx} - 2) = 2\frac{dy}{dx} \qquad \textit{simplify}$$

$$4\frac{dy}{dx} - 4 = 2\frac{dy}{dx}$$

$$2\frac{dy}{dx} = 4$$

$$\frac{dy}{dx} = 2 \qquad \textit{solve for } \frac{dy}{dx}$$

Hence, the slope of the tangent line is 2 and the tangent line is

$$y - 1 = 2(x - 0)$$
$$y = 2x + 1$$

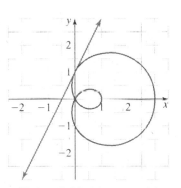

Figure 3.10 Limaçon with tangent line at $(0, 1)$.

The tangent line is shown in Figure 3.10. ◼

Derivatives of logarithms

Implicit differentiation allows us to easily find the derivative of logarithms and power functions.

Derivative of the Natural Logarithm	If $y = \ln x$, then $$\frac{dy}{dx} = \frac{1}{x}$$

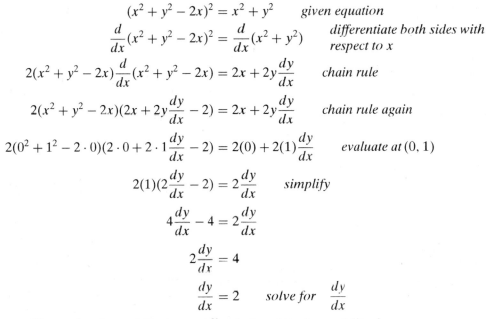

Proof.

$$y = \ln x \qquad \textit{given function}$$

$$e^y = x \qquad \textit{exponentiating both sides}$$

$$\frac{d}{dx}e^y = \frac{d}{dx}(x) \qquad \textit{differentiate both sides}$$

$$e^y\frac{dy}{dx} = 1 \qquad \textit{chain rule}$$

$$\frac{dy}{dx} = \frac{1}{e^y} \qquad \textit{solve for } dy/dx$$

$$= \frac{1}{x} \qquad \textit{substitute}$$

In the problem set of this section you are asked to prove the more general statements of this result; namely, if $y = \ln |x|$ then, for $x \neq 0$, $\dfrac{dy}{dx} = \dfrac{1}{x}$.

The next example deals with the clearance rate—which, as we saw in Example 7 of Section 3.1 in the context of viral particles, is the constant rate of decay—of a drug from the blood stream of an individual.

Example 7   Clearance of acetaminophen

Scientists have estimated that the clearance rate of the drug acetaminophen in the blood stream of an average adult is 0.28 per hour. This means that after an initial dose of acetaminophen at time $t = 0$, the fraction of acetaminophen in the blood t hours later is $e^{-0.28t}$.

a. Find the time, T, it takes for a fraction x of the drug to clear the body.

b. Find and interpret $\dfrac{dT}{dx}\bigg|_{x=1/2}$.

Solution

a. Since $e^{-0.28t}$ is the fraction of drug remaining in the body at time t and x is the fraction that has left the body, we need to solve

$$1 - x = e^{-0.28T}$$
$$\ln(1 - x) = -0.28T$$
$$T = -3.57\ln(1 - x)$$

b. We use the results of part **a** to find

$$\frac{dT}{dx}\bigg|_{x=1/2} = \frac{(-3.57)(-1)}{1 - x}\bigg|_{x=1/2}$$

$$= \frac{3.57}{1 - 0.5}$$

$$= 7.14$$

Thus, the time it takes to clear an extra percentage of the drug, given 50% ($x = \frac{1}{2}$ is 50%) has cleared, is approximately $7.14 \times 0.01 = 0.0714$ hours or 4 minutes and 17 seconds.

If the base on the logarithm has a base other than the natural base, e, then we use the following result, which you will be asked to verify in the Problem 41 of Problem Set 3.3:

Derivative of a General Logarithm	If b is a positive number (other than 1) and $x > 0$ then
	$$\frac{d}{dx} \log_b x = \frac{1}{x \ln b}$$

Example 8   Derivative of a log with base 2

For $x > 0$ differentiate $f(x) = x \log_2 x$.

Solution

$$f'(x) = \left(\frac{d}{dx} x\right) \log_2 x + x \frac{d}{dx} \log_2 x \qquad by\ the\ product\ rule$$

$$= (1) \log_2 x + x \frac{1}{\ln 2} \frac{1}{x} \qquad by\ derivative\ of\ general\ logarithm$$

$$= \log_2 x + \frac{1}{\ln 2}$$

In Section 3.1, we stated the power rule and promised to prove it later in this chapter for all real numbers. We fulfill this promise in the following example.

Example 9   Power law for positive real numbers

Consider $y = x^n$ where $x > 0$ and n is any real number other than 0. Prove that

$$\frac{dy}{dx} = nx^{n-1}$$

Solution   We will prove this for $x > 0$ by taking the natural logarithm of both sides and then differentiating to find the derivative.

$$y = x^n \qquad given\ equation$$
$$\ln y = \ln x^n \qquad take\ the\ natural\ logarithm\ of\ both\ sides$$
$$\ln y = n \ln x \qquad property\ of\ logarithms$$
$$\frac{1}{y} \frac{dy}{dx} = n \frac{1}{x} \qquad by\ chain\ rule\ and\ derivatives\ of\ natural\ logarithm$$
$$\frac{dy}{dx} = n \frac{y}{x} \qquad solve\ for\ \tfrac{dy}{dx}$$
$$= n \frac{x^n}{x} \qquad since\ y = x^n$$
$$= nx^{n-1} \qquad property\ of\ exponents$$

The proof for $x < 0$ you will encounter in Problem Set 3.3 at the end of this section.

Example 10   Modeling problem using the chain rule

An environmental study of a certain suburban community suggests that when the population is p thousand people, the amount of carbon monoxide in the air can be modeled by the function

$$C(p) = \sqrt{0.5p^2 + 17}$$

Table 3.1 Population as a function of time

Time t	Population $p(t)$
0	4.6696
0.25	4.6717
0.5	4.6779
0.75	4.6884
1	4.7032
1.25	4.7225
1.5	4.7463
1.75	4.7751
2	4.8088
2.25	4.8479
2.5	4.8926
2.75	4.9432
3	5.0000

where C is measured in parts per million. The population (in millions) at various times (in years) for the last three years is given in Table 3.1.

a. Decide through visual inspection (plotting each of the two graphs together with the data) which of the following functions model the population data most accurately. (Note how subscripts we apply to y allow us to distinguish between the values predicted by the two models, although once the best model is selected, we will rename the left-hand side p.) Compute the derivatives for each of these models.

- Linear: $y_l = 0.109t + 4.618$
- Quadratic: $y_q = 0.039t^2 - 0.009t + 4.672$

b. Using the model you selected in part **a**, find the rate at which the level of pollution is changing at the end of year three.

Solution

a. To determine which of the three proposed models best fits the population data, we plot the graphs shown in Figure 3.11. The rates of change for these models are calculated by finding these derivatives:

- Linear: $y_l' = 0.109$ *at* $t = 3$, $y_l = 0.109$ ppm
- Quadratic: $y_q' = 0.078t - 0.009$ *at* $t = 3$, $y_q = 0.225$ ppm

The quadratic function clearly fits much better than the linear function and predictions differ by a factor of 2 at $t = 3$. Renaming the right-hand-side of the quadratic function $p(t)$, the function we use in our analysis is the quadratic function, which after renaming the left-hand-side is

$$p(t) = 0.039t^2 - 0.009t + 4.672$$

You could just use the residual sum-of-squares as discussed in Section 1.2 to decide which is better. Also, see Project 3A at the end of this chapter.

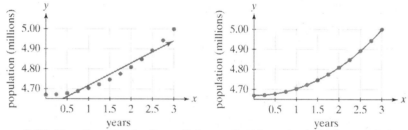

Figure 3.11 Data fitted by the linear (left panel) and quadratic (right panel) functions in part **a** of Example 10.

b. By substituting the quadratic population function $p(t)$ selected in part **a** into the researcher's pollution function $C(p)$, we can represent the level of pollution as $C[p(t)]$, a composite function of time. Applying the chain rule, we find that

$$\frac{dC}{dt} = \frac{dC}{dp}\frac{dp}{dt}$$

$$= \frac{d}{dp}\left[(0.5p^2 + 17)^{1/2}\right]\frac{d}{dt}\left[0.039t^2 - 0.009t + 4.672\right]$$

$$= \left[\frac{1}{2}(0.5p^2 + 17)^{-1/2}(0.5)(2p)\right][0.039(2t) - 0.009]$$

$$= 0.5p(0.5p^2 + 17)^{-1/2}(0.078t - 0.009)$$

When $t = 3$, $p(3) = 0.039(3)^2 - 0.009(3) + 4.672 = 4.996$. Therefore, at $t = 3$ it follows that

$$\frac{dC}{dt}\Big|_{t=3} - 0.5(4.996)\left[0.5(4.996)^2 + 17\right]^{-1/2}[0.078(3) - 0.009]$$

$$\approx 0.104$$

Thus, our analysis suggests that after three years, the level of pollution is increasing at the rate of 0.104 parts per million per year.

PROBLEM SET 3.3

Level 1 DRILL PROBLEMS

Use the chain rule to compute the derivative dy/dx for the functions given in Problems 1 to 4.

1. $y = u^2 + 1; u = 3x - 2$

2. $y = 2u^2 - u + 5; u = 1 - x^2$

3. $y = \dfrac{2}{u^2}; u = x^2 - 9$

4. $y = u^2; u = \ln x$

Differentiate each function in Problems 5 to 8 with respect to the given variable of the function.

5. a. $g(u) = u^5$

   b. $u(x) = 3x - 1$

   c. $f(x) = (3x - 1)^5$

6. a. $g(u) = u^3$

   b. $u(x) = x^2 + 1$

   c. $f(x) = (x^2 + 1)^2$

7. a. $g(u) = u^{15}$

   b. $u(x) = 3x^2 + 5x - 7$

   c. $f(x) = (3x^2 + 5x - 7)^{15}$

8. a. $g(u) = u^7$

   b. $u(x) = 5 - 8x - 12x^2$

   c. $f(x) = (5 - 8x - 12x^2)^7$

Differentiate each function in Problems 9 to 18.

9. $y = (5 - x + x^4)^9$

10. $y = e^{2+x^2}$

11. $y = \dfrac{1}{(1 + x - x^5)^{12}}$

12. $y = e^{(x+1)^7}$

13. $y = \ln x^2$

14. $y = (2x + 12)^\pi$

15. $y - \ln(2x + 5)$

16. $y - xe^{-x^2}$

17. $y = (x^4 - 1)^{10}(2x^4 + 3)^7$

18. $y = \sqrt{\dfrac{x^3 - x}{4 - x^2}}$

Find dy/dx by implicit differentiation in Problems 19 to 25.

19. $x^2 + y = x^3 + y^3$

20. $xy = 25$

21. $xy(2x + 3y) = 2$

22. $\dfrac{1}{y} + \dfrac{1}{x} = 1$

23. $(2x + 3y)^2 = 10$

24. $\ln(xy) = e^{2x}$

25. $e^{xy} + \ln y^2 = x$

26. Consider the functions $y = f(x)$ and $y = g(x)$ whose graphs in red and blue, respectively, are shown in Figure 3.12.

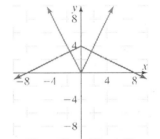

Figure 3.12 Functions $y = f(x)$ (red) and $y = g(x)$ (blue).

   a. Find $\dfrac{d}{dx} f[g(x)]\Big|_{x=2}$ **b.** Find $\dfrac{d}{dx} g[f(x)]\Big|_{x=2}$

27. The graphs of $u = g(x)$ and $y = f(u)$ are shown in Figure 3.13.

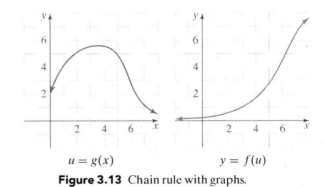

$u = g(x)$ $y = f(u)$

Figure 3.13 Chain rule with graphs.

   a. Find the approximate value of u at $x = 2$. What is the slope of the tangent line at that point?

   b. Find the approximate value of y at $x = 5$. What is the slope of the tangent line at that point?

   c. Find the slope of $y = f[g(x)]$ at $x = 2$.

28. Let $g(x) = f[u(x)]$, where $u(-3) = 5$, $u'(-3) = 2$, $f(5) = 3$, and $f'(5) = -3$. Find an equation for the tangent to the graph of g at the point where $x = -3$.

29. Let f be a function for which

$$f'(x) = \frac{1}{x^2 + 1}$$

a. If $g(x) = f(3x - 1)$, what is $g'(x)$?

b. If $h(x) = f\left(\frac{1}{x}\right)$, what is $h'(x)$?

30. The cissoid of Diocles is a curve of the general form represented by the following particular equation

$$y^2(6 - x) = x^3$$

as illustrated in Figure 3.14.

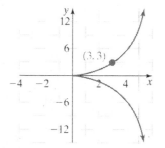

Figure 3.14 Cissoid of Diocles.

Find the equation of the tangent line to this graph at $(3, 3)$.

31. The folium of Descartes is a curve of the general form represented by the following particular equation

$$x^3 + y^3 - \frac{9}{2}xy = 0$$

as illustrated in Figure 3.15.

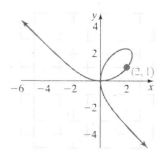

Figure 3.15 Folium of Descartes.

Find the equation of the tangent line to this graph at $(2, 1)$.

32. Another version of the folium of Descartes is given by the equation

$$x^3 + y^3 = 3xy$$

as illustrated in Figure 3.16

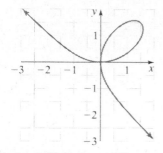

Figure 3.16 Folium of Descartes.

Find at what points the tangent line is horizontal.

Level 2 APPLIED AND THEORY PROBLEMS

33. Arteriosclerosis develops when plaque forms in the arterial walls, blocking the flow of blood; this, in turn, often leads to heart attack or stroke (Figure 3.17). Model the cross-section of an artery as a circle with radius R centimeters, and assume that plaque is deposited in such a way that when the patient is t years old, the plaque is $p(t)$ cm thick, where

$$p(t) = R[1 - 0.009(12{,}350 - t^2)^{1/2}]$$

Find the rate at which the cross-sectional area covered by plaque is changing with respect to time in a sixty-year-old patient.

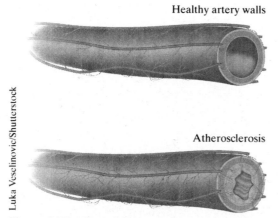

Healthy artery walls

Atherosclerosis

Figure 3.17 Blood flow in a healthy artery (top) and in an artery narrowed by arteriosclerosis (bottom).

34. In Problem 38 in Problem Set 3.2, the energy expended by a species of Australian parakeet during flight was modeled by the function

$$E(v) = \frac{[0.074(v - 35)^2 + 22]}{v} \quad \begin{array}{l} \text{calories per} \\ \text{kilometer} \end{array}$$

where v is the bird's velocity (km/h). Assume at one point in time (say $t = 0$) in its flight, a parakeet's velocity is 25 km/hour and its velocity is increasing at a rate of 2 km/hour². Find the instantaneous rate of change of this parakeet's energy use at $t = 0$. Be sure to identify the correct units for your answer.

35. In Example 5 of Section 2.4, we found that the predation rate of wolves in North America could be modeled by

$$f(x) = \frac{3.36x}{0.46 + x} \qquad \begin{array}{l} \text{moose killed per wolf} \\ \text{per hundred days} \end{array}$$

where x is measured in number of moose per square kilometer. If the current moose density is $x = 0.5$ and is increasing at a rate of 0.1 per year, determine the rate at which the predation rate is increasing.

36. In Problem 42 in Problem Set 2.4, we modeled how wolf densities in North America depend on moose densities with the following function

$$f(x) = \frac{58.7(x - 0.03)}{0.76 + x} \text{ wolves per } 1000 \text{ km}^2$$

where x is the number of moose per square kilometer. If the current moose density is $x = 2.0$ and decreasing at a rate of 0.2 per year, determine the current rate of change of the wolf densities.

37. The proportion of a species of aphid that escapes parasitism is

$$f(x) = e^{-0.02x}$$

where x is the density of parasitoids. If the density of parasitoids is currently 10 wasps per acre and decreasing at a rate 20 wasps per acre per day, find at what rate the likelihood of escaping parasitism is changing.

38. In Example 10 we saw that an environmental study of a certain suburban community suggested the following relationship between the population level p (thousand people) and the amount of carbon monoxide C (ppm) in the air:

$$C(p) = \sqrt{0.5p^2 + 17}$$

Now suppose that the population p (in thousands) at time t is modeled by the function

$$p(t) = 0.10626e^{0.023t}$$

Use the chain rule to find the rate at which the pollution level is changing after three years and compare this with the estimate obtained in Example 10.

39. The bicorn (also called the cocked hat) is a quartic curve studied by mathematician James Sylvester (1814–1897) in 1864. As illustrated in Figure 3.18, it is given by the set of points that satisfy the equation

$$y^2(1 - x^2) = (x^2 + 2y - 1)^2$$

Find the formulas for the two tangent lines at $x = 1/2$.

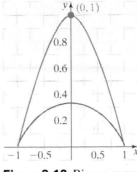

Figure 3.18 Bicorn curve.

40. Prove that if f is differentiable at $u(a)$ and u is continuous at a, then

$$G(h) = \begin{cases} \dfrac{f[u(a + h)] - f(u(a))}{u(a + h) - u(a)} & \text{if } u(a + h) - u(a) \neq 0 \\[3mm] f'[u(a)] & \text{otherwise} \end{cases}$$

is continuous at $h = 0$.

41. Prove that $\dfrac{d}{dx} \log_b x = \dfrac{1}{x \ln b}$ for $b \neq 1$, $x > 0$.

42. Prove that

$$\frac{dy}{dx} = nx^{n-1}$$

for $y = x^n$ where $x < 0$ and n is any real number other than 0.

43. The average height of boys in the United States as a function of age is shown in Figure 3.19. This relationship is well described by the linear function

$$h(t) = 32 + 0.19t \text{ inches}$$

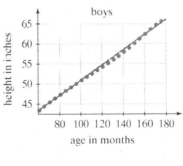

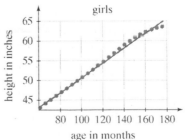

Figure 3.19 Heights in inches of boys and girls in the United States as a function of time in months.

where t is measured in months. The relationship between height and weight can be modeled by the power function

$$W(h) = 0.0024h^{2.6} \text{ lb}$$

Find the instantaneous rates at which height and weight are changing at age ten years.

44. The average height of girls in the United States as a function of age is shown in Figure 3.19. This relationship is well-described by the linear function

$$h(t) = 32 + 0.185t \text{ inches}$$

where t is measured in months. The relationship between height and weight can be modeled by the power function

$$W(h) = 0.0024h^{2.6} \text{ lb}$$

Find the instantaneous rates at which height and weight are changing at age ten years.

3.4   Derivatives of Trigonometric Functions

Many physical and biological processes change periodically over time and consequently are represented by a periodic function. A powerful result in mathematical analysis proves that periodic functions can be represented as a sum of sines and cosines; this is called the *Fourier series representation*. In this section, we find the derivative of these fundamental functions and their functional relatives—tangent, secant, cotangent, and cosecant. Recall from Chapter 1, we assume that the trigonometric functions are functions of real numbers or of angles measured in radians. We make this assumption because the trigonometric differentiation formulas rely on limit formulas that become more complicated if degrees, rather than radians, are used to measure angles.

Derivatives of sine and cosine

Before stating the theorem regarding the derivatives of the sine and cosine functions, we look at the graph of $\dfrac{\sin(x + h) - \sin x}{h}$ for small values of h. In particular, for $h = 0.01$, the expression $\dfrac{\sin(x + 0.01) - \sin x}{0.01}$ has the following graph:

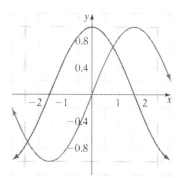

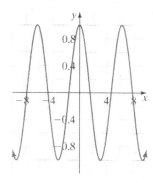

Figure 3.20 Graphs of cosine (blue) and sine (red).

From this graph, it appears that the derivative of $f(x) = \sin x$ is $f'(x) = \cos x$. This relationship appears to match up, as illustrated in Figure 3.20: sine is increasing on intervals where cosine is positive and has turning points where cosine is zero.

Before verifying this assertion, we need two important limits. The first limit is presented numerically in Example 1. You will be asked to give analytical derivations of the limits in Problems 29 and 30 in Problem Set 3.4.

Two Important Trigonometric Limits	$\displaystyle\lim_{x \to 0} \frac{\sin x}{x} = 1 \qquad \lim_{x \to 0} \frac{\cos x - 1}{x} = 0$

Example 1   Numerical approach to one of the trigonometric limits

Find $\lim\limits_{x \to 0} \dfrac{\sin x}{x}$ numerically and graphically using technology.

Solution   Note that

$$\frac{\sin(-x)}{-x} = \frac{-\sin x}{-x} = \frac{\sin x}{x}$$

so the left- and right-hand limits should be the same. Thus, for the numerical approach, we develop a table for x values approaching 0 from the right.

x	$\dfrac{\sin x}{x}$	x	$\dfrac{\sin x}{x}$
$\dfrac{1}{10}$	0.998334	$\dfrac{1}{70}$	0.999966
$\dfrac{1}{20}$	0.999583	$\dfrac{1}{80}$	0.999974
$\dfrac{1}{30}$	0.999815	$\dfrac{1}{90}$	0.999979
$\dfrac{1}{40}$	0.999896	$\dfrac{1}{100}$	0.999983
$\dfrac{1}{50}$	0.999933	$\dfrac{1}{110}$	0.999986
$\dfrac{1}{60}$	0.999954	$\dfrac{1}{120}$	0.999988

The numbers in this table appear to be approaching 1 as x tends toward 0 from the right $(x > 0)$. Thus, we might infer from the table that

$$\lim_{x \to 0} \frac{\sin x}{x} = 1$$

Plotting $\sin x / x$ near 0 in Figure 3.21 reaffirms our tabular approach to finding the limit.

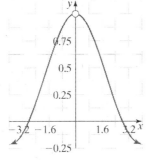

Figure 3.21 Graph of $y = \dfrac{\sin x}{x}$ near the point $x = 0$

We can now state the derivative rule for the sine and cosine functions.

Derivative Rules for Sine and Cosine

The functions $\sin x$ and $\cos x$ are differentiable for all x and

$$\frac{d}{dx} \sin x = \cos x \qquad \text{and} \qquad \frac{d}{dx} \cos x = -\sin x$$

Proof.   We will prove the first derivative formula using the trigonometric identity

$$\sin(x + h) = \sin x \cos h + \cos x \sin h$$

and the definition of derivative. For a fixed x

$$
\begin{aligned}
\frac{d}{dx} \sin x &= \lim_{h \to 0} \frac{\sin(x + h) - \sin x}{h} && \textit{definition of derivative} \\
&= \lim_{h \to 0} \frac{\sin x \cos h + \cos x \sin h - \sin x}{h} && \textit{trigonometric identity} \\
&= \lim_{h \to 0} \frac{\sin x (\cos h - 1) + \cos x \sin h}{h} && \textit{factoring} \\
&= \lim_{h \to 0} \left[\sin x \left(\frac{\cos h - 1}{h} \right) + \cos x \left(\frac{\sin h}{h} \right) \right] \\
&= \lim_{h \to 0} \left[\sin x \left(\frac{\cos h - 1}{h} \right) \right] + \lim_{h \to 0} \left[\cos x \left(\frac{\sin h}{h} \right) \right] && \textit{sum limit law} \\
&= \sin x \lim_{h \to 0} \frac{\cos h - 1}{h} + \cos x \lim_{h \to 0} \frac{\sin h}{h} && \textit{product limit law} \\
&= (\sin x)(0) + (\cos x)(1) && \textit{important trigonometric limits} \\
&= \cos x
\end{aligned}
$$

To find the derivative of cosine, we use the trigonometric identities

$$\cos x = \sin\left(x + \frac{\pi}{2}\right) \qquad \text{and} \qquad \cos\left(x + \frac{\pi}{2}\right) = -\sin x$$

and the chain rule

$$\frac{d}{dx}\cos x = \frac{d}{dx}\sin\left(x + \frac{\pi}{2}\right)$$

$$= \cos\left(x + \frac{\pi}{2}\right)$$

$$= -\sin x$$

Example 2   Derivatives involving sine and cosine functions

Differentiate the functions

a. $f(x) = \sin 2x$ **b.** $f(x) = x^2 \sin x$ **c.** $f(x) = \dfrac{\sqrt{x}}{\cos x}$

Solution

a. Setting $u = 2x$ and $y = f(u) = \sin u$, the chain rule implies that

$$\frac{dy}{dx} = f'(u)\frac{du}{dx}$$

$$= (\cos u)2$$

$$= 2\cos 2x$$

b. By the product rule,

$$f'(x) = \sin x \frac{d}{dx}x^2 + x^2 \frac{d}{dx}\sin x$$

$$= 2x\sin x + x^2\cos x$$

c.
$$f'(x) = \frac{d}{dx}\left[\frac{x^{1/2}}{\cos x}\right]$$

$$= \frac{\cos x \frac{d}{dx}(x^{1/2}) - x^{1/2}\frac{d}{dx}\cos x}{\cos^2 x} \qquad \textit{quotient rule}$$

$$= \frac{\frac{1}{2}x^{-1/2}\cos x - x^{1/2}(-\sin x)}{\cos^2 x} \qquad \textit{power rule}$$

$$= \frac{\frac{1}{2}x^{-1/2}(\cos x + 2x\sin x)}{\cos^2 x} \qquad \textit{common factor}$$

$$= \frac{\cos x + 2x\sin x}{2\sqrt{x}\cos^2 x}$$

Example 3   Rate of change of CO_2

In Section 1.2, we initially approximated the concentration of CO_2 (in ppm) at the Mauna Loa Observatory in Hawaii with the function

$$h(t) = 329.3 + 0.1225\,t + 3\cos\left(\frac{\pi t}{6}\right)$$

Find $h'(3)$ and compare it to the approximation found in Example 2 of Section 2.1.

Solution

$$h(t) = 329.3 + 0.1225\,t + 3\cos\left(\frac{\pi t}{6}\right) \qquad \textit{given function}$$

$$h'(t) = 0 + 0.1225 + 3\left[-\sin\left(\frac{\pi t}{6}\right)\left(\frac{\pi}{6}\right)\right] \qquad \textit{elementary derivatives and chain rule}$$

$$= 0.1225 - \frac{\pi}{2}\sin\left(\frac{\pi t}{6}\right)$$

Evaluating at $t = 3$ yields

$$h'(3) = 0.1225 - \frac{\pi}{2}\sin\left(\frac{\pi}{2}\right) = 0.1225 - \frac{\pi}{2} \approx -1.4483$$

This agrees with the numerical solution of Example 2 in Section 2.1. ■

Periodic fluctuations in biological systems can be internally or externally driven, as the next two examples illustrate.

Example 4   Circadian rhythms

Circadian rhythms are roughly twenty-four-hour cycles in physiological processes of an organism that are primarily driven by the individual's circadian clock. Examples in mammals include heart and breathing patterns and daily fluctuations in body temperature and hormones. In humans, the circadian clock driving these periodic patterns is formed by a cluster of neurons found in the hypothalamus, a part of the brain. However, many brainless organisms, ranging from yeast cells to plants, also exhibit circadian rhythms.

A simple model of circadian rhythm for body temperature in an organism is

$$T(t) = A + B\sin\left(\frac{\pi}{12}(t - C)\right) \text{ degrees Celsius}$$

where t is measured in hours. Assume that $0 \le C \le 6$.

a. Sketch $T(t)$ and discuss the meaning of A, B, and C.

b. Find and sketch $T'(t)$. Discuss what this plot tells you about the circadian rhythm of body temperature.

Solution

a. Using what we studied about trigonometric functions in Chapter 1, we have that $T(t)$ oscillates around the value A with an amplitude of B and a period of 24 hours. The $-C$ term shifts the graph to the right by C hours. Therefore, we get the following plot of $T(t)$:

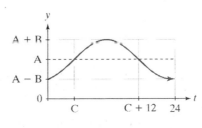

Therefore, the body temperature of $A°$ Celsius occurs at hours C and $C + 12$ each day and the maximum temperature $A + B°$ Celsius occurs at hour $C + 6$ each day.

b. Taking the derivative of T yields

$$T'(t) = \frac{d}{dt}A + B\frac{d}{dt}\sin\left(\frac{\pi}{12}(t - C)\right) \qquad \textit{derivative rules}$$

$$= 0 + B\frac{d}{dt}\sin\left(\frac{\pi}{12}(t - C)\right)$$

$$= 0 + B\cos\left(\frac{\pi}{12}(t - C)\right)\frac{\pi}{12} \qquad \textit{derivative of sine and chain rule}$$

Plotting the derivative using what we learned in Chapter 1 gives

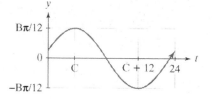

The maximum instantaneous rate of change of body temperature occurs at hour C each day, while the minimum rate of change occurs at hour $C + 12$ each day. Since $T'(t) > 0$ on $[0, C + 6)$ and $T'(t) < 0$ on $(C + 6, C + 18)$, body temperature is increasing between hours 0 and $C + 6$ and decreasing between hours $C + 6$ and $C + 18$.

Example 5   Periodic populations

Many populations live in environments that change in a periodic fashion with time (e.g., diurnal and seasonal cycles). To understand the dynamics of an algal population growing in a climate chamber programmed to have a particular light-dark cycle, a research scientist conducted an experiment in which she found that the algae abundance (in cells per liter) over time t in hours could be modeled by the function

$$N(t) = 10{,}000e^{\sin t}$$

a. Verify that $N(t)$ satisfies the relationship

$$N'(t) = \cos t\, N(t)$$

Explain what this relationship means. Based on the assumption that the growth rate of the population is proportional to the intensity of light, at what times are the light intensity greatest?

b. Determine at what times the population is increasing and at what times the population is decreasing.

Solution

a. Taking the derivative of $N(t)$ with the chain rule, we get

$$N'(t) = 10{,}000\, e^{\sin t}\frac{d}{dt}\sin t = 10{,}000\, e^{\sin t}\cos t$$

Hence, by the definition of $N(t)$, we have

$$N'(t) = \cos t\, N(t)$$

We can interpret $\cos t$ as the per capita growth rate of the population. This per capita growth is greatest (i.e., equals one) at $t = 0, \pm 2\pi, \pm 4\pi, \ldots$ Hence, at these moments of time the light intensity must be the greatest.

b. The population increases when $N'(t) > 0$. This occurs when $\cos t > 0$, in other words, when t is in the intervals $(0, \pi/2)$, $(3\pi/2, 5\pi/2)$, ... On the complementary intervals, the population is decreasing; that is, on these intervals, those algal cells that are dying are doing so faster than those that are dividing.

Derivatives of other trigonometric functions

If you know the derivatives of sine and cosine and the basic rules of differentiation, then all the other trigonometric derivatives follow.

Derivative Rules for Trigonometric Functions	The six basic trigonometric functions $\sin x$, $\cos x$, $\tan x$, $\csc x$, $\sec x$, and $\cot x$ are all differentiable wherever they are defined and

$$\frac{d}{dx}\sin x = \cos x \qquad \frac{d}{dx}\cos x = -\sin x$$

$$\frac{d}{dx}\tan x = \sec^2 x \qquad \frac{d}{dx}\cot x = -\csc^2 x$$

$$\frac{d}{dx}\sec x = \sec x \tan x \qquad \frac{d}{dx}\csc x = -\csc x \cot x$$

All the additional derivative rules are proved by using the quotient rule along with formulas for the derivative of sine and cosine. Here we will obtain the derivative of the tangent function and leave the rest to Problem Set 3.4.

$$\frac{d}{dx}\tan x = \frac{d}{dx}\frac{\sin x}{\cos x} \qquad \textit{trigonometric identity}$$

$$= \frac{\cos x \frac{d}{dx}(\sin x) - \sin x \frac{d}{dx}(\cos x)}{\cos^2 x} \qquad \textit{quotient rule}$$

$$= \frac{\cos x(\cos x) - \sin x(-\sin x)}{\cos^2 x} \qquad \textit{derivatives of sine and cosine}$$

$$= \frac{\cos^2 x + \sin^2 x}{\cos^2 x}$$

$$= \frac{1}{\cos^2 x} \qquad \textit{trigonometric identity}$$

$$= \sec^2 x \qquad \textit{trigonometric identity}$$

Notice that the derivatives of all "co" trig functions have the "co-trig" derivative form of their corresponding trigonometric partners, but with a sign change. Thus, for example, because the derivative of tangent is secant squared, this rule implies that the derivative of cotangent is the negative of cosecant squared.

Example 6 Derivative of a product of trigonometric functions
- -

Differentiate $f(x) = \sec x \tan x$.

Solution

$$f'(x) = \frac{d}{dx}(\sec x \tan x)$$

$$= \sec x \frac{d}{dx}(\tan x) + \tan x \frac{d}{dx}(\sec x) \qquad \textit{product rule}$$

$$= \sec x(\sec^2 x) + \tan x(\sec x \tan x)$$

$$= \sec^3 x + \sec x \tan^2 x$$

PROBLEM SET 3.4

Level 1 DRILL PROBLEMS

Differentiate the functions given in Problems 1 to 20.

1. $f(x) = \sin x + \cos x$

2. $g(x) = 2 \sin x + \tan x$

3. $y = \sin 2x$

4. $y = \cos 2x$

5. $f(t) = t^2 + \cos t + \cos \dfrac{\pi}{4}$

6. $g(t) = 2 \sec t + 3 \tan t - \tan \dfrac{\pi}{3}$

7. $y = e^{-x} \sin x$

8. $y = \tan x^2$

9. $f(\theta) = \sin^2 \theta$

10. $g(\theta) = \cos^2 \theta$

11. $y = \cos x^{101}$

12. $y = (\cos x)^{101}$

13. $p(t) = (t^2 + 2) \sin t$

14. $y = x \sec x$

15. $q(t) = \dfrac{\sin t}{t}$

16. $f(x) = \dfrac{\sin x}{1 - \cos x}$

17. $g(x) = \dfrac{x}{1 - \sin x}$

18. $y = \sin(2t^3 + 1)$

19. $y = \ln(\sin x + \cos x)$

20. $y = \ln(\sec x + \tan x)$

Use the given trigonometric identity in parentheses and the basic rules of differentiation to find the derivatives of the functions given in Problems 21 to 24.

21. $f(x) = \sec x \left(\sec x = \dfrac{1}{\cos x} \right)$

22. $f(x) = \csc x, \left(\csc x = \dfrac{1}{\sin x} \right)$

23. $f(x) = \cot x, \left(\cot x = \dfrac{1}{\tan x} \right)$

24. $f(x) = \cot x, \left(\cot = \dfrac{\sin x}{\cos x} \right)$

25. Differentiate $y = \dfrac{\sec x + \tan x}{\csc x + \cot x}$

26. Differentiate $y = \dfrac{\sqrt{\sin x}}{\cot x}$

27. Differentiate $y = \ln \sin^2 x$

28. a. If $F(x) = \ln |\cos x|$ show that $F'(x) = -\tan x$.

   b. If $f(x) = \ln |\sec x + \tan x|$, show that $f'(x) = \sec x$.

Level 2 APPLIED AND THEORY PROBLEMS

29. Consider three areas as shown in Figure 3.22.

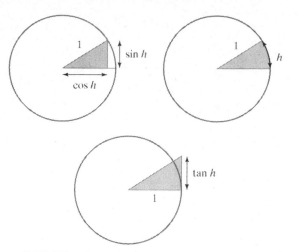

Figure 3.22 Triangles and a unit circle with subtended angle h.

   a. What is the area $g(h)$ of the blue-shaded triangle?

   b. What is the area $f(h)$ of the pink-shaded sector? Hint: The area of a sector of a circle of radius r and central angle θ measured in radians is
$$A = \frac{1}{2}r^2\theta.$$

   c. What is the area $k(h)$ of the green-shaded triangle?

   d. How can you use the fact that $g(h) \le f(h) \le k(h)$ for small $h > 0$ to prove that
$$\lim_{x \to 0} \frac{\sin x}{x} = 1$$
by beginning with the inequality

   BLUE AREA $\le$ PINK AREA $\le$ GREEN AREA

30. Prove
$$\lim_{x \to 0} \frac{\cos x - 1}{x} = 0$$
Hint: Multiply by 1 written as $\left(\dfrac{\cos x + 1}{\cos x + 1} \right)$ and use a fundamental trigonometric identity.

31. A researcher studying a certain species of fish in a northern lake models the population after t months of the study by the function
$$P(t) = 100e^{-t} \sin t + 800$$
At what rate is the population changing after two months? Is the population growing or declining at this time?

32. In an experiment with algae, a research scientist manipulated the light in growth chambers so that
$$P(t) = 7{,}000 \, e^{\cos(\pi t/12)}$$

described the population density (in cells per liter) as a function of t (in hours).

a. Find a function $r(t)$ such that
$$P'(t) = r(t) P(t)$$

b. Under the assumption that the growth rate of the population is proportional to the intensity of light, what is the period of the light fluctuations in the chamber?

c. Determine at what times (if any) the population is decreasing in abundance.

33. In a more ambitious experiment with algae, a research scientist manipulated the light in algal tanks so that
$$P(t) = 5{,}000\, e^{\cos t + t}$$
describes the population density (in cells per liter) as a function of t (in hours).

a. Find a function $r(t)$ such that
$$P'(t) = r(t) P(t)$$

b. Under the assumption that the growth rate of the population is proportional to the intensity of light, what is the period of the light fluctuations in the tank?

c. Determine at what times (if any) the population is decreasing in abundance.

34. In Example 4 of Section 1.5, we modeled the tides for Toms Cove in Assateague Beach, Virginia, on August 19, 2004 with the function
$$H(t) = 1.8 \cos\left[\frac{\pi}{6}(t - 11)\right] + 2.2$$
where H is the height of the tide (in feet) and t is the time (in hours after midnight). Find and interpret $\dfrac{dH}{dt}\Big|_{t=6}$.

35. The temperature in a swimming pool is given by
$$T(t) = 25 - 4\sin(\pi t/12) \text{ degrees Celsius}$$
where t is measured in hours since midnight.

a. Find $T'(12)$ and interpret.

b. During what hours is the temperature of the pool increasing?

36. The human heart goes through cycles of contraction and relaxation (called systoles). During these cycles, blood pressure goes up and down repeatedly; as the heart contracts, pressure rises, and as the heart relaxes (for a split second), the pressure drops. Consider the following approximate function for the blood pressure of a patient:
$$P(t) = 100 + 20\cos\left(\frac{\pi t}{35}\right) \text{ mmHg}$$
where t is measured in minutes. Find and interpret $P'(t)$.

3.5   Linear Approximation

We have seen that the tangent line is the line that just touches a curve at a single point. In this section, we will discover that the tangent line can be used to provide a reasonable approximation to a curve. Using these linear approximations we will be able to make projections about the size of a bison population (Figure 3.23) estimate $\sqrt{10}$, and estimate the effects of measurement error.

Figure 3.23 The North American plain's bison (*Bison bison*) is one of two subspecies of bison that roamed the Great Plains. Their numbers have dropped from tens of millions to thousands over the last 200 years.

Approximating with the tangent line

We begin with an example that illustrates how well a tangent line can approximate a curve.

Example 1   Zooming in at a point

Consider the function $y = \ln x$.

a. Find the tangent line at $x = 1$.

b. Graph $y = \ln x$ and the tangent line over the intervals $[0.1, 2]$, $[0.5, 1.5]$, $[0.9, 1.1]$. Discuss what you find.

Solution

a. Since

$$\frac{d}{dx} \ln x \bigg|_{x=1} = \frac{1}{x} \bigg|_{x=1} = 1$$

we get that the tangent line is the line of slope 1 through the point $(1, 0)$—that is, the equation

$$(y - 0) = 1 \cdot (x - 1) \quad \Rightarrow \quad y = x - 1$$

as we claimed in Section 2.1.

b. The graphs $y = \ln x$ (in blue) and $y = x - 1$ (in red) on the intervals $[0.1, 2]$, $[0.5, 1.5]$, and $[0.9, 1.1]$ are shown in Figure 3.24. This figure illustrates that as we zoom into the point $(1, 0)$, the tangent line provides a better and better approximation of our original function.

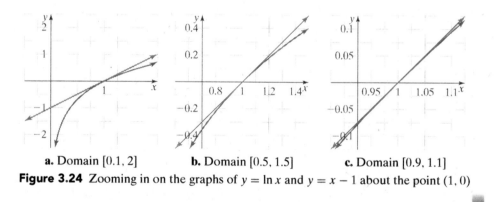

a. Domain $[0.1, 2]$ **b.** Domain $[0.5, 1.5]$ **c.** Domain $[0.9, 1.1]$

Figure 3.24 Zooming in on the graphs of $y = \ln x$ and $y = x - 1$ about the point $(1, 0)$

The difference between a tangent line and the associated curve becomes more and more negligible as you zoom into the point of contact. Thus, it seems quite reasonable to approximate the function with the tangent line in a neighborhood of the point at which this tangent is constructed. This is called the **linearization** of a function.

Linear Approximation

If f is differentiable at $x = a$, then the **linear approximation** of f around a is given by

$$f(x) \approx f(a) + f'(a)(x - a)$$

for x near a.

With linear approximations, we can make predictions about the future, as illustrated in the next example. We use data on the abundance of the North American bison in Yellowstone National Park going back as early as 1902. (Estimates of bison population levels in Yellowstone from 1902–1931 can be found at http://www.seattlecentral.edu/qelp/Data.html.) Annual abundances for bison in Yellowstone for the twenty-nine-year period 1902 to 1931 are shown in Figure 3.25. These data suggest that the bison population was recovering in the first part of the twentieth century after years of intense hunting in the nineteenth century.

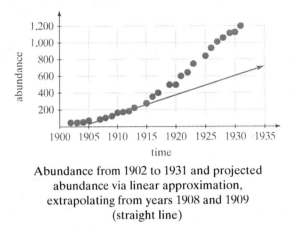

Abundance from 1902 to 1931 and projected
abundance via linear approximation,
extrapolating from years 1908 and 1909
(straight line)

Figure 3.25 Bison abundance in Yellowstone National Park.

In the next example, we use the data only from 1908 to 1915. However, a project involving all the data is outlined at the end of the chapter.

Example 2   **Predicting bison abundance**

Suppose it is January 1910, and you are the Yellowstone National Park manager.

a. Use a linear function to extrapolate what the abundance of bison might be in 1910 through 1915, given that you know the bison abundance in 1908 and 1909 are 95 and 118, respectively.

b. Compare your estimates to the actual population size in 1910 to 1915 as given in the last column in Table 3.2.

Table 3.2 Estimate and measured abundance of Bison in Yellowstone National Park, 1910–1915

Year	t	Abundance Estimated	Measured
1910	10	141	149
1911	11	164	168
1912	12	187	192
1913	13	210	215
1914	14	233	Unknown
1915	15	256	270

Solution

a. Let $N(t)$ denote the number of bison in year t, and for the sake of simplicity, set $t = 0$ at the year 1900. If we approximate $N(t)$ at $t = 8$ by a linear function we get

$$N(t) \approx N(8) + N'(8)(t - 8)$$

To approximate $N'(8)$, we can use

$$N'(8) \approx \frac{N(9) - N(8)}{9 - 8} = 23$$

Hence,

$$N(t) \approx 95 + 23(t - 8)$$

for t "near" 8. Hence, our approximation yields the predictions shown in Table 3.2, with actual abundance in the last column.

b. As we can see in Figure 3.25, our estimates are pretty good; nevertheless, they underestimate the actual population size more and more as time moves on. This is consistent with our expectation that population growth might be exponential.

Using linear approximation, we can estimate the value of a function at points near known values of the function. As we will see, however, linear approximations of nonlinear functions generally get increasingly worse as we move away from the point of approximation.

Example 3   Approximating $\sqrt{10}$

Consider the function $f(x) = \sqrt{x}$.

a. Find the linear approximation of f at $x = 9$.

b. Use the linear approximation found in part **a** to approximate $\sqrt{10}$. Compare this approximation to a calculator approximation.

c. How well does this same approximation work for $\sqrt{16}$?

Solution

a. $f'(x) = \frac{1}{2}x^{-1/2}$, so $f'(9) = \frac{1}{2}(9)^{-1/2} = \frac{1}{6}$ and the linear approximation for $\sqrt{x}$ at $x = 9$ is

$$\sqrt{x} \approx f(9) + f'(9)(x - 9)$$
$$= 3 + \frac{1}{6}(x - 9)$$

for x near 9.

b. If we now apply the approximation in part **a** to find $\sqrt{10}$, we obtain

$$\sqrt{10} \approx 3 + \frac{1}{6}(10 - 9) = 3\frac{1}{6} \approx 3.16667$$

This is fairly close to the calculator approximation

$$\sqrt{10} \approx 3.16228$$

So the error is 0.004 (to three decimal places)

c. Similarly,

$$\sqrt{16} \approx 4 + \frac{1}{6}(16 - 9) = 4\frac{7}{6} \approx 5.16666$$

Since we know the answer is 4, the approximation now has an error of more than 1.1.

The next example shows that the linear approximation of $\sin x$ in the neighborhood of 0 is very simple, but it fails badly as the approximation is pushed too far beyond 0.

Example 4   Approximating sin x

Consider $y = \sin x$

a. Find the linear approximation of $\sin x$ at $x = 0$.

b. Plot the difference between $y = \sin x$ and its linear approximation on the intervals $[-1, 1]$, $[-0.5, 0.5]$, and $[-0.1, 0.1]$. Discuss the meaning of these plots.

c. Approximate $\sin 2$, $\sin 1$, and $\sin 0.25$ with the linear approximation from part **a**. Compare your approximations to calculator approximations.

Solution

a. Since $\dfrac{d}{dx} \sin x \Big|_{x=0} = \cos 0 = 1$, we get the linear approximation at 0:

$$\sin x \approx f(0) + f'(0)(x - 0)$$
$$= 0 + 1(x - 0)$$
$$= x$$

b. The graphs of $\sin x - x$ on the intervals $[-1, 1]$, $[-0.5, 0.5]$ and $[-0.1, 0.1]$ are illustrated in Figure 3.26. These figures illustrate that the difference between $\sin x$ and x gets smaller and smaller as you zoom around the point $x = 0$. Hence, $y = x$ is a better and better approximation for $\sin x$ as x approaches 0.

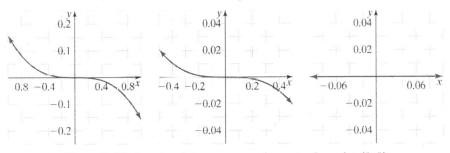

Figure 3.26 Graphs of $\sin x - x$ zooming onto the point $(0, 0)$

c.

linear approximation	calculator approximation	error
$\sin 0.25 \approx 0.25$	$\sin 0.25 \approx 0.247404$	small: $<0.5\%$
$\sin 1 \approx 1$	$\sin 1 \approx 0.841471$	moderate: around 15%
$\sin 2 \approx 2$	$\sin 2 \approx 0.909297$	large: $>100\%$

Development of organisms from immature forms, like eggs or seeds, to adult forms depends on a series of biochemical reactions. These biochemical reactions are often temperature sensitive, breaking down at too low or too high temperatures. For plants and insects whose internal temperatures are largely determined by the temperature of their environment, it follows that developmental rates depend on the temperature of the environment. This temperature dependence can be measured experimentally, as the following example illustrates.

Example 5   Developmental rates of the spider mite destroyer

Roy and colleagues estimated how developmental rates of a beetle (*Stethorus punctillum*) varied with temperature. They modeled the rate at which the fourth stage of development is completed with the following function

$$D(T) = 0.03T(T - 10.7)\sqrt{38 - T} \text{ percent development completed per day}$$

where T is measured in degrees Celsius. This model and the data used to parameterize the model are shown in Figure 3.27. This figure suggests that the developmental rate is approximately linear in T for temperatures near 20°C.

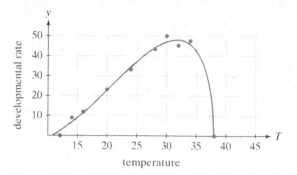

Figure 3.27 Developmental rate (percent completed per day) for a stage of development of the beetle *Stethorus punctillum* (also known as *spider mite destroyer*).

Data Source: Michèle Roy, Jacques Brodeur, and Conrad Cloutier. "Relationship between temperature and developmental rate of *Stethorus punctillum* (Coleoptera: Coccinellidae) and its prey *Tetranychus mcdanieli* (Acari: Tetranychidae)," *Environmental Entomology* 31 (2002), 177–187.

a. Find a linear approximation to $D(T)$ near the value $T = 20$.

b. Plot the linear approximation found in part a. How does this compare to the data?

Solution

a. To find the linear approximation at $T = 20$, we need to compute $D'(20)$. Using the product rule and the chain rule, we get

$$D'(T) = 0.03(T - 10.7)\sqrt{38 - T} + 0.03T\sqrt{38 - T} + 0.03\frac{T(T - 10.7)}{\sqrt{38 - T}}(-1/2)$$

Evaluating this expression at $T = 20$ yields

$$D'(20) \approx 3.07$$

Using the point slope formula for a line, we get the linear approximation

$$D(T) - D(20) \approx D'(20)(T - 20)$$
$$D(T) - 23.67 \approx 3.07(T - 20)$$

Equivalently,

$$D(T) \approx 3.07T - 37.73$$

b. Plotting the linear approximation (red line) from part **a** against $D(T)$ and the data yields

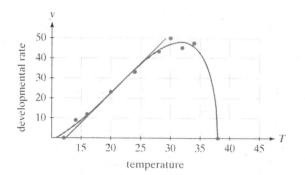

The linear approximation works quite well, and it even appears to provide a better estimate for the lower developmental threshold where the developmental rate equals zero at $T = 12$.

Error analysis

When a scientist makes a measurement, it is always subject to some measurement error. Hence, we have

$$\text{measurement} = \text{actual value} + \text{measurement error}$$

For instance, when the clearance rate of acetaminophen is given as 0.28 per hour, this estimate is the average of a series of measurements, each of which may vary by 0.05 or so. Consequently, when we estimate the half-life of acetaminophen, or the amount in the blood stream several hours after taking the drug, it is important to understand how small variations in the estimate 0.28 influence half-life estimates.

Example 6 **Professor Getz's headache**

Professor Getz takes 1000 mg of acetaminophen to combat a headache.

a. Solve for the half-life T of the drug as a function of the clearance rate x per hour.

b. Determine the half-life of the acetaminophen, assuming that $x = 0.28$ is a good estimate of the clearance rate.

c. What is the derivative of the half-life T with respect to x and its value at $x = 0.28$?

d. Use linear approximation to estimate the change ΔT in the estimated half-life if the estimate $x = 0.28$ is off by Δx. Interpret this result.

Solution

a. Let $A(t)$ denote the amount of acetaminophen in the body at time t hours. Since the clearance rate is x, we have

$$A(t) = A(0)e^{-xt}$$

The half-life is the time $t = T$ such that

$$A(T) = \frac{A(0)}{2}$$

$$e^{-xT} = \frac{1}{2}$$

$$-xT = \ln\frac{1}{2}$$

$$T = \frac{\ln 2}{x}$$

Hence, the half-life as a function of x is

$$T(x) = \frac{\ln 2}{x}$$

b. Evaluating T at $x = 0.28$ yields $T(0.28) = 2.47553$ hours.

c. Differentiating the half-life function derived in part **a** yields

$$T'(x) = -\frac{\ln 2}{x^2}$$

from which we can calculate $T'(0.28) = -8.84116$.

d. If $x = 0.28 + \Delta x$ where Δx can be viewed as a small measurement error, then by linear approximation we have

$$T(0.28 + \Delta x) \approx T(0.28) + T'(0.28)\Delta x$$
$$= 2.47553 - 8.84116\,\Delta x$$

Thus,

$$\Delta T = T(0.28 + \Delta x) - T(0.28)$$
$$\approx 2.47553 - 8.84116\,\Delta x - 2.47553$$
$$= -8.84116\,\Delta x$$

Hence, for a measurement error of Δx per hour, half-life changes by approximately $-8.84116\,\Delta x$ hours. For instance, if the measurement error in the clearance rate is $\Delta x = 0.05$, then our estimate of the half-life decreases approximately by $8.84116 \cdot 0.05 = 0.4421$ hours. Thus the estimate of the half-life, T, is quite sensitive to the estimate of the clearance rate.

Example 6 illustrates how an error in the measurement of the independent variable x propagates to an error in the dependent variable y—a process called **error propagation**.

Error Estimates and Sensitivity

Suppose $y = f(x)$ is a quantity of interest and $x = a$ is the true value of x. If there is an error of Δx in measuring $x = a$, then the approximate resulting error in y is given by

$$\Delta y = f(a + \Delta x) - f(a)$$
$$\approx f(a) + f'(a)\Delta x - f(a)$$
$$= f'(a)\Delta x$$

$f'(a)$ is called the **sensitivity** of y to x at $x = a$. The greater the sensitivity the greater the propagation of error.

Consider another example.

Example 7 Estimating metabolic rates

In Example 12 of Section 1.6 (below we changed the names of the variables from x and y to M and R), we discovered that the mouse-to-elephant curve describing how the metabolic rate R (in kilocalories/day) depends on body mass M (in kilograms) is approximately given by

$$\ln R = 0.75 \ln M + 4.2$$

Thus, taking exponentials yields the equation

$$R = e^{4.2} M^{0.75}$$

a. Estimate the metabolic rate of a California condor weighing 10 kg.

b. Determine the sensitivity of your estimate to the measurement of 10 kg. Discuss how a small error ΔM propagates to an error ΔR in your estimate for R.

Solution

a. For the 10 kg condor, we get $R = e^{4.2} \times 10^{0.75} \approx 375$ kilocalories/day.

b. The sensitivity of this estimate to our estimate for the condor weight is

$$R'(10) = 50.01 M^{-0.25}\Big|_{M=10} \approx 28.13$$

Hence, $\Delta R \approx 28.13 \Delta M$. For example, an error of $\Delta M = 0.1$ kg yields an error of $\Delta R = 2.81$ kilocalories/day in estimating R.

Elasticity

Often scientists are more interested in the percent error and not the absolute error. For example, a scientist may ask this question: How does a 10% error in the measurement of the clearance rate result in a percentage error in the estimate of the half-life? If $x = a$ is the true value of the independent variable and there is a measurement error of Δx, then the **percent error** in x is

$$\frac{\Delta x}{a} \times 100\%$$

With an error of Δx in the independent variable, we get an error of $\Delta y = f(a + \Delta x) - f(a)$ in y. Hence, the *percent error in y* is

$$\frac{\Delta y}{f(a)} \times 100\%$$

The ratio of the percentage error in y over the percentage error in x is given by

$$\frac{\dfrac{\Delta y}{f(a)} \times 100\%}{\dfrac{\Delta x}{a} \times 100\%} = \frac{\Delta y}{\Delta x} \frac{a}{f(a)}$$

and can be approximated by

$$f'(a) \frac{a}{f(a)}$$

This quantity is used quite commonly in the analysis of biological models and, consequently, has a special name: elasticity.

Elasticity	Let $y = f(x)$ be a function that is differentiable at $x = a$. The **elasticity** of f with respect to x at a is $$E = f'(a) \frac{a}{f(a)}$$ We can interpret E as stating that for a 1% error in the measurement of $x = a$, there is a $E\%$ error in the measurement of y.

Example 8 Elasticity of metabolic rates

Let us revisit Example 7 where we estimated the metabolic rate of a California condor weighing 10 kg.

a. Find the elasticity of your estimate of the metabolic rate to the estimate of the condor's weight.

b. Interpret your elasticity in terms of 10% error in the estimate of the condor's weight.

Solution

a. To compute the elasticity, recall we found that $R(10) \approx 375$ kilocalories/day and $R'(10) \approx 28.13$. Hence, the elasticity at $M = 10$ is

$$R'(10) \frac{10}{R(10)} \approx 28.13 \frac{10}{375} \approx 0.75$$

b. Since the elasticity is 0.75, a 10% measurement error in the weight of the condor would result in approximately a 7.5% error in the estimate of the metabolic rate.

Using elasticity, we can estimate with what accuracy we need to measure an independent variable to ensure a certain accuracy in the estimate of a dependent variable.

Example 9 Determining measurement accuracy

The body mass index (BMI) for individual weighing w pounds and h inches tall is given by

$$B = \frac{703w}{h^2}$$

a. Determine the elasticity of B with respect to the variable h for a particular weight class w (i.e., we regard w as constant, so that B is a function of the variable h alone).

b. Estimate how accurate your height measurement needs to be to guarantee less than a $\pm5\%$ error in your BMI measurement.

Solution

a. To compute the elasticity, we first need the derivative

$$\frac{dB}{dh} = -\frac{1406w}{h^3}$$

Hence, the elasticity is

$$\frac{dB}{dh}\frac{h}{B} = -\frac{1406w}{h^3}\frac{h}{703w/h^2}$$
$$= -2$$

Note that this answer does not depend on w or h but is a pure number! Think about why this is the case.

b. Since the elasticity is -2, an $x\%$ error in h results in a $-2x\%$ error in our estimate for BMI. To ensure that our error is no greater than $\pm5\%$, we need to ensure that the error in the measurement of the height is no greater than $\pm2.5\%$. ■

PROBLEM SET 3.5

Level 1 DRILL PROBLEMS

In Problems 1 to 6 find the linear approximation of $y = f(x)$ at the specified point, and use technology to graph the function and its linear approximation to determine whether the linear approximation tends to overestimate or underestimate $y = f(x)$ near the specified point.

1. $y = \cos x$ at $x = \dfrac{\pi}{2}$ **2.** $y = e^x$ at $x = 0$.

3. $y = \sin x$ at $x = \dfrac{\pi}{2}$ **4.** $y = x^2$ at $x = -2$

5. $y = \dfrac{1}{1 + x^2}$ at $x = 2$ **6.** $y = xe^{-x}$ at $x = \ln 2$

In Problems 7 to 12, estimate the indicated quantity using a linear approximation around the given point x and compare to the true value obtained using technology.

7. $\sqrt{26}, x = 25$ **8.** $\sqrt{0.99}, x = 1$

9. $\ln 0.9, x = 1$ **10.** $\cos\left(\dfrac{\pi}{2} + 0.01\right), x = \dfrac{\pi}{2}$

11. $\tan 0.2, x = 0$ **12.** $e^{-0.2}, x = 0$

Find the sensitivity of $y = f(x)$ at the point specified in Problems 13 to 18, and use it to estimate Δy for the given measurement error Δx.

13. $y = \sqrt{x}$ at $x = 9$, with $\Delta x = 0.01$

14. $y = \sqrt{2x^2 + 1}$ at $x = -2$, with $\Delta x = 0.01$

15. $y = \ln x$ at $x = 2$, with $\Delta x = -0.2$

16. $y = \cot x$ at $x = \dfrac{\pi}{2}$, with $\Delta x = 0.1$

17. $y = \cos x$ at $x = \dfrac{\pi}{2}$, with $\Delta x = -0.01$

18. $y = \dfrac{1}{x + 1}$ at $x = 0$, with $\Delta x = -0.05$

Find the elasticity of $y = f(x)$ at the point specified in Problems 19 to 24 and use it to estimate the percent error in y for the given percent error in x.

19. $y = \sqrt{x}$ at $x = 9$, with 1% error in x

20. $y = \sqrt{2x^2 + 1}$ at $x = -2$, with 8% error in x

21. $y = \ln x$ at $x = 2$, with 5% error in x

22. $y = \cot x$ at $x = \dfrac{\pi}{2}$, with 10% error in x

23. $y = \sin x$ at $x = \dfrac{\pi}{2}$, with 10% error in x

24. $y = \dfrac{1}{x+1}$ at $x = 0$, with 12% error in x

Level 2 APPLIED AND THEORY PROBLEMS

25. In Example 5, we saw that Roy and colleagues estimated how developmental rates of a beetle (*Stethorus punctillum*) varied with temperature. They modeled the rate at which egg development is completed with the following function

$$D(T) = 0.021\,T(T - 11.9)\sqrt{37 - T} \text{ percent}$$
$$\text{development completed per day}$$

where T is measured in degrees Celsius. This model and the data used to parameterize the model are shown in Figure 3.28. This figure suggests that the developmental rate is approximately linear in T for temperatures near 20°C.

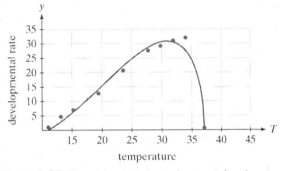

Figure 3.28 Developmental rate (percent development completed per day) for egg development of the beetle *Stethorus punctillum* (spider mite destroyer).

a. Find a linear approximation to $D(T)$ near the value $T = 20$.

b. Sketch the linear approximation on top of the graph in Figure 3.28. How does this compare to the data?

26. In Example 5, we saw that Roy and colleagues estimated how developmental rates of a beetle (*Stethorus punctillum*) varied with temperature. They modeled the rate at which the first stage of larval development is completed with the following function

$$D(T) = 0.07\,T(T - 11.8)\sqrt{37 - T} \text{ percent}$$
$$\text{development completed per day}$$

where T is measured in degrees Celsius. This model and the data used to parameterize the model are shown in Figure 3.29. This figure suggests that the developmental rate is approximately linear in T for temperatures near 20°C.

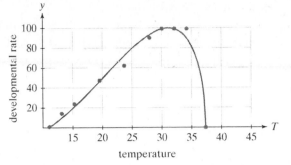

Figure 3.29 Developmental rate (percent completed per day) for the first stage of larval development for the beetle *Stethorus punctillum* (spider mite destroyer).

a. Find a linear approximation to $D(T)$ near the value $T = 20$.

b. Sketch the linear approximation on top of the graph in Figure 3.29. How does this compare to the data?

27. If your measurement of the radius of a circle is accurate to within 3%, approximately how accurate (to the nearest percentage) is your calculation to the area A when the radius is $r = 12$ cm? (Recall the formula $A = \pi r^2$).

28. Suppose a 12-ounce can of Coke® (i.e., Coca-Cola) has a height of 4.5 inches. If your measurement of the radius has an accuracy to within 1%, how accurate is your measurement for the volume? Check your answer by examining a Coke can.

29. An environmental study suggests that t years from now, the average level of carbon monoxide in the air will be

$$Q(t) = 0.05t^2 + 0.1t + 3.4$$

parts per million (ppm). By approximately how much will the carbon monoxide level change during the next six months?

30. A certain cell is modeled as a sphere. If the formulas $S = 4\pi r^2$ and $V = \frac{4}{3}\pi r^3$ are used to compute the surface area and volume of the sphere, respectively, estimate the effect of S and V produced by a 1% increase in the radius r.

31. In a model developed by John Helms ("Environmental Control of Net Photosynthesis in Naturally Grown *Pinus Ponderosa* Nets," *Ecology* (Winter 1972, p. 92), the water evaporation $E(T)$ for a ponderosa pine is modeled by

$$E(T) = 4.6e^{17.3T/(T+237)}$$

where T (degrees Celsius) is the surrounding air temperature.

a. Compute the elasticity of $E(T)$ at $T = 30$.

b. If the temperature is increased by 5% from 30°C, estimate the corresponding percentage change in $E(T)$.

32. In a healthy person of height x inches, the average pulse rate in beats per minute is modeled by the formula

$$P(x) = \frac{596}{\sqrt{x}} \qquad 30 \leq x \leq 100$$

a. Compute the sensitivity of P at $x = 60$.

b. Use your answer to part **a** to estimate the change in pulse rate that corresponds to a height change from 59 to 60 inches.

c. Compute the elasticity of P. Does it depend on x?

d. Determine how accurate the measurement of x needs to be to ensure the estimate for P has an error of less than 10%.

33. In Example 6, we showed that the half-life, T, of a drug with clearance rate x is given by

$$T(x) = \frac{\ln 2}{x}$$

Suppose that the true value of the clearance rate of some drug is given by $x = a$.

a. Find the elasticity of T with respect to x.

b. If you want to estimate the half-life of this drug within an error of 2%, how accurately do you have to measure the clearance rate of the drug?

34. A drug is injected into a patient's blood stream. The concentration of the drug in the blood stream t hours after the drug is injected is modeled by the formula

$$C(t) = \frac{0.12t}{t^2 + t + 1}$$

where C is measured in milligrams per cubic centimeter.

a. Compute the sensitivity of C at $t = 30$.

b. Use your answer to part **a** to estimate the change in concentration over the time period from 30 to 35 minutes after injection.

35. According to Poiseuille's law, the speed of blood flowing along the central axis of an artery of radius R is modeled by the formula

$$S(R) = cR^2$$

where c is a constant. What percentage error (rounded to the nearest percent) will you make in the calculation of $S(R)$ from this formula if you make a 1% error in the measurement of R?

36. The gross U.S. federal debt (in trillions of dollars) from 2000 to 2004 is given in the following table

Year	Gross federal debt
2000	5.629
2001	5.770
2002	6.198
2003	6.760
2004	7.355

Data source: From the historical tables of the Office of Management and Budget, 2006, as downloaded from www.whitehouse.gov/omb/budget/Historicals.

a. Plot the data and the linear approximation of the data at $t = 0$ (2000). Discuss the quality of this approximation.

b. Use a linear approximation to estimate the federal debt in 2010. Look up the actual gross federal debt to see how well the approximation worked.

37. In Example 7 of Section 2.6, the function

$$S(t) = 7.292 + 0.023t - 0.004t^2$$

was used to fit data on the extent of the Arctic sea ice S (million square kilometers) as a function of years t since 1980 (corresponding to $t = 0$).

a. What is the sensitivity of S in 1980?

b. How has the sensitivity changed from 1980 to 2000? Does this make sense? If not, why not?

38. Consider a power function $f(x) = ax^b$ with $a > 0$ and $b \neq 0$. Show that the elasticity of $f(x)$ is independent of the value x. What does it depend on? Use this answer to quickly solve the following problems.

a. If there is a 5% error in estimating the mass M of a weightlifter, what is approximately the percent error in estimating the lift $L = 20.15 M^{2/3}$ kg of the weightlifter?

b. If there is a 10% error in estimating the mass M of an organism, then what is approximately the percent error in estimating the metabolic rate $R \propto M^{2/3}$ kcal/hour of the organism?

c. If there is a 2% error in measuring the weight W of a person, what is approximately the percent error in estimating the body mass index $B \propto W$ of the person?

39. In Problem 31 in Problem Set 3.2, we used the following function (here we replace c with the constant $k = e^{-c-10}$ and x with $\ln y$)

$$T = a + \frac{b - a}{1 + ky}$$

to model T—the concentration of bound ligand I per milligram of tissue—in terms of y representing the concentration of a second ligand II in the solution.

a. What is the elasticity of T with respect to changes in y?

b. If there is a 10% error in estimating the concentration y of ligand II, then what is the error in calculating the level of ligand I as a function of y for the case $a = 1, b = 2$, and $k = 1$.

40. In Example 2 of Section 2.4, we used the function

$$R(x) = \frac{100e^x}{e^x + e^{-5}}$$

to represent the percent of patients exhibiting an above normal temperature response to dose x millimoles (mM) of a particular histamine.

a. What is the elasticity of R with respect to changes in x?

b. If there is a 5% error in estimating the dose x when $x = -5$ (mM), then what is the percent error in calculating the response R?

3.6   Higher Derivatives and Approximations

The derivative of a function can be interpreted as the instantaneous rate of change, and it yields linear approximations to the function. Since the derivative of a function is also a function, this latter function also has a derivative. What does this derivative of a derivative represent? How useful is it? The goal of this section is to answer these questions—and considerably more.

Second derivatives

The **second derivative** of a function f is the derivative of f' and is denoted f''. In other words,

$$f''(x) = \frac{d}{dx}\left(\frac{d}{dx} f(x)\right)$$

Equivalently, we write

$$f''(x) = \frac{d^2}{dx^2} f(x) = f^{(2)}(x)$$

or if $y = f(x)$,

$$f''(x) = \frac{d}{dx}\left(\frac{dy}{dx}\right) = \frac{d^2 y}{dx^2}$$

Note that $\dfrac{d^2}{dx^2}$ is regarded as the symbol for the "operation of taking the second derivative of a function with respect to its argument x."

Example 1   Finding second derivatives

Find $f''(x)$ for the given functions.

a. $f(x) = \sin x$ **b.** $f(x) = x^2$ **c.** $f(x) = x2^x$

Solution

a. Since $f'(x) = \cos x$, we get that $f''(x) = \dfrac{d}{dx} \cos x = -\sin x$.

b. Since $f'(x) = 2x$, we get that $f''(x) = \dfrac{d}{dx} 2x = 2$.

c. Since $f'(x) = 2^x + x(\ln 2)2^x = 2^x(1 + x \ln 2)$, we get that

$$f''(x) = 2^x \ln 2 + 2^x \ln 2(1 + x \ln 2)$$
$$= 2^x \ln 2(1 + 1 + x \ln 2)$$
$$= 2^x \ln 2(2 + x \ln 2)$$

What do these second derivatives represent? Consider the following definition.

| Concave Up/Concave Down | If the graph of a function f lies above all its tangents on an interval I, then it is said to be **concave up** on I. If the graph of f lies below all of its tangents on I, it is said to be **concave down**. |

Since f'' is the derivative of f', the mean value theorem implies that if $f'' > 0$ on an interval, then f' is increasing on this interval. What does this mean? In terms of tangent lines, this means that the slope of the tangent line is increasing in the interval. Hence, f is "bending upward" or, equivalently, is concave up on this interval. Alternatively, if $f'' < 0$, then the slope of the tangent line is decreasing and f is "bending downward" or, equivalently, is concave down.

| Concavity | Let f be a function whose first and second derivatives are defined at $x = a$. If $f''(a) < 0$, then $y = f(x)$ is concave down near $x = a$. If $f''(a) > 0$, then $y = f(x)$ is concave up near $x = a$. |

Example 2   Identifying concavities

Identify the concavities of the function defined by the given graphs. In other words, determine where the graphs are concave up and where they are concave down.

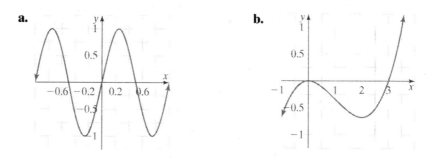

Solution

a. The easiest way to proceed is to place a straight edge (*e.g.*, ruler, pencil) on the graph; keeping it tangent to the curve, move from left to right. Whenever the straight edge is rotating in a counterclockwise fashion, the slope of the tangent line is increasing and $f'' > 0$. Hence, the function is concave up for these values of x. Alternatively, whenever the straight edge is rotating in a clockwise fashion, the slope of the tangent line is decreasing and $f'' < 0$. Hence, the function is concave down for these value of x.

For the graph in part **a** of the example, there is a clockwise rotation from $x = -1$ to $x = -0.5$ and from $x = 0$ to $x = 0.5$. Hence, the function is concave down on $(-1, -0.5)$ and $(0, 0.5)$. Alternatively, there is a counterclockwise rotation from $x = -0.5$ to $x = 0$ and from $x = 0.5$ to $x = 1$. Hence, the function is concave up on $(-0.5, 0)$ and $(0.5, 1)$.

b. Using the approach described in part **a**, we find that this graph is concave down over $(-1, 1)$ and concave up on $(1, 4)$.

A point on a continuous graph that separates a concave downward portion of a curve from a concave upward portion is called an **inflection point**. The following example illustrates this idea using data from mortality due to airborne diseases.

Example 3   Sigmoidal decay in deaths due to airborne diseases

In a study of deaths in the United States, Ausubel and colleagues found that deaths from aerially transmitted diseases as a fraction of all deaths could be very well described by the sigmoidal function shown in Figure 3.30. Determine where this function is concave up and down. Find the point of inflection. Discuss what these changes in concavity mean.

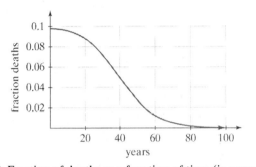

Figure 3.30 Fraction of deaths as a function of time (in years) after 1880.

Data: J. H. Ausubel, P. S. Meyer, and I. K. Wernick, "Death and the Human Environment: The United States in the 20th Century," *Technology in Society* 23(2) (2001): 131–146. Reprinted with permission.

Solution   To estimate the intervals of concavity, we can place a ruler as a tangent to the curve and slowly move it from the left side to the right side. Doing so, we notice that the ruler is rotating clockwise from $x = 0$ to $x \approx 40$ and rotating counterclockwise from $x \approx 40$ to $x = 120$. Hence, the point of inflection appears to be located at $x = 40$, and the fraction of deaths due to airborne diseases is decreasing at a faster and faster rate from 1880 $(x = 0)$ to 1920 $(x = 40)$; that is, the curve is concave down. The fraction of deaths is decreasing at a slower and slower rate from 1920 $(x = 40)$ to 1980 $(x = 100)$; that is, the curve is concave up.

The curve in Example 3 is an example of a *sigmoidal curve*, a curve that is monotonic, with horizontal asymptotes at positive and negative infinity and a single point of inflection. Another example of a sigmoidal curve is Figure 1.28 in Section 1.4; this is a model of population growth in the United States where growth is initially exponential and then levels off asymptotically. The following graphs show both forms of sigmoidal curves.

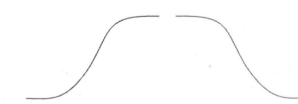

Graphs of increasing (in blue) and decreasing (in red) sigmoidal functions.

Changing rates of change

Recall from Section 2.1 the interpretation of the derivative of a function as the rate of change of that function with respect to increasing values of the function's argument. If we go back to the origins of the calculus, we see that velocity was interpreted by Newton as the instantaneous rate of change over time of the position of a particle in space, and acceleration was interpreted as the instantaneous rate of change over time of velocity. These interpretations led Newton to formulate his famous second law on the relationship between the force acting on an object, the mass of the object, and its resulting acceleration.

Average and Instantaneous Acceleration

Let $v(t)$ be the velocity of an object at time t in a predetermined direction. The **average acceleration** of an object from time t to time $t + h$ is

$$\text{AVERAGE ACCELERATION} = \frac{\text{change in velocity}}{\text{time elapsed}} = \frac{v(t + h) - v(t)}{h}$$

while the **instantaneous acceleration** of an object at time t is

$$\text{INSTANTANEOUS ACCELERATION} = \lim_{h \to 0} \frac{\text{change in velocity}}{\text{time elapsed}} = \lim_{h \to 0} \frac{v(t + h) - v(t)}{h}$$

The field of kinematics—that is, the motion of points or bodies through space—and the application of calculus to physics are developed in physics courses. But no calculus book is complete without at least one example dealing with acceleration, and here we focus on a biological one.

Example 4   When does Usain Bolt slow down?

Example 3 of Section 2.1 provides data on times for the 10-meter splits of Usain Bolt's record-breaking 100-meter win in the 2008 Beijing Olympic Games. Use these data to answer the following questions.

a. Use technology to fit a fifth-order polynomial $s(t)$ to these data that specifies the distance covered by Bolt as a function of time, beginning with the moment he leaves the starting blocks until the end of this race.

b. Calculate and plot the first and second derivatives of $s(t)$ to obtain graphs of Bolt's instantaneous velocity and acceleration during the race.

c. From the plots in part **b**, determine the time t_s during the race that Bolt switches from speeding up to slowing down, and calculate his velocity v_{max}, which is a maximum, at this time.

d. What is Bolt's average deceleration (negative of acceleration) from time t_s until the end of the race?

Solution

a. From Table 2.1 in Example 3 of Section 2.1, and taking into account that it takes 0.17 second for Usain Bolt to leave his starting block, we can construct the following table of how long it takes Usain Bolt to reach each of the successive 10-meter marks along the race.

Time (seconds) at	0	1.68	2.70	3.61	4.48	5.33	6.15	6.97	7.79	8.62	9.52
Distance (meters)	0	10	20	30	40	50	60	70	80	90	100

From these data we can use technology to obtain the following function $s(t)$ that specifies distance covered as time progress from leaving the blocks at $t = 0$ to finishing the race at $t = 9.52$, which with the time it takes for Usain Bolt to leave blocks, gives him a final race time of $9.52 + 0.17 = 9.69$ seconds (each term is specified to five significant figures):

$$s(t) = 2.0288t + 3.0905t^2 - 0.52044t^3 + 0.046520t^4 - 0.0016942t^5$$

This function is illustrated in the right panel of Figure 3.31.

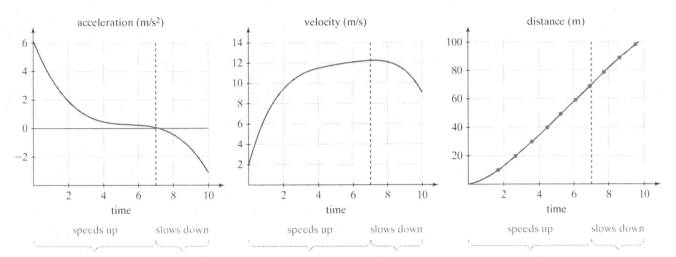

Figure 3.31 Distance covered as a function of time (seconds) by Usain Bolt in his record-breaking 100-meter win in the 2008 Beijing Olympic Games. Right panel: data and five-degree polynomial fit; middle panel: corresponding velocity profile; left panel: acceleration profile. Maximum velocity $v_{max} = 12.28$ is achieved (dotted vertical line) at $t = 7.17$ seconds, when the acceleration curve passes through zero.

b. Taking the first derivative, we obtain the velocity function (middle panel in Figure 3.31)

$$s'(t) = 2.0288 + 6.1811t - 1.5613t^2 + 0.18608t^3 - 0.0084710t^4$$

and taking the second derivative we obtain the acceleration function (left panel in Figure 3.31)

$$s''(t) = 6.1811 - 3.1227t + 0.55824t^2 - 0.033884t^3$$

c. The function $s''(t)$ has a root at $t_s = 7.17$. We see from Figure 3.31 that $s''(t)$ is decreasing and goes from positive on $[0, 7.16]$ to negative on $[7.18, 9.52]$. Thus, the velocity and acceleration plots show that Bolt accelerates, first strongly, and then more slowly until $t_s = 7.17$, at which time he reaches his maximum instantaneous velocity of $v_{max} = 12.28$ meters/second (m/s).

d. The average acceleration from time $t_s = 7.17$ to the end of the race at $t = 9.52$ is, by definition with $v(t) = s'(t)$,

$$\frac{s'(7.17) - s'(9.52)}{7.17 - 9.52} = -0.83$$

so taking the negative sign into account, the average deceleration is 0.83 m/s^2.

The reason for choosing a fifth-order polynomial rather than a fourth or sixth is that the runners accelerate strongly at the beginning and tend to decelerate as they tire at the end. Thus, acceleration is initially positive and eventually negative. Since this type of behavior is best modeled by odd-ordered rather than even-ordered polynomials, we choose an odd-ordered polynomial for distance, as it becomes odd again after taking two derivatives. We choose a fifth-order instead of third-order polynomial as it does a better job modeling the intermediate, close to zero acceleration segment that we see occur approximately around seconds 4 to 7 during the course of the race (see Problem 53 in Problem Set 3.6).

Example 5 Declining rates

A recent news article reported that SAT scores are declining at a slower rate. Use calculus to describe this report.

Solution   The key statement is that "SAT scores are declining at a slower rate." If $S(t)$ denotes the average SAT score as a function of time, then the phrase "SAT scores are declining" means that $S'(t) < 0$ and the phrase "at a slower rate" means that $S''(t) > 0$ as the rate $S'(t)$ is increasing. In other words, SAT scores are decreasing, yet concave up and so "leveling off"! ▪

Using our interpretations of the first and second derivative, we should be able to identify the graph of one from the other.

Example 6 Finding f, f', and f''

The graphs of $y = f(x)$, $y = f'(x)$, and $y = f''(x)$ are shown in Figure 3.32. Identify f, f', and f''.

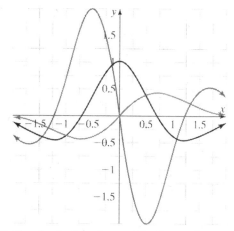

Figure 3.32 Graph of a function and its first and second derivatives.

Solution   To identify f, f', f'', we can start with one graph—say, the black one—and determine when it is rising and falling. We can see that it is falling roughly on the intervals $[-2, -1.25]$ and $[0, 1.25]$ and rising on the complementary intervals. Since the blue curve is negative on $[-2, -1.25]$ and $[0, 1.25]$ and positive on the complementary intervals, the blue curve may be the graph of the derivative of function defined by the black curve. On the other hand, the black curve appears to be negative where the red curve is falling and positive where the red curve is rising. Hence, the black curve appears to be the graph of the derivative of the function defined by the red curve. Therefore, we conclude that $y = f(x)$ is defined by the red curve, $y = f'(x)$ is defined by the black curve, and $y = f''(x)$ is defined by the blue curve. ▪

Second-order approximations

In Section 3.5, we approximated functions with their tangent lines. While a good start, these approximations can be improved upon by using first and second derivatives.

Example 7   Stripping away the tangent line

Consider $y = e^{2x}$.

a. Find the tangent line at $x = 0$.

b. Compute $\dfrac{d^2y}{dx^2}\Big|_{x=0}$ and determine whether the linear approximation overestimates or underestimates $y = e^{2x}$ near $x = 0$.

c. Plot the difference between $y = e^{2x}$ and its tangent line. Discuss what you notice.

Solution

a. Since $\dfrac{dy}{dx}\Big|_{x=0} = 2e^{2x}\Big|_{x=0} = 2e^0 = 2$, the tangent line has slope 2 and passes through the point $(0, 1)$ — that is, the line

$$(y - 1) = 2(x - 0) \quad \Rightarrow \quad y = 2x + 1$$

b. $\dfrac{d^2y}{dx^2} = \dfrac{d}{dx} 2e^{2x} = 4e^{2x}$, which is 4 at $x = 0$. Since the second derivative is positive, $\dfrac{dy}{dx}$ is increasing near $x = 0$, and we would expect the tangent line to underestimate (*i.e.*, lie under) $y = e^{2x}$ near $x = 0$. Indeed, graphing the function $y = e^{2x}$ (blue curve) and $y = 2x + 1$ (red curve) confirms this prediction.

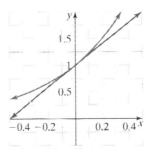

c. Plotting $y = e^{2x} - 2x - 1$ yields a function that looks like a parabola.

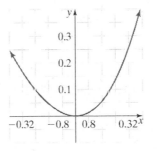

The preceding example suggests that function obtained by taking the difference between the original function and its derivative is approximately parabolic. If we want to approximate this function by a quadratic function, how do we find the best quadratic approximation? To answer this question, we develop the following procedure for finding the best quadratic approximation to a function f around the point $x = 0$. To find

$$f(x) \approx a + bx + cx^2$$

near $x = 0$, we require

$$a = f(0)$$

To have the first derivatives of $f(x)$ and the approximation $a + bx + cx^2$ agree at $x = 0$, we can take derivatives of both sides

$$f'(x) \approx b + 2cx$$

At $x = 0$, we want $f'(0) = b$, so we define $b = f'(x)$. Finally, to have their second derivatives agree at $x = 0$, we differentiate one more time:

$$f''(x) \approx 2c$$

This leads us to define $c = \dfrac{f''(0)}{2}$. This gives a **quadratic** (*second-order* or *parabolic*) **approximation** at $x = 0$:

$$f(x) \approx f(0) + f'(0)x + \frac{1}{2}f''(0)x^2$$

Let us see how well this approximation works.

Example 8 Quadratic approximation

Find the quadratic approximation to $y = e^{2x}$ at $x = 0$. Plot $y = e^{2x}$, its linear approximation, and its quadratic approximation.

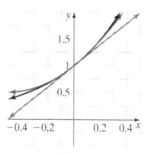

Figure 3.33 Graph of a function $f(x) = e^{2x}$ (in black) along with its linear (in red) and quadratic approximations (in blue).

Solution   Let $f(x) = e^{2x}$, so from the previous example $f'(x) = 2e^{2x}$ and $f''(x) = 4e^{2x}$. The linear approximation is

$$f(x) \approx f(0) + f'(0)(x - 0) = 1 + 2x$$

The quadratic approximation is

$$f(x) = f(0) + f'(0)x + \frac{1}{2}f''(0)x^2$$

$$= 1 + 2x + 2x^2$$

The graphs of $y = e^{2x}$, $y = 2x + 1$, and $y = 1 + 2x + 2x^2$ are shown in Figure 3.33. The quadratic approximation does a significantly better job of approximating the function $y = e^{2x}$.

In cases where the linear approximation is a horizontal line, the quadratic approximation is the first approximation to give real information about the concavity of the curve in question.

Example 9 Approximating the cosine

a. Find the linear and quadratic approximations of $y = \cos x$ at $x = 0$.

b. Use the quadratic approximation to estimate $\cos 1$, $\cos 0.5$, and $\cos 0.1$. Compare your approximations to the answers given by a calculator.

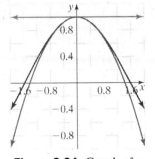

Figure 3.34 Graph of a function $f(x) = \cos x$ (in black) along with its linear (in red) and quadratic approximations (in blue).

Solution

a. Let $f(x) = \cos x$, so $f'(0) = -\sin 0 = 0$ and $f''(0) = -\cos 0 = -1$. The linear approximation is

$$y = 1$$

The quadratic approximation is

$$f(x) = f(0) + f'(0)x + \frac{1}{2}f''(0)x^2$$

$$= 1 - \frac{1}{2}x^2$$

The graph is a downward facing parabola. The graphs of $y = \cos x$, $y = 1$, and $y = 1 - \frac{1}{2}x^2$ are shown in Figure 3.34.

b. We compare the quadratic and calculator approximations.

Quadratic approximation	Calculator approximation	Comment (dp ≡ decimal places)
$\cos 1 \approx 1 - \frac{1}{2} = 0.5$	$\cos 1 \approx 0.540302$	fair: correct to 1 dp
$\cos 0.5 \approx 1 - \frac{1}{2}(0.5)^2 = 0.875$	$\cos 0.5 \approx 0.877583$	better: correct to 2 dp
$\cos 0.1 \approx 1 - \frac{1}{2}(0.1)^2 = 0.995$	$\cos 0.1 \approx 0.995004$	better yet: correct to 6 dp!

The approximations get better and better as you get closer and closer to $x = 0$.

More generally, we may wish to approximate a function near a point $x = a$ with a parabola. As an exercise, you can verify that by forcing the quadratic approximation and the function to agree up to the second derivative at $x = a$, you obtain the following **second-order approximation** of f at $x = a$.

Second-Order Approximation

Let f have a first and second derivative defined at $x = a$. The *second-order approximation* of f around $x = a$ is given by

$$f(x) \approx f(a) + f'(a)(x - a) + \frac{1}{2}f''(a)(x - a)^2$$

Example 10   Professor Getz's headache continues

Recall in Example 6 of Section 3.5 that we found that the half-life for a drug as a function of the clearance rate x per hour is given by

$$T(x) = \frac{\ln 2}{x} \text{ hours}$$

For a dose of 1000 mg of acetaminophen, we estimated a clearance rate of approximately 0.28 per hour.

a. Compute the first- and second-order approximation of $T(x)$ at $x = 0.28$.

b. Plot both approximations together with the function $T(x)$.

c. Discuss whether an error analysis using the sensitivity $T'(0.28)$ overestimates or underestimates the propagation of error from estimating x to estimating $T(x)$.

Solution

a. Computing the first and second derivatives of $T(x)$ at $x = 0.28$ gives

$$T'(0.28) = \frac{d}{dx}\bigg|_{x=0.28} \frac{\ln 2}{x}$$

$$= -\frac{\ln 2}{x^2}\bigg|_{x=0.28} \approx -8.841$$

$$T''(0.28) = \frac{d}{dx}\bigg|_{x=0.28} -\frac{\ln 2}{x^2}$$

$$= \frac{2\ln 2}{x^3}\bigg|_{x=0.28} \approx 63.151$$

Therefore, the first-order approximation is given by

$$T(x) \approx T(0.28) + T'(0.28)(x - 0.28)$$

$$\approx 2.475 - 8.841(x - 0.28)$$

and the second-order approximation is given by

$$T(x) \approx T(0.28) + T'(0.28)(x - 0.28) + \frac{1}{2}T''(0.28)(x - 0.28)^2$$

$$\approx 2.476 - 8.841(x - 0.28) + \frac{1}{2}63.151(x - 0.28)^2$$

b. Plotting $T(x)$ (in black), the first-order approximation (in blue), and the second-order approximation (in red) yields

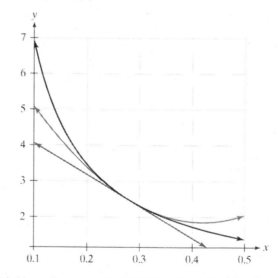

c. Since the sensitivity analysis using $T'(0.28)$ is based on the linear approximation of $T(x)$ near $x = 0.28$ and T is concave up, the sensitivity analysis underestimates the propagation of error from estimating x to estimating $T(x)$. This underestimation corresponds to the tangent line (in black) in part **a** lying under the graph of $T(x)$.

Even higher derivatives

Once we have taken second derivatives, there is no reason to stop. We can attempt to take the derivative of the second derivative, and the derivative of the resulting derivatives until the function obtained is 0; or we can continue indefinitely (e.g., see parts **b** and **c** of the next example). These **higher derivatives** and the associated notations are defined as follows:

- **First derivatives:** $f^{(1)}(x) = f'(x) = \dfrac{d}{dx} f(x) = \dfrac{df}{dx}$

- **Second derivatives:** $f^{(2)}(x) = f''(x) = \dfrac{d}{dx}\left(\dfrac{d}{dx} f(x)\right) = \dfrac{d^2}{dx^2} f(x) = \dfrac{d^2 f}{dx^2}.$

- **Third derivatives:** $f^{(3)}(x) = f'''(x) = \dfrac{d}{dx}\left[\dfrac{d}{dx}\left(\dfrac{d}{dx} f(x)\right)\right] = \dfrac{d^3}{dx^3} f(x) = \dfrac{d^3 f}{dx^3}$

- **nth derivatives:** $f^{(n)}(x) = \dfrac{d}{dx}\left(f^{(n-1)}(x)\right) = \dfrac{d}{dx}\left(\dfrac{d^{n-1} f}{dx^{n-1}}\right) = \dfrac{d^n f}{dx^n}$

Example 11   Higher derivatives

Find the following higher derivatives.

a. $\dfrac{d^3}{dx^3}(1 + x + x^3)$

b. $\dfrac{d^5}{dx^5} e^{2x}$

c. $f^{(101)}(x)$ where $f(x) = \sin x$

Solution

a. If $y = 1 + x + x^3$, then

$$\frac{dy}{dx} = \frac{d}{dy}(1 + x + x^3) = 1 + 3x^2$$

$$\frac{d^2 y}{dx^2} = \frac{d}{dy}(1 + 3x^2) = 6x$$

$$\frac{d^3 y}{dx^3} = \frac{d}{dy}(6x) = 6$$

b. If $f(x) = e^{2x}$, then

$$f'(x) = 2e^{2x}$$
$$f''(x) = 4e^{2x}$$
$$f'''(x) = 8e^{2x}$$
$$f^{(4)}(x) = 16e^{2x}$$
$$f^{(5)}(x) = 32e^{2x}$$

c. At first this problem might seem insane. Take 101 derivatives of a function? However, if we proceed calmly, a pattern will quickly emerge that will dispel this insanity. If $f(x) = \sin x$, then

$$f'(x) = \cos x$$
$$f''(x) = -\sin x$$
$$f'''(x) = -\cos x$$
$$f^{(4)}(x) = \sin x$$

We are back to where we started, and the derivatives cycle in a fixed pattern of period four; that is, repetition occurs every four derivatives so that $f^{(1)}(x) = f^{(5)}(x) = f^{(9)}(x) = \cdots \cos x$, $f^{(2)}(x) = f^{(6)}(x) = f^{(10)}(x) = \cdots - \sin x$, and so on. Hence, $f^{(100)}(x) = \sin x$ and $f^{(101)}(x) = \dfrac{d}{dx} \sin x = \cos x$. ∎

We conclude with an application of higher derivatives from politics.

Example 12   Presidential proclamation

In the fall of 1972, President Nixon announced that the rate of increase of inflation was decreasing. This was the first time a sitting president used the third derivative to advance his case for reelection.

So reported Hugo Rossi in "Mathematics Is an Edifice, Not a Toolbox" (*Notices of the AMS*, 43, October 1996). Discuss how a third derivative was being used by President Nixon.

Solution   Let V denote the "value of a dollar" at time t in years. Inflation means that the value of a dollar is decreasing, so $\dfrac{dV}{dt} < 0$. If inflation is increasing, then the value of a dollar is decreasing at a faster rate; that is, $\dfrac{d^2 V}{dt^2} < 0$. Finally, if the rate of increase of inflation is decreasing, we get $\dfrac{d^3 V}{dt^3} > 0$. Hence, at the level of the third derivative, things were looking less bleak for the value of the dollar! ∎

PROBLEM SET 3.6

Level 1 DRILL PROBLEMS

Find the higher derivatives indicated in Problems 1 to 12.

1. $\dfrac{d^2}{dx^2}(x\,e^{-x})$

2. $\dfrac{d^3}{dx^3}(2^x)$

3. $f^{(4)}(x)$, where $f(x) = 1 + x + x^2 + x^3 + x^4$

4. $f^{(103)}(x)$, where $f(x) = \cos x$

5. $\dfrac{d^{99}}{dx^{99}}(\sin 3x)$

6. $\dfrac{d^3}{dw^3}(1 + w + w^2 + w^3 + w^4)$

7. $\dfrac{d^4}{dt^4}\left(\dfrac{1}{4}t^8 - \dfrac{1}{2}t^6 - t^2 + 2\right)$

8. $\dfrac{d^{n+1}}{dx^{n+1}}x^n$

9. $f^{(10)}(x)$, where $f(x) = (1+x)^{10}$

10. $f^{(4)}(x)$, where $f(x) = \dfrac{4}{\sqrt{x}}$

11. $\dfrac{d^2}{dw^2}\dfrac{1}{1+w}$

12. $\dfrac{d^2 y}{dx^2}$, where $y = (x^2 + 4)(1 - 3x^3)$

In Problems 13 to 18 you are given the function $s(t)$ that specifies the position of an object on a line as a function of time t. Find expressions for the velocity and acceleration as a function of time for $t \geq 0$. Solve for t when the acceleration is 0; use technology where needed to find the values and where multiple values exist, the two closest $t = 0$.

13. $s(t) = t^2 - 3t$

14. $s(t) = t^3 - 5t^2 - 8t$

15. $s(t) = 1 - \cos t/3$

16. $s(t) = 1 - \cos t^2$

17. $s(t) = te^{-t}$

18. $s(t) = \dfrac{1}{1 + e^t}$

In Problems 19 to 24 find the linear approximations of the given functions $f(x)$ around $x = a$. Using second-order derivatives, determine whether the linear approximation tends to overestimate or underestimate $f(x)$ near $x = a$.

19. $f(x) = e^x$ at $x = 0$

20. $f(x) = \cos x$ at $x = 0$

21. $f(x) = 1 - x^2$ at $x = 2$

22. $f(x) = \tan x$ at $x = \pi$

23. $f(x) = \dfrac{1}{1 + x}$ at $x = 2$

24. $f(x) = xe^{-x}$ at $x = 1$

In Problems 25 to 34 determine on what intervals f is increasing, decreasing, concave up, concave down, and find the points of inflection.

25. $y = 1 - x + x^3$

26. $y = 1 + 2x + 18/x$

27. $y = xe^{-x}$

28. $y = e^{-x^2}$

29. $y = \dfrac{x}{1+x}$

30. $y = \dfrac{x}{x^2+1}$

31. $y = 3x^4 - 2x^3 - 12x^2 + 18x - 5$

32. $y = x^4 + 6x^3 - 12x^2 + 18x - 5$

33. $y = \sec x$

34. $y = x^3 + \sin x$ on $\left[-\dfrac{\pi}{2}, \dfrac{\pi}{2}\right]$

Find the first- and second-order approximations of $y = f(x)$ around $x = a$ in Problems 35 to 40. Use technology to plot the function and its approximations near $x = a$.

35. $y = \sin x$ at $x = 0$

36. $y = 1 + x^2$ at $x = 2$

37. $y = e^x$ at $x = 0$

38. $y = \sec x$ at $x = 0$

39. $y = \sqrt{x}$ at $x = 4$

40. $y = \sqrt[3]{x}$ at $x = 27$

In Problems 41 to 44, identify $y = f(x)$, $y = f'(x)$, and $y = f''(x)$.

41.

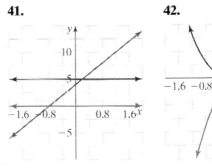

42.

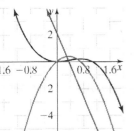

43.

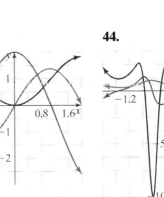

44.

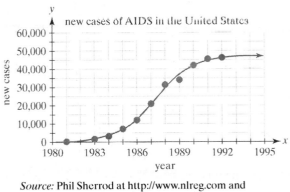

45. Sketch the graph of a function with all of the following properties:

$f'(x) > 0$ when $x < -1$

$f'(x) > 0$ when $x > 3$

$f'(x) < 0$ when $-1 < x < 3$

$f''(x) < 0$ when $x < 2$

$f''(x) > 0$ when $x > 2$

46. Sketch the graph of a function with all of the following properties:

$f'(x) > 0$ when $x < 2$ and when $2 < x < 5$

$f'(x) < 0$ when $x > 5$

$f'(2) = 0$

$f''(x) < 0$ when $x < 2$ and when $4 < x < 7$

$f''(x) > 0$ when $2 < x < 4$ and when $x > 7$

Level 2 APPLIED AND THEORY PROBLEMS

47. The slogan of a particular home improvement company is "Improving Home Improvement." Explain the role of derivatives in this slogan.

48. A politician claims that "Under a new law, prices would rise slower than if the law were not passed." Explain the role of higher derivatives in this statement.

49. At the website **http://www.nlreg.com/aids.htm**, you can find the following figure that graphs the number of new cases of AIDS since 1980.

   a. Estimate where the function is concave up and concave down.

   b. Describe in words what these changes in the concavity mean for the AIDS epidemic.

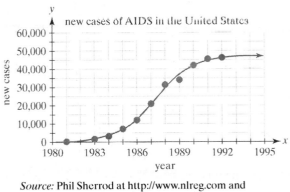

Source: Phil Sherrod at http://www.nlreg.com and http://www.dtreg.com

50. In Example 2 of Section 2.4, a dose-response curve for patients responding to a dose of histamine is given by

$$R = \dfrac{100e^x}{e^x + e^{-5}}$$

where x is the natural logarithm of the dose in millimoles (mmol).

a. Compute $\dfrac{d^2R}{dx^2}$

b. Determine for what dose ranges R is concave up and concave down. Interpret your results.

51. 𝕳𝖎𝖘𝖙𝖔𝖗𝖎𝖈𝖆𝖑 𝕼𝖚𝖊𝖘𝖙

Maria Gaetana Agnesi 1718–1799

One of the most famous women in the history of mathematics is Maria Gaetana Agnesi.

She was born in Milan, the first of twenty-one children. Her first publication was at age nine, when she wrote a Latin discourse defending higher education for women. Her most important work was a now classic calculus textbook published in 1748. Agnesi is primarily remembered for a curve defined by the equation

$$y = \frac{a^3}{x^2 + a^2}$$

for a positive constant a. The curve was named *versiera* (from the Italian verb *to turn*) by Agnesi, but John Colson, an Englishman who translated her work, confused the word *versiera* with the word *avversiera*, which means "wife of the devil" in Italian; the curve has ever since been called the "witch of Agnesi." This was particularly unfortunate because Colson wanted Agnesi's work to serve as a model for budding young mathematicians, especially young women. Graph this curve, find the points of inflection (if any), and discuss its concavity.

52. The spruce budworm is a moth whose larvae eat the leaves of coniferous trees. These insects suffer predation by birds. Ludwig and others* suggested a model for the per capita predation rate, $p(x)$:

$$p(x) = \frac{bx^2}{a^2 + x^2}$$

where b is the maximum predation rate and a is the number of budworms at which the predation rate is half its maximum rate. What is the concavity of this curve, and is there a point of inflection?

53. In Example 4 of this section, we fitted a fifth-order polynomial to the data on the distance covered as a function of time during Usain Bolt's record-breaking 100-meter win in the 2008 Beijing Olympic Games. Use technology to fit a third-order polynomial to these data; then differentiate this polynomial to obtain the corresponding velocity and acceleration functions of time. Plot these three functions (displacement, velocity, acceleration) and estimate the time t_s at which Bolt switches from acceleration to deceleration during the course of the race and his velocity v_{max}, which is a maximum, at this switching point. What is the average deceleration from the switching point to the end of the race? Compare your values of t_s, v_{max}, and average deceleration with those obtained in Example 4.

54. In Example 4 of this section, we fitted a fifth-order polynomial to the data on the distance covered as a function of time during Usain Bolt's record-breaking 100-meter win in the 2008 Beijing Olympic Games. Use technology to fit a seventh-order polynomial to these data; then differentiate this polynomial to obtain the corresponding velocity and acceleration functions of time. Plot these three functions (displacement, velocity, acceleration) and estimate the time t_s at which Bolt switches from acceleration to deceleration during the course of the race and his velocity v_{max}, which is a maximum, at this switching point. What is the average deceleration from the switching point to the end of the race? Compare your values of t_s, v_{max}, and average deceleration with those obtained in Example 4.

55. In Example 4 of this section, we fitted a fifth-order polynomial to the data on the distance covered as a function of time during Usain Bolt's record-breaking 100-meter win in the 2008 Beijing Olympic Games. Use Ben Johnson's split times given in Table 2.1 in Example 3 of Section 2.1 to obtain data relating distance and time of Johnson's performance during the 1988 Seoul Olympics 100-meter final. Fit a fifth-order polynomial to the data; then differentiate this polynomial to obtain the corresponding velocity and acceleration functions of time. Plot these three functions (displacement, velocity, acceleration) and estimate the time t_s at which Johnson switches from acceleration to deceleration during the course of the race. What is Johnson's maximum velocity, which occurs at t_s, and what is his average deceleration from time t_s until the end of the race?

*D. Ludwig, D. D. Hones, and C. S. Holling, "Qualitative Analysis of Insect Outbreak Systems: The Spruce Budworm and Forest," *Journal of Animal Ecology* 47(1978): 315–332.

Compare your results to Bolt's performance analyzed in Example 4.

56. Let f be a function that is twice differentiable on an interval I containing the point $x = a$. If there exists a $K > 0$ such that $\left|f''(x)\right| \leq K$ for all x in I, then show that

$$\left|f(x) - f(a) - f'(a)(x - a)\right| \leq \frac{K}{2}|x - a|^2$$

for all x in I. This result gives the error of the first-order approximation. Hint: Pick any point $b \neq a$ in I. Define

$$G(x) = f(x) - f(a) - f'(a)(x - a) - C(x - a)^2$$

where C is chosen such that $G(b) = 0$. Differentiate G and apply the mean value theorem to G and f'.

57. Let f be a function with first- and second-order derivatives at $x = a$. Consider a quadratic of the form $q(x) = b + c(x - a) + d(x - a)^2$. Show that $f(a) = q(a)$, $f'(a) = q'(a)$, and $f''(a) = q''(a)$ if and only if $b = f(a)$, $c = f'(a)$ and $d = f''(a)/2$.

3.7 l'Hôpital's Rule

In models of tumor or population growth, spread of rumors, and risk of being infected, one may encounter limits of the form

$$\lim_{x \to a} \frac{f(x)}{g(x)}$$

where $\lim_{x \to a} f(x)$ and $\lim_{x \to a} g(x)$ are both zero or both infinite. Such limits are called **0/0 indeterminate form** and **∞/∞ indeterminate form**, respectively, because their value cannot be determined without further analysis. In this section, we study an approach to handling these limits and explore some applications.

The 0/0 and ∞/∞ indeterminate forms

In 1694, French mathematician Guillaume de l'Hôpital (see Historical Quest in Problem Set 3.7) found a useful method for evaluating limits involving indeterminate forms. He considered the special case where $f(a) = g(a) = 0$, f and g are differentiable at $x = a$, and $g'(a) \neq 0$. Under these assumptions, we have

$$\lim_{x \to a} \frac{f(x)}{g(x)} = \lim_{x \to a} \frac{f(x)}{x - a} \frac{x - a}{g(x)} \qquad \textit{multiplying by } \frac{x - a}{x - a}$$

$$= \lim_{x \to a} \frac{f(x)}{x - a} \lim_{x \to a} \frac{x - a}{g(x)} \qquad \textit{product limit law}$$

$$= \lim_{x \to a} \frac{f(x) - f(a)}{x - a} \lim_{x \to a} \frac{x - a}{g(x) - g(a)} \qquad \textit{as } g(a) = f(a) = 0$$

$$= f'(a) \frac{1}{g'(a)} \qquad \textit{by definition of derivative and } g'(a) \neq 0$$

The following example illustrates how replacing the original limit with a limit involving derivatives can be helpful.

Example 1   Using l'Hôpital's argument

Evaluate the following limits.

a. $\displaystyle\lim_{x \to 0} \frac{\sin x}{x}$

b. $\displaystyle\lim_{x \to 2} \frac{x^7 - 128}{x^3 - 8}$

Solution

a. This limit is of indeterminate form because $\sin x$ and x both approach 0 as $x \to 0$. l'Hôpital's rule applies because both $\sin x$ and x are differentiable at $x = 0$. Thus

$$\lim_{x \to 0} \frac{\sin x}{x} = \frac{\cos x}{1}\Big|_{x=0} = 1$$

b. For this example, $f(x) = x^7 - 128$ and $g(x) = x^3 - 8$ and the limit is of the form 0/0. Since $f'(2) = 7 \cdot 2^6$ and $g'(2) = 3 \cdot 2^2 \neq 0$, we can apply l'Hôpital's argument to obtain

$$\lim_{x \to 2} \frac{x^7 - 128}{x^3 - 8} = \frac{f'(2)}{g'(2)} = \frac{7 \cdot 2^6}{3 \cdot 2^2} = \frac{112}{3}$$

∎

This approach to computing limits is known as *l'Hôpital's rule*. The general statement of this rule is given in the following theorem.

Theorem 3.1   l'Hôpital's rule

Let f and g be differentiable functions on an open interval containing a (except possibly at a itself). Suppose $\lim_{x \to a} \dfrac{f(x)}{g(x)}$ produces an indeterminate form $\dfrac{0}{0}$ or $\dfrac{\infty}{\infty}$ and that

$$\lim_{x \to a} \frac{f'(x)}{g'(x)} = L$$

where L is either a finite number, $-\infty$, or ∞. Then

$$\lim_{x \to a} \frac{f(x)}{g(x)} = L$$

The theorem also applies to one-sided limits and to limits at infinity where $x \to \infty$ and $x \to -\infty$.

When we use l'Hôpital's rule, we use the symbol $\overset{H}{=}$ as shown in the following example.

Example 2   Using l'Hôpital's rule

Find the following limits.

a. $\displaystyle\lim_{x \to 3} \frac{\sin(x - 3)}{x - 3}$ **b.** $\displaystyle\lim_{x \to \infty} \frac{x + e^{-x}}{2x + 1}$ **c.** $\displaystyle\lim_{x \to \pi/2^+} \frac{\cos x}{1 - \sin x}$ **d.** $\displaystyle\lim_{x \to \infty} \frac{\sqrt{x}}{\ln x}$

Solution

a. Since $\sin(3 - 3) = 3 - 3 = 0$, this limit is of an 0/0 indeterminate form. Since both $\sin(x - 3)$ and $x - 3$ are differentiable near $x = 3$, we can apply l'Hôpital's rule as follows:

$$\lim_{x \to 3} \frac{\sin(x - 3)}{x - 3} \overset{H}{=} \lim_{x \to 3} \frac{\cos(x - 3)}{1}$$
$$= 1$$

b. Since $\lim_{x \to \infty} x + e^{-x} = \infty$ and $\lim_{x \to \infty} 2x + 1 = \infty$, this limit is an ∞/∞ indeterminate form. Since both $x + e^{-x}$ and $2x + 1$ are differentiable for large x, we can apply l'Hôpital's rule as follows:

$$\lim_{x \to \infty} \frac{x + e^{-x}}{2x + 1} \overset{H}{=} \lim_{x \to \infty} \frac{1 - e^{-x}}{2}$$
$$= \frac{1}{2}$$

c. Since $\cos \pi/2 = 1 - \sin \pi/2 = 0$, this limit is of a $0/0$ indeterminate form. Since both $\cos x$ and $1 - \sin x$ are differentiable near $x = \pi/2$, we can apply l'Hôpital's rule as follows:

$$\lim_{x \to \pi/2^+} \frac{\cos x}{1 - \sin x} \overset{H}{=} \lim_{x \to \pi/2^+} \frac{-\sin x}{-\cos x}$$

$$= -\infty$$

d. Since $\lim_{x \to \infty} \sqrt{x} = \infty$ and $\lim_{x \to \infty} \ln x = \infty$, this limit is an ∞/∞ indeterminate form. Since both $\sqrt{x}$ and $\ln x$ are differentiable for large x, we can apply l'Hôpital's rule as follows:

$$\lim_{x \to \infty} \frac{\sqrt{x}}{\ln x} \overset{H}{=} \lim_{x \to \infty} \frac{\dfrac{1}{2\sqrt{x}}}{\dfrac{1}{x}}$$

$$= \lim_{x \to \infty} \frac{\sqrt{x}}{2} = \infty$$

We consider two applications of l'Hôpital's rule to models of population growth.

Example 3   Exponential versus arithmetic growth

In *An Essay on the Principle of Population*, first published anonymously in 1798, but later attributed to Thomas Malthus, we find the following text:

"Population, when unchecked, increases in a geometrical ratio. Subsistence increases only in an arithmetical ratio. A slight acquaintance with numbers will shew [sic] the immensity of the first power in comparison of the second."

While Example 4 of Section 1.4 explored a special case of this observation, l'Hôpital's rule allows us to fully appreciate the observation of Malthus. Let $P(t) = P_0 c^t$ for some $c > 1$ and $P_0 > 0$ represent the size of a population at time t, and let $F(t) = a + bt$ for some $a > 0$ and $b > 0$ represent the total amount of food available at time t. Find

$$\lim_{t \to \infty} \frac{F(t)}{P(t)}$$

and discuss its implications.

Solution   Since both $P_0 c^t$ and $a + bt$ approach infinity as t approaches infinity, we obtain

$$\lim_{t \to \infty} \frac{a + bt}{P_0 c^t} \overset{H}{=} \lim_{t \to \infty} \frac{b}{P_0 c^t \ln c}$$

$$= 0$$

Hence, as time marches on, the amount of food per individual approaches nothing.

What do tumor growth, sales of mobile phones, spread of rumor or infection, and population growth have in common? They all can be modeled mathematically by specifying how the growth rate of the tumor, rumor, or population depends on its current size, frequency, or abundance. The next example looks an important family of growth functions introduced by F. J. Richards in a 1959 article that appeared in the *Journal of Experimental Botany* [(2): 290–301].

Example 4 Generalized logistic growth function and indeterminate form 0/0

Whether it be the spread of a rumor, tumor growth, or population growth, an important class of models describing the rate at which the size N of a population, or a tumor for that matter, changes is

$$G(N) = (r/v)N(1 - (N/K)^v)$$

where $r > 0$, $v > 0$, and $K > 0$ are positive constants that influence the shape of the growth function.

a. For what population sizes N does the population grow?

b. Let $r = 1$ and $K = 100$. Plot $G(N)$ on the interval $[0, 110]$ for $v = 2, 1, 0.1, 0.01$. Discuss what you find.

c. For $K > N > 0$, $r = 1$, and $K = 100$, find

$$\lim_{v \to 0}(r/v)N(1 - N/K)^v)$$

and sketch the resulting curve.

Solution

a. Since r, v, and K are positive, the population growth rate $G(N)$ is positive if

$$1 - (N/K)^v > 0$$
$$1 > (N/K)^v$$
$$1 > N/K$$
$$K > N$$

Therefore, the population grows whenever its population size is positive and less than K.

b. Plotting $G(N)$ for the different v values yields the dashed colored curves in Figure 3.35. Smaller v values correspond to higher curves. Hence, as v gets smaller, the growth rate gets larger. Moreover, the growth function G appears to be approaching a limiting function as v approaches zero.

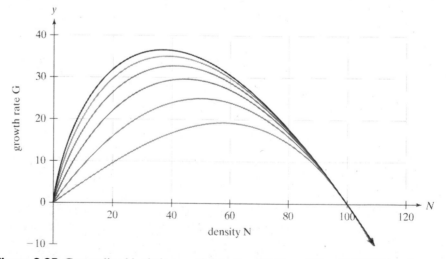

Figure 3.35 Generalized logistic growth function $G(N) = N(1 - (N/100)^v)/v$ for $v = 2$ (in red), 1 (in green), 0.5 (in purple), 0.25 (in cyan), and 0.1 (in magenta). The limiting Gompertz growth function $G(N) = -N\log(N/100)$ is shown as a solid black curve.

c. For $0 < N < K$, $G(N)$ is positive and the limit

$$\lim_{v \to 0} \frac{rN(1 - (N/K)^v)}{v}$$

is of indeterminate form $0/0$ as $r N(1 - (N/K)^v)$ and v equal zero at $v = 0$. Therefore, taking derivatives with respect to v gives

$$\lim_{v \to 0} \frac{r N(1 - (N/K)^v)}{v} \overset{H}{=} \lim_{v \to 0} \frac{-r N \ln(N/K)(N/K)^v}{1} = -r N \ln(N/K)$$

for $N > 0$. This limiting growth function $-r N \ln(N/K)$ is known as the Gompertz growth function, which has been used extensively to model tumor growth. Figure 3.35 plots this function (in black) for $K = 100$ and $r = 1$. As anticipated in part **b**, the plots of the generalized logistic growth functions approach the Gompertz growth function as v approaches zero.

Sometimes repeated applications of l'Hôpital's rule are necessary to get anywhere.

Example 5   Applying l'Hôpital's rule twice

Evaluate $\displaystyle\lim_{x \to \infty} \frac{2x^2 - 3x + 1}{3x^2 + 5x - 2}$.

Solution   If we consider the limit of the numerator and denominator separately, we obtain ∞/∞. However, if we apply l'Hôpital's rule twice we obtain

$$\lim_{x \to \infty} \frac{2x^2 - 3x + 1}{3x^2 + 5x - 2} \overset{H}{=} \lim_{x \to \infty} \frac{4x - 3}{6x + 5} \overset{H}{=} \lim_{x \to \infty} \frac{4}{6} = \frac{2}{3}$$

Note that L'Hôpital's rule is not the only way to solve the above example. We could have divided both the numerator and denominator by x^2 to obtain

$$\lim_{x \to \infty} \frac{2x^2 - 3x + 1}{3x^2 + 5x - 2} = \lim_{x \to \infty} \frac{2 - 3/x + 1/x^2}{3 + 5/x - 2/x^2} = \frac{2 - 0 + 0}{3 + 0 - 0} = \frac{2}{3}$$

Most examples in this section, however, do not yield to this simple procedure, so l'Hôpital's rule must be used. Before applying l'Hôpital's rule, however, we must check that the conditions of Theorem 3.1 apply. If they do not hold, then the analysis is not valid, as illustrated by the next two examples.

Example 6   Limit is not an indeterminate form

Evaluate $\displaystyle\lim_{x \to 0} \frac{1 - \cos x}{\sec x}$.

Solution   You must always remember to check that you have an indeterminate form before applying l'Hôpital's rule. The limit is

$$\lim_{x \to 0} \frac{1 - \cos x}{\sec x} = \frac{\displaystyle\lim_{x \to 0} (1 - \cos x)}{\displaystyle\lim_{x \to 0} \sec x} = \frac{0}{1} = 0$$

If you apply l'Hôpital's rule in Example 6, you obtain the WRONG answer:

$$\lim_{x \to 0} \frac{1 - \cos x}{\sec x} \overset{H}{=} \lim_{x \to 0} \frac{\sin x}{\sec x \tan x} \qquad \textit{this is NOT correct}$$

$$= \lim_{x \to 0} \frac{\cos x}{\sec x}$$

$$= \frac{1}{1}$$

$$= 1 \qquad \textit{hence the answer is WRONG}$$

Example 7   Conditions of l'Hôpital's rule are not satisfied

Evaluate $\lim\limits_{x \to \infty} \dfrac{x + \sin x}{x - \cos x}$.

Solution   This limit has the indeterminate form ∞/∞. If you try to apply l'Hôpital's rule, you find

$$\lim_{x \to \infty} \frac{x + \sin x}{x - \cos x} \overset{H}{=} \lim_{x \to \infty} \frac{1 + \cos x}{1 + \sin x}$$

The limit on the right does not exist, because both $\sin x$ and $\cos x$ oscillate between -1 and 1 as $x \to \infty$. Recall that l'Hôpital's rule applies only if $\lim\limits_{x \to c} \dfrac{f'(x)}{g'(x)} = L$ is finite or is $\pm\infty$. This does not mean that the limit of the original expression does not exist or that we cannot find it; it simply means that we cannot apply l'Hôpital's rule. To find this limit, factor out an x from the numerator and denominator and proceed as follows:

$$\lim_{x \to \infty} \frac{x + \sin x}{x - \cos x} = \lim_{x \to \infty} \frac{x \left(1 + \dfrac{\sin x}{x}\right)}{x \left(1 - \dfrac{\cos x}{x}\right)}$$

$$= \lim_{x \to \infty} \frac{1 + \dfrac{\sin x}{x}}{1 - \dfrac{\cos x}{x}}$$

$$= \frac{1 + 0}{1 - 0}$$

$$= 1$$

Other indeterminate forms

Remember that l'Hôpital's rule itself applies only to the indeterminate forms $0/0$ and ∞/∞. Other indeterminate forms, such as 1^∞, 0^0, ∞^0, $\infty - \infty$, and $0 \cdot \infty$, can often be manipulated algebraically, or by taking logarithms, into one of the standard forms $0/0$ or ∞/∞, and then evaluated using l'Hôpital's rule. In a case where we have taken the logarithm to obtain one of the standard forms, we need to remember to transform back by applying exponentiation to our solution.

Example 8   Limit of the form 0^0

Find $\lim\limits_{x \to 0^+} x^{\sin x}$.

Solution   This is a 0^0 indeterminate form. From the graph shown in Figure 3.36, it looks as though the desired limit is 1.

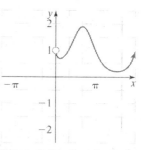

Figure 3.36 Graph of $x^{\sin x}$.

We can verify this conjecture analytically. We proceed as with the previous example by using properties of logarithms.

$$L = \lim_{x \to 0^+} x^{\sin x} \qquad \textit{given equation}$$

$\textit{taking logarithms} \qquad \ln L = \ln\left[\lim_{x \to 0^+} x^{\sin x} \right]$

$$= \lim_{x \to 0^+} \left[\ln x^{\sin x} \right] \qquad \textit{the natural logarithm is continuous}$$

$$= \lim_{x \to 0^+} [(\sin x) \ln x] \qquad \textit{property of logarithms}$$

$$= \lim_{x \to 0^+} \frac{\ln x}{\csc x} \qquad \textit{this is } \frac{\infty}{\infty} \textit{ form}$$

$$\overset{H}{=} \lim_{x \to 0^+} \frac{1/x}{-\csc x \cot x} \qquad \textit{l'Hôpital's rule}$$

$$= \lim_{x \to 0^+} \frac{-\sin^2 x}{x \cos x} \qquad \textit{algebraically simplify}$$

$$= \lim_{x \to 0^+} \left(\frac{\sin x}{x} \right) \left(\frac{-\sin x}{\cos x} \right)$$

$$= (1)(0)$$

$$= 0$$

$\textit{taking inverse of logarithms} \qquad L = e^0 = 1$

Example 9 Escaping infection and the indeterminate form $0^{-\infty}$

In models of host-pathogen and host-parasite interactions, the fraction of hosts escaping parasitism is often given by a negative-binomial escape function

$$f(P) = (1 + aP/k)^{-k}$$

where P is the density of the parasites or pathogens, $a > 0$ is the rate at which hosts encounter parasites or pathogens, and $k > 0$ is a clumping parameter. Small values of k correspond to parasites or pathogens being highly aggregated in the environment and large values of k correspond to parasites or pathogens being more evenly distributed across the environment. Assume $a = 0.1$.

a. For $k = 0.1, 1, 5, 10$, plot $f(P)$ over the interval $[0, 10]$. What effect does k have on the risk of being parasitized or infected?

b. For $P > 0$, find $\lim_{k \to \infty} f(P)$.

Solution

a. Plots of $f(P)$ for $k = 0.1, 1, 5, 10$ shown in Figure 3.37 suggest that as k increases the likelihood of escaping parasitism or infection goes down. Hence, as k increases and parasites or pathogens are more evenly distributed across the environment, the risk of parasitism or infection goes up.

b. For $P > 0$, $1 + aP/k$ approaches 0 and $-k$ approaches $-\infty$ as k approaches ∞. Therefore we have an indeterminate form of $0^{-\infty}$. To turn this problem to an indeterminate form of $0/0$, we take the $\ln$ of $f(P)$ which yields

$$g(P) = \ln f(P) = -k \ln(1 + aP/k) = \frac{\ln(1 + aP/k)}{-1/k}$$

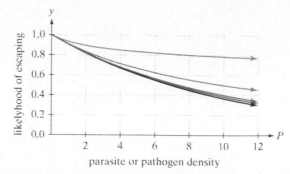

Figure 3.37 Negative binomial escape function $f(P) = (1 + 0.1P/k)^{-k}$ for $k = 0.1$ (in red), 1 (in green), 5 (in purple), and 10 (in cyan). The limiting Poisson escape function $f(P) = \exp(-0.1P)$ is shown as a solid black curve.

Since $\ln(1 + aP/k)$ and $-1/k$ approach zero as k approaches ∞, we can apply l'Hôpital's rule.

$$\lim_{k \to \infty} \frac{\ln(1 + aP/k)}{-1/k} \overset{H}{=} \lim_{k \to \infty} \frac{\frac{1}{1+aP/k} \frac{-aP}{k^2}}{\frac{1}{k^2}}$$

$$= \lim_{k \to \infty} \frac{-aP}{1 + aP/k} = -aP$$

Therefore, we get $\lim_{k \to \infty} \ln f(P) = -aP$ and by exponentiating

$$\lim_{k \to \infty} f(P) = e^{-aP}$$

for $P > 0$. This limiting escape function is known as the Poisson escape function that corresponds to parasitism or infection events occurring randomly among all hosts. This limiting function is plotted in black in Figure 3.37 and illustrates that the greatest risk of infection or parasitism occurs in this limiting case.

Example 10   Finding a horizontal asymptote and the indeterminate form ∞^0

Find the horizontal asymptote of the graph $f(x) = x^{1/x}$ for $x > 0$.

Solution   To determine if the graph of f has a horizontal asymptote for $x > 0$, we evaluate

$$\lim_{x \to \infty} x^{1/x}.$$

This limit is indeterminate of the form ∞^0. To evaluate it, we take the natural logarithm and proceed as follows:

$$L = \lim_{x \to \infty} x^{1/x}$$

taking logarithms $$\ln L = \ln \left[\lim_{x \to \infty} x^{1/x} \right]$$

$$= \lim_{x \to \infty} \left[\ln x^{1/x} \right]$$

$$= \lim_{x \to \infty} \left[\left(\frac{1}{x} \right) \ln x \right]$$

$$= \lim_{x \to \infty} \frac{\ln x}{x} \qquad form \frac{\infty}{\infty}$$

$$\overset{H}{=} \lim_{x \to \infty} \frac{\frac{1}{x}}{1}$$

$$= 0$$

taking inverse of logarithms $$L = e^0 = 1$$

Thus, $y = 1$ is a horizontal asymptote for the graph of $y = x^{1/x}$, as shown in Figure 3.38.

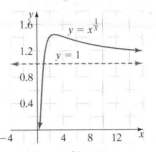

Figure 3.38 Graph of $y = x^{1/x}$ with horizontal asymptote.

We saw in Figure 3.38 that the graph of $f(x) = x^{1/x}$ approaches the line $y = 1$ asymptotically as $x \to \infty$, but how does $f(x)$ behave as $x \to 0^+$? That is, what is

$$\lim_{x \to 0^+} x^{1/x}?$$

It may seem that to answer this question, we need to apply l'Hôpital's rule again, but this limit has the form 0^∞, which is simply 0 and is not indeterminate at all. Other forms that may appear to be indeterminate, but really are not, are $0/\infty, \infty \cdot \infty$, $\infty + \infty$ and $-\infty - \infty$.

PROBLEM SET 3.7

Level 1 DRILL PROBLEMS

1. An incorrect use of l'Hôpital's rule is illustrated in the following limit computations. In each case, explain what is wrong and find the correct value of the limit.

   a. $\lim_{x \to \pi} \dfrac{1 - \cos x}{x} = \lim_{x \to \pi} \dfrac{\sin x}{1} = 0$

   b. $\lim_{x \to \pi/2} \dfrac{\sin x}{x} = \lim_{x \to \pi/2} \dfrac{\cos x}{1} = 0$

2. Sometimes l'Hôpital's rule leads nowhere. For example, observe what happens when the rule is applied to

   $$\lim_{x \to \infty} \frac{x}{\sqrt{x^2 - 1}}$$

   Use any method you wish to evaluate this limit.

Find the limits, if possible, in Problems 3 to 18.

3. $\lim_{x \to 1} \dfrac{x^3 - 1}{x^2 - 1}$

4. $\lim_{x \to 1} \dfrac{x^{10} - 1}{x - 1}$

5. $\lim_{x \to 0} \dfrac{1 - \cos^2 x}{\sin^2 x}$

6. $\lim_{x \to 0} \dfrac{1 - \cos x}{x^2}$

7. $\lim_{x \to \infty} x^{-5} \ln x$

8. $\lim_{x \to 0^+} x^{-5} \ln x$

9. $\lim_{x \to 0^+} \sin x / \ln x$

10. $\lim_{x \to \infty} \dfrac{\ln(\ln x)}{x}$

11. $\lim_{x \to \infty} \left(1 - \dfrac{3}{x}\right)^{2x}$

12. $\lim_{x \to \infty} \left(1 + \dfrac{1}{2x}\right)^{3x}$

13. $\lim_{x \to \infty} (\ln x)^{1/x}$

14. $\lim_{x \to 0^+} (e^x + x)^{1/x}$

15. $\lim_{x \to 0^+} (e^x - 1)^{1/\ln x}$

16. $\lim_{x \to 0} \dfrac{e^x - 1 - x - x^{3/2}}{x^3}$

17. $\lim_{x \to \infty} (\sqrt{x^2 - x} - x)$

18. $\lim_{x \to 0^+} \left(\dfrac{1}{x^2} - \ln \sqrt{x}\right)$

In Problems 19 to 22, use l'Hôpital's rule to determine all horizontal asymptotes to the graph of the given function. You are NOT required to sketch the graph.

19. $f(x) = x^{-3} e^{-0.01x}$

20. $f(x) = \dfrac{\ln x^5}{x^{0.02}}$

21. $f(x) = (\ln \sqrt{x})^{2/x}$

22. $f(x) = \left(\dfrac{x + 3}{x + 2}\right)^{2x}$

Verify the statements in Problems 23 to 25.

23. For positive integer n, $\lim_{x \to 0^+} \dfrac{\ln x}{x^n} = -\infty$

24. For positive integer n, $\lim_{x \to \infty} \dfrac{\ln x}{x^n} = 0$

25. For positive integer n and any $k > 0$,
    $$\lim_{x \to \infty} x^n e^{-kx} = 0$$

Level 2 APPLIED AND THEORY PROBLEMS

26. Fisheries scientists have found that a Ricker stock-recruitment relationship, which has the form

$$y = axe^{-bx}$$

where y is a measure (also called an *index*) of the number of individuals recruited to the fishery each year (typically one-year-olds), and x is an index of the spawning stock biomass (sometimes measured in terms of eggs produced), provides a reasonable fit to various species. Consider the case where the parameter values are $a = 5.9$ and $b = 0.0018$.

   a. What is the value of the recruitment index as $x \to \infty$?

   b. What is the maximum value of the recruitment index and at what spawning stock index value does it occur?

   c. Over what range of spawning stock index values is the recruitment function concave up and over what values is it concave down?

   d. Use the information obtained in parts **a**, **b**, and **c** to sketch this function.

27. An agronomist experimenting with a new breed of giant potato has found that individual tubers x months after planting have a biomass in kilograms given by the equation $y(x) = 2e^{-1/(5x)}$ for $x > 0$.

   a. Calculate the rate of growth of the tuber over time and determine what happens to this rate in the limit as $x \to 0$ and $x \to \infty$.

   b. Find the time after planting when the growth rate of the tuber is maximized.

   c. Show that the growth rate is positive for all $x > 0$ and determine the regions over which the growth is accelerating and decelerating.

   d. Sketch the biomass of the potato, as well as its growth rate, indicating the important points and regions calculated in parts **a**, **b**, and **c**.

28. Determine which function, $f(x) = x^n$ with $n > 0$ or $g(x) = e^{ax}$ with $a > 0$, grows faster at ∞ by computing $\lim\limits_{x \to \infty} \dfrac{f(x)}{g(x)}$.

29. Determine which function, $f(x) = x^n$ with $n > 0$ or $g(x) = \ln x$, grows faster at ∞ by computing $\lim\limits_{x \to \infty} \dfrac{f(x)}{g(x)}$.

30. Consider a drug in the body whose current concentration is 1 mg/liter. In this problem, you investigate the meaning of exponential decay of the drug.

   a. If one-half of the drug particles cleared the body after one hour, determine the concentration of the drug that remains after one hour.

   b. If one-quarter of the drug particles cleared the body every half an hour, determine the concentration of the drug that remains after one hour.

   c. If one-twentieth of the drug particles cleared the body every six minutes, determine the concentration of the drug that remains after one hour.

   d. If $\dfrac{1}{(2n)}$ of the drug particles cleared the body every $1/nth$ of an hour, determine the concentration c_n of the drug that remains after one hour.

   e. Find $\lim\limits_{n \to \infty} c_n$.

31. 𝕳𝖎𝖘𝖙𝖔𝖗𝖎𝖈𝖆𝖑 𝕼𝖚𝖊𝖘𝖙   The French mathematician Guillaume de l'Hôpital (1661–1704) is best known today for the rule that bears his name, but that rule was discovered by l'Hôpital's teacher, Johann Bernoulli. Not only did l'Hôpital neglect to cite his sources in his book, but there is also evidence that he paid Bernoulli for his results and for keeping their arrangements for payment confidential. In a letter dated March 17, 1694, he asked Bernoulli "to communicate to me your discoveries"—with the request not to mention them to others: "it would not please me if they were made public." (See D. J. Stuik, *A Source Book in Mathematics*, 1200–1800, Cambridge, MA: Harvard University Press, 1969, 313–316.) L'Hôpital's argument, which was originally given without using functional notation, can easily be reproduced:

$$\frac{f(a+dx)}{g(a+dx)} = \frac{f(a)+f'(a)\,dx}{g(a)+g'(a)\,dx}$$
$$= \frac{f'(a)\,dx}{g'(a)\,dx}$$
$$= \frac{f'(a)}{g'(a)}$$

First, place some conditions on the functions f and g that will make this argument true. Next, supply reasons for this argument, and give necessary conditions for the functions f and g.

32. Consider the general logistic growth function

$$G(N) = (r/v)N(1 - (N/K)^v)$$

from Example 4.

   a. For $v > 0$, find the density $N > 0$ that maximizes $G(N)$; that is, solve $G'(N) = 0$. The answer will depend on the parameters r, v, and K.

   b. Take your answer from part **a** and compute its limit as $v \to 0$.

   c. Find density $N > 0$ that maximizes $-rN\log(N/K)$ and compare your answer to what you found in part **b**.

CHAPTER 3 REVIEW QUESTIONS

1. Find $\dfrac{dy}{dt}$ for the following expressions.

   a. $x^3 + x\sqrt{x} + \sin 3x$

   b. $xy + y^3 = 25$

   c. $y = \dfrac{\ln(x^2 - 1)}{\sqrt[3]{x}(2 - x)^3}$

   d. $y = x^2 e^{-\sqrt{x}}$

   e. $y = x\sqrt{x}\cos 2x$

   f. $y = \sin^2\left(\dfrac{\pi x}{4}\right)$

2. Approximate $65^{1/3}$ and determine whether this approximation overestimates or underestimates the true answer. Justify your answers by using derivatives.

3. Find $\dfrac{d^2 y}{dx^2}$ where $y = x^2(2x - 3)^3$.

4. Use the definition of derivative to calculate, showing all details, $\dfrac{d}{dx}(x - 3x^2)$.

5. Find the first- and second-order approximations to $y = e^{x^2}$ at $x = 0$. Graph the function and its approximations.

6. In Figure 3.39, which graph represents the function and which graph the derivative?

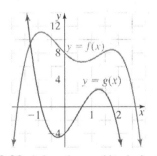

Figure 3.39 A function and its derivative.

7. Sketch the graph of a function with the following properties:

$f'(x) > 0$	when	$x < 1$
$f'(x) < 0$	when	$x > 1$
$f''(x) > 0$	when	$x < 1$
$f''(x) > 0$	when	$x > 1$

   What can you say about the derivative of f when $x = 1$?

8. The developmental rate of insects and plants as a function of temperature T can be modeled by the

Briere model

$$D(T) = a T(T - T_L)\sqrt{T_U - T} \quad \begin{array}{l}\text{percent development} \\ \text{per day}\end{array}$$

where T_L is the lower developmental threshold below which an individual does not develop, T_U is the upper developmental threshold above which an individual does not develop, and a is a proportionality constant. Find a linear approximation to $D(T)$ at $T = T_L$, discuss what it means, and discuss where it breaks down.

9. Let f be a function defined by

$$y = x^3 + 35x^2 - 125x - 9{,}375$$

   Determine where the function is increasing, where it is decreasing, and where the graph is concave up and where it is concave down.

10. Suppose the proportion of insect hosts escaping parasitism depends on the parasitoid density, d, and is modeled by the function $f(d) = e^{-.05d}$. Does the proportion escaping parasitism increase or decrease with parasitoid density? What is the concavity of this curve, and is there a point of inflection?

11. Determine the concavity and inflection points and use l'Hôpital's rule to find the horizontal asymptotes of the graph of

$$g(t) = \dfrac{t^2 + t + 1}{t^2 + 1}$$

12. Suppose the concentration in the blood at time t of a drug injected into the body is modeled by

$$C(t) = te^{-2t}$$

   Use l'Hôpital's rule to find the horizontal asymptote. Find the time when $C'(t) = 0$. Graph this curve and verify that the largest concentration occurs at the solution to $C'(t) = 0$.

13. Say you want to estimate the height of a tall tree. To do so, you cannot simply drop a tape measure from the top of the tree. However, you can determine the height by using a sextant to determine the angle θ between the ground and the tip of the tree at a distance of 100 feet from the base of the tree.

   a. Find the height of the tree, H, as a function of θ.

   b. If you measure an angle $\theta = 1.1$ radians, determine the height of the tree.

   c. Determine the elasticity of the height in part **b** to θ. Discuss how a 10% error in measuring θ influences the estimate for the height of the tree when $\theta = 1.1$.

14. A bacterial colony is estimated to have a population of P thousand individuals, where

$$P(t) = \frac{24t + 10}{t^2 + 1}$$

and t is the number of hours after a toxin is introduced.

a. At what rate is the population changing when $t = 0$ and $t = 1$?

b. Is the rate increasing or decreasing at $t = 0$ and $t = 1$?

c. At what time does the population begin to decrease?

15. As we saw in Example 6 of Section 1.5, scientists at Woods Hole Oceanographic Institution measured the uptake rate of glucose by bacterial populations from the coast of Peru. In one field experiment, they found that the uptake rate can be modeled by

$$f(x) = \frac{1.2078x}{1 + 0.0506x} \text{ micrograms per hour, where}$$

x is micrograms of glucose per liter. If the current uptake rate is twelve, determine the current level of glucose and, hence, determine the rate at which this uptake rate is itself changing per unit increase in glucose.

16. The gross U.S. federal debt (in trillions of dollars) is plotted below.

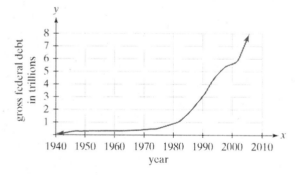

Regarding this debt, President Ronald Reagan stated in 1979 that the United States is "going deeper into debt at a faster rate than we ever have before." Discuss the role of higher-order derivatives in the graph of federal debt from 1950 to the end of the graph in the context of President Reagan's statement.

17. The figure eight curve shown below is defined implicitly by the equation $x^4 = x^2 - y^2$.

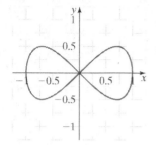

Find all the points on this curve that have horizontal tangents.

18. Consider the functions $y = f(x)$ (in blue) and $y = g(x)$ (in red) whose graphs are shown below.

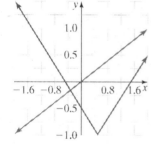

Find $\dfrac{d}{dx} f(g(x))$ at $x = -1$ and $x = 1$.

19. Find the tangent line of $y = (1 + \sin 2x)^{100}$ at $x = \pi/2$.

20. We modeled the concentration of carbon dioxide (in ppm) at the Mauna Loa Observatory of Hawaii with the function

$$h(t) = 329.3 + 0.1225\,t + 3\cos\left(\frac{\pi t}{6}\right)$$

where t is months since May 1974. Find for what months h is increasing and decreasing over the interval $[0, 12]$.

GROUP PROJECTS

Seeing a project through on your own, or working in a small group to complete a project, teaches important skills. The following project provide opportunities to develop such skills.

Project 3   Modeling North American Bison Population

If we look closely at the data plotted in Example 2 of Section 3.5, on the abundance of North American bison in Yellowstone National Park from 1902 to 1931, we get the distinct impression that the data can be represented much better by two linear functions than by one: the first representing data from 1902 to 1915 and the second representing the data from 1915 to 1931. We can fit these two functions by eye, or we can work more precisely using the concept of a *sum-of-squares* measure to gauge how well the functions fit the data. This concept requires that we know the actual values of the data points. Specifically, if we have n data points, indexed by $i = 1, \ldots, n$, then we need to know the values (x_i, y_i) for each data point. For the bison, these data are specified in Table 3.3. (Note that the data for some years are missing. This is not a problem if we just ignore these missing points when indexing the data.)

Table 3.3 Population for the North American bison

Index (i)	Year (x_i)	Abundance (y_i)
1	1902	44
2	1903	47
3	1904	51
4	1905	74
5	1907	84
6	1908	95
7	1909	118
8	1910	149
9	1911	168
10	1912	192
11	1913	215
12	1915	270
13	1916	348
14	1917	397
15	1919	504
16	1920	501
17	1921	602
18	1922	647
19	1923	748
20	1925	830
21	1926	931
22	1927	1008
23	1928	1057
24	1929	1109
25	1930	1124
26	1931	1192

For the bison data, consider piecing together two linear functions so that they both meet at the point $(x_{12}, y_{12}) = (1915, 270)$. Since both lines pass through this point, they must both satisfy the equation

$$\frac{y - 270}{x - 1915} = c$$

for some constant c. If the line fitted to the 1902–1915 date is specified by a constant c_1 and the line fitted to

the 1915–1931 data is specified by a constant c_2, then the the actual function fitted to the data is $y = f(x)$ where

$$f(x) = \begin{cases} c_1 x + (270 - 1915c_1) & 1902 \leq x \leq 1915 \\ c_2 x + (270 - 1915c_2) & 1915 < x \leq 1931 \end{cases}$$

The question now is to find the values of c_1 and c_2 that provide the best fit of the function $f(x)$ to the data in the sense of minimizing the sum-of-squares measure, denoted by S, of the fit.

Before we do this, recall, that for any sequence of n points $a_1, a_2, a_3, \cdots, a_n$, the sum of these points can be written as:

$$\sum_{i=1}^{n} a_i = a_1 + a_2 + a_3 + \cdots + a_n$$

(Also note that i does not have to start at $i = 1$, but could start at any integer value less than or equal to n).

Returning to our problem, if we define the value of this measure to be S, where

$$S = \sum_{i=1}^{26} (y_i - f(x_i))^2$$

then we can plot the value of S for different choices of c_1 and c_2. This is best done by considering separately the sums

$$S_1(c_1) = \sum_{i=1}^{11} (y_i - f(x_i))^2$$

and

$$S_2(c_2) = \sum_{i=12}^{26} (y_i - f(x_i))^2$$

1. By calculating S_1 for a range of values of c_1 and S_2 for a range of values of c_2 and then plotting the results, find to two significant figures for the values of c_1 and c_2 that minimize the sum $S = S_1 + S_2$. (Find these by "playing around" with the functions until you find the appropriate intervals over which to plot the two sums.) This is a graphical approach to finding the best-fitting function $f(x)$ defined above.

2. Can you think of a way that you might use differential calculus to solve this problem analytically? Once you find a way to do this, then solve the problem analytically and compare this analytical solution with your graphical solution.

3. What advantages does the analytical solution have over the graphical solution and vice versa?

ANSWERS TO SELECTED PROBLEMS

CHAPTER 3

Problem Set 3.1, Page 210

1. a. $7x^6$ **b.** $(\ln 7)7^x$ **3. a.** $15x^4$ **b.** 0 **5. a.** $2x$ **b.** -2 **7.** $5x^4 - 6x$
9. $4e^t - 5$ **11.** $4.78(2.25)^t$ **13.** $2Cx + 5 - 2e^{-2x}$

15. increasing: $(-\infty, 0)$, $\left(\frac{2}{3}, \infty\right)$; decreasing: $\left(0, \frac{2}{3}\right)$

17. increasing: $(-\infty, -17.9)$, $(-7.8, 5.3)$, $(16.4, \infty)$; decreasing: $(-17.9, -7.8)$, $(5.3, 16.4)$ **19.** increasing:
$(-\infty, \ln 2)$; decreasing: $(\ln 2, \infty)$ **21.** $\frac{3}{2}x^{1/2}$

23. $-\frac{5}{3}x^{-8/3}$, $x \neq 0$ **25.** $\left(\frac{3}{2}\right)^t \ln\left(\frac{3}{2}\right) - \left(\frac{1}{6}\right)^t \ln 6$

27. Write b^x as $f(x) = e^{x(\ln b)}$ so that $f'(x) = (\ln b)e^{x(\ln b)}$ and this can be written as $f'(x) = (\ln b)b^x$. **31. a.** $0.34D - 0.41$; rate of change of weight with respect to dose level
b. $1.21 \le D \le 8$ **33. a.** 0.8 **b.** 2.43 people/day
35. $L'(W) = 1.064W^{-0.05}$; $L'(5) = 0.982$ vs. $L'(50) = 0.875$
37. 2.88 lb/mass; the additional kilogram, each lifter can be expected to lift with a kilogram increase in the lifter's body weight **39. a.** $41{,}850$ children/year **b.** 2014

Problem Set 3.2, Page 221

1. $30x^4 - 6x^2 + 42x$ **3.** $\dfrac{2(x - 2)(2x - 3)}{(x^2 - 3)^2}$ **5.** $2^x(x \ln 2 + 1)$

7. $(x^2 + 3x + 2)e^x$ **9.** $-6L^5 + 4L^3 - 3L^2 + 1$ **11.** $32x + 24$

13. $\dfrac{e^x}{(e^x + 1)^2}$ **15.** $\dfrac{a[(1 + 2^p) - p(\ln 2)2^p]}{(1 + 2^p)^2}$ **17.** $\dfrac{-x^3 - 3x - 4}{3x^3}$

19. $4x + y - 1 = 0$ **21.** $2x + y + 1 = 0$ **23.** $9x - y + 5 = 0$
25. $4x - 5$ **27. a.** 0.177 among all adults who are 63 inches tall; this is the amount that the BMI changes per unit weight increase at a weight of 130 lbs. **b.** -0.54; among all children who weigh 60 lbs, this is the amount that the BMI changes per unit increase in height at a height of 54 inches **29. a.** 98.0%
b. decreasing at a rate of 0.5%/week (at the start of the fifth week of the year) **c.** 97.5%. **31. a.** a is the "steepness of the graph." For $b > a$, the curve changes from "down" to "up," then b translates the curve up. For example,

$a > 0; b = 1, c = 1$ $a > 0, b > a, c = 1$

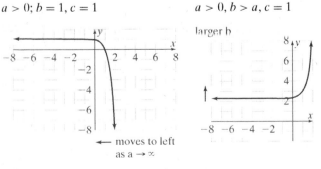

← moves to left as $a \to \infty$

b. $\dfrac{(a - b)10^{x-c}}{(1 + 10^{x-c})^2}\ln 10$

Finally, c moves the graph to the right or left.

33. $f'(0.5) = \dfrac{161}{96} \approx 1.7$; $f'(2.0) = \dfrac{1.288}{5.043} \approx 0.3$. The values represent the per unit rate of increase in the predation rate of wolves on moose for a unit increase in the moose population abundance of 0.5 and 2 moose per square kilometer, respectively. **35.** increasing on $(0, \infty)$ **37.** increasing on $(0, 17)$ and decreasing on $(17, \infty)$

Problem Set 3.3, Page 233

1. $6(3x - 2)$ **3.** $\dfrac{-8x}{(x^2 - 9)^3}$ **5. a.** $5u^4$ **b.** 3 **c.** $15(3x - 1)^4$

7. a. $15u^{14}$ **b.** $6x + 5$ **c.** $15(3x^2 + 5x - 7)^{14}(6x + 5)$
9. $9(x^4 - x + 5)^8(4x^3 - 1)$ **11.** $-12(1 + x - x^5)^{(13)}(1 - 5x^4)$

13. $\dfrac{2}{x}$ **15.** $\dfrac{2}{2x + 5}$ **17.** $8x^3(x^4 - 1)^9(2x^4 + 3)^6(17x^4 + 8)$

19. $\dfrac{-x(3x - 2)}{3y^2 - 1}$ **21.** $\dfrac{-y(4x + 3y)}{2x(x + 3y)}$ **23.** $\dfrac{-2}{3}$ **25.** $\dfrac{y - y^2e^{(xy)}}{xye^{(xy)} + 2}$

27. a. 5; $m = \dfrac{1}{2}$ **b.** 3; $m = \dfrac{3}{2}$ **c.** $m = \dfrac{3}{4}$ **29. a.** $\dfrac{3}{(3x - 1)^2 + 1}$

b. $\dfrac{-1}{x^2 + 1}$ **31.** $5x - 4y - 6 = 0$ **33.** $0.031R$ cm/yr
35. The predation rate is increasing at 0.477 moose/year.
37. -0.3275 **39.** $y = -0.296x + 0.410$, $y = -1.219x + 1.271$
43. 0.19 inches/month and 0.72 pounds/month

Problem Set 3.4, Page 242

1. $\cos x - \sin x$ **3.** $2\cos 2x$ **5.** $2t - \sin t$
7. $e^{-x}\cos x - e^{-x}\sin x$ **9.** $2\sin\theta\cos\theta$ **11.** $-101x^{100}\sin x^{101}$
13. $(t^2 + 2)\cos t + 2t\sin t$ **15.** $\dfrac{t\cos t - \sin t}{t^2}$

17. $\dfrac{x\cos x - \sin x + 1}{(1 - \sin x)^2}$ **19.** $\dfrac{\cos x - \sin x}{\cos x + \sin x}$

21. $\dfrac{\sin x}{\cos^2 x}$ or $\sec x \tan x$ **23.** $-\csc^2 x$

25. $\dfrac{\sec x(\tan x - \sec x + \csc x - 1)}{\csc x + \cot x}$ **27.** $2\cot x$

29. a. $g(h) = \dfrac{1}{2}(\cos h)(\sin h)$ **b.** $f(h) = \dfrac{1}{2}(1)h$

c. $k(h) = \dfrac{1}{2}(1)\tan h$ **31.** The population is decreasing by about 18 fish/month. **33. a.** $r(t) = 1 - \sin t$ **b.** 2π
c. population is increasing on $(0, \infty)$ **35. a.** At noon, the temperature in the pool is increasing at a rate of $T'(12) = \dfrac{\pi}{3}$ degrees Celsius per hour. **b.** from 6 A.M. until 6 P.M.

Problem Set 3.5, Page 252

(Note: Answers may vary depending on the point around which the approximation is made. In some cases, the best point is obvious in terms of the simplicity of the calculation.)

1

1. $y = -x + \dfrac{\pi}{2}$; over for $x < \dfrac{\pi}{2}$; under for $x > \dfrac{\pi}{2}$ **3.** $y = 1$;

over   **5.** $y = -\dfrac{4}{25}x + \dfrac{13}{25}$; under   **7.** 5.2 vs. 5.0990195   **9.** -0.01

vs. -0.10536052 **11.** 0.2 vs. 0.20271   **13.** $\dfrac{1}{6}$; $0.001\overline{6}$ **15.** $\dfrac{1}{2}$;

-0.1 **17.** -1; 0.01   **19.** $\dfrac{1}{2}$; 0.5%   **21.** $\dfrac{1}{\ln 2}$; 7.2%   **23.** 0; 0%

25. a. $D(t) \approx 2.02T - 26.38$

b.

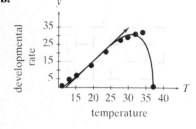

27. 6%   **29.** 0.05 ppm   **31. a.** 1.725   **b.** 8.625%   **33. a.** -1
b. $\pm 2\%$ **35.** $\pm 2\%$ **37. a.** 0.23   **b.** -0.137
39. a. $E = \dfrac{k(a-b)y}{(ky+1)(b+aky)}$ **b.** $\dfrac{-y}{(y+1)(y+2)} \cdot 10\%$

Problem Set 3.6, Page 266

1. $e^{-x}(x-2)$ **3.** 24   **5.** $-3^{99}\cos 3x$ **7.** $60t^2(7t^2-3)$ **9.** 10!

11. $\dfrac{2}{(w+1)^3}$ **13.** velocity: $s'(t) = 2t - 3$; acceleration:

$s''(t) = 2$; $s''(t) \neq 0$ **15.** velocity: $s'(t) = \dfrac{1}{3}\sin\dfrac{t}{3}$; acceleration:

$s''(t) = \dfrac{1}{9}\cos\dfrac{t}{3}$; $s''\left(\dfrac{3\pi}{2}\right) = s''\left(\dfrac{9\pi}{2}\right) = 0$ **17.** velocity:

$s'(t) = (1-t)e^{-t}$; acceleration: $s''(t) = (t-2)e^{-t}$; $s''(2) = 0$
and as the limit as $t \to \infty$ **19.** $y = 1 + x$; underestimates

21. $y = 5 - 4x$: overestimates   **23.** $y = -\dfrac{1}{9}x + \dfrac{5}{9}$;

underestimates   **25.** increasing: $\left(-\infty, -\dfrac{\sqrt{3}}{3}\right) \cup \left(\dfrac{\sqrt{3}}{3}, \infty\right)$;

decreasing: $\left(-\dfrac{\sqrt{3}}{3}, \dfrac{\sqrt{3}}{3}\right)$; concave up: $(0, \infty)$; concave down:
$(-\infty, 0)$; point of inflection: $(0, 1)$ **27.** increasing: $(-\infty, 1)$;
decreasing: $(1, \infty)$; concave up: $(2, \infty)$; concave down:
$(-\infty, 2)$; point of inflection: $(2, 2e^{-2})$ **29.** increasing:
$(-\infty, -1) \cup (-1, \infty)$; concave up: $(-\infty, -1)$; concave down:
$(-1, \infty)$; no point of inflection   **31.** increasing: $\left(-\dfrac{3}{2}, \infty\right)$;

decreasing: $\left(-\infty, -\dfrac{3}{2}\right)$; concave up: $\left(-\infty, -\dfrac{2}{3}\right) \cup (1, \infty)$;

concave down: $\left(-\dfrac{2}{3}, 1\right)$; points of inflection: $\left(-\dfrac{2}{3}, -\dfrac{571}{27}\right)$

and $(1, 2)$ **33.** increasing: $\left(0 + 2n\pi, \dfrac{\pi}{2} + 2n\pi\right) \cup$

$\left(\dfrac{\pi}{2} + 2n\pi, \pi + 2n\pi\right)$; decreasing: $\left(-\dfrac{\pi}{2} + 2n\pi, 2n\pi\right) \cup$

$\left(\pi + 2n\pi, \dfrac{3\pi}{2} + 2n\pi\right)$; concave up: $\left(-\dfrac{\pi}{2} + n\pi, \dfrac{\pi}{2} + n\pi\right)$;

concave down: $\left(\dfrac{\pi}{2} + n\pi, \dfrac{3\pi}{2} + n\pi\right)$; no points of inflection

35. first: $y = x$
second: $y = x$

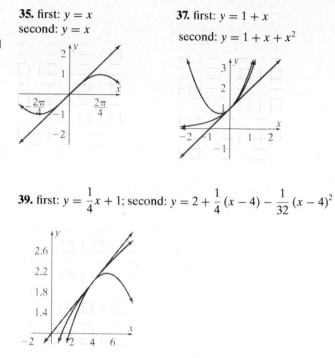

37. first: $y = 1 + x$

second: $y = 1 + x + x^2$

39. first: $y = \dfrac{1}{4}x + 1$; second: $y = 2 + \dfrac{1}{4}(x-4) - \dfrac{1}{32}(x-4)^2$

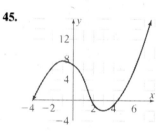

41. f is blue, f' is black, and f'' is red   **43.** f is black, f' is
red, and f'' is blue

45.

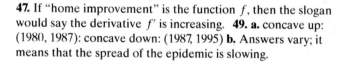

47. If "home improvement" is the function f, then the slogan
would say the derivative f' is increasing.   **49. a.** concave up:
(1980, 1987): concave down: (1987, 1995)   **b.** Answers vary; it
means that the spread of the epidemic is slowing.

51.

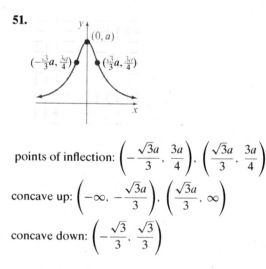

points of inflection: $\left(-\dfrac{\sqrt{3}a}{3}, \dfrac{3a}{4}\right)$, $\left(\dfrac{\sqrt{3}a}{3}, \dfrac{3a}{4}\right)$

concave up: $\left(-\infty, -\dfrac{\sqrt{3}a}{3}\right)$, $\left(\dfrac{\sqrt{3}a}{3}, \infty\right)$

concave down: $\left(-\dfrac{\sqrt{3}}{3}, \dfrac{\sqrt{3}}{3}\right)$

53.

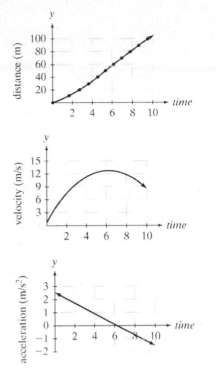

$t_s = 6.27$, $v_{max} = 12.49$; average deceleration is about 0.66

55.

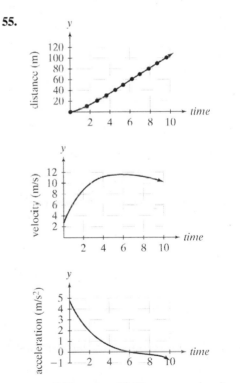

$t_s = 5.81$, $v_{max} = 12.00$; average deceleration is about -0.30

57. By definition, $f(a) = a(a) = b$ if and only if $q(a) = b$. Since $q'(a) = c$, $q'(c) = f'(a)$ if and only if $f'(x) = c$. Finally, since $q''(a) = 2d$, $q''(a) = f''(a)$ if and only if $d = f''(a)/2$.

Problem Set 3.7, Page 277

1. a. $\lim\limits_{x \to \pi} \dfrac{1 - \cos x}{x}$ is not of the form $\dfrac{0}{0}$ or $\dfrac{\infty}{\infty}$; $\dfrac{2}{\pi}$

b. $\lim\limits_{x \to \pi/2} \dfrac{\sin x}{x}$ is not of the form $\dfrac{0}{0}$ or $\dfrac{\infty}{\infty}$; $\dfrac{2}{\pi}$ **3.** $\dfrac{3}{2}$ **5.** 1 **7.** 0

9. 0 **11.** e^{-6} **13.** 1 **15.** e **17.** $-\dfrac{1}{2}$ **19.** $y = 0$ **21.** $y = 1$

27. a. As $x \to 0$, growth rate is 0 kg/month; as $x \to \infty$, growth rate is 2 kg/month **b.** At three days **c.** growth acceleration: $(0, 0.1)$; growth deceleration: $(0.1, \infty)$

d.

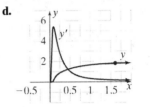

29. x^n grows faster **31.** f and g must be differentiable functions on an open interval containing c where each statement is proceeded by $\lim\limits_{x-e}$.

Chapter 3 Review Questions, Page 279

1. a. $3x^2 + \dfrac{3}{2}\sqrt{x} + 3\cos 3x$ **b.** $\dfrac{-y}{x + 3y^2}$

c. $\dfrac{2(x^2 - 1)(5x - 1)\ln(x^2 - 1) - 6x^2(x - 2)}{3x^{4/3}(x + 1)(x - 1)(x - 2)^4}$

d. $\dfrac{1}{2}xe^{-\sqrt{x}}(4 - \sqrt{x})$ **e.** $\dfrac{\sqrt{x}}{2}(3\cos 2x - 4x\sin 2x)$

f. $\dfrac{\pi}{4}\sin\left(\dfrac{\pi x}{2}\right)$ **3.** $2(2x - 3)(40x^2 - 48x + 9)$

5. first order: $y = 1$
second order: $y = 1 + x^2$

7. graphs vary

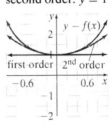

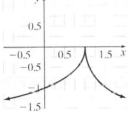

Derivative at $x = 1$ does not exist.

9. increasing: $(-\infty, -25) \cup \left(\dfrac{5}{3}, \infty\right)$; decreasing: $\left(-25, \dfrac{5}{3}\right)$;

concave up: $\left(-\dfrac{35}{3}, \infty\right)$; concave down: $\left(-\infty, -\dfrac{35}{3}\right)$

11. concave up on $(-\sqrt{3}, 0)$ union $(\sqrt{3}, 0)$; concave down on $(-\infty, -\sqrt{3})$ union $(0, \sqrt{3})$; inflection points at $t = 0$ $t = -\sqrt{3}$, and $t = \sqrt{3}$, and asymptote $g(t) = 1$

13. a. $H = 100\tan\theta$ **b.** 196 ft **c.** 27.2% error is the estimate of H. **15.** $f'(19.98) \approx 0.299$ micrograms/hour

17. $\left(\pm\dfrac{1}{\sqrt{2}}, \dfrac{1}{2}\right)$, $\left(\pm\dfrac{1}{\sqrt{2}}, -\dfrac{1}{2}\right)$ **19.** $y = -200x + 100\pi + 1$

CHAPTER 4

Applications of Differentiation

Figure 4.1 A great tit is a species of bird whose foraging behavior was studied by biologist Richard Cowie and whose behavior can be predicted by optimal foraging models.

Santiago Bañón / Flickr / Getty Images

Preview

"'If one way be better than another, that you may be sure is nature's way.' Aristotle clearly stated the basic premise of optimization in biology, yet it was almost 2,000 years before the power of this idea was appreciated. The essence of optimization is to calculate the most efficient solution to a given problem, and then to test the prediction. The concept has already revolutionized some aspects of biology, but it has the potential for much wider application."

William Sutherland, on "The best solution" in Nature (2005) 435:569

One of the central ideas in physics, chemistry, and biology is that processes act to optimize some physically or biologically meaningful quantity. For example, from physics we know that light in a vacuum travels along a path that is the shortest distance between two points (taking into account that gravity "bends" space), and from biochemistry we know that proteins fold in a way that minimizes the energy of their constituent amino acid configuration.

Differential calculus is an important tool for analyzing optimization (maximization or minimization). In this chapter we show how optimization applies to various biological problems and processes. Before we do this, however, we study how calculus can be used to construct the graphs of a variety of functions; in particular, we identify where the graph has turning points corresponding to local minimum or maximum values. We then develop procedures for modeling and solving optimization problems, including how to draw the best-fitting line through data plotted on a graph. After considering a number of biological applications, we study how calculus provides insight into dynamic processes such as the growth of populations and the spread of deleterious or mutant genes (e.g., the gene that causes sickle cell anemia) within populations. We end the chapter with an application of difference equations that is at the heart of many numerical methods used by current technologies for finding solutions to nonlinear equations.

4.1 Graphing Using Calculus

In this section, we combine many of the tools that we have studied so far (e.g., limits involving infinity, first and second derivatives) to graph a function. In graphing a function, envision walking along the graph and indicating all the highlights of your walk. For instance, *vertical asymptotes* are places with such a rapid ascent or descent that they make climbing Mount Everest seem like a stroll in a park. *Horizontal asymptotes* are places where the landscape levels out into a never-ending plain. Where the derivative is positive, the graph is ascending; and where the derivative is negative, the graph is descending. Switches in the sign of the slope correspond to either hilltops or valley bottoms along your walk. On ascents where the second derivative is positive, the walk is getting harder. On descents where the second derivative is negative, the descent becomes faster.

Properties of graphs

When graphing the function $y = f(x)$ by hand, follow these procedures to find the highlights of the function shape:

Vertical asymptotes: Determine at what points the function is not well defined (e.g., division by zero). At each of these points, say $x = a$, evaluate the one-sided limits, $\lim_{x \to a^+} f(x)$ and $\lim_{x \to a^-} f(x)$, to determine what the graph looks like near $x = a$. If either of these one-sided limits is $+\infty$ or $-\infty$, then there is a vertical asymptote at this point.

Intervals of increase and decrease: Compute the first derivative $f'(x)$ of $f(x)$ and determine on which intervals $f'(x) > 0$ and on which intervals $f'(x) < 0$. On these intervals, f is increasing and decreasing, respectively.

Intervals of concavity: Compute the second derivative $f''(x)$ and determine on which intervals $f''(x) > 0$ and $f''(x) < 0$. On these intervals, f is concave up and concave down, respectively.

The x and y intercepts Find the x intercepts (i.e., where $f(x) = 0$) and the y intercept (i.e., $y = f(0)$). These points help pin down the placement of the graph.

After identifying these highlights of a function, you are ready to sketch the function.

Example 1   Dropping whelks: a graphical approach

In Example 6 of Section 3.2, we considered how often $D(h)$ a whelk had to be dropped by a crow from a height of h meters before breaking. The function, based on data collected by Reto Zach ("Selection and dropping of whelks, Behaviour," Vol. 67, pp. 134–148, 1978) is given by

$$D(h) = 1 + \frac{20.4}{h - 0.84} \text{ drops}$$

a. Find the horizontal and vertical asymptotes and where D is positive.

b. Find on what intervals D is increasing and on what intervals D is decreasing.

c. Find on what intervals D is concave up and on what intervals D is concave down.

d. Take this information and sketch $D(h)$. Discuss for which h values this function is biologically meaningful.

Solution

a. There is a vertical asymptote at $h = 0.84$. Moreover, $\lim_{h \to 0.84^+} D(h) = +\infty$ and $\lim_{h \to 0.84^-} D(h) = -\infty$. Since $\lim_{h \to \pm\infty} D(h) = 1$, D has a horizontal asymptote of $D = 1$.

$D(h) > 0$ only if $1 + \frac{20.4}{h - 0.84} > 0$, equivalently $\frac{20.4}{h - 0.84} > -1$. If $h > 0.84$, the inequality is always satisfied. If $h < 0.84$, then $h - 0.84$ is negative and multiplying by $h - 0.84$ reverses the direction of the inequality, yielding $20.4 < 0.84 - h$, equivalently $-19.56 > h$. Hence, D is positive on the intervals $(0.84, \infty)$ and $(-\infty, -19.56)$ as indicated by the third ribbon at the bottom of Figure 4.2.

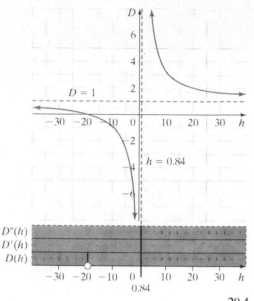

Figure 4.2 Graph of the whelk-dropping function $D(h) = 1 + \dfrac{20.4}{h - 0.84}$. The ribbons below the graph indicate where D, D', and D'' are negative (in red) and positive (in green).

b. Taking the first derivative yields

$$D'(h) = -\frac{20.4}{(h - 0.84)^2}$$

Since $(h - 0.84)^2$ is always positive for $h \neq 0.84$, we get $D'(h) < 0$ for all $h \neq 0.84$, as indicated by the second ribbon at the bottom of Figure 4.2. Therefore, D is decreasing for all $h \neq 0.84$.

c. Taking the second derivative yields

$$D''(h) = \frac{40.8}{(h - 0.84)^3}$$

which is positive for $h > 0.84$ and negative for $h < 0.84$, as indicated by the first ribbon at the bottom of Figure 4.2. Hence, D is concave up for $h > 0.84$ and concave down for $h < 0.84$.

d. Putting all this together yields the graph in Figure 4.2. From the crow's point of view, we require that $h > 0$ (since the crow does not burrow under ground!). Also, this graph is only meaningful for $h > 0.84$, since for $0 < h < 0.84$ the number of drops predicted is negative. For $h > 0.84$, the graph we drew is very similar to the graph shown in Figure 3.6 of Chapter 3. ∎

Many functions have no horizontal asymptotes. Nonetheless, understanding the limits as x approaches $\pm\infty$ may help graph the function.

Example 2   A "W" shaped curve

Consider the function $y = x^4 - 2x^2$.

a. Find the asymptotes, the intervals where the function is increasing or decreasing, the intervals where the function is concave up or down, the roots (x intercepts), and the y intercept.

b. Use all the information found in part **a** to graph the function.

Solution

a. The function is continuous for all real numbers. Hence, there are no vertical asymptotes. We have $\lim\limits_{x \to \pm\infty} x^4 - 2x^2 = \lim\limits_{x \to \pm\infty} x^2(x^2 - 2) = \infty$. Hence, there are no horizontal asymptotes, and y gets arbitrarily large as x approaches $\pm$infinity. Factoring the function $y = x^2(x^2 - 2)$ reveals that it is zero at $x^2 = 0$ and $x^2 = 2$; that is, $x = 0$ and $x = \pm\sqrt{2}$ are roots of the equation. The function is thus negative over the intervals $-\sqrt{2} < x < 0$ and $0 < x < \sqrt{2}$, as depicted in the panel below Figure 4.3. Further, the y intercept is $y = 0$.

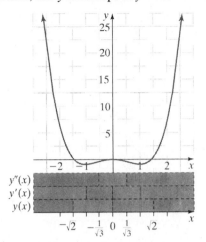

Figure 4.3 Graph of the function $y = x^4 - 2x^2$ with the sign of the function and its first and second derivatives indicated by the green (positive) and red (negative) ribbons below the graph.

To determine where the function is increasing, we first find the roots of the derivative, which solve the equation

$$0 = \frac{dy}{dx} = 4x^3 - 4x$$

$$0 = 4x(x^2 - 1)$$

Hence, the derivative vanishes at $x = 0, \pm 1$. Since $\frac{dy}{dx} = 24$ at $x = 2$, $\frac{dy}{dx} > 0$ on $(1, \infty)$. Since $\frac{dy}{dx} = -\frac{3}{2}$ at $x = \frac{1}{2}$, $\frac{dy}{dx} < 0$ on $(0, 1)$, as depicted in the panel below Figure 4.3. Since $\frac{dy}{dx} = \frac{3}{2}$ at $x = -\frac{1}{2}$, $\frac{dy}{dx} > 0$ on $(-1, 0)$. Since $\frac{dy}{dx} = -24$ at $x = -2$, $\frac{dy}{dx} < 0$ on $(-\infty, -1)$. Therefore, the function is increasing on the intervals $(-1, 0)$ and $(1, \infty)$ and decreasing on the intervals $(-\infty, -1)$ and $(0, 1)$, as depicted in the panel below Figure 4.3.

To determine intervals of concave up and concave down, we determine where the second derivative equals zero.

$$0 = \frac{d^2y}{dx^2} = 12x^2 - 4$$

$$x = \pm\frac{1}{\sqrt{3}}$$

Since $\frac{d^2y}{dx^2} = -4$ at $x = 0$, y is concave down on $\left(-\frac{1}{\sqrt{3}}, \frac{1}{\sqrt{3}}\right)$. Since $\frac{d^2y}{dx^2} = 8$ at $x = \pm 1$, y is concave up on $\left(-\infty, -\frac{1}{\sqrt{3}}\right)$ and $\left(\frac{1}{\sqrt{3}}, \infty\right)$.

b. To sketch the graph using the information from part **a**, we can envision how the graph of the function changes as we move from $-\infty$ to ∞. Since $\lim_{x \to -\infty} y = \infty$, $\frac{dy}{dx} < 0$ on $(-\infty, 1)$, and $y = 0$ at $x = -\sqrt{2}$, the function decreases from $+\infty$, crosses the x axis at $x = -\sqrt{2}$, and continues to decrease to the value $y = -1$ at

$x = -1$. Since $\dfrac{dy}{dx} > 0$ on $(-1, 0)$, the function increases to $y = 0$ at $x = 0$. Since $\dfrac{dy}{dx} < 0$ on $(0, 1)$, the function decreases to $y = -1$ at $x = 1$. Since $\dfrac{dy}{dx} > 0$ on $(1, \infty)$, $y = 0$ at $x = \sqrt{2}$, and $\lim\limits_{x \to \infty} y = \infty$, the function increases, crosses the x axis again at $x = \sqrt{2}$, and approaches $+\infty$ as x approaches $+\infty$. The function changes concavity at the points $\pm 1/\sqrt{3}$. Hence, the graph has the general characteristics depicted in Figure 4.3.   ◼

Example 3   **Linear asymptotes**

Consider the function $y = \dfrac{x^2 + 2}{x}$.

a. Find the asymptotes, the intervals where the function is increasing or decreasing, the intervals where the function is concave up or down, and the x and y intercepts.

b. Use all the information found in part **a** to graph the function.

Solution

a. Rewriting the function as $y = x + \dfrac{2}{x}$ helps us see that a vertical asymptote exists at $x = 0$. In fact, $\lim\limits_{x \to 0^+} y = +\infty$ and $\lim\limits_{x \to 0^-} y = -\infty$. Since $\lim\limits_{x \to \infty} y = \infty$ and $\lim\limits_{x \to -\infty} y = -\infty$, y has no horizontal asymptotes. Indeed since $\dfrac{2}{x}$ goes to zero as x gets large, we expect the graph of $y = x + \dfrac{2}{x}$ to approach the line $y = x$ for large x.

To find the boundaries between the intervals of increase and decrease, we determine where the first derivative equals zero:

$$0 = \frac{dy}{dx} = 1 - \frac{2}{x^2}$$

$$\frac{2}{x^2} = 1$$

$$x^2 = 2$$

$$x = \pm\sqrt{2}$$

Since $\dfrac{dy}{dx} = \dfrac{1}{2}$ at $x = \pm 2$ and $\dfrac{dy}{dx} = -1$ at $x = \pm 1$, we find that y is increasing on the intervals $(-\infty, -\sqrt{2})$ and $(\sqrt{2}, \infty)$ and decreasing on the intervals $(-\sqrt{2}, 0)$ and $(0, \sqrt{2})$.

To determine concavity, we compute the second derivative $\dfrac{d^2 y}{dx^2} = \dfrac{4}{x^3}$, which is positive when $x > 0$ and negative when $x < 0$. Hence, y is concave up on $(0, \infty)$ and y is concave down on $(-\infty, 0)$.

There is no y intercept, as the function has a vertical asymptote at $x = 0$. The roots (x intercepts) must satisfy

$$0 = y = x + \frac{2}{x}$$

$$0 = x^2 + 2$$

for which there is no real-valued solution. Hence there are no roots.

b. To graph $y = x + \dfrac{2}{x}$, think about what happens as you move from $-\infty$ to ∞. Since $\lim\limits_{x \to -\infty} y = -\infty$ and $\dfrac{dy}{dx} > 0$ on $(-\infty, -\sqrt{2})$, we find the graph increases from ∞ to $y = -2\sqrt{2}$ at $x = -\sqrt{2}$. Since $\dfrac{dy}{dx} < 0$ on $(-\sqrt{2}, 0)$ and $\lim\limits_{x \to 0} y = -\infty$, the graph decreases to infinity as x approaches 0 from the left. Since $\lim\limits_{x \to 0^+} y = \infty$

and $\dfrac{dy}{dx} < 0$ on $(0, \sqrt{2})$, the graph decreases from ∞ to $y = 2\sqrt{2}$ at $x = \sqrt{2}$.

Since $\dfrac{dy}{dx} > 0$ on $(\sqrt{2}, \infty)$ and $\lim\limits_{x \to \infty} y = +\infty$, the graph increases toward $+\infty$ as x approaches $+\infty$. Moreover, the concavity only changes at $x = 0$. Finally, since $\lim\limits_{x \to \pm\infty} \dfrac{2}{x} = 0$, it follows that $y = x + \dfrac{2}{x}$ behaves like $y = x$ for sufficiently positive or negative values of x. Using this information, we obtain a sketch that looks something like this:

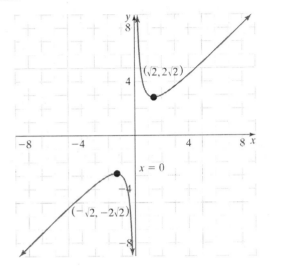

Sometimes just using limits and first derivatives is enough to get a good sense of the graph.

Example 4   Tylenol in the blood stream

As a project for a mathematical biology class, three college students developed a model of how acetaminophen (Tylenol) levels diffuse from the stomach and intestines to the blood stream after taking a dose of 1000 mg. Using data from the Federal Drug Administration (FDA), the students found that the concentration of acetaminophen in the blood was modeled by

$$C(t) = 28.6(e^{-0.3t} - e^{-t}) \text{ micrograms/milliliter}$$

where t is hours after taking the dose. Use information about asymptotes and first derivatives to sketch this function. Discuss the meaning of the graph.

Solution   Since $C(t)$ is continuous everywhere, there are no vertical asymptotes. Since $e^{-0.3t}$ and e^{-t} approach zero as t gets large, $\lim\limits_{t \to +\infty} C(t) = 0$. Therefore, there is a horizontal asymptote at $C = 0$. Alternatively, since $e^{-0.3t} - e^{-t} = e^{-0.7t}(e^{0.4t} - 1)$, $\lim\limits_{t \to -\infty} e^{0.4t} = 0$, and $\lim\limits_{t \to \infty} e^{-0.7t} = \infty$, we get $\lim\limits_{t \to \infty} C(t) = -\infty$.

Taking the first derivative yields

$$C'(t) = 28.6\,(e^{-t} - 0.3e^{-0.3t})$$

We have $C'(t) = 0$ if and only if

$$e^{-t} = 0.3e^{-0.3t}$$
$$e^{-0.7t} = 0.3$$
$$-0.7t = \ln 0.3$$
$$t = \frac{\ln 0.3}{-0.7} \approx 1.72 \text{ hours}$$

Since $C'(0) \approx 20$, we have $C'(t) > 0$ on $(-\infty, 1.72)$. Since $C'(t) < 0$ for very large t, we have $C'(t) < 0$ on $(1.72, \infty)$. Hence, as t goes from $-\infty$ to 0, the function increases up from $-\infty$ and passes through 0 at $t = 0$. $C(t)$ increases from $t = 0$ to $t \approx 1.72$, at which point it takes on the value of approximately 12 micrograms/milliliter. For t greater than 1.72, $C(t)$ decreases toward zero as t approaches $+\infty$. Therefore, we can graph the function as follows:

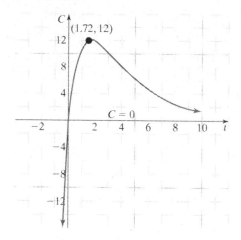

This graph is only meaningful for $t \geq 0$. It shows that initially there is no drug in the blood stream and then that the concentration of drug increases to a maximum concentration of 12 mcg/ml after 1.7 hours. Hence, the maximum effect of Tylenol is felt after approximately two hours. After reaching the maximum value, the concentration decays to zero.

In the previous example, we note that because the function has a maximum above zero and then approaches 0 as $x \to \infty$, the graph necessarily has a point of inflection where $C''(t)$ switches from being positive to negative. In Problem Set 4.1, we ask you to discuss the sign of the second derivative and to solve for the value of x where this point of inflection occurs.

Graphing families of functions

The shape of some functions, such as $f(x) = 3x + a$, does not depend in any critical sense on the value of the parameter a. All a does is move the line of slope 3 up and down the xy plane. As we see in this subsection, however, in more complicated functions the value of a parameter can have a surprising effect, and we can use calculus to discover such effects.

Example 5   To infinity and back

Consider the function $f(x) = \dfrac{1}{x^2 - a}$ with the parameter a. Using first derivatives and asymptotes, determine how the shape of this function depends on the parameter a.

Solution   Since $\lim\limits_{x \to \pm\infty} \dfrac{1}{x^2 - a} = 0$, $f(x)$ has a horizontal asymptote $y = 0$ as $x \to \pm\infty$. If $a < 0$, then $x^2 - a$ is positive for all x and there are no vertical asymptotes. If $a = 0$, then there is a vertical asymptote at $x = 0$. If $a > 0$, then there are vertical asymptotes at $x = \pm\sqrt{a}$. Computing the first derivative yields

$$f'(x) = -\frac{2x}{(x^2 - a)^2}$$

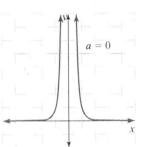

Since the denominator of this expression is positive whenever $x^2 \neq a$, $f'(x) < 0$ for all positive x with $x^2 \neq a$ and $f'(x) > 0$ for all negative x with $x^2 \neq a$.

These computations suggest there are qualitatively three distinctive graphs. First, consider the case where $a < 0$. In this case, there are no vertical asymptotes. There are horizontal asymptotes of 0 as $x \to \pm\infty$. Moreover, $f(x)$ is increasing for negative x and $f(x)$ is decreasing for positive x. Hence, the graph looks something like the figure on the left.

Next, consider the case where $a = 0$. In this case, $f(x) = \dfrac{1}{x^2}$ and there is a vertical asymptote at $x = 0$. In fact, $\lim\limits_{x \to 0} \dfrac{1}{x^2} = \infty$. There are horizontal asymptotes of $y = 0$ as $x \to \pm\infty$. Moreover, $f(x)$ is increasing for negative x and $f(x)$ is decreasing for positive x. Hence the graph, as you by now know, looks something like the figure on the left.

Finally, consider the case where $a > 0$. In this case, there are vertical asymptotes at $x = \pm\sqrt{a}$. In fact, evaluating all the limits as x approaches $\pm\sqrt{a}$ yields

$$\lim_{x \to \sqrt{a}^+} \frac{1}{x^2 - a} = \infty$$

$$\lim_{x \to \sqrt{a}^-} \frac{1}{x^2 - a} = -\infty$$

$$\lim_{x \to -\sqrt{a}^+} \frac{1}{x^2 - a} = -\infty$$

$$\lim_{x \to -\sqrt{a}^-} \frac{1}{x^2 - a} = \infty$$

There are horizontal asymptotes of $y = 0$ as $x \to \pm\infty$. Moreover, $f(x)$ is increasing for negative x and $f(x)$ is decreasing for positive x. Hence, if we walk along the graph of f from $+\infty$ to $-\infty$, then we initially ascend from 0. The ascent gets exceptionally steep as x approaches $-\sqrt{a}$. As we cross $x = -\sqrt{a}$, we suddenly fall down to $y = -\infty$. After crossing both infinities, we continue to ascend until reaching a maximum of $y = -\dfrac{1}{a}$ at $x = 0$. From there, we descend through $-\infty$ and skyrocket to $+\infty$ at $x = \sqrt{a}$. After this harrowing jump through infinities, we continue with a descent to zero. In other words, our graph looks something like the figure on the left.

Example 6   Dose-response curves

Dose-response curves can be used to plot the response of an individual to a dose of a drug or hormone. This response can almost be anything. For instance, the response may be heart rate, dilation of an artery, membrane potential, enzyme activity, or the secretion of a hormone. We previously encountered dose-response curves in Example 2 of Section 2.4 and Problem 31 in Problem Set 3.2. A general form of a dose-response curve is

$$y = a + \frac{b - a}{1 + e^{x - c}}$$

where y is the response of the individual and x is the concentration of the dose of drug or hormone. The parameters $a > 0$, $b > 0$, and $c > 0$ affect the shape of the dose-response curve and often can be used to fit the function to particular data sets. Assuming $c = 0$, use limits and first derivatives to determine how the shape of this curve depends on the parameters a and b.

Solution　Consider $f(x) = a + \dfrac{b - a}{1 + e^x}$. Since $f(x)$ is continuous for all reals, there are no vertical asymptotes. Since

$$\lim_{x \to \infty} a + \frac{b - a}{1 + e^x} = a \quad \text{and} \quad \lim_{x \to -\infty} a + \frac{b - a}{1 + e^x} = a + b - a = b,$$

there is a horizontal asymptote $y = a$ as x approaches $+\infty$ and a horizontal asymptote $y = b$ as x approaches $-\infty$.

Taking the first derivative of f, we obtain

$$f'(x) = \frac{(a - b)e^x}{(1 + e^x)^2}$$

This derivative is negative for all x if $b > a$, positive for all x if $b < a$, and zero for all x if $b = a$.

Hence, the graph of $f(x)$ comes in three flavors. If $b > a$, then the function decreases from an asymptote of $y - b$ to an asymptote of $y - a$. If $b < a$, then the function increases from an asymptote of $y - b$ to an asymptote of $y - a$. Finally, if $b = a$, then the function is the constant function $y = a$. These three graphs are sketched below.

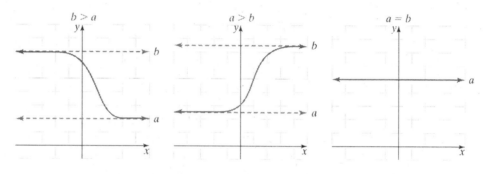

Note that when $b > a$, the graph goes from concave down to concave up and hence passes through an inflection point. Similarly, when $a > b$, the graph goes from concave up to concave down and hence also passes through an inflection point. You are asked to explore this further in Problem Set 4.1.

Example 7　**Stock-recruitment curves**

In conservation biology and fisheries management, stock-recruitment curves are used to describe the relationship between the current abundance of a population (i.e., the stock) and the number of juveniles entering the system in the next year (i.e., the recruits). A general class of stock-recruitment curves are given by the functions

$$F(N) = \frac{a N^b}{1 + N^b}$$

where N is the current population size, $F(N)$ is the number of recruits in the next generation, and a and b are positive parameters. A useful way to categorize these functions is to consider the relationship between the current population abundance and the average of number recruits per individual, that is,

$$f(N) = \frac{F(N)}{N} = \frac{a N^{b-1}}{1 + N^b}$$

Use limits and first derivatives to determine how the parameter b influences the shape of $f(N)$ for $N \geq 0$. Discuss the possible meaning.

Solution   Notice that if $0 < b < 1$, then there is a vertical asymptote at $N = 0$ and $\lim_{N \to 0^+} f(N) = \infty$. If $b \geq 1$, there is no vertical asymptote. To determine the horizontal asymptote as $N \to \infty$, notice that the power of the numerator is less than the power of the higher order term in the denominator. Hence, $\lim_{N \to \infty} f(N) = 0$.

The first derivative of $f(N)$ is given by

$$f'(N) = a\frac{(b-1)N^{b-2}(1+N^b) - bN^{b-1}N^{b-1}}{(1+N^b)^2}$$

$$= a\frac{N^{b-2}(b-1) - N^{2b-2}}{(1+N^b)^2}$$

$$= a\frac{N^{b-2}(b-1-N^b)}{(1+N^b)^2}$$

Hence, if $b \leq 1$, $f'(N) < 0$ for all $N > 0$. However, if $b > 1$, then $f'(N) > 0$ for $0 \leq N \leq (b-1)^{1/b}$ and $f'(N) < 0$ otherwise. Therefore, we get three types of graphs, depending on whether $b < 1$, $b = 1$, or $b > 1$:

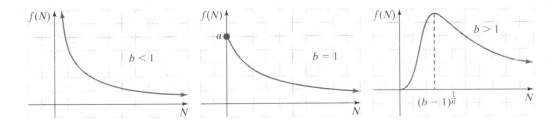

For $b < 1$, the number of recruits constantly decreases with stock levels. One interpretation of this fact is at higher population densities, there are fewer resources per individuals and, consequently, fewer recruits produced per individual. For $b > 1$, the number of recruits per individual initially increases and then decreases. One possible explanation is that for $b > 1$, individuals have difficulty finding mates for reproduction. Therefore, at low densities as densities increase, the chance of finding mates increases and the number of recruits produced per individual increases. However, as the population density increases too much (i.e., beyond $(b-1)^{1/b}$), the advantage of finding mates is outweighed by the limited resources available per individual. Consequently, at higher densities, the number of recruits per individual decreases. For $b > 1$, the population exhibits what ecologists call *depensation* or a *strong Allee effect*. Working with data from 128 species, Ran Myers and colleagues used $F(N)$ to evaluate to what extent fish populations exhibit depensation and discussed the implications for populations to recover from environmental disturbances. (See R. A. Myers, N. J. Barrowman, J. A. Hutchings, and A. A. J. Rosenberg, "Population Dynamics of Exploited Fish Stocks at Low Population Levels," *Science* 269 (1995): 1106–1108.)

PROBLEM SET 4.1

Level 1 DRILL PROBLEMS

In Problems 1 to 14, graph the functions by hand by finding asymptotes and using first and second derivatives. Compare your graphs to what you get using technology.

1. $y = x^2 - x$

2. $y = x^2 + 5x - 3$

3. $y = \dfrac{1}{1+x^2}$

4. $y = \dfrac{x}{1+x^2}$

5. $y = x + \dfrac{1}{2+x}$

6. $y = \dfrac{1}{x-1} + x$

7. $y = -12x - \dfrac{9x^2}{2} + x^3$

8. $y = \dfrac{1}{3}x^3 - 9x + 2$

9. $y = e^x + 2e^{-x}$

10. $y = 2e^x + e^{-x}$

11. $y = x - x^3$

12. $y = \dfrac{2+x}{1+x}$

13. $y = \dfrac{x-3}{x+1}$

14. $y = \dfrac{x^2}{1+x^4}$

In Problems 15 to 20, graph the families of functions by finding asymptotes and using first and second derivatives. In particular, determine how the graph of the functions depends on the parameter $a > 0$.

15. $y = x^4 - ax^2$

16. $y = \dfrac{ax}{x^2+1}$

17. $y = ae^x + e^{-x}$

18. $y = e^x + ae^{-x}$

19. $y = \dfrac{a+x}{1+x}$

20. $y = ax + \dfrac{1}{x}$

In Problems 21 and 22, sketch the graph of a function with the given properties.

21. $y = 2, y = -2$ are horizontal asymptotes

f is increasing for $0 < x < 2$ and $x > 2$

f is decreasing for $x < -2$ and $-2 < x < 0$

graph is concave down on $(-\infty, -2)$ and $(2, \infty)$

intercepts are $(-1, 0)$, $(0, -4)$ and $(1, 0)$

22. $y = 1, y = -1$ are horizontal asymptotes

f is increasing for $x < -\dfrac{3}{2}$ and for $x > \dfrac{3}{2}$

f is decreasing for $-1 < x < 1$

graph is concave down for $x < -1$ and for $0 < x < 1$

graph is concave up for $x > 1$ and for $-1 < x < 0$

Level 2 APPLIED AND THEORY PROBLEMS

23. Consider the graph of $y = ax^2 + bx + c$ for constants $a, b,$ and c. Use second derivatives to determine what happens to the graph as a changes.

24. Consider the graph of $y = \dfrac{e^{ax}}{1 + e^{ax}}$. Use limits and first derivatives to determine how the shape of this curve depends on the parameter a.

25. In Example 6, we saw that the dose-response curve

$$y = a + \dfrac{b-a}{1 + e^x}$$

has asymptotes $y = a$ and $y = b$, respectively, as x approaches, plus and minus infinity. Find the second derivative $y''(x)$ and discuss its properties including the derivation of an equation that can be used to identify any points of inflection, if they exist.

26. In Example 4 of Section 2.7, we consider patterns of local species richness of ants along an elevational gradient. A function that best fits the data is

$$S = -10.3 + 24.9\,x - 7.7\,x^2$$

where x is elevation measured in kilometers and S is the number of species. Plot this function using information about first derivatives.

27. In Example 6 of Section 1.5, we develop the Michaelis-Menton model for the rate at which an organism consumes its resource. For bacterial populations in the ocean, this model was given by

$$f(x) = \dfrac{1.2078x}{1 + 0.0506x}$$

micrograms of glucose per hour

where x is the concentration of glucose (micrograms per liter) in the environment. Use asymptotes and first derivatives to sketch this function by hand.

28. In Example 5 of Section 2.4 we found that the rate at which wolves kill moose can be modeled by

$$f(x) = \dfrac{3.36x}{0.42 + x}$$

moose killed per wolf per hundred days

where x is measured in number of moose per square kilometer. Use asymptotes and first derivatives to sketch this function.

29. In Problem 42 in Problem Section 2.4, we examined how wolf densities in North America depend on moose densities. We found that the following function provides a good fit to the data:

$$f(x) = \dfrac{58.7(x - 0.03)}{0.76 + x} \text{ wolves per } 1000\,km^2$$

where x is number of moose per square kilometer.

a. Find the horizontal and vertical asymptotes.

b. Determine on which intervals f is increasing and decreasing.

c. Determine on which intervals f is concave up and concave down.

d. Use the information from parts **a–c** to sketch the graph of $f(x)$.

30. Two mathematicians, W. O. Kermack and A. G. McKendrick, showed that the weekly mortality rate during the outbreak of the plague in Bombay (1905–1906) is reasonably well described by the function

$$f(t) = 890\,\text{sech}^2(0.2t - 3.4) \text{ deaths/week}$$

where t is measured in weeks. Sketch this function using information about asymptotes and first derivatives. Recall that

$$\text{sech}\,x = \dfrac{2}{e^x + e^{-x}}$$

31. In Example 4 we modeled the rate at which acetaminophen diffuses from the stomach and intestines to the blood stream using this equation:

$$C(t) = 28.6(e^{-0.3t} - e^{-t}) \text{ micrograms/milliliter}$$

Calculate the second derivative and discuss its behavior. Identify if the function $C(t)$ has any points of inflection for $t > 0$.

32. In an experiment, a microbiologist introduces a toxin into a bacterial colony growing in an agar dish. The data on the area of the dish covered by living colony members at time t minutes after the introduction of the toxin are given by this equation:

$$A(t) = 5 + e^{-0.04t+1}$$

Sketch the graph of $A(t)$ showing its salient features.

33. Let f be a function that represents the weight of a fish at age t. Write a function that satisfies the following properties.

- The weight of the fish at birth must be positive.
- As the fish ages, the weight increases at decreasing rate.
- No fish can grow bigger than 2 kg.

34. *Aerobic rate* is the rate of a person's oxygen consumption and is sometimes modeled by the function A defined by

$$A(x) = 110 \left(\frac{\ln x - 2}{x} \right)$$

for $x \geq 10$. Graph this function.

35. As a project for their mathematical biology class, three college students developed a model of how acetaminophen levels varied in the blood stream of a child after taking a dose of 325 milligrams. Using FDA data, they found that

$$C(t) = 23.725 \left(-e^{-0.7t} + e^{-0.5t} \right)$$

micrograms/milliliter

where t is hours after taking the dose.

a. Use information about asymptotes and first derivatives to sketch this function.

b. Discuss the meaning of your graph. In particular, address when the maximum concentration is achieved and what the maximum concentration is.

36. A naturalist at an animal sanctuary determined that the function

$$f(x) = \frac{4e^{-(\ln x)^2}}{\sqrt{\pi} x}$$

provides a good measure of the number of animals in the sanctuary that are x years old. Sketch the graph of f for $x > 0$.

4.2   Getting Extreme

When viewing the graph of a function as a landscape of hilltops and valley bottoms, each top and each bottom corresponds to a place where the function in question has an extremum. Methods to identify extrema play an important role in applications. For instance, if the function of interest represents how profits due to harvesting a crop depend on the amount of seeds planted, then the farmer would like to know how many seeds per acre yield the greatest profits. In other words, the farmer would like to identify the largest hilltop of the function. Alternatively, if a northwestern crow minimizes the amount of energy required to break whelk shells, then the optimal behavior for a crow corresponds to the deepest valley of a function. In this section, we develop methods to find these hilltops and valleys.

Local extrema

Local Maxima and Minima

Let $f(x)$ be a function of x. We say that f has a **local maximum** at $x = a$ if

$$f(a) \geq f(x)$$

for all x near a. We say that f has a **local minimum** at $x = a$ if

$$f(a) \leq f(x)$$

for all x near a. We say f has a **local extremum** at $x = a$ if there is a local maximum or a local minimum at $x = a$.

Example 1   Finding Extrema

Estimate for what x values, $y = f(x)$, as graphed below, has local maxima and local minima on the domain $D = \{x : -3 \leq x \leq 3\}$.

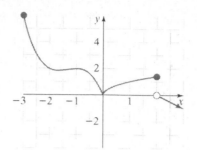

Solution   There are local minima at $x \approx -1.75$, $x = 0$, and $x = 3$. There are local maxima at $x = -3$, $x \approx -1$, and $x = 2$.

The previous example suggests that either extrema occur at end points of the domain, points where f is not differentiable, or points where the derivative of f equals zero. The following theorem verifies these observations.

Theorem 4.1   Fermat's theorem

If f is defined on (a, b) and has a local extremum at $c \in (a, b)$, then either $f'(c) = 0$ or $f'(c)$ is not defined.

Proof.   Suppose that f is defined on (a, b) and has a local extremum at $c \in (a, b)$. This extremum is either a local maximum or a local minimum. Suppose that this extremum is a local minimum. Then we have $f(c) \leq f(x)$ for all x near c. Equivalently, $f(c) \leq f(c + h)$ for all h sufficiently small. Taking a difference quotient yields that

$$\frac{f(c + h) - f(c)}{h} \geq 0$$

for all sufficiently small positive h and

$$\frac{f(c + h) - f(c)}{h} \leq 0$$

for all sufficiently small negative h. Assume $f'(c)$ exists. Then, taking one-sided limits yields

$$f'(c) = \lim_{h \to 0^+} \frac{f(c + h) - f(c)}{h} \geq 0$$

and

$$f'(c) = \lim_{h \to 0^-} \frac{f(c + h) - f(c)}{h} \leq 0$$

Therefore, $f'(c) = 0$. The case of a local maximum can be proved similarly, which you see in Problem 31 in Problem Set 4.2.

Fermat's theorem shows that we can find possible local maxima and local minima by finding points where $f'(x) = 0$ or f' is not defined. Such points have a special name.

| Critical Points and Values | If $f'(c) = 0$ or $f'(c)$ is not defined, then c is a **critical point** for f. The value of f at a critical point is called a **critical value**. |

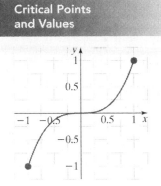

Although all local extrema are critical values, not all critical values are local extrema. Consider, for example, $y = x^3$ plotted on the left for $-1 \le x \le 1$.

The derivative is $\dfrac{dy}{dx} = 3x^2$. Hence, $x = 0$ is the only critical point. However as $y = x^3$ increases over all the reals, $x = 0$ is neither a local maximum nor a local minimum.

Example 2   **Finding and classifying critical points**

Find the critical points of $y = x^3 - 3x^2 - 4$ and determine whether these critical points are local maxima, local minima, or neither.

Solution   We have $\dfrac{dy}{dx} = 3x^2 - 6x = 3x(x - 2)$. Hence, $\dfrac{dy}{dx} = 0$ at $x = 0$ and $x = 2$. These are the critical points of y. To determine whether these critical points correspond to local maxima, local minima, or neither, we can consider how the sign of the derivative varies over the real line. Since $\dfrac{dy}{dx} < 0$ for $0 < x < 2$ and $\dfrac{dy}{dx} > 0$ for $x > 2$, the function decreases over the interval $(0, 2)$ and increases on $(2, \infty)$. Hence, there is a local minimum of $y = -8$ at $x = 2$. Alternatively, since $\dfrac{dy}{dx} > 0$ for $x < 0$ and $\dfrac{dy}{dx} < 0$ for $0 < x < 2$, the function increases until $x = 0$ and then decreases. Thus, there is a local maximum $y = -4$ at $x = 0$. Graphing $y = x^3 - 3x^2 - 4$ with technology in the plot on the left corroborates these statements.

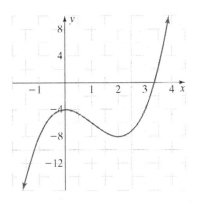

Example 2 illustrates one method for identifying local maxima and local minima; this is called the *first derivative test.*

| First Derivative Test | Assume $f'(c) = 0$ and f is differentiable near $x = c$.

• If the sign of f' changes from positive to negative at $x = c$ (i.e., f changes from increasing to decreasing), then f has a local maximum at $x = c$.

• If the sign of f' changes from negative to positive (i.e., f changes from decreasing to increasing) at $x = c$, then f has a local maximum at $x = c$. |

Example 3   Thermodilution

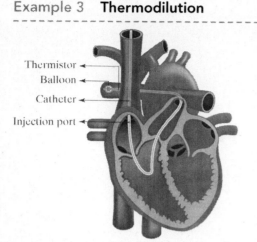

Thermistor
Balloon
Catheter
Injection port

Figure 4.4 Thermodilution involves injecting a cold dextrose solution in the vena cava of the heart and measuring the temperature of the blood leaving the heart (e.g., from the aorta).

Cardiac output can be determined by thermodilution as illustrated in Figure 4.4. Let's say a doctor injects 10 milliliters (ml) of a cold dextrose solution into a vein entering the heart. As the cold solution mixes with the blood in the heart, the temperature variations in the blood leaving the heart are measured. A typical temperature variation curve (i.e., degrees below normal temperature), may be described by the function $T(t) = 0.2t^2 e^{-t}$ degrees Celsius, where t is measured in seconds. Find the critical points and classify them. Discuss the meaning of your results.

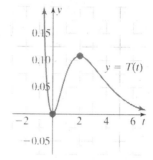

Solution   Taking the derivative yields

$$T'(t) = 0.2(2t)e^{-t} - 0.2t^2 e^{-t}$$

$$= 0.2te^{-t}(2 - t)$$

We have $T'(t) = 0$ at $t = 0$ and $t = 2$. Hence, $t = 0$ and $t = 2$ are the critical points of T. To apply the first derivative test, we need to determine the sign of T' on the intervals $(-\infty, 0)$, $(0, 2)$, and $(2, \infty)$. Since T' is continuous everywhere, it can only have sign changes at the points $t = 0, 2$. Therefore, it suffices to check the sign of T' at one point in each of the intervals. Since $T'(-1) = -0.6e^1 < 0$, T' is negative on $(-\infty, 0)$. Since $T'(1) = 0.2e^{-1} > 0$, T' is positive on $(0, 2)$. Since $T'(3) = -0.6e^{-3} < 0$, T' is negative on $(2, \infty)$. Since at $t = 0$ the sign of T' changes from negative to positive, we have a local minimum at $t = 0$. Since at $t = 2$ the sign of T' changes from positive to negative, at $t = 2$ we have a local maximum. Hence, the temperature of blood leaving the heart drops $T(2) \approx 0.11$ degrees Celsius after two seconds, before returning to its normal temperature. ∎

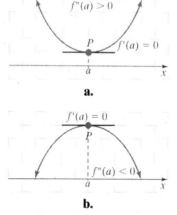

a.

b.

Figure 4.5 The second derivative test determines whether a critical point $x = a$ where $f'(a) = 0$ is a local minimum (a) or a local maximum (b).

Another possibility for identifying local maxima and local minima is using the second derivative. Suppose f has a critical point at $x = a$ and has second-order derivatives at $x = a$. In Section 3.6, we saw that a second-order approximation of $f(x)$ is given by

$$f(x) \approx f(a) + f'(a)(x - a) + \frac{1}{2}f''(a)(x - a)^2$$

Since a is a critical point, $f'(a) = 0$ and the second-order approximation reduces to

$$f(x) \approx f(a) + \frac{1}{2}f''(a)(x - a)^2$$

Provided that $f''(a) \neq 0$, the graph of this approximation is given by a parabola whose vertex is at $x = a$. Furthermore, if $f''(a) > 0$, then this parabola is facing up, which suggests that there is a local minimum at $x = a$ as shown in Figure 4.5a.

Alternatively, if $f''(a) < 0$, then this parabola is facing down, which suggests that there is a local maximum at $x = a$ as shown in Figure 4.5b. In fact, what is suggested by the second approximation can be proven, thereby providing an alternative test for classifying extrema.

Second Derivative Test	Let f have first and second derivatives at $x = a$. Assume that $f'(a) = 0$.

Local maximum If $f''(a) < 0$, then there is a local maximum at $x = a$.

Local minimum If $f''(a) > 0$, then there is a local minimum at $x = a$.

Inconclusive If $f''(a) = 0$, then we can not determine whether the critical point is a maximum or minimum from the second derivative.

Example 4   Using the second derivative test

Find and classify the critical points of $y = -x^3 + 6x^2 + 2$ using the second derivative test.

Solution   Computing the first and second derivatives of $y = -x^3 + 6x^2 + 2$ yields

$$\frac{dy}{dx} = -3x^2 + 12x = -3x(x - 4)$$

$$\frac{d^2y}{dx^2} = -6x + 12$$

This derivative always exists, so the critical points correspond to the solutions of $-3x(x - 4) = 0$. Hence, they are given by $x = 0$ and $x = 4$. Evaluating the second derivatives at $x = 0$ and $x = 4$ yields

$$\left.\frac{d^2y}{dx^2}\right|_{x=0} = 12$$

$$\left.\frac{d^2y}{dx^2}\right|_{x=4} = -12$$

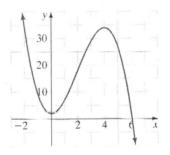

Hence, there is a local minimum at $x = 0$ and a local maximum at $x = 4$. Graphing the function $y = -x^3 + 6x^2 + 2$ demonstrates these conclusions in the graph on the left.

Global extrema

Often in applied problems, we want to find the largest or small value of a function on its domain.

Global Extrema	Let f be a function with domain D.

f has a **global minimum** at $x = a$ if

$$f(a) \leq f(x) \text{ for all } x \text{ in } D.$$

f has a **global maximum** at $x = a$ if

$$f(a) \geq f(x) \text{ for all } x \text{ in } D.$$

A global maximum or a global minimum is called a **global extremum**.

Example 5   Finding global extrema

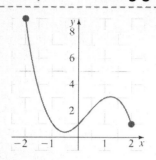

Consider the function whose graph is given by find the global extrema of this function.

Solution   The global maximum of $y = 9$ occurs at $x = -2$ and the global minimum of approximately 0.1 occurs approximately at $x = -0.6$. ■

Example 5 illustrates that global extrema may occur at critical points or end points for a continuous function on a closed interval. Thus, we have the following procedure for finding global extrema.

Closed Interval Method

Let f be a continuous function defined on the closed interval $[a, b]$. To find the global extrema of f, do the following:

Find critical points on the interval (a, b).

Evaluate f at all critical points and at end points a and b.

Identify the global extrema The largest value of f at a critical point or end point is the global maximum of f. The smallest value of f at a critical point or end point is the global minimum of f.

Example 6   Using the closed interval method

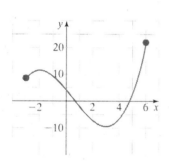

Find the global extrema of $f(x) = \frac{1}{3}x^3 - \frac{1}{2}x^2 - 6x + 4$ on the interval $[-3, 6]$.

Solution   Taking the derivative of f yields

$$f'(x) = x^2 - x - 6 = (x - 3)(x + 2)$$

The critical points are $x = 3$ and $x = -2$. Evaluating f at the critical points and end points yields $f(-3) = 8.5$, $f(-2) = 11\frac{1}{3}$, $f(3) = -9.5$, and $f(6) = 22$. Therefore, the global maximum of 22 occurs at the end point $x = 6$. The global minimum of -9.5 occurs at the critical point $x = 3$. Plotting this function on the left demonstrates our findings. ■

Example 7   Getting extreme with carbon dioxide

In Example 4 of Section 1.2, we examined how CO_2 concentrations in parts per million (ppm) varied from 1974 to 1985 at the Mauna Loa Observatory in Hawaii. Using linear and periodic functions, we found that the following function gives an excellent fit to the data:

$$f(x) = 0.1225x + 329.3 + 3\cos\left(\frac{\pi x}{6}\right) \text{ ppm}$$

where x is months after April 1974. Using the closed interval method, find the global maximum and minimum CO_2 levels in the one-year interval $[0, 12]$.

Solution   To find the critical points of $f(x)$, we differentiate

$$f'(x) = 0.1225 - \frac{\pi}{2}\sin\left(\frac{\pi x}{6}\right)$$

Although we can solve for the critical points by hand by recalling properties of inverse sine, we circumvent such analysis by using a root finder on a graphing calculator. Finding all the roots of $f'(x)$ on the interval $[0, 12]$ yields $x = 0.149$ and $x = 5.851$. Evaluating f to two decimal points at these critical points and the end points yields

$$f(0) = 332.30$$
$$f(0.149) \approx 332.31$$
$$f(5.851) \approx 327.03$$
$$f(12) \approx 333.77$$

Hence, the global minimum CO_2 level occurred at $x = 5.851$ (sometime in late October 1974). The global maximum occurred at $x = 12$ (in April 1975). Plotting the function over the interval $[0, 12]$ demonstrates these extremes:

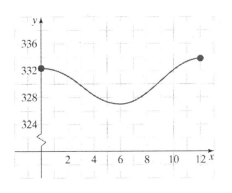

Example 8   Search period of the codling moth

© John T. Fowler/Alamy

Figure 4.6 Codling moth adult.

After a codling moth (*Cydia pomonella*, see Figure 4.6) larva hatches from its egg case, it goes looking for an apple in which to burrow. The period between hatching and finding the apple is called the *search period*. For individual larvae, this period will vary, but the average time s that it takes is known to be a function of temperature T in degrees Celsius. A good fit to the available data illustrated in Figure 4.7 is provided by the equation

$$s(T) = \frac{1}{-0.03T^2 + 1.67T - 13.65} \quad \text{for} \quad 20 \leq T \leq 30$$

Use the tools of calculus to find the largest and smallest values of $s(T)$ over the range $20 \leq T \leq 30$.

Solution   The polynomial $p(T) = -0.03T^2 + 1.67T - 13.65$ has roots at $T \approx 9.95$ and $T \approx 45.7$. Hence, $p(T) \neq 0$ for $20 \leq T \leq 30$ so that $s(T) = \dfrac{1}{p(T)}$ is continuous on this interval. Using the quotient rule, its derivative is

$$s'(T) = \frac{2(0.03T) - 1.67}{(-0.03T^2 + 1.67T - 13.65)^2}$$

which satisfies $s'(T) = 0$ only if $0.06T = 1.67$, equivalently $T \approx 27.83°$C. Evaluating $s(T)$ at this critical point and at the end points we obtain

$$s(20) \approx 0.129 \qquad s(27.83) \approx 0.104 \qquad s(30) \approx 0.106.$$

Hence, on the interval $20 \leq T \leq 30$, $s(T)$ has a minimum at $T \approx 27.33$ and a maximum at $T = 20$.

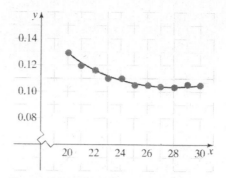

Figure 4.7 Codling moth search period.

Data Source: P. L. Shaffer, and H. J. Gold, "A Simulation Model of Population Dynamics of the Codling Moth, *Cydia pomonella*," *Ecological Modeling* 30 (1985): 247–274.

In many problems we need to find the global extrema on open intervals, half-closed intervals, or intervals involving infinity. For each of these cases, we deal with the limits as we approach the end points of the intervals, as illustrated with the open interval method. (The other cases appear as exercises in Problem Set 4.2.)

Open Interval Method

Let f be a continuous function defined on the open interval (a, b). Assume the limits $L = \lim\limits_{x \to a^+} f(x)$ and $M = \lim\limits_{x \to b^-} f(x)$ are well defined. Here we allow L and M to be $\pm\infty$, a to be $-\infty$, and b to be $+\infty$. To find the global extrema of f on (a, b), do the following:

Find critical points Find all the critical points on the interval (a, b).

Evaluate at critical points Evaluate f at all critical points.

Identify the extrema If L or M is greater than f evaluated at any critical point, then f has no global maximum on (a, b). Alternatively, if f evaluated at a critical point $x = c$ is greater than or equal to L, M, and f evaluated at any other critical point, then $f(c)$ is the global maximum. If L or M is less than f evaluated at any critical point, then f has no global minimum on (a, b). Alternatively, if f evaluated at a critical point $x = c$ is less than or equal to L, M, and f evaluated at any other critical point, then $f(c)$ is the global minimum.

Example 9   **Using the open interval method**

Use the open interval method to find the global extrema of the following functions on the indicated intervals.

a. $f(x) = \dfrac{1}{3x - x^2 - 2}$ on $(1, 2)$ **b.** $f(x) = \dfrac{x}{1 + x^2}$ on $(-\infty, \infty)$

Solution

a. We have $f(x) = \dfrac{1}{3x - x^2 - 2} = \dfrac{1}{(2 - x)(x - 1)}$ is continuous on $(1, 2)$. Note $f'(x)$ exists for all x on $(1, 2)$. Moreover,

$$\lim_{x \to 2^-} \frac{1}{(2 - x)(x - 1)} = +\infty$$

$$\lim_{x \to 1^+} \frac{1}{(2 - x)(x - 1)} = +\infty$$

Hence, $f(x)$ has no global maximum on $(1, 2)$. Solving for the critical points on $(1, 2)$, we get

$$f'(x) = 0$$

$$-\frac{3 - 2x}{(3x - x^2 - 2)^2} = 0$$

$$2x = 3$$

$$x = 1.5$$

Since f has only one critical point and $f(1.5) = 4$ is less than $\lim_{x \to 1^+} f(x)$ and $\lim_{x \to 2^-} f(x)$, the global minimum is 4 and occurs at $x = 1.5$.

b. Since $1 + x^2$ is positive for all x, $f(x) = \dfrac{x}{1 + x^2}$ is continuous on $(-\infty, \infty)$. Taking limits at infinity, we get

$$\lim_{x \to \infty} \frac{x}{1 + x^2} \frac{1/x}{1/x} = \lim_{x \to \infty} \frac{1}{1/x + x} = 0$$

$$\lim_{x \to -\infty} \frac{x}{1 + x^2} \frac{1/x}{1/x} = \lim_{x \to -\infty} \frac{1}{1/x + x} = 0$$

Solving for the critical points, we get

$$f'(x) = 0$$

$$\frac{1(1 + x^2) - x(2x)}{(1 + x^2)^2} = 0$$

$$\frac{1 - x^2}{(1 + x^2)^2} = 0$$

$$x = \pm 1$$

Since $f(1) = \dfrac{1}{2}$ and $f(1) = -\dfrac{1}{2}$ are greater than 0 and less than 0, respectively, these correspond to the global minimum and global maximum. ∎

PROBLEM SET 4.2

Level 1 DRILL PROBLEMS

In Problems 1 to 4, identify the local and global extrema.

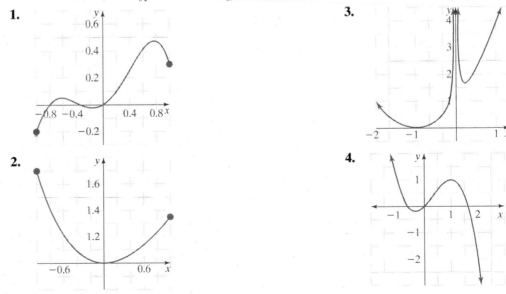

1.

2.

3.

4.

In Problems 5 to 12, find the critical points and use the first derivative test to classify them.

5. $y = 1 + 3x + 4x^2$

6. $f(x) = 10 + 6x - x^2$

7. $f(t) = t^2 e^{-t}$

8. $y = x^3 - \dfrac{3x^4}{4} + 5$

9. $f(x) = \dfrac{x}{1 + x}$

10. $y = -3x - x^2 + \dfrac{x^3}{3}$

11. $y = -x + \dfrac{3x^2}{4} + \dfrac{x^3}{3}$

12. $y = e^{t^2 - 2t + 1}$

In Problems 13 to 16, find the critical points and use the second derivative test to classify them.

13. $y = -12x - \dfrac{9x^2}{2} + x^3$

14. $y = 1 - \exp(-x^2)$

15. $y = x + \dfrac{1}{2 + x}$

16. $y = \dfrac{2x^2 - x^4}{4}$

In Problems 17 to 20, use the closed interval method to find the global extrema on the indicated intervals.

17. $f(x) = x^2 - 4x + 2$ on $[0, 3]$

18. $f(x) = x^3 - 12x + 2$ on $[-3, 3]$

19. $f(x) = x + \dfrac{1}{x}$ on $[0.1, 10]$

20. $f(x) = xe^{-x}$ on $[0, 100]$

In Problems 21 to 24, use the open interval method to find the global extrema on the indicated intervals.

21. $f(x) = x^2 - 4x + 2$ on $(-\infty, \infty)$

22. $f(x) = x^3 - 12x + 2$ on $(0, \infty)$

23. $f(x) = x + \dfrac{1}{x}$ on $(0, \infty)$

24. $f(x) = xe^{-x}$ on $(-\infty, \infty)$

25. Let f be continuous on the half-open interval $[a, b)$ with b possibly equal to $+\infty$. Devise a method to find the global extrema of f on this interval.

26. Let f be continuous on the half-open interval $(a, b]$ with a possibly equal to $-\infty$. Devise a method to find the global extrema of f on this interval.

In Problems 27 to 30, use the half-open interval methods you developed in Problems 25 and 26 to find the global extrema on the indicated intervals.

27. $f(x) = x^2 - 4x + 2$ on $[0, \infty)$

28. $f(x) = x^3 - 12x + 2$ on $[1, 10)$

29. $f(x) = x + \dfrac{1}{x + 2}$ on $[-1, \infty)$

30. $f(x) = xe^{-x}$ on $(-\infty, -1]$

Level 2 APPLIED AND THEORY PROBLEMS

31. Let f be defined on (a, b) and $c \in (a, b)$. Prove that if $x = c$ is a local maximum and f is differentiable at $x = c$, then $f'(c) = 0$.

32. In Example 4 of Section 1.2, we examined how CO_2 concentrations (in ppm) have varied from 1974 to 1985. Using linear and periodic functions, we found that the following function gives an excellent fit to the data:

$$f(x) = 0.122463x + 329.253 + 3\cos\left(\frac{\pi x}{6}\right) \text{ ppm}$$

where x is months after April 1974. Using the closed interval method, find the global maximum and minimum CO_2 levels on the interval $[12, 24]$.

33. In the previous problem, use the closed interval method and find the global maximum and minimum CO_2 levels between April 2000 and April 2001.

34. A close relative of the codling moth is the pea moth, *Cydia nigricana*, which is a pest of cultivated and garden peas in several European countries. If its search period in one of the regions where it is a pest is given by the function

$$s(T) = \frac{1}{-0.04T^2 + 2T - 15} \quad \text{for} \quad 20 \leq T \leq 30,$$

then graph $s(T)$ using information about the first derivative over the domain $20 \leq T \leq 30$. Be sure that your graph indicates the largest and smallest value of s over this interval.

35. In Problem 30 of Problem Set 4.1, we saw that the weekly mortality rate during the outbreak of the plague in Bombay (1905–1906) can be reasonably well described by the function

$$f(t) = 890 \operatorname{sech}^2(0.2t - 3.4) \text{ deaths/week}$$

where t is measured in weeks. Find the global maximum of this function. Recall that

$$\operatorname{sech} x = \frac{2}{e^x + e^{-x}}$$

36. Some species of plants (e.g., bamboo) flower once and then die. A well-known formula for the average growth rate r of a *semelparous species* (a species that breeds only once) that breeds at age x is

$$r(x) = \frac{\ln[s(x)n(x)p]}{x}$$

where $s(x)$ represents the proportion of plants that survive from germination to age x, $n(x)$ is the number of seeds produced at age x, and p is the proportion of seeds that germinate.

a. Find the age of reproduction that maximizes r in terms of the parameters a, b, c, and p where

$$s(x) = e^{-ax} \qquad a > 0$$

and

$$n(x) = bx^c \qquad b > 0$$

$0 < c < 1$.

b. Sketch the graph of $y = r(x)$ for the case where $a = 0.2, b = 3, c = 0.8$, and $p = 0.5$.

37. The production of blood cells plays an important role in medical research involving leukemia and other so-called *dynamical diseases*. In 1977, a mathematical model was developed by A. Lasota. (See W. B. Gearhart and M. Martelli, "A Blood Cell Population Model, Dynamical Diseases, and Chaos," in UMAP Modules 1990: *Tools for Teaching* [Arlington, MA: Consortium for Mathematics and Its Applications, 1991].) The model involved the cell production function

$$P(x) = Ax^s e^{-sx/r}$$

where A, s, and r are positive constants and x is the number of granulocytes (a type of white blood cell) present.

a. Find the granulocyte level x that maximizes the production function P. How do you know it is a maximum?

b. Graph this function.

38. When you cough, the radius of your trachea (windpipe) decreases, thereby affecting the speed of the air in the trachea. If r is the normal radius of the trachea, the relationship between the speed S of the air and the radius r of the trachea during a cough is given by a function of the form

$$S(r) = ar^2(r_0 - r)$$

where a is a positive constant. (Philip M. Tuchinsky, "The Human Cough," UMAP Modules 1976: *Tools for Teaching* [Lexington, MA: Consortium for Mathematics and Its Applications, 1977].) Find the radius r for which the speed of the air is the greatest.

39. Research indicates that the power P required by a bird to maintain flight is given by the formula

$$P = \frac{w^2}{2\rho Sv} + \frac{1}{2}\rho Av^3$$

where v is the relative speed of the bird, w is its weight, ρ is the density of air, and S and A are constants associated with the bird's size and shape. (See C. J. Pennycuick, "The Mechanics of Bird Migration," *IBIS III* (1969): 525–556.) What speed will minimize the power? You may assume that w, ρ, S, and A are all positive and constant.

40. An epidemic spreads through a community in such a way that t weeks after its outbreak, the number of residents who have been infected is given by a function of the form

$$f(t) = \frac{A}{1 + Ce^{kt}}$$

where A is the total number of susceptible residents. Show that the epidemic is spreading most rapidly when half the susceptible residents have been infected.

Optimization in Biology

One of the most important applications of calculus to biology in particular, and science and technology in general, involves finding the extrema of functions. Consider, for example, the problem of determining the most effective treatment regimen for a malignant tumor using chemo- or radiation therapy. Such treatments are toxic to the body, so physicians want to prescribe the minimum dosage that will do the job. Typically, a single treatment will not destroy the tumor. Instead, the tumor will initially shrink in size after treatment and sometime later will begin to regrow. Ideally, therapy should be readministered immediately—when the tumor is at its smallest—before this regrowth phase. Using calculus in conjunction with tumor growth data, we can estimate the time when therapy should be reapplied. As another example, think of a farmer planting a corn crop. The farmer might be interested in knowing the planting density of seeds that would maximize his or her profit. To find out, the farmer could formulate a function that describes how profits depend on planting density, and maximizing this function. In this section, we consider these problems as well as the behavior of dogs fetching balls, sustainable harvesting of arctic fin whales, and vascular branching. More examples appear in the problem set. We end this section with applications to finding best-fitting functions to empirically collected data.

Steps to solve an optimization problem

Optimization problems typically require that we develop an appropriate model for the problem being considered, then analyze this model to find the optimal solution for the problem. To tackle these problems successfully, use the following steps:

1. **Read, understand, and visualize.** Take the time to carefully read the problem so that you fully understand what is being asked. In particular, ask yourself: What am I trying to maximize or minimize? What information am I given? Is it sufficient to solve the problem at hand? When appropriate, draw a picture or figure that summarizes the problem.

2. **Identify key variables and quantities.** Ask yourself: What are the important quantities in the problem? What quantity is being optimized? This is the dependent variable. Which of the variables is the one whose value I can control to obtain my optimal solution? This is the independent variable. What additional quantities presented in the problem do I need to obtain the sought after relationship between the dependent and independent variable? Associate units with each of these variables.

3. **Write the function.** In this step, you need to determine how the dependent variable is determined by the quantities that you identified in the previous step. Think carefully about this crucial step. Make sure that units on both sides of your equation agree.

4. **Optimize.** Determine whether you need to minimize or maximize the function and over what interval you need to perform the optimization. To find the optimal value, it suffices to find the critical points and evaluate the function at these critical points and at the end points of the interval. Whichever of these values is the largest (smallest) yields the maximum (minimum).

5. **Interpret your answer.** Interpret the results of your optimization. Ask yourself whether your answer makes sense. If not, check your work.

In this next example, we demonstrate how these steps are applied to the problem of determining the density of seedlings that a farmer needs to plant to optimize profits from a particular crop. In the remaining examples in this section, we do not stress the steps involved, but these steps are implicit in our approach. Remember to you these steps whenever you get stuck in solving an optimization problem. The examples relate to behavior, physiology, resource management, and fitting functions to data. You won't necessarily have time to study them all, so you can pick and choose those of greatest interest to you.

Example 1   Maximum economic yield

In an article titled "*A 'Cookbook' Approach for Determining the 'Point of Maximum Economic Return,*' " Gaspar and colleagues lay out procedures for farmers to conduct field trials to determine the impact of different planting densities on crop yields. In an experiment to assess the impact of planting densities on yield Y of a corn hybrid, they fitted the following function to the data depicted in Figure 4.8.

$$\text{Yield:} \qquad Y(x) = -0.1181x^2 + 8.525x + 12.95 \text{ bushels per acre}$$

where x is thousands of seeds planted per acre.

In a particular year, suppose that the price a farmer can obtain for his corn is $1.50 per bushel and that the cost of seed is $3 per thousand seeds. Use this information to determine the density of seeds (i.e., seeds per acre) that maximizes the farmer's net profit per acre.

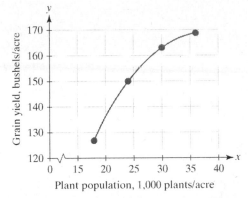

Figure 4.8 Yield of a corn hybrid as a function of seed density.

Data Source: Gaspar, P.E., S. Paszkiewicz, P. Carter, M. McLeod, T. Doerge, and S. Butzen. 1999. Corn hybrid response to plant populations. Pioneer Hi-Bred International Inc. Northern Agronomic Research Summary. pp. 29–40.

Solution   We follow the five steps for solving an optimization problem.

1. From the statement of the problem, we realize that the farmer wants to maximize his net profit, measured in dollars per acre, rather than his yield, measured in bushels per acre. The planting density of seeds is the quantity that can be varied.

2. The independent variable is x, with units 1,000 seeds per acre; the dependent variable is net profit $P(x)$, with units dollars per acre.

3. Since $P(x)$ is determined by the total revenue $R(x)$ generated from the crops each season minus the cost $C(x)$ of the seeds each season, it follows that

$$\textit{Net profit:} \qquad P(x) = R(x) - C(x) \text{ dollars per acre}$$

where $R(x)$ is the yield $Y(x)$ in bushels per acre multiplied by the price $p = 1.5$ in dollars per bushel of corn; that is,

$$\textit{Total revenue:} \qquad R(x) = pY(x) \text{ dollars per bushel} \times \text{bushels per acre}$$
$$= 1.5(-0.1181x^2 + 8.525x + 12.95) \text{ dollars per acre}$$

On the other hand, the cost per acre is \$3 for each thousand seeds, so that for x thousand seeds per acre the cost is

$$\textit{Cost:} \qquad C(x) = 3x \text{ dollars per acre}$$

Hence, we can *write the function*

$$P(x) = \overbrace{-0.1772\,x^2 + 12.7875\,x + 19.425}^{R(x)} - \overbrace{3x}^{C(x)}$$
$$= -0.1772\,x^2 + 9.7875\,x + 19.425$$

that we want to *maximize with respect to x on the interval* $[0, \infty)$. If we plot $P(x)$ verus x, then the red line in the figure on the left indicates optimum planting density.

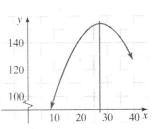

4. The point at which $P(x)$ is maximized can be found by solving for the critical points of $P(x)$. Since

$$P'(x) = -0.3544\,x + 9.7875$$

it follows that $x = \dfrac{9.7875}{0.3544} = 27.617$ is the unique critical point. Since the graph of $P(x)$ is a downward facing parabola, $x = 27.617$ is where the global maximum occurs.

5. Our *interpretation* of 27.617 is that the farmer should plant approximately 27.6 thousand seeds per acre and, in doing so, should obtain a net profit of $P(27.6) \approx \$155$ per acre. ■

In many problems in population biology, a variable x is used to represent the density (or number) of individuals in a population and the function $G(x)$ is used to represent the population growth rate. For instance, for the discrete logistic equation presented in Example 7 of Section 2.5, we modeled the growth using the function.

$$G(x) = rx \left(1 - \frac{x}{K}\right)$$

where $r > 0$ has the interpretation of the maximum per capita growth rate and $K > 0$ has the interpretation of the environmental carrying capacity. Here, we use the function $G(x)$ to determine the optimal rate at which a population of whales should be harvested, if not illegal to do so.

The Arctic fin whale *Balaenoptera physalus*, which at fifty to seventy tons for adults of both sexes is second in size to the blue whale, was a highly desirable catch during the whaling heydays of the nineteenth and twentieth centuries. As many as 30,000 individuals were slaughtered each year from 1935 to 1965. This level of exploitation could not be sustained for long, so today population levels are estimated to be an order of magnitude (i.e., a factor of 10) below historical highs of around a half million individuals. Some individuals are still taken each year for purposes of subsistence by aboriginal people in Greenland. A moratorium on whale hunting is needed, however, to allow this species to recover to levels where the populations can be safely exploited on a sustainable basis.

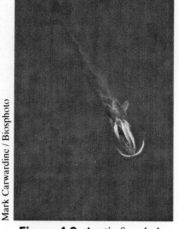

Mark Carwardine / Biosphoto

Figure 4.9 Arctic fin whale.

Example 2   Sustainable exploitation of the Arctic fin whale

Assume the Arctic fin whale growth rate is modeled by the logistic function $G(x) = rx(1 - x/K)$ with $r = 0.08$ (i.e., an 8% annual growth rate when the whale densities are low) and $K = 500,000$ (i.e., prior to exploitation, the Arctic fin whale population was estimated to be around half a million individuals). If the population is harvested at a constant rate of H individuals per year for an extended period of time, then this harvesting rate is *sustainable* if there exists a positive number x of whales at which the growth rate $G(x)$ equals the harvesting rate H. That is, it is possible for the growth to keep pace with the loss from harvesting. Determine the maximal sustainable harvesting rate.

Solution   According to the statement of the problem, a harvesting rate H is sustainable if there is a positive x such that

$$H = G(x) = 0.08x \left(1 - \frac{x}{500,000}\right)$$

Hence, maximizing a sustainable harvesting rate is equivalent to finding $x > 0$ which maximizes $G(x)$. Since the graph of G is a downward facing parabola, we can find its maximum by taking the derivative of G, setting it equal to zero, and solving for x:

$$0 = G'(x) = 0.08 - 0.16 \frac{x}{500,000}$$

$$0.16 \frac{x}{500,000} = 0.08$$

$$x = 250,000$$

Hence, the maximum sustainable yield occurs at a harvesting rate of $H = G(250,000) = 10,000$ whales per year at which the whale population consists of 250,000 individuals. This maximum sustainable harvesting rate of 10,000 whales per year is *three times smaller* than the harvesting rate in the early twentieth century. Hence, the model reaffirms the statement that harvesting at 30,000 whales per year in the early twentieth century was not sustainable and may explain why the current population sizes are an order of magnitude lower than half a million. ∎

Sometimes when solving a problem it is useful to sketch a figure, as illustrated in the next example.

Example 3   Do dogs know calculus?

Professor Tim Pennings from Hope College wanted to determine whether his dog, Elvis, fetched balls thrown into Lake Michigan in an optimal way. (See T. Pennings, "Do Dogs Know Calculus?" *College Mathematics Journal* 34(2003):178–182.) Standing along the shoreline with Elvis at his side, Tim would throw the ball into the water. Elvis could choose to swim out directly from where Tim was standing to get the ball, hence taking a minimal-distance trajectory. Alternatively, he could run along the shore before he jumped into the water and swam to the ball. Because Elvis can only swim at an average speed of 0.91 meters per second whereas he can run at an average speed of 6.4 meters per second, it is likely that he ran for some distance along the shore. But how far along the shore should Elvis run?

Tim performed an experiment to assess what strategy Elvis was playing by throwing the ball repeatedly into the water and keeping track of where Elvis entered the water. For one throw, the ball landed 6 meters from the shore, as illustrated in Figure 4.10**a**.

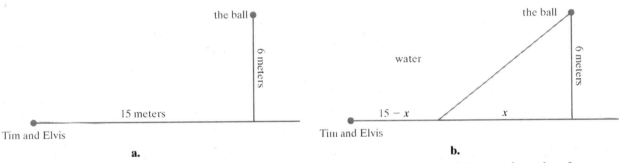

Figure 4.10 How will Elvis fetch a ball that landed 6 meters from shore?

What path would Elvis take if he were to minimize that amount of time it took him to retrieve the ball?

Solution   Let us begin by sketching a figure that indicates a hypothetical path Elvis could take (see Figure 4.10**b**). In this drawing, $15 - x$ is the distance Elvis runs along the shore. Assuming that Elvis wants to minimize the time to getting to the ball, we need to write a function that describes how the amount of time to get to the ball depends on x. Since he is running at a speed of 6.4 meters per second and runs a distance of $15 - x$ meters along the shore, we get that the time he spends running on the shore is

$$\frac{(15 - x) \text{ meters}}{6.4 \text{ meters per second}} = \frac{15 - x}{6.4} \text{ seconds}$$

By the Pythagorean theorem, the distance Elvis swims to the ball is $\sqrt{36 + x^2}$. Hence, the time he spends swimming is

$$\frac{\sqrt{36 + x^2} \text{ meters}}{0.91 \text{ meters per second}} = \frac{\sqrt{36 + x^2}}{0.91} \text{ seconds}$$

Hence, the total time T it takes him to get to the ball as a function of x is given by

$$T(x) = \frac{15 - x}{6.4} + \frac{\sqrt{36 + x^2}}{0.91} \text{ seconds}$$

We want to understand the graph of this function for $0 \le x \le 15$, so let us take the derivative of T.

$$T'(x) = -\frac{1}{6.4} + \frac{x}{0.91\sqrt{36 + x^2}}$$

To find the critical points, we need to solve $T'(x) = 0$. Doing so yields

$$\frac{x}{0.91\sqrt{36 + x^2}} = \frac{1}{6.4}$$

$$\frac{x^2}{0.91^2(36 + x^2)} = \frac{1}{6.4^2} \qquad \textit{square both sides}$$

$$x^2 = 0.02(36 + x^2) \qquad \textit{multiply both sides by common denominator}$$

$$0.98\,x^2 = 0.72 \qquad\qquad\qquad \textit{and isolate } x^2$$

$$x^2 = 0.735$$

$$x \approx \pm 0.86$$

Hence, on the interval $[0, 15]$, T' vanishes only at $x = 0.86$. Since $T'(2) \approx 0.19 > 0$, we see that T is increasing on the interval $(0.86, 15]$. On the other hand, since $T'(0) \approx -0.16$, T is decreasing on $[0, 0.86)$. Thus, the minimum time is achieved at $x = 0.86$. Therefore, Elvis should run 14.1 meters along the shore before jumping into the water. ∎

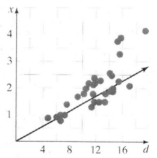

Figure 4.11 Scatter plot of distance of ball from shore (in the horizontal direction) and Elvis's point of entry $15 - d$ in the water (in the vertical direction). The best-fitting line $x = 0.144\,d$ passes through the center of the scatter plot.

So what was the outcome of Tim's experiment? When Tim measured the point at which Elvis entered the water, he found that Elvis ran $15 - x = 14.1$ meters along the shore (i.e., $x = 0.9$). Does this dog know calculus? Well, he could have been lucky on this one throw. So Tim performed thirty-five throws, with the ball landing different distances d from the shoreline. Tim measured the point x where Elvis entered the water on each throw. In the problems at the end of this section, you will be asked to show that the optimal place to enter the water as a function of the distance d the ball lands from the shore is

$$x = 0.144\,d \text{ meters}$$

A scatter plot of the data and the line is shown in Figure 4.11. This figure illustrates that Elvis is on average acting pretty optimal, which is quite remarkable.

The next example concerns treating tumors with chemotherapy (Figure 4.12), which was mentioned in the introduction to this section. Refer to Problems 44 and 45 in Problem Set 1.4 and Problem Set 44 in Problem Set 1.5 for further insights into modeling tumor growth.

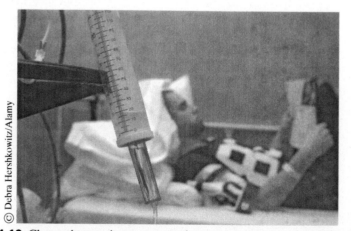

© Debra Hershkowitz/Alamy

Figure 4.12 Chemotherapy is a treatment for cancer patients in which powerful drugs are used to kill cancer cells. Often it is used in conjunction with other treatments, including radiation therapy and surgery.

Example 4   Tumor regrowth

In an experimental study performed at Dartmouth College (E. Demidenko. Mixed Models: Theory and Applications. Wiley 2004), two groups of mice with tumors were treated with the chemotherapeutic drug cisplatin. Before the therapy, the tumor consisted of proliferating cells (also known as *clonogenic cells*) that grew exponentially with a doubling time of approximately 2.9 days. Each of the mice was given a dose of 10 mg/kg of cisplatin. At the time of the therapy, the average tumor size was approximately 0.5 cm^3. After treatment, 99% of the proliferating cells became quiescent cells (also known as *nonproliferating* or *resting cells*). These quiescent cells do not divide and decay with a half-life of approximately 5.7 days.

a. Write a function $V(t)$ that represents the volume of the tumor t days after therapy. The tumor volume includes the volume of the proliferating cells and the quiescent cells.

b. Determine at what point in time the tumor starts to regrow and therapy should be readministered.

Solution

a. If $P(t)$ and $Q(t)$ represent the respective volumes of proliferating and quiescent cells in a tumor, then the total volume $V(t)$ of the tumor is given by

$$V(t) = P(t) + Q(t)$$

Assume the proliferating cells are increasing at an exponential rate and have an initial volume of $P(0) = 0.01 \times 0.5 = 0.005$ cm^3 (i.e., 1% of the previous untreated average size). Hence, $P(t) = 0.005e^{at}$ where we need to solve for a. Since the doubling time is 2.9 days, we can solve for a as follows:

$$P(2.9) = 2(0.005) \qquad \textit{tumor has doubled in size by } t = 2.9$$

$$0.005e^{2.9a} = 0.01$$

$$e^{2.9a} = 2 \qquad \textit{dividing by } 0.005$$

$$a = \ln 2/2.9 \approx 0.24$$

Hence, $P(t) = 0.005e^{0.24t}$.

Similarly, we have $Q(0) = 0.99(0.5) = 0.495$ and $Q(t) = 0.495e^{bt}$ where we have to solve for b. Since the half-life of quiescent cells is 5.7 days, we can solve for b as follows:

$$Q(5.7) = 0.5(0.495)$$

$$0.495e^{5.7b} = 0.5(0.495)$$

$$e^{5.7b} = 0.5$$

$$b = \ln 0.5/5.7 \approx -0.12$$

Hence, $Q(t) = 0.495e^{-0.12t}$.

Thus, it follows from the first equation that

$$V(t) = 0.005e^{0.24t} + 0.495e^{-0.12t}$$

b. To determine when $V(t)$ is increasing or decreasing, we need to compute its derivative:

$$V'(t) = 0.0012e^{0.24t} - 0.0594e^{-0.12t}$$

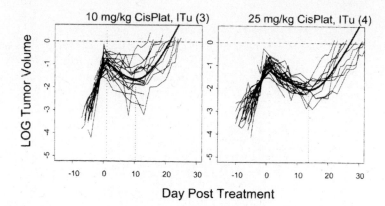

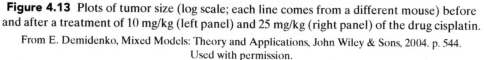

Figure 4.13 Plots of tumor size (log scale; each line comes from a different mouse) before and after a treatment of 10 mg/kg (left panel) and 25 mg/kg (right panel) of the drug cisplatin.

From E. Demidenko, Mixed Models: Theory and Applications, John Wiley & Sons, 2004. p. 544. Used with permission.

Since $V'(0) \approx -0.0582$, the volume of the tumor is initially decreasing after therapy. To see when $V'(t)$ changes sign, we solve

$$0.0012e^{0.24t} - 0.0594e^{-0.12t} = 0$$
$$0.0012e^{0.24t} = 0.0594e^{-0.12t}$$
$$0.0012e^{0.36t} = 0.0594$$
$$e^{0.36t} = 49.5$$
$$t = \frac{\ln 49.5}{0.36} \approx 10.84 \text{ days}$$

Hence, after 10.84 days, the tumor begins to regrow and therapy should be read-ministered. Indeed, this prediction is supported by the data shown in the left panel of Figure 4.13. (The data in the right panel are examined in Problem Set 4.3.)

In the next example, we consider the vascular system, which consists of arteries and veins that branch in different directions to pump blood through all parts of the body. Ideally, the body is designed to minimize the amount of energy it expends in pumping blood. According to one of Poiseuille's laws, the resistance blood experiences by traveling down the center of a blood vessel with radius r and length L is proportional to

$$\frac{L}{r^4}$$

Without loss of generality, we assume that this proportionality constant equals one, and use this law to determine optimal branching angles in the vascular system of animals.

Example 5   Vascular branching

Consider a blood vessel that branches as illustrated below:

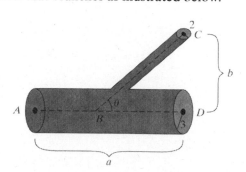

where a and b are positive constants. Given a and b, determine the angle θ which minimizes the total resistance in the blood flow from the point A to the point C.

Solution   We want to minimize the total resistance along the blood vessel from A to C. Let B be the point where the vessel branches. We need to determine the resistance from A to B and the resistance from B to C. To determine the resistance along the blood vessel from A to B, we need to determine how the distance from A to B depends on θ. Using the right triangle as shown below

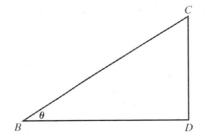

we get that the length from B to D is given by $b\cot\theta$. Hence, the distance from A to B is

$$a - b\cot\theta$$

and, as the radius of the vessel from A to B is 3, the resistance from A to B is

$$\frac{a - b\cot\theta}{3^4}$$

Using the same right triangle, we get that the distance from B to C is $b\csc\theta$. Hence, the resistance from B to C is

$$\frac{b\csc\theta}{2^4}$$

as the radius of the vessel from B to C is 2. Adding the resistance from A to B to the resistance from B to C, we get that the resistance from A to C is given by

$$R(\theta) = \frac{a - b\cot\theta}{81} + \frac{b}{16}\csc\theta$$

To minimize the resistance on the half-open interval $\left(0, \dfrac{\pi}{2}\right]$, we need to determine the critical points along this interval as follows:

$$R'(\theta) = 0$$

$$\frac{b}{81}\csc^2\theta - \frac{b}{16}\csc^2\theta\cos\theta = 0 \quad \textit{taking the derivative and using the fact that}$$
$$\cot\theta = \csc\theta\cos\theta$$

$$b\csc^2\theta\left(\frac{1}{16}\cos\theta - \frac{1}{81}\right) = 0 \quad \textit{common factor}$$

$$\textit{This implies} \quad \cos\theta = \frac{16}{81}$$

$$\theta \approx 1.37 \quad \textit{solving for } \theta$$

Hence, the optimal angle is given by ≈ 1.37 radians. Equivalently, since one radian is approximately 57.3 degrees, $\theta \approx 78.5$ degrees. ■

Regression

Regression, loosely speaking, is the process of drawing a graph through a set of data, where the graph represents the information in the data after process and measurement errors have been "averaged out." The term *regression* dates back to Sir Francis

Galton's work on measuring heritable traits in humans, such as height, and his publication of this work in 1886 under the title "Regression Towards Mediocrity in Hereditary Status" (*Journal of the Anthropological Institute of Great Britain and Ireland*, 15 (1886): 246–263). To simplify our notation in developing some of the ideas associated with regression theory, we introduce the summation notation, a notation that we revisit in Chapter 5 when developing integral calculus.

Summation Notation

The sum of a sequence of n real numbers $a_1, a_2, a_3, \cdots, a_n$ is

$$\sum_{i=1}^{n} a_i = a_1 + a_2 + a_3 + \cdots + a_n$$

The index i does not have to start at $i = 1$, but could start at any integer value less than or equal to n.

The following three properties of this summation notation are easily verified.

Properties of Summations

Let $a_1, a_2, a_3, \ldots, a_n, b_1, b_2, b_3, \ldots, b_n$, and c be real numbers. Then

$$\sum_{i=1}^{n}(a_i + b_i) = \sum_{i=1}^{n} a_i + \sum_{i=1}^{n} b_i$$

$$\sum_{i=1}^{n}(a_i - b_i) = \sum_{i=1}^{n} a_i - \sum_{i=1}^{n} b_i$$

$$\sum_{i=1}^{n} ca_i = c \sum_{i=1}^{n} a_i$$

In our development of regression, we use the following definition that we informally introduced in Section 1.2 and depicted in Figure 1.14 for the case of linear regression. Here we provide a definition for any function $f(x)$, not just the linear function $f(x) = mx + c$.

Residual Sum-of-Squares

The residual sum-of-squares S of the function $y = f(x)$ from a data set

$$D = \{(x_1, y_1), (x_2, y_2), \cdots, (x_n, y_n)\}$$

is the residuals

$$e_i = y_i - f(x_i)$$

squared and then summed to obtain

$$S = \sum_{i=1}^{n} e_i^2$$

If we interpret the residuals e_i as "errors" from the true value, then S is the **sum of squared errors**. To find a best-fitting function to a data set, regression aims to minimize the sum of these squared errors.

Example 6   Best line through the origin

In Example 7 of Section 2.2, we determined the slope a of how the rate (cells/hour) at which copepods feed on diatoms increases as a function of diatom density (cells/milliliter). In the first two rows of data in Table 4.1 we have extracted eleven representative points from these data, as diatom density increases from 0 to 200 cells/milliliter.

Table 4.1 Diatom densities x (cells/milliliter) and copepod feeding rates y (cells/hour)

i	1	2	3	4	5	6	7	8	9	10	11	$\sum_{i=1}^{11}$
x_i	19	20	39	68	73	100	106	149	155	174	193	
y_i	102	156	297	313	523	484	797	680	938	1328	914	
x_i^2	373	412	1494	4574	5392	10097	11295	22139	23898	30246	37340	147260
$x_i y_i$	1963	3170	11473	21135	38436	48617	84692	101132	144928	230978	176630	863210

a. Find the slope a of the line $f(x) = ax$ through the origin that minimizes the residual sum-of-squares through the data. This is the so-called *best-fitting* or *regression* line.

b. Plot these data and the regression line on the same graph.

Solution

a. From definition of the residual sum-of-squares with $f(x) = ax$ and properties of summations, we have

$$S(a) = \sum_{i=1}^{11} (y_i - ax_i)^2$$

$$= \sum_{i=1}^{11} (y_i^2 - 2ax_i y_i + a^2 x_i^2) \qquad \text{expanding the quadratic term}$$

$$= \sum_{i=1}^{11} y_i^2 - 2a \sum_{i=1}^{11} x_i y_i + a^2 \sum_{i=1}^{11} x_i^2 \qquad \text{from summation properties}$$

S is a quadratic function of a. Since the coefficient of a^2 is positive, the graph of $S(a)$ is an upward facing parabola and, hence, has a unique minimum. To minimize $S(a)$ with respect to a simply requires finding where its derivative $S'(a)$ equals 0. Differentiating S yields

$$S'(a) = -2 \sum_{i=1}^{11} x_i y_i + 2a \sum_{i=1}^{11} x_i^2$$

Setting $S'(a) = 0$ and solving yields

$$a^* = \frac{\sum_{i=1}^{11} x_i y_i}{\sum_{i=1}^{11} x_i^2}$$

Using the values of the sums, as given in Table 4.1, we obtain that

$$a^* = \frac{863210}{147260} = 5.86$$

is the value of a that minimizes $S(a)$.

b. The line $f(x) = 5.86x$ and the data are plotted below

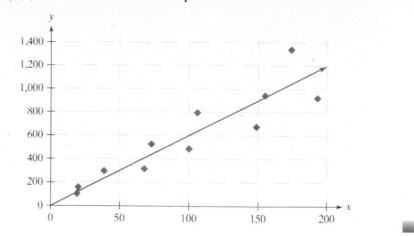

Recall Example 5 of Section 1.7. We plotted the data in Figure 1.46 of that example on the decline of the Glued gene in a species of fruit fly. The data, which exhibit an exponential decline from 0.5 to 0.0036 over six generations, are reported in Table 4.2. To model how rapidly the Glued gene is lost from the experimental fruit fly population in each generation, we used the function $f(t) = 0.5e^{-rt}$ for some appropriately chosen constant $r > 0$. Taking the logarithm of this equation yields the linear function $\ln 0.5 - rt$ of t. In the next example, we use this observation to find the best-fitting line to the logarithmically transformed data.

Table 4.2 Changes in the frequency x of the Glued gene in a species of fruit fly over seven (generation 0 is also experimentally generated) experimental generations t (values to two significant digits)

t (generation)	0	1	2	3	4	5	6
x_t	0.50	0.45	0.32	0.23	0.23	0.067	0.036

Example 7   Regression and lethal genes

a. Find the value of the decay rate parameter $r > 0$ of the function $\ln 0.5 - rt$ that minimizes the residual sum-of-squares of this function with respect to the data $(1, \ln x_1), (2, \ln x_2), \ldots, (6, \ln x_6)$ from Table 4.2.

b. Provide a semi-log plot of these data and the best-fitting, log-transformed, exponential decay function on the same graph.

Solution

a. Following the approach of Example 6, we want to minimize

$$S(r) = \sum_{t=1}^{6} (\ln x_t - (\ln 0.5 - rt))^2$$

Differentiating S with respect to r yields

$$S'(r) = \sum_{t=1}^{6} 2t (\ln x_t - \ln 0.5 + rt) = 2\sum_{t=1}^{6} t \ln x_t - 2\ln 0.5 \sum_{t=1}^{6} t + 2r \sum_{t=1}^{6} t^2$$

Setting $S'(r) = 0$ and solving for r yields

$$r = \frac{\ln 0.5 \sum_{t=1}^{6} t - \sum_{t=1}^{6} t \ln x_t}{\sum_{t=1}^{6} t^2}$$

Calculating relevant sums from Table 4.2, we obtain the following table.

t	0	1	2	3	4	5	6	$\sum_{t=1}^{6} t = 21$
x_t	0.50	0.45	0.32	0.23	0.23	0.067	0.036	
t^2	0	1	4	9	16	25	36	$\sum_{t=1}^{6} t^2 = 91$
$\ln x_t$	−0.69	−0.80	−1.14	−1.47	−1.47	−2.70	−3.32	
$t \ln x_t$	0	−0.80	−2.28	−4.41	−5.88	−13.5	−19.92	$\sum_{t=1}^{6} t \ln x_t = 46.8$

Thus, from the above equation for r we have

$$r = \frac{64.5}{182} = 0.35$$

We conclude that the best estimate of the rate at which the Glued gene is purged from the fruit fly population during the experiment is very close to 33% per generation.

b. The log-transformed data $\ln x_t$ and the best-fitting function $\ln 0.5 - rt$ are shown below.

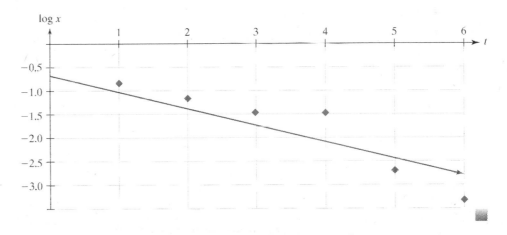

PROBLEM SET 4.3

Level 1 DRILL PROBLEMS

1. In Example 1, the selling price of corn was $1.50 per bushel and the seeds cost $3 per thousand seeds. Determine the density of seeds that maximize profit if the selling price and cost are both doubled.

2. In Example 1, determine the density of seeds that maximize profit if the selling price is $5 per bushel and the seeds cost $2 per thousand seeds.

3. In Example 1, determine the density of seeds that maximize profit if the selling price is $2.20 per bushel and the seeds cost $2.50 per thousand seeds.

4. In Example 2, we estimated that the maximum per capita growth rate of the Arctic fin whale is $r = 0.08$.

Suppose a better estimate is $r = 0.1$. Determine the maximum sustainable harvesting rate for this value of r.

5. In Example 2, we estimated that the long-term abundance of the arctic fin whales in the absence of harvesting is $K = 500,000$ of the Arctic fin whale is $K = 500,000$. Suppose a better estimate is $K = 400,000$. Determine the maximum sustainable harvesting rate for this value of K.

6. In a species of fish the growth rate function is given by $G(x) = 1.4x(1 - x/K)$, where $K = 5$ million metric tons (i.e., the population of fish is measured in metric tons rather than number of individuals). If

the harvest rate is a function of the harvesting effort h and the total amount of fish x, that is $H = hx$, find the harvesting effort value h that corresponds to the maximum sustainable yield.

7. In a species of fish, the growth rate function is given by $G(x) = 2.1x(1 - x/K)$, where $K = 8$ million metric tons. If the harvest rate is $H = hx$, find the harvesting effort value h that corresponds to the maximum sustainable yield.

In Problems 8 to 12, find the optimal angle for the following vascular branching problems, as considered in Example 5.

8. A larger artery has a radius of 0.05 mm, and a smaller artery of radius 0.025 mm branches from the larger artery with branching angle θ.

9. A larger artery has a radius of 0.06 mm, and a smaller artery of radius 0.04 mm branches from the larger artery with branching angle θ.

10. The radius of the main blood vessel is $r_1 = 2$ and the radius of the branching vessel is $r_2 = 1$.

11. The radius of the main blood vessel is $r_1 = 4$ and the radius of the branching vessel is $r_2 = 3$.

12. In a general case, the radius of the main blood vessel is r_1 and the radius of the branching vessel is r_2. Assume that $r_1 > r_2$.

13. In Example 3, calculate at what point x along the shore Elvis should enter the water if the distance of the ball from the shore is 20 meters rather than 6.

14. In Example 3, calculate at what point x along the shore Elvis should enter the water if the distance of the ball from the shore is 10 meters rather than 6.

15. In Example 3, calculate at what point x along the shore Elvis should enter the water if the distance of the ball from the shore is d meters.

In Problems 16 to 22, calculate the residual sum-of-squares of the listed function through this data set:

t	1	2	3	4	5
x_t	1	3	6	12	16

Draw a graph of the function and the data on the same plot. In problems Problems 21 to 22, plot the residual sum-of-squares graph as a function of the free parameter and selected range for this parameter. Note that you are not being asked to fit the exponential functions in the relevant examples below on a semi-log plot, but to use the function itself directly in the calculations of the residuals with respect to the data as it stands.

16. $f(x) = 2x$

17. $f(x) = 2x + 1$

18. $f(x) = 3x - 1$

19. $f(x) = 0.4e^{0.8t}$

20. $f(x) = 0.2e^{0.9t}$

21. $f(x) = mx, 0 \le m \le 4$

22. $f(x) = 0.2e^{rt}, 0 \le r \le 1$

Level 2 APPLIED AND THEORY PROBLEMS

23. Find a general formula for which Example 3 is a specific case that describes how to calculate at what point x along the shore Elvis should enter the water if the distance of the ball from the shore is d meters (rather than 6) and the point on the shore to which this distance d holds is k meters (rather than 15) from where Tim is standing.

24. In a species of fish, the growth rate function is given by $G(x) = 1.5x(1 - x/K)$, where $K = 6,000$ metric tons (i.e., the population of fish, x, is measured in metric tons rather than number of individuals). The price a fisher can get is $p = \$600$ per metric ton. If the amount the fisher can harvest is determined by the function $H = hx$, where each unit of h costs the fisher $c = \$100$, what is the maximum amount of money the fisher can expect to make on a sustainable basis? (Hint: The fisher's sustainable income is given by $pH - ch$, where H is a sustainable harvesting rate.)

25. In the tumor growth study described in Example 4, the tumor consisted of proliferating cells (clonogenic cells) that grew exponentially with a doubling time of approximately 2.9 days. Suppose that each mouse was given a dose of 25 mg/kg of cisplatin per treatment with the following results: At the time of the therapy, the average tumor size was approximately 0.44 cm^3. After treatment, 99.73% of the proliferating cells became quiescent cells and decayed with a half-life of approximately 6.24 days.

   a. Write a function $V(t)$ that represents the size of the tumor (proliferating plus quiescent cells) t days after therapy.

   b. Determine at what point in time the tumor starts to regrow and therapy should be readministered.

   c. Compare your answer to the data figure in Example 4.

26. In a follow-up study to the tumor growth study described in Example 4, mice were infected with a relatively aggressive line of proliferating clonogenic cells that grew exponentially with a doubling time of approximately 1.8 days. Each mouse was given a dose of 20 mg/kg of cisplatin per treatment with the following results: At the time of the therapy, the average tumor size was approximately 0.6 cm^3. After treatment, 99.10% of the proliferating cells became

quiescent cells and decayed with a half-life of approximately 4.4 days.

a. Write a function $V(t)$ that represents the size of the tumor (proliferating plus quiescent cells) t days after therapy.

b. Determine at what point in time the tumor starts to regrow and therapy should be readministered.

27. In certain tissues, cells exist in the shape of circular cylinders. Suppose such a cylinder has radius r and height h. If the volume is fixed (say, at v), find the value of r that minimizes the total surface area $(S = 2\pi r^2 + 2\pi rh)$ of the cell.

28. Farmers regularly use fertilizers to enhance the productivity of their crops. Determining the appropriate amount of fertilizer to use requires balancing the costs of fertilization with the increases in yield. In a 2004 study, Baker and colleagues studied the relationship between nitrogen fertilization and yield of hard red spring wheat. (See Dustin A. Baker, Douglas L. Young, David R. Huggins, and William L. Pan, "Economically Optimal Nitrogen Fertilization for Yield and Protein in Hard Red Spring Wheat," *Agronomy Journal* 96 (2004): 116–123.) For conventional tillage practices in eastern Washington in the late 1980s, they found that the grain yield (in kilograms per hectare) as a function of nitrogen (in kilograms per hectare) is well approximated by

$$Y(N) = 1.86 + 0.02741N - 0.00009N^2$$

These researchers suggested that a high selling price for wheat would be \$191.1/kg and low cost for nitrogen would be \$0.49/kg. Determine the amount of nitrogen that maximizes profits per hectare.

29. Baker and colleagues suggested that a low selling price for wheat would be \$139.65/kg and a high cost for nitrogen would be \$0.71/kg. Using the same yield function as in the previous problem, determine the amount of nitrogen that maximizes profits per hectare.

30. If the effects of density dependence in a whale population set in less rapidly closer to the final carrying capacity, K, than the logistic equation used in Example 2, then the equation should be replaced by an asymmetric growth model

$$G(x) = 0.08x\left[1 - \left(\frac{x}{500,000}\right)^\alpha\right] \text{ whales per year}$$

for some $\alpha \in (0, 1)$. For the case $\alpha = 0.5$, calculate the stock level x that provides the maximum sustainable.

31. If the effects of density dependence in a whale population set in less rapidly or more rapidly closer to the final carrying capacity, K, than the logistic

equation used in Example 2, then the equation should be replaced by an asymmetric growth model

$$G(x) = rx\left[1 - \left(\frac{x}{K}\right)^\alpha\right] \text{ whales per year}$$

For $\alpha > 0$, $r > 0$, and $K > 0$, calculate the stock level x that provides the maximum sustainable yield. Discuss whether rapid onset of density dependence (i.e., large α) or gradual onset of density dependence (i.e., small α) leads to larger sustainable yields.

32. During the winter, a species of bird migrates from the coast of a mainland to an island 500 miles southeast. If the energy the bird requires to fly one mile over the water is twice more than the amount of energy it requires to fly over the land, determine what path the species should fly to minimize the amount of energy used.

33. The Statue of Liberty is 92 meters high, including the 46 meter pedestal upon which it stands. How far from the base should an individual stand to ensure that the view angle, θ, is maximized?

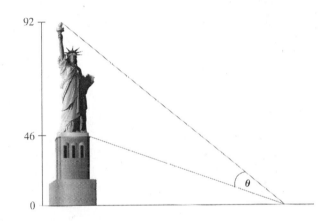

34. In the northeastern part of Sweet Water County, a large dam is being constructed on the Shuga River to produce *hydroelectricity* (i.e., the generation of electricity through water pressure). An important part of this project is running power lines from the power stations at the downstream side of the dam to various parts of the county, including Pickle City, the largest city in the county. On the recommendation of a number of other counties, Sweet Water County officials have hired you as consultant to resolve cost issues for running these power lines.

County officials have informed you that the Shuga River runs due east, and on its southern side lies an expanse of federally protected wetlands. Pickle City lies several miles to the south of these wetlands, as shown in the map below.

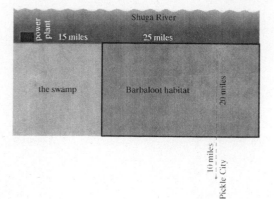

The federally protected wetlands are divided into two regions. In the western region, county officials expect that due to federal regulations it will cost 40% more to run conduit here than it does through non-wetland ground. The eastern region of the wetlands is a habitat for the endangered Brown Barbaloots. Consequently, federal law prevents the county from running conduits through this region.

As the county officials intend to submit a budget proposal for the project to the county council in the next week, they would like you to determine the path from the power station to downtown Pickle City that minimizes the cost of installing the conduit.

35. An oil spill has fouled 200 miles of Pacific shoreline. The oil company responsible has been given fourteen days to clean up the shoreline, after which a fine will be levied in the amount of $10,000/day. The local cleanup crew can scrub five miles of beach per day at a cost of $500/day. Additional crews can be brought in at a cost of $18,000, plus $800/day for each crew. Determine how many additional crews should be brought in to minimize the total cost to the company and how much the cleanup will cost.

36. Consider a spherical cell with radius r. Assume that the cell gains energy at a rate proportional to its surface area (i.e., nutrients diffusing in from outside of the cell) and that the cell loses energy at a rate proportional to its volume (i.e., all parts of the cell are using energy). If the cell is trying to maximize its net gain of energy, determine the optimal radius of the cell. Note: Your final expression will depend on your proportionality constants.

37. Consider a cylindrical cell with radius r and height $r/2$. Assume that the cell gains energy at a rate proportional to its surface area (i.e., nutrients diffusing in from outside of the cell) and that the cell loses energy at a rate proportional to its volume (i.e., all parts of the cell are using energy). If the cell

is trying to maximize its net gain of energy, determine the optimal value of r. Note: Your final expression will depend on your proportionality constants.

38. A dune buggy is in the desert at a point A located 40 km from a point B, which lies on a long, straight road, as shown in Figure 4.14. The driver can travel at 45 km/hour on the desert and 75 km/hour on the road. The driver will win a prize if she arrives at the finish line at point D, 50 km from B, in 85 minutes or less. Set up and analyze a model to help her decide on a route to minimize the time of travel. Does she win the prize?

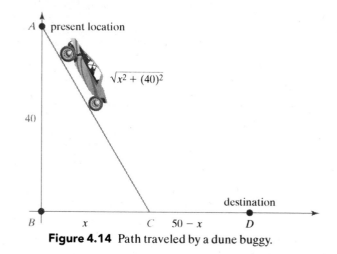

Figure 4.14 Path traveled by a dune buggy.

39. The question of whether an optimal body size exists for different kinds of animals is one that is of great interest to biologists. The reproductive power P of an individual can be modeled, following the ideas of ecologist James H. Brown (see his book *Macroecology*, University of Chicago Press, 1995), as the harmonic mean of two limiting rates. The harmonic mean of two numbers a and b is the reciprocals of the average of the inverses of the two numbers: $1/(1/a + 1/b) = ab/(a + b)$. The two rates are a per-unit-mass rate R_1 at which individuals acquire resources, and a per-unit-mass rate R_2 at which individuals convert those resources into new individuals; that is,

$$P = \frac{R_1 R_2}{R_1 + R_2}$$

Assuming both R_1 and R_2 are the following allometric functions of body mass measure in kilograms

$$R_1 = 2M^{3/4} \qquad \text{and} \qquad R_2 = 3M^{-1/4},$$

find the body mass M that maximizes the reproductive power P, and show that this extremum is a maximum for the case $b_1 = 0.75$ and $b_2 = -0.25$.

40. Suppose that we express the two rate functions in Problem 39 using the general form $R_1 = c_1 M^{b_1}$ and $R_2 = c_2 M^{-b_2}$. Show in this case that the maximum body size is given by the expression

$$M^* = \left(\frac{-c_2 b_1}{c_1 b_2} \right)^{1/(b_1 - b_2)}$$

41. In Example 6, we determined the slope a of the linear component of a type I functional response for the rate (cells/hour) at which copepods feed on diatoms as a function of diatom density (cells/milliliter). Suppose now that only the following partial set of data (Table 4.3) is available for estimating the parameter a.

Table 4.3 Diatom densities x (cells/milliliter) and copepod feeding rates y (cells/hour)

i	1	2	3	4	5	6
x_i	19	39	68	106	149	174
y_i	102	297	313	797	680	1328

a. Find the slope a of the line $f(x) = ax$ through the origin that minimizes the residual sum-of-squares through the data.

b. Plot these data and the best-fit line on the same graph.

42. In Table 1.4, the CO_2 concentrations at the Mauna Loa Observatory in Hawaii are listed by month, starting at month 1 (May 1974) until month 140 (December 1985). The data for the month of May, for the twelve periods spanning May 1974 to May 1985, are shown in Table 4.4.

a. Find the slope m of the regression line $f(x) = mx + 333.2$ through the point $(t, x_t) = (0, 333.2)$ that minimizes the residual sum-of-squares through the remaining eleven data points.

b. Plot these data and the regression line on the same graph.

43. In Example 7, we found the value of the decay rate parameter $r > 0$ using linear regression to fit a semi-log plot of the frequency of Glued genes in an experimental fruit fly population. This experiment was repeated by the same group of researchers and the following data were obtained:

t	0	1	2	3	4	5
x_t	0.59	0.37	0.21	0.16	0.047	0.015

Use these data to find the value r of the best-fitting exponential decay function $x_t = 0.59 e^{-rt}$ through the starting point $(t, \ln x_t) = (0, -0.53)$. Present the solution on a semi-log plot together with a plot of the data.

44. In Section 1.4, we presented the following data on the growth of the United States from 1815 until 1895.

Year	Population (in millions)
1815	8.3
1825	11.0
1835	14.7
1845	19.7
1855	26.7
1865	35.2
1875	44.4
1885	55.9
1895	68.9

Use linear regression on a semi-log transformation of the above data to find the best estimate of the annual growth rate $r > 0$ in the population model $x(t) = 8.3 e^{rt}$ (million individuals) for $t \in [0, 80]$ (years), with $t = 0$ corresponding to the year 1815.

Table 4.4 CO_2 x (cell/milliliter) in year t

t	0	1	2	3	4	5	6	7	8	9	10	11
x_t	333.2	333.9	334.8	336.8	338.0	339.0	341.5	343.0	344.3	345.8	347.5	348.7

4.4   Decisions and Optimization

Optimal decisions

The behavior of animals has been honed by natural selection to maximize the reproductive potential of individuals. Thus, from an individual point of view, individuals should act in ways that maximize the number of offspring they rear to sexual maturity. This number is referred to as an **individual's fitness**. From a genetic point of view, a gene encoding for a behavior that maximizes an individual's fitness will have a greater representation in the gene pool of future generations than a gene that encodes for a behavior that is detrimental to an individual's fitness (e.g., a gene that causes an individual to be excessively reckless, making it likely that the individual will die before reaching sexual maturity). Theories of optimal behavior are based on the premise that organisms maximize their fitness by behaving in a certain way. Using models, researchers can develop hypotheses about these optimal behaviors. These hypotheses can be tested experimentally or through comparative studies.

In our first example in this section, we obtain insights into the reason why Northwestern crows consistently drop whelks from a specific height to break them open. If the crows fly too low, the shells require too many drops to get them to break open. If they fly too high, the crows waste energy. Assuming that crows have evolved to minimize energy expenditures, scientists might be interested in testing this hypothesis by formulating a suitable function to minimize. This function would characterize the number of of drops, and hence work, required to break open a whelk as a function of the height from which the shell is dropped. In addition to modeling the dropping behavior of Northwestern crows, this section investigates optimal foraging in a patchy environment, optimal timing of seed production, and optimal time to harvest crops. In addition to these examples, we present a key theorem called the *marginal value theorem*, which has applications to problems maximizing or minimizing average rates of change.

The Northwestern crow, illustrated in Figure 4.15, feeds on whelks, a type of mollusk. To get the meat from inside the whelk's shell, individual crows lift whelks into the air and drop them onto a rock to break open the shell. The biologist Reto Zach (see Example 6 of Section 3.2) observed that individual crows typically drop the shells from a height of five meters. This led him to ask this question: Does the height from which Northwestern crows drop whelk shells minimize the amount energy required to open a shell?

Figure 4.15 A Northwestern crow.

Example 1　Northwestern crows and whelks

After collecting data by dropping whelks from different heights, Zach found that, on average, the number of drops required to break a whelk dropped from h meters is modeled by the function

$$D(h) = 1 + \frac{20.4}{h - 0.84} \text{ drops}, \quad h > 0.84$$

This relationship implies $\lim_{h \to 0.84^+} D(h) = \infty$, which in turn implies that if $h \leq 0.84$, the shell will never open. Use this equation

$$work = force \times distance$$

to find the optimal height from which a whelk should be dropped to minimize the amount of work required to break a whelk shell.

Solution　Since work is force times distance, the amount of work required to drop a shell of fixed weight is in proportion to the total height the crow flies when breaking a whelk. The total height is given by the number of drops times the height of the drop. In other words, up to a proportionality constant that depends on the units of measurement, the average amount of work that it will take a crow to break open a whelk shell is given by

$$W(h) = hD(h) = h + \frac{20.4h}{h - 0.84}$$

To determine where this function takes on its smallest value, we need to understand the graph of the function. It has a vertical asymptote at $h = 0.84$. Taking the derivative yields

$$W'(h) = 1 - \frac{0.84 \cdot 20.4}{(h - 0.84)^2}$$

$$= \frac{-16.4304 - 1.68\,h + h^2}{(h - 0.84)^2}$$

Since the denominator is positive wherever $h \neq 0.84$, we only need to understand when the numerator is positive or negative. Solving $-16.4304 - 1.68\,h + h^2 = 0$ for h yields $h \approx -3.3$ meters and $h \approx 4.98$ meters. Since this quadratic corresponds to an upward facing parabola, we get that the numerator of $W'(h)$ is positive when $h > 4.98$ and negative on the interval $(0.84, 4.98)$. Hence, $W(h)$ decreases on the interval $(0.84, 4.98)$ and increases on the interval $(4.98, \infty)$. The height $h \approx 4.98$ is a global minimum for $h > 0.84$.

Hence, the height that minimizes the amount of work is approximately five meters, the height observed by Reto Zach! ∎

The next example explores the optimal time for a plant to produce seeds. This is just one in a class of optimal time-to-reproduction problems including the optimal time for a honey bee colony to swarm and the optimal time for salmon to return from the ocean to lay eggs upriver.

Example 2   Optimal time for producing seeds

A particular plant is known to have the following growth and seed production characteristics. At time of planting ($t = 0$), the seedling has a mass of 5 grams. At time ($t > 0$) days after planting, the seedling has grown into a plant that weighs $w(t) = 5 + 400t - t^2$ grams. The plant has a gene that can be manipulated to control the age t at which the plant matures. The number of seeds $S(t)$ produced by a plant maturing at age t is

$$S(t) = 0.1w(t) = 0.5 + 40t - 0.1t^2$$

A farmer asks the geneticists to genetically engineer a plant line that accounts for the fact that on his farm, because of losses from pests, drought, and disease, only a proportion

$$P(t) = \frac{100}{100 + t}$$

of germinating seeds develop and survive to age t. What age of maturity should the geneticist select for the plants to maximize the seed production of the mature crop for the farmer?

Solution   For every N seeds that the farmer plants on his land at time $t = 0$, $N \times P(t)$ will mature at time $t > 0$. The total yield from these plants is then

$$Y(t) = N \times P(t)S(t) = \frac{100N(0.5 + 40t - 0.1t^2)}{100 + t}$$

Since N is just a scaling factor that depends on the number of acres that farmer plants, we can set it to any convenient value such as $N = 1$. To find the germination time that maximizes this yield, we need to understand the first derivative:

$$Y'(t) = \frac{d}{dt}\left[\frac{50 + 4000t - 10t^2}{100 + t}\right]$$

$$= \frac{(100 + t)(4000 - 20t) - (50 + 4000t - 10t^2)}{(100 + t)^2}$$

$$= \frac{-10t^2 - 2000t + 399950}{(100 + t)^2}$$

Thus, $Y'(t)$ exists for $t > 0$ and the derivative vanishes at solutions to the equation

$$10t^2 + 2{,}000t - 399{,}950 = 0$$

We can use technology or the quadratic formula to obtain the roots

$$t^* = -323.6 \text{ and } 123.6$$

Since $Y'(0) > 0$ and $Y'(200) < 0$, we get that Y increases on the interval $(0, 123.6)$ and decreases on the interval $(123.6, \infty)$. Hence, $Y(t)$ is maximized at $t \approx 123.6$. We verify this directly by plotting Y as a function of time, as illustrated in Figure 4.16. The vertical line indicates the optimal maturation time $t^* = 123$ days.

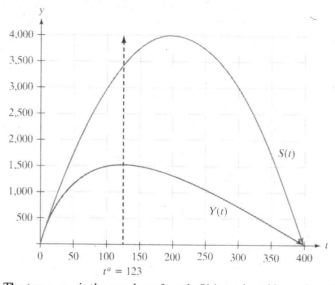

Figure 4.16 The top curve is the number of seeds $S(t)$ produced by a plant that survives to age t. The bottom curve, which has its maximum value at t^*, is the expected number of seeds that plant will produce after taking into account the probability it may die before starting to seed.

Optimal foraging and marginal value

Very often, food is not distributed homogeneously over the environment; rather, it occurs in discrete patches in the environment. For fruit bats, a patch may correspond to a fruit tree or a stand of fruit trees. For a hummingbird, which feeds on the nectar of flowers, a patch may correspond to a single flower or a field of flowers. In *optimal foraging theory*, we want to know how long an animal should continue to collect resources in a patch when it has the choice of traveling to another resource-rich patch. The question of when to leave a patch as resources in the patch are being depleted is known as the *optimal residence time* problem.

Example 3   Optimal foraging in a multi-patch environment

Figure 4.17 House martin parent feeding its young

House martins make sorties from their nests to collect food to bring back to their young. In an experiment carried out in the early 1980s, two British scientists, D. M. Bryant and A. K. Turner, found that the travel time of martins from a particular nest to nearby foraging areas ranged from half a minute to several minutes, and the weight of the load of insects the martins collected and brought back to their nest to feed their chicks (see Figure 4.17) varied between 20 and 100 mg. (See Central place foraging by swallows (Hirundinidae): The question of load size. *Animal Behavior* 30 (1982): 845–856.) On an average foraging bout, Bryant and Turner observed that these martins collected insects at the rate of (roughly) 10 mg/minute from time of departure from the nest. Assume one of these martins encounters a patch three minutes after leaving its nest, and its cumulative load of insects after foraging for t minutes is given by the function

$$B(t) = \frac{200t}{6+t} \text{ mg}$$

If the martin is trying to maximize the average load accumulated per minute since leaving its nest, then what is the optimal time for the martin to quit foraging in this patch?

Solution   Since it takes three minutes for the martin to reach the patch, the average load accumulated per minute after t minutes in the patch is $R(t) = B(t)/(t+3)$. To determine the best time to leave the patch, we need to understand the graph of $R(t)$ for $t \geq 0$. Taking the first derivative of R we get

$$R'(t) = \frac{d}{dt}\left[\frac{200t}{(6+t)(t+3)}\right]$$

$$= \frac{d}{dt}\left[\frac{200t}{t^2 + 9t + 18}\right]$$

$$= \frac{200(t^2 + 9t + 18) - (2t + 9)200t}{(t^2 + 9t + 18)^2}$$

$$= \frac{200(18 - t^2)}{(t^2 + 9t + 18)^2}$$

We have $\frac{dR}{dt} = 0$ when $t^2 = 18$. Equivalently, $t = \pm\sqrt{18} \approx \pm 4.24$ minutes. Only the positive solution is relevant. Since $R'(0) > 0$ and $R'(18) < 0$, R is increasing on the interval $(0, \sqrt{18})$ and decreasing on the interval $(\sqrt{18}, \infty)$. Hence, the maximum is achieved at $t = \sqrt{18}$ at which

$$R(\sqrt{18}) \approx 11.44 \text{ mg/minute}$$

which exceeds the background average rate of 10 mg/minute. This conclusion is reaffirmed by graphing $R(t)$ as follows:

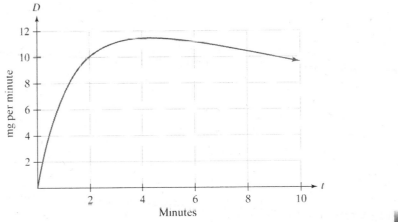

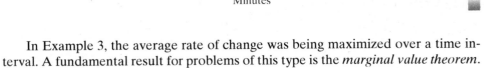

In Example 3, the average rate of change was being maximized over a time interval. A fundamental result for problems of this type is the *marginal value theorem*.

Theorem 4.2   Marginal value theorem

Let $V(t)$ be a function defined on an interval $[a, \infty)$. If $V(t)$ represents the accumulated value of the resource by time $t \geq a$, then the average rate of resource accumulation over *time $t - a$ is given by*

$$A(t) = \frac{V(t) - V(a)}{t - a}$$

If a maximum or minimum of $A(t)$ occurs at $t = b > a$ and V is differentiable at $t = b$, then b satisfies the equation

$$V'(b) = \frac{V(b) - V(a)}{b - a}$$

In other words, this maximum or minimum occurs at a time where the average rate of change equals the instantaneous rate of change.

Proof.   Since V achieves a maximum or minimum at $t = b > a$, we have $A'(b) = 0$. Computing the derivative yields

$$
\begin{aligned}
A'(b) &= \frac{d}{dt}\Big|_{t=b} \left(\frac{V(t) - V(a)}{t - a} \right) \\
&= \frac{V'(b)(b - a) - (V(b) - V(a))}{(b - a)^2} \qquad \text{by the quotient rule}
\end{aligned}
$$

Setting $A'(b) = 0$ and multiplying both sides of the equation by $(b - a)^2$, we get

$$V'(b)(b - a) - (V(b) - V(a)) = 0$$
$$V'(b)(b - a) = V(b) - V(a)$$

Equivalently, $V'(b) = \dfrac{V(b) - V(a)}{b - a}$. ∎

Example 4   Optimal foraging of great tits

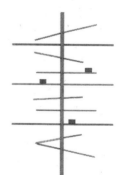

Figure 4.18 Experimental tree in Cowie's experiments.

In a classic paper on animal behavior, biologist Richard Cowie studied the foraging behavior of great tits by constructing experimental trees in an aviary (see Figure 4.18). On these experimental trees, food was placed in plastic containers in a manner that would allow Cowie to manipulate the average travel time T between food containers. Through these experiments, Cowie estimated that the energy gained by a bird after eating from a container for $t \geq 0$ seconds is

$$E(t) = 6.3587(1 - e^{-0.0081\,t}) \text{ calories}$$

Assuming the great tits are maximizing their average energy gain, do the following:

a. Use the marginal value theorem to determine the relationship between the average travel time T and the optimal residence time t in a patch.

b. Solve for T in terms of the optimal residence time and plot it.

c. Discuss your findings with respect to data collected by Cowie, as depicted in Figure 4.19.

Solution

a. Assume that at $t = 0$ the bird arrives at a food container. Since it takes T seconds to get to a container, we are interested in the time interval $[-T, \infty)$ where $t = -T$ corresponds to the moment that the bird begins traveling to the container. Since we assume there is no energy gain during the flight, we define $E(t) = 0$ for $t \leq 0$.

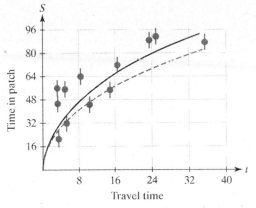

Figure 4.19 Amount of time spent by great tits in a foraging patch is plotted as the solid line through the data (solid points with measurement error bars) as a function of the amount of time taken by individuals to reach the patch. The dotted line is discussed in the solution to part **c** of Example 4.

Data Source: R. Cowie, "Optimal Foraging in Great Tits (*Parus major*)," *Nature* 268 (1977): 137–139.

Clearly, the maximum cannot occur during the interval $[-T, 0]$. By the marginal value theorem with $a = -T$, the time t at which the maximum occurs must satisfy

$$E'(t) = \frac{E(t) - E(-T)}{t + T}$$

$$0.0515e^{-0.0081t} = \frac{6.3587(1 - e^{-0.0081t})}{t + T}$$

b. Solving for the average travel time T in terms of the optimal residence time t yields

$$0.0515e^{-0.0081t} = \frac{6.3587(1 - e^{-0.0081t})}{t + T}$$

$$t + T = \frac{6.3587(1 - e^{-0.0081t})}{0.0515e^{-0.0081t}}$$

$$t + T = 123.5(e^{0.0081t} - 1)$$

$$T = 123.5(e^{0.0081t} - 1) - t$$

Plotting T as a function of t yields this graph:

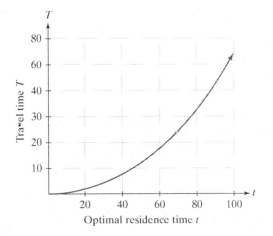

c. The graph plotted in part **b** implies that as the average travel time T between patches increases, the optimal residence time t within a patch should increase at a greater than linear rate (i.e., it is concave up). Notice that in the graph of Cowie's data in Figure 4.19 the axes are switched, so that the inverse of our function $T = f(t)$ is plotted rather than the function itself as the dashed line in this figure. While five of the twelve data points are very close to the dashed line, the remaining seven data points lie significantly above it. In other words, for these seven experiments, the birds were spending more time in the patches than predicted by the model. One possible explanation for this discrepancy is that the model does not account for the energetic costs of traveling. Cowie adjusted the model to account for these energetic costs and the resulting prediction is plotted as a solid curve in Figure 4.19. In Problem 4 of this section's problem set, you will be asked to redo the analysis in this example in a way that accounts for these energetic costs.

The marginal value theorem has a simple graphical interpretation, which is explored in the next example.

Example 5   Optimal time to harvest

Over a six-decade period, a forestry company has collected data on the profit $P(t)$ of stands of trees harvested at various ages t (units are decades). Initially, $P(t)$ is zero because the costs required to bring in the heavy equipment needed to harvest the trees exceeds the value of the harvest itself, and the company will not harvest before making a profit. Once the trees reach a certain size, a profit is possible and it steadily increases as the stand of trees ages. The company found that the function that best fit its data has the following graph:

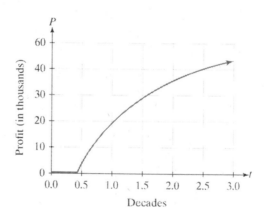

where the profit P is measured in thousands of U.S. dollars and t is measured in decades.

The company wants to maximize the profits it makes per unit time. Write the function $A(t)$ that the company wants to maximize and illustrate where the maximum occurs graphically.

Solution   The company wants to maximize the average rate of accumulation of profit $P(t)$, which is $A(t) = P(t)/t$. Since $P(0) = 0$, we can apply the marginal value theorem, which asserts that the average rate of change $P(a)/a$ equal the instantaneous rate of change $P'(a)$, where $t = a$ is the optimal harvesting time. Graphically, this corresponds to the line from $(0, 0)$ to $(a, P(a))$ being tangent to the graph of $P(t)$ at $t = a$. To find the optimal value a, we take a ruler and place one end at $(0, 0)$ and rotate the ruler until the line determined by its edge is tangent to the graph of $P(t)$. Doing so yields the following plot:

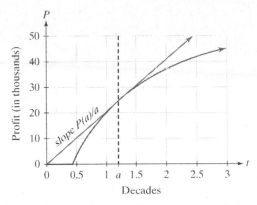

where the optimal time to harvest is approximately $a \approx 1.2$ decades, about 12 years.

Our final example in this section introduces the concept of discounting when optimizing a *sustainable stream of revenue* calculated for all time in the future. Discounting arises if someone promises to pay you D dollars next year, and the current interest rate compounded continuously is $r\%$; then this person should be willing to receive $De^{-r/100}$ dollars now. Namely, if this person took the $De^{-r/100}$ dollars now and invested it, then a year later the investment would yield $e^{r/100}$ dollars for each dollar invested. Hence, a year later the person would have $e^{r/100}De^{-r/100} = D$ dollars. As a result of this reasoning, economists use the *discount factor* $e^{-\delta t}$, where $\delta = r/100$ to reduce D dollars needed at time t in the future to their current value $De^{-\delta t}$ dollars now.

Example 6   Optimal rotation period for a plantation

In the mid-nineteenth century, a German forester by the name of Faustmann developed a theory for the optimal rotation period of a plantation. He calculated that if one planted a stand and harvested it every T years, and received the same value $V(T)$ each time, then the sum of all the discounted amounts (i.e., the sum of $V(T)e^{-\delta T}$ obtained after T years, $V(T)e^{-\delta 2T}$ obtained after $2T$ years, $V(T)e^{-\delta 3T}$ obtained after $3T$ years, and so on for all time into the future) constitutes the so-called *present value* $P(T)$ of the stand given by the formula

$$P(T) = \frac{V(T)}{e^{\delta T} - 1}$$

Now continue his analysis by doing the following:

a. Using his formula for $P(T)$, find a general expression for the optimal stand rotation period T^* that is defined to be the value of T on $(0, \infty)$ that maximizes the present value $P(T)$ of the stand.

b. What does the expression in part **a** imply as $\delta \to 0$?

c. Use your technology to find the optimal rotation period when

$$V(T) = \left(\frac{2T^{5/2}}{1 + T^2} - 1\right)$$

and the discount rate is $\delta = 0.1$.

Solution

a. The optimal rotation period T^* is an extremum of $P(T)$. Thus, if a maximum exists on an open interval, T^* will satisfy the equation $P'(T) = 0$ where

$$P'(T) = \frac{d}{dT}\left[\frac{V(T)}{e^{\delta T} - 1}\right]$$
$$= \frac{V'(T)(e^{\delta t} - 1) - V(T)\delta e^{\delta T}}{(e^{\delta T} - 1)^2} \qquad \textit{quotient rule}$$

Therefore, if $\delta > 0$, $P'(T) = 0$ implies that

$$V'(T) = \frac{\delta e^{\delta T}}{e^{\delta T} - 1} V(T)$$

b. Using l'Hôpital's rule to calculate the limit as δ approaches 0, we obtain that the optimal rotation period T^* satisfies the equation

$$V'(T) = V(T) \lim_{\delta \to 0} \frac{\delta e^{\delta T}}{e^{\delta T} - 1} = \frac{V(T)}{T}$$

By the marginal value theorem, this equation implies that T^* maximizes the average profit accumulation rate over each harvesting period in the limit $\delta = 0$.

c. From part **a** and the specific form for $V(T)$, the optimal rotation period when $\delta = 0.1$ is the solution to

$$\left(\frac{2T^{3/2}}{2} \right) \frac{T^2 + 5}{(1 + T^2)^2} = \left(\frac{2T^{5/2}}{1 + T^2} - 1 \right) \left(\frac{0.1 e^{0.1T}}{e^{0.1T} - 1} \right)$$

$$T^{3/2}(T^2 + 5)(e^{0.1T} - 1) = 0.1(1 + T^2)(2T^{5/2} - T^2 - 1)e^{0.1T}$$

$$T^* = 2.68361 \quad \textit{using technology}$$

PROBLEM SET 4.4

Level 1 DRILL PROBLEMS

In Problems 1 to 6, the amount of energy a hummingbird gains after remaining in a patch for t seconds is given. For each problem, find how long a hummingbird should stay in a patch if it wants to maximize its average energy intake rate.

1. The travel time between patches is 15 seconds and

$$f(t) = \frac{180t}{1 + 0.15t} \quad \text{calories}$$

2. The travel time between patches is 5 seconds and

$$f(t) = \frac{180t}{1 + 0.15t} \quad \text{calories}$$

3. The travel time between patches is 10 seconds and

$$f(t) = \frac{360t}{1 + 0.5t} \quad \text{calories}$$

4. The travel time between patches is 5 seconds and

$$f(t) = \frac{360t}{1 + 0.5t} \quad \text{calories}$$

5. The travel time between patches is 5 seconds and

$$f(t) = \frac{360t}{1 + 0.3t} \quad \text{calories}$$

6. The travel time between patches is 10 seconds and

$$f(t) = \frac{360t}{1 + 0.3t} \quad \text{calories}$$

In Problems 7 to 10, rework Example 5 with the given graphs.

7.

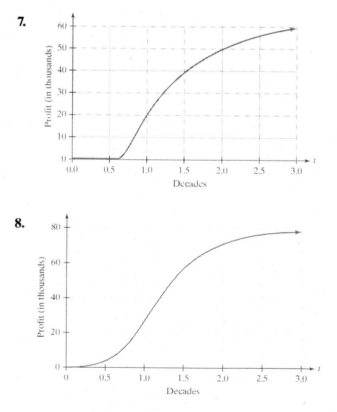

8.

9.

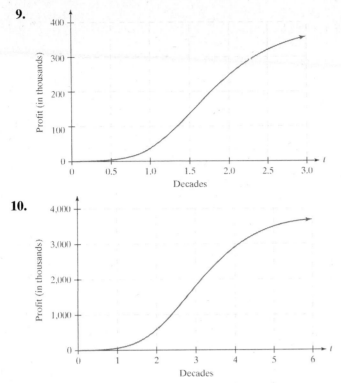

10.

Assume the house martins in Example 3 can choose between two patches. In Problems 11 to 16, the time to fly to a patch and the energy yield as a function of patch residence time (t minutes) are given for two patches. If an individual can visit only one patch and wants to maximize the average amount of calories it receives, then which patch of each pair should it choose?

11. $B(t) = \dfrac{150t}{3+t}$ calories with a travel time of 2 minutes or $B(t) = \dfrac{250t}{5+t}$ calories with a travel time of 3 minutes.

12. $B(t) = \dfrac{150t}{3+t}$ calories with a travel time of 1 minute or $B(t) = \dfrac{250t}{5+t}$ calories with a travel time of 2 minutes.

13. $B(t) = \dfrac{150t}{3+t}$ calories with a travel time of 3 minutes or $B(t) = \dfrac{150t}{4+t}$ calories with a travel time of 2 minutes.

14. $B(t) = \dfrac{150t}{3+t}$ calories with a travel time of 2 minutes or $B(t) = \dfrac{150t}{4+t}$ calories with a travel time of 3 minutes.

15. $B(t) = \dfrac{250t}{5+t}$ calories with a travel time of 2 minutes or $B(t) = \dfrac{150t}{4+t}$ calories with a travel time of 3 minutes.

16. $B(t) = \dfrac{250t}{4+t}$ calories with a travel time of 2 minutes or $B(t) = \dfrac{150t}{4+t}$ calories with a travel time of 15 seconds.

In Example 5 (optimal time to harvest), assume that the profit function P(t) has the form specified in Problems 17 to 22. For these profit functions, find the optimal age at which to harvest the stands of trees to maximize profit where t is measured in decades.

17. $P(t) = \dfrac{2t^{5/2}}{1+t^2} - 1$ whenever $\dfrac{2t^{5/2}}{1+t^2} - 1 > 0$ and 0 otherwise.

18. $P(t) = \dfrac{3t^{5/2}}{1+t^2} - 1$ whenever $\dfrac{3t^{5/2}}{1+t^2} - 1$ is positive and 0 otherwise.

19. $P(t) = \dfrac{2t^{5/2}}{1+2t^2} - 1$ whenever $\dfrac{2t^{5/2}}{1+2t^2} - 1$ is positive and 0 otherwise.

20. $P(t) = \dfrac{3t^{5/2}}{1+2t^2} - 1$ whenever $\dfrac{3t^{5/2}}{1+2t^2} - 1$ is positive and 0 otherwise.

21. $P(t) = \dfrac{5t^{5/2}}{1+2t^2} - 2$ whenever $\dfrac{5t^{5/2}}{1+2t^2} - 2$ is positive and 0 otherwise.

22. $P(t) = \dfrac{4t^{5/2}}{1+2t^2} - 3$ whenever $\dfrac{4t^{5/2}}{1+2t^2} - 3$ is positive and 0 otherwise.

23. Find the optimal rotation period for a forest stand that has a value $V(T) = \left(\dfrac{2T^{5/2}}{1+T^2} - 1\right)$ when $\delta = 0.2$.

24. Find the optimal rotation period for a forest stand that has a value $V(T) = \left(\dfrac{2T^{5/2}}{1+T^2} - 3/2\right)$ when $\delta = 0.1$.

25. Find the optimal rotation period for a forest stand that has a value $V(T) = \left(\dfrac{(7/3)T^{5/2}}{1+T^2} - 1\right)$ when $\delta = 0.15$.

26. Find the optimal rotation period for a forest stand that has a value $V(T) = \left(\dfrac{(5/3)T^{5/2}}{2/3+T^2} - 1\right)$ when $\delta = 0.1$.

Level 2 APPLIED AND THEORY PROBLEMS

27. At the National Council of Teachers of Mathematics (NCTM) illuminations website, students are encouraged to collect data on how many drops are required to break a blanched peanut in two pieces. The sample data provided at this website are shown in the following graph.

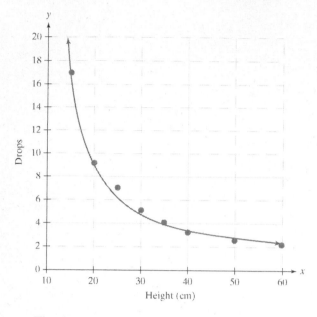

The data can be modeled by the function

$$f(h) = 0.8 + \frac{80}{h - 10} \text{ drops}$$

where h is the height in centimeters. Suppose that the "peanut hummingbird" collects peanuts and wants to minimize the amount of work required to break a peanut into two halves. Determine the height which minimizes the amount of work to break open the peanuts.

28. In Example 4, we found how the optimal residence time in a patch for a great tit depended on the travel time between patches. Although our prediction described the data reasonably well, more than half of the data points lay above the optimal curve. Cowie proposed that part of the reason for this result was that the birds expend energy traveling between patches and searching for food within a patch. In this problem, determine how these expenditures of energy influence the optimal residence time. Let

$$E(t) = 6.3587(1 - e^{-0.0081\,t}) \text{ calories}$$

denote the amount of energy gained by a bird after residing in a patch for t seconds. Assume that the bird requires T seconds to travel the patch. Cowie found that great tits expend approximately 0.697 calories per second while traveling between patches and expend approximately 0.155 calories per second while searching for food in a patch.

a. Write a function $V(t)$ that represents the average gain in energy in a patch after residing there for $t \geq 0$ seconds.

b. Use the marginal value theorem to find an expression relating the optimal residence time t to the travel time T.

c. Compare your solution to the solution found in Example 4.

29. Suppose the crop developed by plant geneticists, as discussed in Example 2—that is, the weight of the crop t days after planting satisfies the growth equation $w(t) = 5 + 400t - t^2$—is grown in a location that is relatively pest free, so that the proportion of germinating seeds is

$$P(t) = \frac{900}{900 + t}$$

The crop, however, must be harvested on or before the first frosty day of fall. Suppose the crop has relative value 1 when harvested at its optimum time of maturity, as represented by the day T on which the yield $Y = aw(t)P(t)$ is maximized and that this value is reduced by $10t_e\%$, where t_e is the number of days prior to T that harvest actually occurs, so that the relative crop value is 0 if harvested at time $T - 10$ or earlier.

a. What is the value of T?

b. If the expected number of days t_s in the growing season—that is the number of frost-free days plus 1—is equally likely to fall on any day from day 165 to day 190, then what is the expected value of the harvest in any year?

30. When a codling moth larva hatches from its egg, it goes looking for an apple. The period between hatching and finding an apple is called the *search period*. The search period S seems to be a function of the temperature, as shown in Table 4.5.

Table 4.5 Search period for the codling moth

Temperature	S, in days
20° C	0.129
21° C	0.122
22° C	0.116
23° C	0.112
24° C	0.109
25° C	0.106
26° C	0.105
27° C	0.104
28° C	0.104
29° C	0.105
30° C	0.106

Source: P.L. Shaffer and H.J. Gold, 1985. "A simulation model of population dynamics of the codling moth, *Cydia pomonella*" *Ecological Modeling* 30:247–274.

Following the lead of Shaffer and Gold (see Section 4.2, Example 8), find $1/S$ for each data value and then use technology to fit a quadratic function to the data. Find the largest and smallest value of this fitted function S.

31. In a plantation of a particular species of trees, a forest economist estimated the number of board feet

that can be harvested as a function of the age of the plantation. Data are given in Table 4.6. By using your technology to fit a quadratic function to the data, estimate at what age the plantation should be harvested to maximize the yield of board per acre.

Table 4.6 Harvest yield for a lumber crop

Age (years)	Yield (board feet per acre)
15	6013
20	7021
25	8793
30	9411
35	9786
40	9958
45	9921
50	9766

32. By using your technology to fit a cubic equation to the data in Problem 31, find the age in $[15, 50]$ at which the plantation represented by the data should be harvested to maximize the yield.

33. By using your technology to fit a quartic equation to the data in Problem 31, find the age in $[15, 50]$ at which the plantation represented by this data should be harvested to maximize the yield.

34. By using your technology to fit a quintic equation to the data in Problem 31, find the age in $[15, 50]$ at which the plantation represented by the data should be harvested to maximize the yield.

4.5 Linearization and Difference Equations

As we have seen in earlier chapters, difference equations $x_{n+1} = f(x_n)$ are useful for describing biological dynamics. The simplest dynamics occur at an equilibrium, because by definition, these equilibria are the solutions of the difference equation that remain constant for all time. Specifically, if a given first value x_0 satisfies $x_0 = f(x_0)$, then our difference equation implies $x_1 = x_0$. Repeated application results in $x_{n+1} = x_n = \cdots = x_0$ for all $n > 0$.

While equilibria may be easily identified, as discussed in Section 1.7, by solving the equation $x = f(x)$, their biological relevance depends on their *stability*. Many biological systems, when perturbed, naturally return to their equilibrium state. The temperature of the human body is a case in point. If a person's temperature is perturbed because of an infection, it returns to its equilibrium value of 98.6 °F once he or she is well again. Not all equilibria, however, are stable. If we stand up a six-month-old child, the child may stay upright for a second or two, but until the child is around a year old, he or she will soon fall over. Standing vertically without feedback control from muscles constantly moving to correct the tendency to fall over is an unstable situation.

Thus, when a biological system is perturbed away from equilibrium, it may do one of two things. A system may return to the equilibrium state, in which case the equilibrium is considered *stable*. Alternatively, even if the perturbation is small, a system may continue to drift away from the equilibrium. In this case, the equilibrium is *unstable*. In this section, we make the notion of stability precise and provide a simple algebraic method for checking stability—a method that relies on linearizing the difference equation near the equilibrium. These ideas and methods are applied to models of population growth and population genetics.

We conclude the section by considering another application of linearization and difference equations, namely, numerically solving for the roots of a nonlinear equation. This numerical method is an important alternative to the bisection method presented in Example 10 of Section 2.3.

Equilibrium stability

We begin with the following example, which motivates the notion of a stable equilibrium.

Example 1   Logistic equation

In Example 7 of Section 2.5, we introduced the *discrete logistic equation*, which is a simple model of population growth. If x_n denotes the population density (e.g., average number of individuals per acre) in the nth generation, then the model is given by

$$x_{n+1} = x_n + r x_n \left(1 - \frac{x_n}{K}\right) \qquad x_0 \text{ specified}$$

where r is the per capita growth rate at low densities and K is the carrying capacity of the population. The only two equilibrium solutions are $x = 0$ and $x = K$. For $K = 100$ and $r = 0.5, 1.5, 3.0$, simulate the model for the initial condition $x_0 = 99$. Discuss what you find.

Solution   Simulating the model with $x_0 = 99$ for twenty-five iterations yields the following figures:

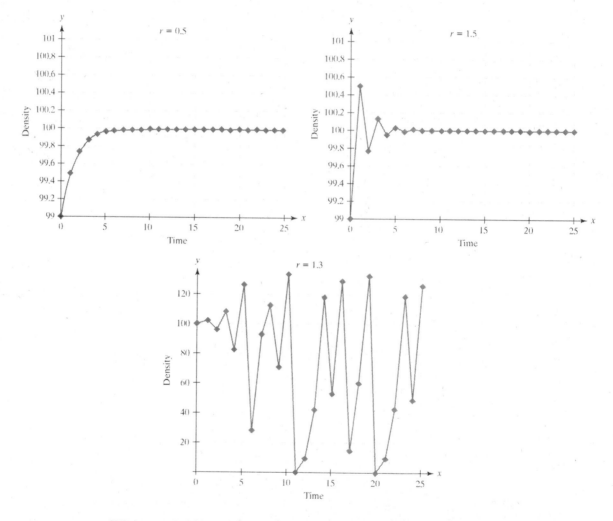

When $r = 0.5$, the population density gradually increases from the density 99 to the equilibrium density 100. When $r = 1.5$, the population density exhibits oscillations that dampen toward the equilibrium density 100. When $r = 3$, the population exhibits irregular oscillations that never approach the equilibrium density 100, despite having started near this equilibrium density.

Example 1 illustrates that some solutions starting near the equilibria approach the equilibrium, while other solutions starting near an equilibrium move away. These observations suggest the following definitions.

<table>
<tr><td>**Equilibrium Stability**</td><td></td></tr>
</table>

An equilibrium to $x_{n+1} = f(x_n)$, that is a solution satisfying $x^* = f(x^*)$, is:

stable provided that there exists an open interval (a, b) containing x^* such that $\lim_{n \to \infty} x_n = x^*$ and x_1 lies in (a, b); whenever x_0 lies in (a, b);

unstable provided that there is an interval (a, b) containing x^* such that all solutions x_n eventually leave (a, b) whenever x_0 lies in (a, b) but $x_0 \neq x^*$;

Note: The second condition that "x_1 lies in (a, b) whenever x_0 lines in (a, b)" is equivalent to the image of (a, b) under f lies in (a, b).

Stated more simply, stability of an equilibrium means that if the solution starts near the equilibrium, then it remains nears the equilibrium and asymptotically approaches the equilibrium. Alternatively, solutions starting near (but not at) an unstable equilibrium eventually move further away from the unstable equilibrium.

Example 2   Stability the hard way

Find the equilibria of the following difference equations and verify stability using the definitions of stable and unstable.

a. $x_{n+1} = \dfrac{x_n}{2}$

b. $x_{n+1} = x_n^2$

Solution

a. The equilibria are given by solutions of $x = x/2$. Hence, the only equilibrium is $x = 0$. Given any x_0, and using the methods developed in Section 1.7, it follows that $x_n = \dfrac{1}{2^n} x_0$. Therefore, given any $a > 0$, we get that $\lim_{n \to \infty} x_n = 0$ for any x_0 in $(-a, a)$. In addition, the image of $(-a, a)$ under f is $\left(-\dfrac{a}{2}, \dfrac{a}{2}\right)$. Therefore, x^* is stable.

b. The equilibria of $x_{n+1} = x_n^2$ must sastisfy $x = x^2$. Hence, the equilibria are given by $x = 0$ and $x = 1$. For any x_0, we have that $x_1 = x_0^2, x_2 = x_1^2 = x_0^4, x_3 = x_2^2 = x_0^8$. Hence, $x_n = x_0^{2n}$. If x_0 lies in the interval $(-1, 1)$, then $\lim_{n \to \infty} x_0^{2n} = 0$. Moreover, the image of $(-1, 1)$ under the function $f(x) = x^2$ is $[0, 1)$, which lies in $(-1, 1)$. Hence, 0 is a stable equilibrium for this difference equation. For any $x_0 > 1$ or $x_0 < -1$, $x_n = x_0^{2n}$ approaches $+\infty$ as n approaches ∞. Hence, for any initial condition near 1, the solution moves away from 1 so that the equilibrium 1 is unstable.

Example 3   Stability of linear difference equations

Consider the linear difference equation

$$x_{n+1} = r x_n$$

For this difference equation, the origin, $x = 0$, is always an equilibrium. Determine for which r values, the origin is stable or unstable.

Solution   The solution of this difference equation is given by $x_n = r^n x_0$. Suppose $x_0 \neq 0$. If $|r| < 1$, then $|x_n| = |r|^n |x_0|$ is decreasing to zero at a geometric rate. Therefore, if $|r| < 1$, then $x = 0$ is stable. Alternatively, if $|r| > 1$, then $|x_n| = |r|^n |x_0|$ is increasing without bound. Hence, $x = 0$ is unstable when $|r| > 1$. If $r = 1$, then $x_n = x_0$ for all n. Hence, x_n neither approaches or moves away from 0, so that 0 is neither stable or unstable when $r = 1$. Similarly, if $r = -1$, you can show that $x = 0$ is neither stable nor unstable.

Stability via linearization

Stability of an equilibrium can be verified directly using the definition, but this method can be challenging. To make things easier, we take advantage of linearization and our work in Example 3.

Suppose x^* is an equilibrium of $x_{n+1} = f(x_n)$ and f is differentiable at x^*. If we approximate f by its tangent line at $x = x^*$, we get

$$f(x) \approx f(x^*) + f'(x^*)(x - x^*)$$
$$= x^* + f'(x^*)(x - x^*) \quad \text{since } f(x^*) = x^*$$

Using this linear approximation and setting $r = f'(x^*)$, we get

$$x_{n+1} \approx x^* + r(x_n - x^*)$$

Equivalently,

$$(x_{n+1} - x^*) \approx r(x_n - x^*)$$

Using the change of variables $y_n = x_n - x^*$, we get

$$y_{n+1} \approx r y_n$$

Example 3 suggests that if $|r| < 1$ and x_0 is sufficiently close to x^*, then we expect that y_n approaches zero at a geometric rate. Equivalently, since we defined $y_n = x_n - x^*$, it follows that x_n approaches x^* at a geometric rate. Alternatively, if $|r| > 1$ and x_0 is sufficiently close to x^*, then we expect that y_n increases initially at a geometric rate. Equivalently, x_n initially moves away from x^* at a geometric rate. As it turns out, all of these statements hold provided that x_n is sufficiently close to x^*, as the following theorem states.

Theorem 4.3   Stability via linearization theorem

If $x_{n+1} = f(x_n)$ has an equilibrium at $x = x^*$ and $r = f'(x^*)$ exists, then x^* is stable if $|r| < 1$ and unstable if $|r| > 1$.

Theorem 4.3 is inconclusive about stability if $|f'(x^*)| = 1$.

Example 4   Logistic revisited

Consider the logistic difference equation

$$x_{n+1} = x_n + r x_n \left(\frac{x_n}{100} \right)$$

with $r > 0$. Determine for which r values $x^* = 100$ is stable.

Solution   Let $f(x) = x + rx \left(\dfrac{x_n}{100} \right)$. To determine whether an equilibrium is stable or not, we need to compute

$$f'(x) = 1 + r - \frac{rx}{50} = 1 + r \left(1 - \frac{x}{50} \right)$$

and evaluate at $x = 100$

$$f'(100) = 1 + r(1 - 2) = 1 - r$$

For stability, we need that $|1 - r| < 1$. Equivalently,

$$-1 < 1 - r < 1$$
$$-2 < -r < 0$$
$$2 > r > 0$$

Hence, the equilibrium $x^* = 100$ is stable provided that $0 < r < 2$ and unstable provided that $r > 2$. This conclusion is consistent with the simulations in Example 1.

Indeed, for $r = 0.5$ and $r = 1.5$, the simulations approached the equilibrium $x^* = 100$. However, for $r = 3$, the simulation oscillated irregularly and never converged to any density.

Example 5   Stability of insect population dynamics

Biology professor T. S. Bellows investigated the ability of several different difference equation models to describe the population dynamics of various insect species. (See T. S. Bellows, "The Descriptive Properties of Some Models for Density Dependence." *The Journal of Animal Ecology* 50(1) (Feb. 1981), 139–156) He found that the so-called generalized Beverton-Holt model provided the best mathematical description for the insect species that he studied. If x_n denotes the population density in the nth generation, then the model is of the form

$$x_{n+1} = \frac{r x_n}{1 + x_n^b}$$

where r is the intrinsic fitness of the population and b measures the abruptness of density dependence. For three insect species, Bellows made the following parameter estimates:

- Budworm moth: $r = 3.5$ and $b = 2.7$
- Colorado potato beetle: $r = 75$ and $b = 4.8$
- Meadow plant bug: $r = 2.2$ and $b = 1.4$

These insects are shown in Figure 4.20.

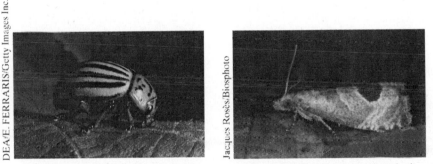

Figure 4.20 Photos of the budworm moth (left), Colorado potato beetle (center), and the meadow plant bug (right).

a. Use these parameter estimates to determine which population, according to the model, supports a stable equilibrium.

b. For the species that do not support a stable equilibrium, simulate their dynamics.

Solution

a. To begin with, we need to find the equilibria of the model that must satisfy $x = r \dfrac{x}{1 + x^b}$. Equivalently, $x = 0$ or

$$1 = \frac{r}{1 + x^b}$$
$$1 + x^b = r$$
$$x^b = r - 1$$
$$x = (r - 1)^{1/b}$$

Hence, for the budworm moth, the equilibria are given by

$$x = 0 \text{ and } x = 2.5^{1/2.7} \approx 1.40$$

For the Colorado potato beetle, the equilibria are given by

$$x = 0 \text{ and } x = 74^{1/4.8} \approx 2.45$$

For the meadow plant bug, the equilibria are given by

$$x = 0 \text{ and } x = 1.2^{1/1.4} \approx 1.14$$

Let $f(x) = \dfrac{rx}{1 + x^b}$. To determine the stability of these equilibria, we need to evaluate the derivative

$$f'(x) = r\frac{1 + x^b - bx^{b-1}x}{(1 + x^b)^2}$$

$$= r\frac{1 + (1 - b)x^b}{(1 + x^b)^2}$$

at the equilibria. Since $f'(0) = r$ and $r > 1$ for all three species, 0 is an unstable equilibrium for all three species.

For the budworm moth, $f'(1.4) \approx -0.93$. Since $|-0.93| = 0.93 < 1$, the equilibrium $x \approx 1.4$ is stable for the budworm moth model. For the Colorado potato beetle, $f'(2.45) \approx -3.75$. Since $|-3.75| > 1$, the equilibrium $x \approx 2.45$ is unstable for the Colorado potato beetle model. Therefore, the Colorado potato beetle model has no stable equilibria. For the meadow plant bug, $f'(1.14) \approx 0.24$. Since $0.24 < 1$, the equilibrium $x \approx 1.14$ is stable for the meadow plant bug model.

b. Since all of the equilibria for the Colorado potato beetle model are unstable, we can ask the question: What is the long-term behavior of a nonequilibrium solution? Simulating the model with $x_0 = 2.4$ (a value "close to" the equilibrium 2.45) yields the following numerical solution.

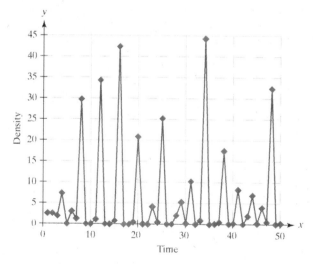

This figure suggests that the Colorado potato beetle is subject to episodic population outbreaks, which is a characteristic associated with agricultural insect pests.

Stability of monotone difference equations

A special, and important, class of difference equations $x_{n+1} = f(x_n)$ was introduced in Section 2.5. For these difference equations, f is a continuous and increasing function over some domain of interest. Within this domain, the solutions to this difference equation are *monotone* (i.e., either increasing for all *n* or decreasing for all *n*). As a consequence of this monotonicity, it is possible to provide a simple graphical approach to stability for these difference equations.

Theorem 4.4   Stability of monotone difference equations theorem

Let f be a continuous, increasing function on an interval (a, b). *Let* x^* *be an equilibrium for* $x_{n+1} = f(x_n)$ *that lies in* (a, b). *Then* x^* *is*

stable *if* $f(x) > x$ *for x in* (a, x^*) *and* $f(x) < x$ *for x in* (x^*, b). *In particular,* $\lim_{n \to \infty} x_n = x^*$ *whenever* x_0 *lies in* (a, b).

unstable *if* $f(x) < x$ *for x in* (a, x^*) *and* $f(x) > x$ *for x in* (x^*, b). *In particular,* x_n *leaves* (a, b) *for some n whenever* x_0 *lies in* (a, x^*) *or* (x^*, b).

Combined with the monotone convergence theorem in Section 2.5, this stability theorem allows us to determine the fate of solutions to difference equations where *f* is a continuous, increasing function.

Example 6   Graphical approach to stability

Consider the difference equation

$$x_{n+1} = f(x_n)$$

where the graph of *f* is given by

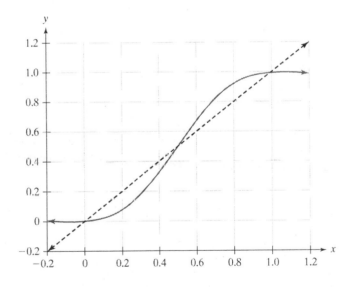

Assuming *f* is increasing on $[0, 1]$, identify the equilibria and determine their stability.

Solution   The equilibria correspond to points where the graph of $y = x$ intersects with the graph of $y = f(x)$. These intersections occur at $x = 0, \frac{1}{2}$, and 1. Inspection of the graph of *f* yields that $f(x) > x$ for *x* in $(-0.2, 0)$ and $(0.5, 1)$. Alternatively, $f(x) < x$ for *x* in $(0, 0.5)$ and $(1, 1.2)$. Applying the stability theorem for monotone difference equations implies that 0 and 1 are stable, while 0.5 is unstable. Moreover, x_n converges to 0 whenever x_0 lies in $(-0.2, 0.5)$ and x_n converges to 1 whenever x_0 lies in $(0.5, 1.2)$.

We can verify this stability with cobwebbing. Cobwebbing with an x_0 slightly above 0.5 and an x_0 slightly below 0.5 leads to the following figures:

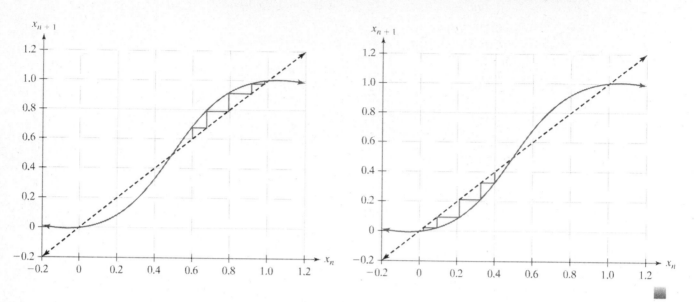

As we saw in Example 5 of Section 1.7, we can construct models that allow us to trace the fate of alleles that code for genes affecting the biological fitness (i.e., the ability to survive and reproduce) of individuals. Recalling our discussion in Section 1.7 regarding genetic models of diploid organisms, we consider an allele that codes for a particular trait. If the frequency of this allele in the population is $x \in [0, 1]$, then a well-known model describing how the frequency of this trait changes from generation n to generation $n + 1$ in a very large (essentially infinite) randomly mating population is

$$x_{n+1} = f(x_n) \quad \text{with} \quad f(x) = \frac{w_1 x^2 + x(1 - x)}{w_1 x^2 + 2x(1 - x) + w_2(1 - x)^2}$$

where w_1 and w_2 are the fitness of individuals who, respectively, have two or no copies, relative to individuals who have only one copy, of the allele in question. Referring back to the equation given in Example 5 of Section 1.7 regarding the spread of a deleterious mutant allele, we see that the equation is the same as the above equation for the special case $w_1 = 0$ and $w_2 = 1$. This case is equivalent to the statement that the allele a in question is recessive (heterozygous Aa individuals are not affected) and lethal (aa individuals die before reproducing). Despite the drastic effect of this lethal allele a, we found that it can take a very long time for it to be eliminated from the population. In the next example, we consider a variant of this model in which the allele that is lethal in the homozygous state actually confers a benefit on an individual when combined with the other allele (i.e., when in the heterozygous state).

Example 7   Fate of the sickle cell allele

In areas of the world where malaria occurs, it is known that individuals who have one sickle cell allele are more resistant to malaria than those who do not have the allele. On the other hand, individuals who have two sickle cell alleles suffer from sickle cell anemia, which can cause premature death. Let x denote the frequency of the allele that does not cause sickle cell anemia. Assume when malaria is prevalent that individuals not protected by the sickle cell allele will, on average, have 10% fewer progeny than individuals who have one sickle cell allele—that is, $w_1 = 0.9$. For the sake of simplicity, we assume that individuals with sickle anemia die before they reproduce (even though, in reality, this assumption is too extreme)—that is, $w_2 = 0$.

a. Write and simplify the difference equation, $x_{n+1} = f(x_n)$, under the assumption that $x \neq 0$.

b. Verify that f is increasing on the interval $(0, 1]$.

c. Find the equilibria on the interval $(0, 1]$ and determine their stability.

d. Interpret your results.

Solution

a. Under the assumption that $w_1 = 0.9$, $w_2 = 0$, and $x \neq 0$, we get

$$f(x) = \frac{0.9\, x^2 + x(1 - x)}{0.9\, x^2 + 2x(1 - x) + 0 \cdot (1 - x)^2}$$

$$= \frac{-0.1\, x^2 + x}{-1.1\, x^2 + 2x}$$

$$= \frac{-0.1\, x + 1}{-1.1\, x + 2} \qquad \textit{assuming } x \neq 0$$

b. To verify that $f(x)$ is increasing on the interval, we can determine the derivative of $f(x)$:

$$f'(x) = \frac{d}{dx}\left[\frac{-0.1\, x + 1}{-1.1\, x + 2}\right]$$

$$= \frac{-0.1(-1.1\, x + 2) + 1.1(-0.1\, x + 1)}{(2 - 1.1\, x)^2}$$

$$= \frac{0.11\, x - 0.2 - 0.11\, x + 1.1}{(2 - 1.1\, x)^2}$$

$$= \frac{0.9}{(2 - 1.1\, x)^2}$$

Hence, $f'(x) > 0$ on $(0, 1]$ and f is increasing on this interval.

c. To find the equilibria in $(0, 1]$, we solve $x = f(x)$:

$$x = \frac{-0.1\, x + 1}{-1.1\, x + 2} \qquad \textit{by definition of equilibrium}$$

$$-1.1\, x^2 + 2x = -0.1\, x + 1$$

$$0 = 1.1\, x^2 - 2.1\, x + 1 = (1.1\, x - 1)(x - 1)$$

Hence, the equilibria are given by $x = 1$ and $x = 1/1.1 \approx 0.91$.

To determine their stability, we can use the derivative calculated in part **b.** We have $f'(1) = \dfrac{0.9}{0.9^2} = \dfrac{1}{0.9} \approx 1.11$. Hence, $x = 1$ is unstable. Alternatively, $f'(1/1.1) = 0.9$ so that $x = 0.91$ is stable. In fact, these calculations imply that $f(x) < x$ on the interval $(0.91, 1)$ and $f(x) > x$ on the interval $(0, 0.91)$. Hence, the stability theorem for monotone difference equations implies that $\lim_{n \to \infty} x_n = 0.91$ whenever x_0 lies in $(0, 1)$.

d. The results imply that as long as both alleles are present in the population, they will persist, and the frequency of the sickle cell anemia allele will approach a value of $1 - 1/1.1 \approx 0.09$. Hence, under the assumptions made, we expect approximately 9% of this population to have the sickle cell allele. ■

Newton's method

The final application of linearization to difference equations is to illustrate the inner workings of an algorithm called **Newton's method**. This method is used to find the roots of nonlinear algebraic equations of the form $f(x) = 0$ that are too difficult or impossible to solve algebraically. The algorithm is based on the *Newton-Raphson* difference equation, which we now describe. Suppose our initial guess for the solution of $f(x) = 0$ is $x = x_0$. Assuming that this guess is not the solution, we need to find an improved guess for the root. Since the nonlinear function in question is too hard to manipulate by hand, we consider the linear approximation of $y = f(x)$ at $x = x_0$:

$$y = f(x_0) + f'(x_0)(x - x_0)$$

To get our next guess, x_1, for the solution to $f(x) = 0$, we set $x = x_1$ and $y = 0$ in the linear approximation and solve for x_1:

$$0 = f(x_0) + f'(x_0)(x_1 - x_0)$$
$$-f(x_0)/f'(x_0) = x_1 - x_0 \qquad \text{assuming that } f'(x_0) \neq 0$$
$$x_1 = x_0 - f(x_0)/f'(x_0)$$

To get the next guess, x_2, we can proceed similarly to get the equation

$$x_2 = x_1 - \frac{f(x_1)}{f'(x_1)}.$$

Proceeding inductively, we get the following difference equation:

$$x_{n+1} = F(x_n) \quad \text{where} \quad F(x) = x - \frac{f(x)}{f'(x)} \quad \text{and} \quad f'(x) \neq 0.$$

This difference equation is illustrated in Figure 4.21. In this figure, r is a root of the equation $f(x) = 0$.

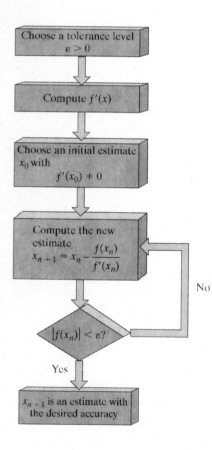

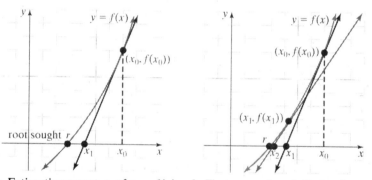

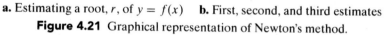

a. Estimating a root, r, of $y = f(x)$ **b.** First, second, and third estimates

Figure 4.21 Graphical representation of Newton's method.

One of the key requirements of the method is to start with a reasonable guess x_0 for the root x^* because the closer x_0 is to x^* the more likely the solution will converge to x^*. For example, if we want to use Newton's method to obtain a numerical solution to the equation $f(x) = x^2 - 10 = 0$, which of course is the same as finding a numerical value for $\sqrt{10}$, we could begin with $x_0 = 3$ or 4. We then use the Newton-Raphson equation to solve for x_1 and carry on iteratively. The following theorem implies that if the sequence converges, then it converges to a root.

Theorem 4.5   **Newton's method**

Let $f(x)$ be a continuously differentiable function with $f'(x) \neq 0$. Any solution to

$$x_{n+1} = x_n - \frac{f(x_n)}{f'(x_n)} \qquad f'(x_n) \neq 0$$

will approach a limit that is a root of the equation or else will not have a limit.

When applying Newton's method, we choose a number $\epsilon > 0$ that determines the allowable tolerance for estimated solutions. Given an appropriate initial guess, x_0, we iteratively compute x_n until $|f(x_n)| < \epsilon$. This procedure is shown in the following flowchart.

Example 8 Time to tumor regrowth

In Example 4 of Section 4.3, we considered the growth of a tumor in a mouse after the mouse was given a drug treatment. To model the volume of the tumor, we used the function (renaming the variable x rather than t)

$$V(x) = 0.005e^{0.24x} + 0.495e^{-0.12x} \text{ cm}^3$$

where x is measured in days after the drug was administered. Using Newton's method, solve for x to within a tolerance of 0.01 for $V(x)$ to shrink and then regrow back to its starting volume of 0.5 cm^3.

Solution   We want to find a root of

$$f(x) = V(x) - 0.5 = 0.005e^{0.24x} + 0.495e^{-0.12x} - 0.5$$

To use Newton's method, we need to compute the first derivative:

$$f'(x) = 0.0012e^{0.24x} - 0.0594e^{-0.12x}$$

We will see what happens if we start with $x_0 = 20$, although other start values close to the anticipated solution can be chosen. To find x_1, we compute

$$x_1 = x_0 - \frac{f(x_0)}{f'(x_0)} = 20 - \frac{f(20)}{f'(20)} \approx 18.914$$

Since $|f(x_1)| \approx 0.02 > 0.01$, our stopping criterion has not been met and we compute

$$x_2 = x_1 - \frac{f(x_1)}{f'(x_1)} = 18.914 - \frac{f(18.914)}{f'(18.914)} \approx 18.732$$

Since $f(18.732) \approx 0.0004$, the stopping criterion has been met and our answer to two decimal places is $r = 18.73$. ◾

Implementation of Newton's method for finding roots is widespread, as a quick search of the Web will reveal. Several websites will turn up that allow you to input a function, an initial condition, and the number of iterations, and you will obtain the corresponding sequence from Newton's method.

Newton's method may not converge to a solution, as shown by the following example.

Example 9 Nonconvergence of Newton's method

Consider the function $f(x) = e^x - 2x$. Use Newton's method with $x_0 = 1$ to find a solution to $f(x) = 0$. Discuss what you find.

Solution   Note that $f'(x) = e^x - 2$ so that

$$x_{n+1} = x_n - \frac{f(x_n)}{f'(x_n)}$$

$$= x_n - \frac{e^{x_n} - 2x_n}{e^{x_n} - 2}$$

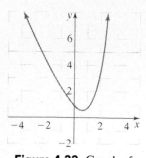

Figure 4.22 Graph of
$y = e^x - 2x$.

If we let $x_0 = 1$, then we find

$$x_1 = 1 - \frac{e^1 - 2(1)}{e^1 - 2} = 0$$

$$x_2 = 0 - \frac{e^0 - 2(0)}{e^0 - 2} = 1$$

$$x_3 = 1 - \frac{e^1 - 2(1)}{e^1 - 2} = 0$$

Note that the values simply alternate, and the method does not converge to a solution. The graph in Figure 4.22 shows why there can be no solution: the graph does not intersect with the x-axis and hence does not have any roots.

PROBLEM SET 4.5

Level 1 DRILL PROBLEMS

In Problems 1 to 4, find the equilibria of $x_{n+1} = f(x_n)$ and determine their stability using cobwebbing.

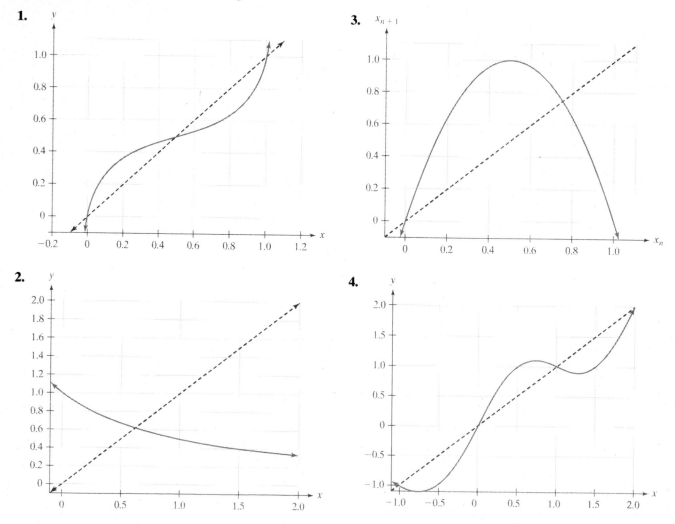

1.

2.

3.

4.

In Problems 5 to 10, find the equilibria of the difference equation. Moreover, use the definitions of an unstable equilibrium and a stable equilibrium to determine their stability.

5. $x_{n+1} = 2x_n$

6. $x_{n+1} = x_n^{1/3}$

7. $x_{n+1} = x_n^{1/2}$

8. $x_{n+1} = x_n^2$

9. $x_{n+1} = \dfrac{2x_n}{1 + 2x_n}$

10. $x_{n+1} = \dfrac{x_n}{2 + 2x_n}$

In Problems 11 to 16, find the equilibria of the difference equation. Moreover, use linearization to determine their stability.

11. $x_{n+1} = x_n^2$

12. $x_{n+1} = \dfrac{x_n}{2 + 2x_n}$

13. $x_{n+1} = \dfrac{2x_n}{1 + 2x_n}$

14. $x_{n+1} = 2x_n(1 - x_n)$

15. $x_{n+1} = 4x_n(1 - x_n)$

16. $x_{n+1} = \dfrac{1}{1 + x_n}$

17. Consider the following alternative formulation of the logistic difference equation, which is different from the formulation presented in Example 1:
$x_{n+1} = rx_n(1 - x_n/100)$ with $r > 0$.

  a. Find the equilibria.

  b. Determine under what conditions the origin is stable.

  c. Determine under what conditions the nonzero equilibrium is positive.

  d. Determine under what conditions the nonzero equilibrium is stable.

18. Consider the logistic difference equation
$x_{n+1} = rx_n(1 - x_n/50)$ with $r > 0$.

  a. Find the equilibria.

  b. Determine under what conditions the origin is stable.

  c. Determine under what conditions the nonzero equilibrium is positive.

  d. Determine under what conditions the nonzero equilibrium is stable.

19. Consider the Beverton-Holt difference equation
$x_{n+1} = \dfrac{rx_n}{1 + x_n}$ with $r > 0$.

  a. Find the equilibria.

  b. Determine under what conditions the origin is stable.

  c. Determine under what conditions the nonzero equilibrium is positive.

  d. Determine under what conditions the nonzero equilibrium is stable.

20. Consider the Beverton-Holt difference equation
$x_{n+1} = \dfrac{rx_n}{1 + 2x_n}$ with $r > 0$.

  a. Find the equilibria.

  b. Determine under what conditions the origin is stable.

  c. Determine under what conditions the nonzero equilibrium is positive.

  d. Determine under what conditions the nonzero equilibrium is stable.

Following the approach laid out in Example 7 (i.e., graphing and using Theorem 4.4) investigate the fate of an allele in a large, randomly mating population when the fitnesses of individuals with two and zero copies of the allele relative to those that have one copy are given in Problems 21 to 24.

21. $w_1 = 1/2$ and $w_2 = 1/2$

22. $w_1 = 2$ and $w_2 = 1$

23. $w_1 = 1/2$ and $w_2 = 2$

24. $w_1 = 2$ and $w_2 = 2$

Use Newton's method to estimate a root of the equations in Problems 25 to 32. Use x_0 as a starting value and iterate twenty times.

25. $x^2 - 2 = 0$, $x_0 = 1$

26. $x^2 + 2 = 0$, $x_0 = 1$

27. $x^3 - x + 1 = 0$, $x_0 = -1$

28. $x^4 + 2x - 1 = 1$, $x_0 = 1$

29. $\cos x = x$, $x_0 = 1$

30. $\sin x + 0.1 = x^2$, $x_0 = 0$

31. $e^x - 5x = 0$, $x_0 = 0$

32. $e^x + x = 0$, $x_0 = -1$

33. Let $f(x) = -2x^4 + 3x^2 + \dfrac{11}{8}$

  a. Show that the equation $f(x) = 0$ has at least two solutions.

  b. Use $x_0 = 2$ and Newton's method to estimate a root of the equation $f(x) = 0$.

  c. Show that Newton's method fails if you choose $x_0 = \dfrac{1}{2}$ as the initial estimate.

34. Let $f(x) = x^6 - x^5 + x^3 - 3$

  a. Show that the equation $f(x) = 0$ has at least two solutions.

  b. Use $x_0 = 2$ and Newton's method to find a root of the equation $f(x) = 0$.

  c. Show that Newton's method fails if you choose $x_0 = 0$ as the initial estimate.

Level 2 APPLIED AND THEORY PROBLEMS

35. For the beetle species *Lasioderma serricorne*, Bellows found that the fraction $f(x)$ of eggs surviving as a function of their initial density x is well described by

$$f(x) = \frac{0.806x}{1 + (0.0114x)^{7.53}}$$

A graph of this function and the corresponding data are shown below:

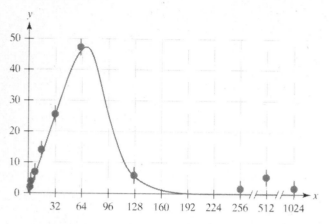

If we assume that each adult produces two eggs, then the dynamics of the population is given by

$$x_{n+1} = 2f(x_n)$$

a. Find the equilibria and determine their stability.

b. Simulate the model with $x_0 = 0.1$

36. For the flour beetle species *Tribolium castaneum*, Bellows found that the fraction $f(x)$ of eggs surviving as a function of their initial density x is well described by

$$f(x) = \frac{0.8x}{1 + (0.0149x)^{4.21}}$$

A graph of this function and the corresponding data are shown below:

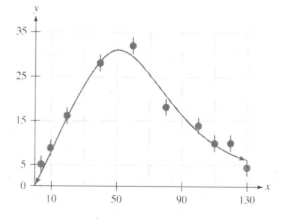

If we assume that each adult produces r eggs, then the dynamics of the population is given by

$$x_{n+1} = rf(x_n)$$

a. Find the equilibria and determine their stability for $r = 2, 4, 6$.

b. Simulate the model with $x_0 = 0.1$ for $r = 2, 4, 6$.

37. Consider the genetic model

$$p_{n+1} = \frac{w_1 p^2 + p(1 - p)}{w_1 p^2 + 2p(1 - p) + w_2(1 - p)^2}$$

Show that the following statements are true:

a. This model has three equilibrium solutions:

$$p = 0, \quad p = 1, \quad \text{and} \quad p^* = \frac{(w_2 - 1)}{(w_1 + w_2 - 2)}.$$

b. $p = 1$ is stable and $p = 0$ is unstable when $w_1 > 1 > w_2 > -1$.

c. (Harder problem) p^* as defined in part **a** is the only stable equilibrium when $w_1 < 1$ and $w_2 < 1$ (a condition known as *heterozygote superiority*).

d. (Harder problem) p^* as defined in part **a** is the only unstable equilibrium when $w_1 > 1$ and $w_2 > 1$ (a condition known as *inbreeding depression*).

38. It can be shown that the volume of a spherical cap is given by

$$V = \frac{\pi}{3} H^2 (3R - H)$$

where R is the radius of the sphere and H is the height of the cap, as shown in Figure 4.23.

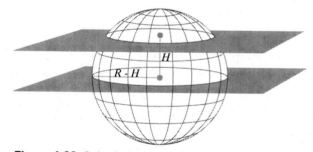

Figure 4.23 Spherical segment is the portion of a sphere between two parallel planes

If $V = 8$ and $R = 2$, use Newton's method to estimate the corresponding H.

39. 𝕳𝖎𝖘𝖙𝖔𝖗𝖎𝖈𝖆𝖑 𝕼𝖚𝖊𝖘𝖙

Archimedes
287–212 BC

The Greek geometer Archimedes is acknowledged to be one of the greatest mathematicians of all time. Ten treatises (as well as traces of some lost works) of Archimedes have survived the rigors of time and are masterpieces of mathematical exposition. In one of these works, *On the Sphere and Cylinder*, Archimedes asks where a sphere should be cut in order to divide it into two pieces whose volumes have a given ratio.

Show that if a plane at distance d from the center of a sphere with $R = 1$ divides the sphere into two parts, one with volume five times that of the other, then

$$3H^3 - 9H^2 + 2 = 0$$

where $H = 1 - d$. Find d by using the Newton-Raphson method to estimate H. (*Hint:* see Problem 38.)

40. Suppose the plane in Problem 38 is located so that it divides the sphere in the ratio of 1:3. Find an equation for d, and estimate the value of d using Newton's method.

41. In Example 4 of Section 4.3, we considered the growth of a tumor in a mouse after the mouse was given a drug treatment. To model the volume of the tumor, we used the function

$$V(x) = 0.005e^{0.24x} + 0.495e^{-0.12x} \text{ cm}^3$$

where x is measured in days after the drug was administered. Using Newton's method, solve within a tolerance of 0.01 for the time x at which the tumor volume has doubled. For an initial guess, use $x = 25$ days.

42. In Example 4 of Section 4.3, we considered the growth of a tumor in a mouse after the mouse was given a drug treatment. To model the volume of the tumor, we used the function

$$V(x) = 0.005e^{0.24x} + 0.495e^{-0.12x} \text{ cm}^3$$

where x is measured in days after the drug was administered. Using Newton's method, solve within a tolerance of 0.01 for the time x at which the tumor volume has quadrupled. For an initial guess, use $x = 30$ days.

43. In Problem 25 in Problem Set 4.3, you found that the volume of a tumor for mice under a different drug regimen was

$$V(x) = 0.0044\, e^{0.239x} + 0.4356e^{-0.111x} \text{ cm}^3$$

where x is days after treatment. Using Newton's method, solve within a tolerance of 0.01 for the time x at which tumor volume has regrown to its original volume. For an initial guess, use $x = 20$ days.

44. In Problem 25 in Problem Set 4.3, you found that the volume of a tumor for mice under a different drug regimen was

$$V(x) = 0.0044\, e^{0.239x} + 0.4356e^{-0.111x} \text{ cm}^3$$

where x is days after treatment. Using Newton's method, solve within a tolerance of 0.01 for the time x at which tumor volume has doubled. For an initial guess, use $x = 25$ days.

45. Show that for different initial values Newton's method converges to a unique solution for the function

$$y = x^3 - 3x^2 + 2x + 0.4$$

but yet converges to one of three solutions for the function

$$y = x^3 - 3x^2 + 2x + 0.3$$

Why is this the case?

46. According to an online article in the *New Scientist* (Catherine Brahic, "Carbon Emissions Rising Faster Than Ever," p. 9), recent research suggests that stabilizing carbon dioxide concentrations in the atmosphere at 450 parts per million (ppm) could limit global warming to 2°C. In Section 1.2, we modeled carbon dioxide concentrations in the atmosphere with the following function (which we now present to higher precision to make more transparent the numerical details of the convergence process):

$$f(x) = 0.122463x + 329.253 + 3\cos\frac{\pi x}{6} \text{ ppm}$$

where x is months after April 1974. In Example 11 of Section 2.3, we used the bisection method to estimate the time that the model predicts carbon dioxide levels of 450 ppm. Use Newton's method to estimate this time with a stopping value of $\epsilon = 0.001$.

47. Repeat Problem 46 except estimate the time until reaching 400 ppm.

CHAPTER 4 REVIEW QUESTIONS

1. Use the first derivative test and the second derivative test to find and classify all the extrema of $g(x) = x^3 - 3x - 4$.

2. Find the global maximum and global minimum of $f(x) = \sqrt{x}e^{-x}$ on $[0, 6]$.

3. Using asymptotes and first derivatives, graph

$$f(x) = \frac{x^3 + 3}{x(x + 1)(x + 2)}$$ by hand and then check

it using a calculator.

4. Consider the family of curves
$$y^2 = x^3 + x^2 + bx + 2b$$
Using calculus, graph the curves for the given values of b.

 a. $b = 0$

 b. $b = 0.05$

 c. $b = 0.01$

 d. $b = -0.05$

 e. $b = -0.1$

5. The canopy height (in meters) of a tropical grass may be modeled by (for $0 \le t \le 30$)

$$h(t) = 0.0000071t^3 - 0.0015852t^2 + 0.1419159t + 3.14$$

where t is the number of days after mowing.

 a. Sketch the graph of $h(t)$.

 b. When was the canopy height growing most rapidly? Least rapidly?

6. Find the value of r in the function $f(x) = e^{-rx}$ that provides the best fit through a semi-log plot of the points $\{(0, 1), (1, 0.6), (2, 0.4), (3, 0.3)\}$.

7. A travel company plans to sponsor a tour to Africa. There will be accommodations for no more than forty people, and the tour will be canceled if no more than ten people book reservations. Based on past experience, the manager determines that if n people book the tour, the profit (in dollars) may be modeled by the function
$$P(n) = -n^3 + 27.6n^2 + 970n - 4{,}235$$
What is the maximum profit?

8. Two towns, A and B, are 12.0 miles apart and are located 5.0 and 3.0 miles, respectively, from a long, straight highway, as shown in Figure 4.24.

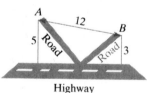

Figure 4.24 Highway construction project.

A construction company has a contract to build a road from A to the highway and then to B. Analyze a model to determine the length (to the nearest tenth of a mile) of the shortest road that meets these requirements.

9. A particular plant is known to have the following growth and seed production characteristics: At time of planting ($t = 0$), the seedling has a mass of 3 grams. At time $t > 0$ days after planting, the seedling has grown into a plant that weighs
$$w(t) = 3 + 450t - t^2$$

grams. The plant has a gene that can be manipulated to control the age t at which the plant matures. At maturity the number of seeds $S(t)$ produced by the plant is given by

$$S(t) = \frac{w(t)}{3}$$

A farmer asks a geneticist to genetically engineer a plant line that accounts for the fact that on his farm, because of losses from pests, drought, and disease, a proportion

$$P(t) = \frac{100}{100 + t}$$

of germinating seeds can be expected to develop and survive to age t as plants. What age of maturity should the geneticist select for the plants to maximize the seed production of the mature crop for the farmer?

10. If the value of a forest stand (units are dollars per square meter) is given by the function

$$V(t) = \frac{100}{1 + e^{-0.1(t-40)}} - 1.8$$

where t represents the number of years after the stand has been clear-cut, and the discount is 0.02 per year, solve for the optimal rotation period, assuming that $V(t)$ applies every time the stand is clear-cut.

11. On a particular island in the tropics, scientists have determined that individuals who are not protected by the sickle cell allele will have, on average, 20% fewer progeny than individuals who have one sickle cell allele, while individuals who have two sickle cell alleles will not reproduce.

 a. Write a difference equation for the proportion x_n of non-sickle-cell alleles in the population in generation n, assuming that initially $x_0 > 0$, under assumptions of random mating and random segregation of alleles.

 b. Find the equilibria proportions for x on the interval $(0, 1]$ and determine if they are stable.

 c. Interpret your results.

12. Let $C(t)$ denote the concentration in the blood at time t of a drug injected into the body intramuscularly. In a now classic paper by E. Heinz ("Probleme bei der Diffusion kleiner Substanzmengen innerhalb des menschlichen Körpers," *Biochem. Z*, 319 (1949): 482–492), the concentration was modeled by the function

$$C(t) = \frac{k}{b - a}(e^{-at} - e^{-bt}) \qquad t \ge 0$$

where a, b (with $b > a$), and k are positive constants that depend on the drug. At what time does the largest concentration occur? What happens to the concentration as $t \to +\infty$?

13. Consider a bird that has arrived at a wooded patch with two trees. If the bird spends x minutes foraging for insects on the first tree, she gains $E_1(x) = 200(1 - e^{-x})$ Calories from insects. If the bird spends x minutes on the second tree, she gains $E_2(x) = 100(1 - e^{-x})$ Calories of insects. Assuming the bird has five minutes to spend in the patch, determine the time she should spend on each tree to optimize her energy intake.

14. For the flour beetle species *Tribolium confusum*, Bellows found that the fraction $f(x)$ of eggs surviving as a function of their initial density x is well described by

$$f(x) = \frac{0.61x}{1 + (0.0116x)^{3.12}}$$

A graph of this function and the corresponding data are shown below:

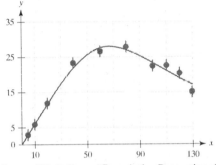

Data Source: T.S. Bellows, "Descriptive Properties of Some Models for Density Dependence," *Journal of Animal Ecology* 50(1)(1981): 139–156.

If we assume that each adult produces r eggs, then the dynamics of the population is given by

$$x_{n+1} = rf(x_n)$$

a. Find the equilibria and determine their stability for $r = 2, 4, 6$.

b. Simulate the model with $x_0 = 0.1$ for $r = 2, 4, 6$.

15. A model for the population growth rate of Eastern Pacific yellowfin tuna is given by

$$G(N) = 2.61N\left(1 - (N/148)^\theta\right)$$

where N is measured in thousands of tons, t is measured in years, and $\theta > 0$ is a parameter that determines the strength of density dependence. Find the population size at the maximum sustainable harvesting rate. Discuss what effect θ has on this population size.

16. The energy gain from nectar for a hummingbird flying at $t = 0$ to a flower is shown in the graph below:

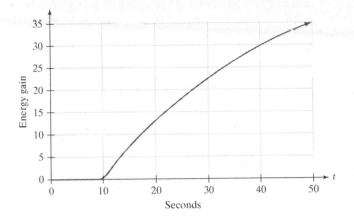

Ignoring the cost of flying constantly, find the time at which the hummingbird's energy gain per unit time is maximal and, consequently, the bird should fly to another flower. Discuss what effect including a fixed energetic cost per unit time would have on your answer.

17. A simple model of a biochemical switch is given by

$$x_{n+1} = \frac{3x_n^2}{1 + x_n^2}$$

where x_n is the concentration of a biochemical at time n.

a. Find the equilibria of this model.

b. Verify that $f(x) = \dfrac{3x^2}{1 + x^2}$ is an increasing function of x for $x > 0$.

c. Discuss what you can say about all nonnegative solutions to this difference equation.

18. Public awareness of a new drug is modeled by

$$P(t) = \frac{5.2t}{0.015t^2 + 0.342} + 0.18$$

where t is the number of months after FDA approval and $P(t)$ is the fraction of people who are aware of the drug and its possible uses.

a. Find the critical points for $P(t)$.

b. Sketch the graph of $P(t)$.

c. At what time, t, during the time interval $0 \le t \le 36$ is $P(t)$ the largest?

19. Suppose that systolic blood pressure of a patient t years old is modeled by

$$P(t) = 38.52 + 21.8\ln(0.98t + 1)$$

for $0 \le t \le 60$, where $P(t)$ is measured in millimeters of mercury.

a. Sketch the graph of $P(t)$.

b. At what rate is $P(t)$ increasing at age t?

20. During the time period 1905–1920, hunters virtually wiped out all large predators on the Kaibab Plateau near the Grand Canyon in northern Arizona. This, in turn, resulted in a rapid increase in the deer population $P(t)$, until food supplies were exhausted and famine led to a steep decline in $P(t)$. A study of this ecological disaster determined that during the time period 1905–1920, the rate of change of the population, $P'(t)$, could be modeled by the function

$$P'(t) = \frac{1}{8}(100 - 5t)t^3$$

$0 \le t \le 20$, where t is the number of years after the base year of 1905.

a. In what year during this period was the deer population the largest?

b. In what year did the rate of growth $P'(t)$ begin to decline?

GROUP PROJECTS

Seeing a project through on your own, or working in a small group to complete a project, teaches important skills. The following projects provide opportunities to develop such skills.

Project 4A   Optimal swimming patterns

In getting from one spot to another, fish have to contend with drag forces and gravity. Drag forces are much greater when a fish is swimming than when it is merely gliding. To reduce the amount of time spent swimming, fish that are heavier than water engage in burst swimming in which they alternate between gliding and swimming upward. This burst swimming leads to a vertical zigzag motion of the fish in the water as shown below:

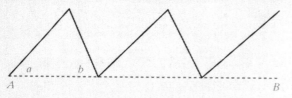

where a is the angle of the upward burst and b is the angle of the downward glide.

In this project, you will investigate the optimal swimming pattern under the following assumptions:

- Throughout its swim, the fish maintains a constant speed s to the right.

- The forces acting on the fish are its weight W relative to the water and drag forces.

- The drag on the gliding fish is D and the drag on the swimming fish is kD where $k \ge 1$.

- The fish has sufficient top/bottom surface area (e.g., a skate) that frictional forces perpendicular to the top/bottom of the fish cancel the component of the gravitational force that is perpendicular to the top/bottom of the fish.

- The energy expended by the fish in swimming is proportional to the force it exerts in moving.

Under these assumptions, your project should do the following:

- Find the ratio of energy in the burst mode to the energy for continuous horizontal swimming from A to B.

- It has been found empirically that $\tan a \approx 0.2$. Given this information, find the optimal value of b for the fish.

- Determine how much energy the fish saves by swimming with this b instead of swimming horizontally.

- Determine how sensitive the amount of energy used is to b, and how sensitive the optimal b is to the estimate of a.

Project 4B   Stability and bifurcation diagrams

Consider the normalized version of the logistic model introduced in the first example in Section 4.5; that is, we set $K = 1$ or, equivalently, interpret the units of x in terms of multiples of K to obtain the equation

$$x_{n+1} = f(x_n) \quad \text{where} \quad f(x) = rx(1 - x)$$

Now explore the behavior of this equation as follows:

1. Solve for the equilibrium solutions as a function of r and determine the stability properties of these equilibria for $r \in [0, 5]$. You will notice that as r increases, an equilibrium solution jumps at some point r_b from being stable on one side of r_b to unstable on the other side of r_b. The value r_b is called a *bifurcation point*.

2. Plot the equilibria in the rx plane (r is the horizontal axis spanning $[0, 5]$) using a solid line to denote where the nontrivial equilibrium solution $\hat{x}$ to $x = f(x)$ is stable and a dotted line where it is unstable.

3. Now consider the equilibria of the iterated logistic map $x_{n+2} = f(f(x_n))$ by constructing (see Section 1.6) the composite map $(f \circ f)(x)$. Use the terminology $f^2 \equiv (f \circ f)$. Find all the equilibria of $f^2(x)$ as a function of r and plot them on the same rx plane as above, but this time plot only the nontrivial stable solutions using a solid line (if you plot where they are unstable, your diagram will become too busy). Note that the equation $x = f^2(x)$ has many more solutions than the equation $x = f(x)$: It has both all the solutions to equation $x = f(x)$ (demonstrate this) and additional solutions that come in pairs, say x^* and x^{**}, such that the sequence $\{x^*, x^{**}, x^*, x^{**}, \ldots\}$ is a two-cycle solution of the original equation $x = f(x)$ (demonstrate this). Further, if for a particular value of r, x^* and x^{**} are stable equilibrium solutions of $x = f^2(x)$,

then the two-cycle $\{x^*, x^{**}, x^*, x^{**}, \ldots\}$ is a stable attractor of the equation $x_{n+1} = f(x_n)$. By this, we mean that for any initial condition x_0 starting close to x^* or x^{**}, the resulting sequence generated by our original equation will oscillate between two values that get closer and closer to x^* and x^{**} as time progresses.

4. You have now reached the limit of what you can probably do analytically. Research the literature (a good source is J. D. Murray's book *Mathematical Biology: I, An Introduction*, 3rd ed., New York: Springer-Verlag, 2001). Then discuss what happens as r increases on $[0, 5]$, focusing in terms of bifurcation values at which stable equilibrium solutions of the logistic equation are replaced by stable two-cycles, as well as stable n-cycles for $n > 2$.

5. If you have command of an appropriate technology, use it to summarize graphically your discussion in what is called a *bifurcation diagram*. (Instructions on how to do this are available in textbooks and on the Web, so locate a set of instructions and see if you can follow them.)

Project 4C   Economic production versus ecological welfare

Economic activities, such as extraction and processing of raw materials and the manufacture of finished goods, always result in some damage to the ecosystem. Because of pollution and the destruction of natural habitats, such activities may even severely degrade the ecosystem's delivery of clean water and clean air. Activities may also compromise the ecosystem's ability to produce food and provide a place for relaxation and recreation. In this project, you are asked to use optimization to explore the trade-off between economic production and ecological welfare. (This problem follows Problem 11.5 in J. Harte, *Consider a Cylindrical Cow*. Sausalito, University Science Books, 2001.)

Suppose the level of economic activity is measured by a variable X, the value of goods and services produced by this activity (also known as *economic output*) is measured by a variable Y, and the value of ecosystem services is measured by an environmental quality variable Z.

A very simple model of human welfare W is based on these assumptions:

- Welfare is proportional to both economic output Y and environmental quality Z.

- Economic output Y is itself proportional to economic activity X and and environmental quality Z. (The first assumption is self-evident and the second arises from the notion that it is much more difficult to produce the same unit of economic output in a poor environment where resources are depleted than in a pristine environment where resources are plentiful.)

- The environment declines from a pristine level linearly with activity X.

The following three equations are equivalent to this mathematical statement: For positive constants a, b, c, and Z_0, our variables satisfy the equations

$$W = aYZ$$
$$Y = bXZ$$
$$Z = Z_0 - cX$$

Figure 4.25 Industrial pollution.

1. Demonstrate that human welfare W is maximized at $X^* = Z_0/3c$ and has the maximum value

$$W^* = \frac{4abZ_0^3}{27c}$$

2. Show that the value of economic activity $\widehat{X}$ that maximizes production Y is 1.5 times larger than X^*; that is, $\rho = \widehat{X}/X^* = 3/2$. Further, show that if $\widehat{W}$ is the welfare obtained when production is maximized, then the "cost of greed" (defined to be the ratio $\gamma = \widehat{W}/W^*$) is $\gamma = 27/32$. Discuss the implications of the fact that $\rho > 1$ and $\gamma < 1$.

3. Assume that the economic production level Y has the more general Cobb-Douglas form $Y = bX^{\alpha}Z^{\beta}$ than assumed in Equation 4.1, where α and β are nonnegative, empirically determined constants with values that depend on the economic sector under consideration. If, in addition, welfare has the general form $W = aX^{\mu}Y^{\nu}$, then find the values of X that maximize both economic output and welfare.

Calculate the ratios ρ and γ for this more general case. What do you conclude?

4. Show in the case of the given equations for W, Y, and Z that the level of economic output that maximizes welfare-per-unit-output—that is, the ratio W/Y—is $X = 0$. Does this hold true for the more general case when α, β, μ, and ν are not necessarily 1?

5. Look through the literature and see how many Cobb-Douglas functions you can find and what values of α and β are associated with various sectors of the world economy. Also, see if you can find a real problem where most of the parameters a, b, c, Z_0, α, β, μ, and ν are known. Describe the problem and the values of the parameters. (If one of or more of α, β, μ, and ν are not known, then set them equal to 1, and it is fine if relative rather than global values of the other constants are known or guessed at.) Now calculate the optimum production levels $\widehat{X}$ and X^* with respect to economic output and welfare, respectively, and elaborate in anyway you think appropriate.

ANSWERS TO SELECTED PROBLEMS

CHAPTER 4

Problem Set 4.1, Page 291

1.

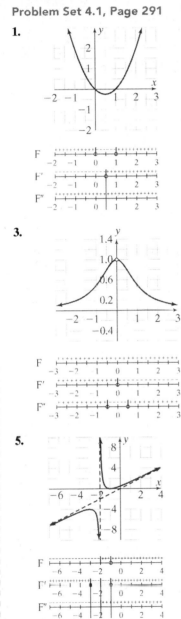

3.

5.

7.

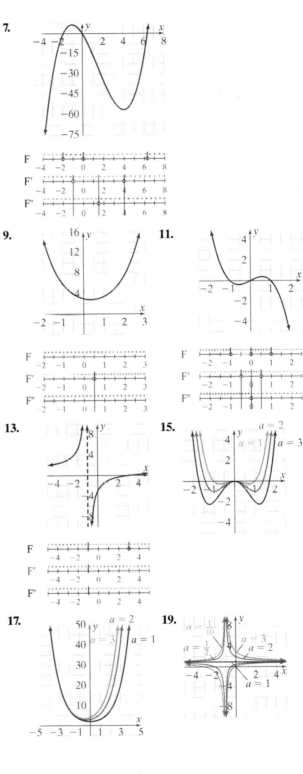

9.

11.

13.

15.

17.

19.

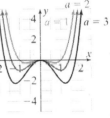

21.

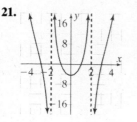

23. As a changes from positive to negative, the graph of the parabola goes from being concave up to being concave down.

25. $y''(x) = \dfrac{(a-b)e^x(1-e^x)}{(1+e^x)^3}$

If $b > a$, concave down for $x < 0$; if $b < a$, concave up for $x < 0$; point of inflection at $x = 0$ and concave up for $x > 0$ and concave down for $x < 0$

27.

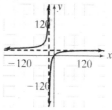

29. The domain is $(0, \infty)$.
a. $y = 58.7$; $x = -0.76$; (outside domain)
b. increasing on $(-\infty, -0.76) \cup (-0.76, \infty)$; thus, the function is increasing on its domain
c. up: $(-\infty, -0.76)$; down $(-0.76, \infty)$; thus the function is concave down on its domain

d.

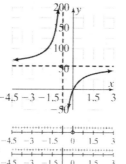

31. $C''(t) = 2.574e^{(-0.3t)} - 28.6e^{(-t)}$; $C''(t) < 0$ for $t < 3.4$ and $C''(t) > 0$ for $t > 3.4$ **33.** Answers vary: one possibility is $\dfrac{2t}{1+t}$; another possibility is $2e^{-1}$.

35. a.

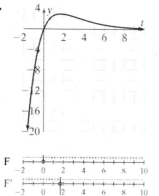

For this problem, the domain is $[0, \infty)$. **b.** Maximum concentration of 2.92 is achieved at $t = 5\ln\dfrac{7}{5}$.

Problem Set 4.2, Page 301

1. Local max at $x = -0.6$; global max at $x = 0.8$; local min at $x = -0.1, 1$; global min at $x = -1$ **3.** global min at $x = -1$, local min at $x \approx 0.25$, local max at $x = -2, 1$
5. There is one critical point at $x = -\frac{3}{8}$ and it is a local minimum.   **7.** $t = 0$ is a local minimum, $t = 2$ is a local maximum.   **9.** The only critical point is at $x = -1$, at which f is not defined.   **11.** $x = \frac{1}{2}$ is a local minimum, $x = -2$ is a local maximum   **13.** There is a local maximum at $x = -1$ and a local minimum at $x = 4$.   **15.** There is a local maximum at $x = -3$ and local minimum at $x = -1$.   **17.** There is a global maximum at $x = 0$ and a global minimum at $x = 2$.   **19.** There is global minimum at $x = 1$ and a global maximum at $x = 0.1, 10$.   **21.** There is a global minimum at $x = 2$ and there is no global maximum.   **23.** There is a global minimum at $x = 1$.   **25.** Find all the critical values. Evaluate f at these critical values and at $x = a$. Let M and m be the largest and smallest values, respectively. Find $\lim\limits_{x \to b} f(x) = L$, assuming it exists. If $M > L$, then M is the global maximum. If $m \leq L$, then m is the global minimum.   **27.** Global minimum at $x = 2$; no global maximum.   **29.** Global minimum at $x = -1$ and no global maximum   **33.** There is a global minimum of 365.1871 at $x \approx 317.8500$ and a global maximum of 371.9310 at $x \approx 324$.   **35.** The global maximum is 890 at $t = 17$.
37. a. The maximum occurs at $x = r$ because $x = r$ is the only critical value and $P(0) = 0$ and $\lim\limits_{x \to \infty} P(x) = 0$.

b.

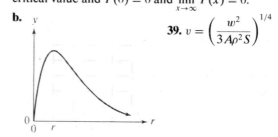

39. $v = \left(\dfrac{w^2}{3A\rho^2 S}\right)^{1/4}$

Problem Set 4.3, Page 315

1. $x = 27.6249$ **3.** 32.3667 **5.** $9,600$/year   **7.** $h = 1.05$
9. $\theta = 1.3720$ **11.** $\theta = 1.2489$ **13.** Elvis should run 12.1 meters along the shore.   **15.** Elvis Should run $15 - 0.1414d$.
17. 43,   **19.** 42.2,

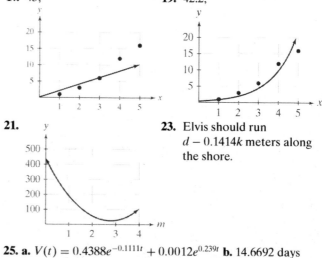

21.   **23.** Elvis should run $d - 0.1414k$ meters along the shore.

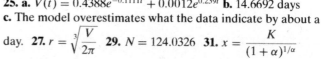

25. a. $V(t) = 0.4388e^{-0.1111t} + 0.0012e^{0.239t}$ **b.** 14.6692 days
c. The model overestimates what the data indicate by about a day.   **27.** $r = \sqrt[3]{\dfrac{V}{2\pi}}$ **29.** $N = 124.0326$ **31.** $x = \dfrac{K}{(1+\alpha)^{1/\alpha}}$

33. 65.05 meters **35.** Two crews (1.86 crews) will minimize cost at $61,284. **37.** If the rate at which energy is accumulated is $E = ar^2 - br^3$, then E is maximized when $r = \dfrac{2a}{3b}$.

39. $P' = \dfrac{-3(2M - 9)}{2M^{1/4}(2M + 3)^2}$ which is zero at $M = 4.5$. This is a maximum since $P' > 0 (< 0)$ for M just less (greater) than 4.5.

41. a. $a^* = 6.44$ **b.**

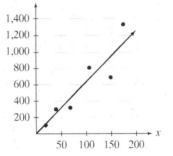

43. $r^* = 0.64$;

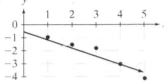

Problem Set 4.4, Page 328

1. 10 seconds **3.** 4.47 seconds **5.** 4.08 seconds

7.

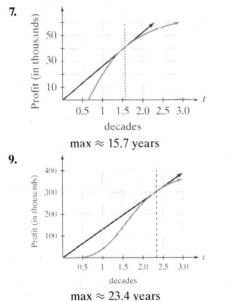

max ≈ 15.7 years

9.

max ≈ 23.4 years

11. Patch 2 **13.** Patch 2 **15.** Patch 1 **17.** 3.11 years
19. 4.93 years **21.** 3.71 years **23.** 2.43 years **25.** 2.38 years
27. $h = 41.6200$ cm **29. a.** 181.75 **b.** 0.54 **31.** 41.48 **33.** 38.40

Problem Set 4.5, Page 342

1. Equilibria are 0 (unstable), 0.5 (stable), and 1 (unstable).
3. Equilibria are 0 (unstable) and 0.75 (unstable).
5. Equilibrium is 0 (unstable). **7.** Equilibria are 0 (unstable) and 1 (stable). **9.** Equilibria are 0 (unstable) and $\frac{1}{2}$ (stable).
11. Equilibria are 0 (stable) and 1 (unstable). **13.** Equilibria are 0 (unstable) and $\frac{1}{2}$ (stable). **15.** Equilibria are 0 (unstable) and $\frac{3}{4}$ (unstable).

17. a. Equilibria are $x = 0$ and $x = 100 - \frac{100}{r}$. **b.** 0 is stable provided that $r < 1$ (remember $r > 0$). **c.** Nonzero equilibrium is positive provided that $r > 1$. **d.** $r < 3$ corresponds to stability. **19. a.** Equilibria are 0 and $r - 1$.
b. $r < 1$ **c.** $r > 1$ **d.** $r > 1$ **21.** Frequency of allele approaches $\frac{1}{2}$ (stable), provided that initially the frequency is between 0 and 1 (unstable). **23.** Frequencies of alleles approach 0 (stable) provided that the initial frequency is less than 1 (unstable) **25.** 1.4142 **27.** -1.3247 **29.** $x_3 = 0.7391$
31. $x = 0.2592$ **33. b.** 1.3668 **35. a.** 0 (unstable), 82.182 (unstable) **39.** $d \approx 0.4817$ **41.** 21.9251 days **43.** 18.7145 days
45. In the first case, only one real root exists, namely -0.1597. In the second case, three real roots exist, namely -0.1254, 1.3389, and 1.7865. **47.** $x = 561.1286$ months after April 1974.

Chapter 4 Review Questions, Page 345

1. Max, -2 at $x = -1$; min, -6 at $x = 1$
3.

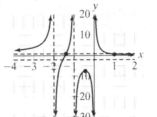

5. a.

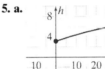

b. Growing most rapidly at $t = 0$ and least rapidly at $t = 30$

7. $22,727.15 **9.** 135 days **11. a.** $x_{n+1} = \dfrac{-0.2x + 1}{-1.2x + 2}$ **b.** $x = 1$ (stable) and $x = 0.833$ (stable) **c.** The results imply that as long as both alleles are present in the population, they will persist and the frequency of the sickle cell anemia allele will approach a value of 16.67%. **13.** The bird should spend $\frac{5}{2} + \frac{1}{2}(\ln 2)$ minutes on the first tree and $\frac{5}{2} - \frac{1}{2}(\ln 2)$ minutes on the second tree. **15.** $N = 148 \left(\dfrac{1}{1 + \theta}\right)^{1/\theta}$ which is an increasing function of θ **17. a.** $0, \frac{1}{2}(3 \pm \sqrt{5})$

b. $f'(x) = \dfrac{6x}{(x^2 + 1)^2} > 0$ for all $x > 0$ **c.** For initial conditions $x_0 < \frac{1}{2}(3 - \sqrt{5})$, x_n converges to 0. For initial conditions $x_0 > \frac{1}{2}(3 - \sqrt{5})$, x_n converges to $\frac{1}{2}(3 + \sqrt{5})$.

19. a.

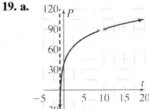

b. $P'(t) = \dfrac{21.364}{0.98t + 1}$

CPSIA information can be obtained at www.ICGtesting.com
Printed in the USA
BVOW00n1932291213

340311BV00004B/6/P